The Voucher Worth

50P

May be redeemed in accordance with the conditions overleaf at any of the establishments whose gazetteer entry shows the symbol Ⓥ.

The Voucher Worth

50P

May be redeemed in accordance with the conditions overleaf at any of the establishments whose gazetteer entry shows the symbol Ⓥ.

The Voucher Worth

50P

May be redeemed in accordance with the conditions overleaf at any of the establishments whose gazetteer entry shows the symbol Ⓥ.

The Voucher Worth

50P

May be redeemed in accordance with the conditions overleaf at any of the establishments whose gazetteer entry shows the symbol Ⓥ.

The Voucher Worth

50P

May be redeemed in accordance with the conditions overleaf at any of the establishments whose gazetteer entry shows the symbol Ⓥ.

The Voucher Worth

50P

May be redeemed in accordance with the conditions overleaf at any of the establishments whose gazetteer entry shows the symbol Ⓥ.

The Voucher Worth

50P

May be redeemed in accordance with the conditions overleaf at any of the establishments whose gazetteer entry shows the symbol Ⓥ.

The Voucher Worth

50P

May be redeemed in accordance with the conditions overleaf at any of the establishments whose gazetteer entry shows the symbol Ⓥ.

A copy of AA Stately Homes, Museums, Castles and Gardens in Britain 1986 must be produced with this voucher.

Only one voucher per person or party accepted.

Not redeemable for cash. No change given.

The voucher is valid during the published opening times of the establishments concerned, and will not be valid after 31st December, 1986.

This voucher cannot be used in conjunction with any other discount voucher.

A copy of AA Stately Homes, Museums, Castles and Gardens in Britain 1986 must be produced with this voucher.

Only one voucher per person or party accepted.

Not redeemable for cash. No change given.

The voucher is valid during the published opening times of the establishments concerned, and will not be valid after 31st December, 1986.

This voucher cannot be used in conjunction with any other discount voucher.

A copy of AA Stately Homes, Museums, Castles and Gardens in Britain 1986 must be produced with this voucher.

Only one voucher per person or party accepted.

Not redeemable for cash. No change given.

The voucher is valid during the published opening times of the establishments concerned, and will not be valid after 31st December, 1986.

This voucher cannot be used in conjunction with any other discount voucher.

A copy of AA Stately Homes, Museums, Castles and Gardens in Britain 1986 must be produced with this voucher.

Only one voucher per person or party accepted.

Not redeemable for cash. No change given.

The voucher is valid during the published opening times of the establishments concerned, and will not be valid after 31st December, 1986.

This voucher cannot be used in conjunction with any other discount voucher.

A copy of AA Stately Homes, Museums, Castles and Gardens in Britain 1986 must be produced with this voucher.

Only one voucher per person or party accepted.

Not redeemable for cash. No change given.

The voucher is valid during the published opening times of the establishments concerned, and will not be valid after 31st December, 1986.

This voucher cannot be used in conjunction with any other discount voucher.

A copy of AA Stately Homes, Museums, Castles and Gardens in Britain 1986 must be produced with this voucher.

Only one voucher per person or party accepted.

Not redeemable for cash. No change given.

The voucher is valid during the published opening times of the establishments concerned, and will not be valid after 31st December, 1986.

This voucher cannot be used in conjunction with any other discount voucher.

A copy of AA Stately Homes, Museums, Castles and Gardens in Britain 1986 must be produced with this voucher.

Only one voucher per person or party accepted.

Not redeemable for cash. No change given.

The voucher is valid during the published opening times of the establishments concerned, and will not be valid after 31st December, 1986.

This voucher cannot be used in conjunction with any other discount voucher.

AA

STATELY HOMES, MUSEUMS, CASTLES AND GARDENS

in Britain

Stately Homes, Museums, Castles and Gardens in Britain 1985

Editor: Penny Hicks
Designer: Andrew Turnbull

Gazetteer: compiled by the Publications Research Unit of the Automobile Association

Maps: prepared by the Cartographic Services Department of the Automobile Association

Cover Picture: Sheffield Park and Gardens

Head of Advertisement Sales: Christopher Heard tel 0256 20123 (ext 2020)
Advertisement Production: Karen Weeks tel 0256 20123 (ext 3525)
Advertisement Sales Representatives:
London, East Anglia, East Midlands, Central Southern and South East England: Edward May tel 0256 20123 (ext 3524) or 0256 467568
South West, West, West Midlands: Bryan Thompson tel 0272 393296
Wales, North of England, Scotland: Arthur Williams tel 0222 620267

Typeset by CCC, printed and bound in Great Britain by William Clowes Limited, Beccles and London.

ISBN 0 86145 307 7

Published by the Automobile Association, Fanum House, Basingstoke, Hampshire RG21 2EA.

AA Ref. 59051

Contents

About this book

In this book we list hundreds of places to visit and try to provide as much information as possible for the intending visitor.

Gazetteer

The gazetteer is listed in strict alphabetical order throughout. As far as possible, the places of interest situated within one or two miles of a town or village are placed under the nearest town or village heading. However, some establishments are too remote for this to be done and such places are listed under their own name. Should you be in any doubt about a particular place, the comprehensive index at the back of the book will indicate where it can be found.

Where the establishment's name is shown in italic type, this indicates that particulars have not been confirmed by the management and you may wish to check by telephone before your visit.

Atlas

If you are planning a day out or a holiday in a particular area, you might find it useful to refer in the first instance to the atlas at the back of the book where all of the towns and individual establishments that we list are located. A useful key at the front of the atlas section will help you to find the area you require. Each gazetteer entry also gives a map reference which includes the atlas page number and grid code (see page 320).

Opening dates

The dates quoted in the gazetteer are inclusive, so that Apr–Oct indicates that the establishment is open from the beginning of April to the end of October. (For Ancient Monuments see page 298).

Prices

As far as possible we publish the prices that will be charged during 1986, but where we have been unable to ascertain what these will be, we quote the prices which were charged in 1985 (if known), prefixed by an asterisk.

Telephone

Unless otherwise stated the telephone exchange given in the gazetteer is that of the town under which the establishment is listed. Where the exchange for a particular establishment is not that of the town under which it appears the name of the exchange is given after the telephone symbol ☏ and before the dialling code and number.

In some areas telephone numbers are likely to be changed by the telephone authorities during the currency of this publication. If you have any difficulty it is advisable to check with the operator.

Disabled persons

If the wheelchair symbol ⵕ is shown in the entry it means that the property has suitable access for wheelchair-bound visitors. However, other facilities such as toilets may be unsuitable and it is advisable to check in advance to confirm that necessary requirements are met.

The Voucher Scheme

At the front of the book you will find eight 50p vouchers, redeemable against the price of admission to certain establishments, and by using them you can effectively save the cost of this book. The conditions for their use will be found on the reverse of each one and places which have agreed to accept the vouchers have the symbol ⓥ at the end of their entry in the gazetteer.

Your Opinions Please

On page 317 you will find a questionnaire which you may like to use to let us know what you think of this book. We are always looking for ways of improving the content and the quality of the guide and who better to help us than those who use it. As an added incentive, we are offering a discount on the price of the 1987 edition to anyone who returns a completed questionnaire.

Once again this year we are pleased to welcome a large number of new establishments to the book, proving not only our concern about preserving our heritage, but also that a variety of new and unusual tourist attractions are being developed. In the pages that follow we tell you about some of these new places—you will find many more within the pages of the gazetteer.

Fairfax House
·
YORK

One of the most remarkable projects we have come across this year has been the restoration of Fairfax House in York's Castlegate, now one of the finest examples of a Georgian town house in existance.

Many years ago it was converted into a 'front of house' for a cinema and more recent neglect had pushed it to the edge of total collapse. Fortunately, the York Civic Trust came to the rescue and in 1982 a massive restoration programme was begun. The finest local craftsmen were employed and over the next two years thousands of man-hours were put into stripping away layers of old paint and whitewash, repairing, replacing and redecorating until, in October 1984, the finishing touches were complete. The house was originally built in the mid 18th-century and soon came into the ownership of Charles Gregory, 9th and last Viscount Fairfax. He spent a great deal on remodelling the interior—indeed, interior decoration was one of his many interests—and much of the décor we see today reflects his influence, notably in the magnificent plaster work.

Rooms on show include two bedrooms, the Saloon and Drawing Room, the Library and a reconstruction of an 18th-century kitchen, complete with massive range, scrubbed table and a variety of utensils and equipment of that era. The original kitchen and servants' quarters were demolished by the cinema company and this reconstruction is in a room probably used as a back parlour. The whole house is furnished in superb style, thanks to the munificent gift of the Noel Terry Collection of furniture and clocks to the York Civic Trust. Noel Terry, of the famous confectionary family, who died in 1980, was for many years the Honorary Treasurer of the Trust and his collection has been described by Christie's as '. . . one of the best collections of the mid-18th century period formed in the last 50 years . . .' The coming together of this collection and the building which it now adorns is fortunate indeed and together they become a great asset to our architectural heritage.

Georgian Theatre & Museum
•
RICHMOND

Still in North Yorkshire and still with the 18th century, we go now to the lovely old town of Richmond. It is, perhaps, an unlikely place in which to find one of Britain's most important theatres, but that is the distinction which has been accorded to the Georgian Theatre Royal. Not important in the sense of West End-style box office hits, perhaps, but in its historic value, for this is the most authentic 18th-century theatre in existence and has been restored, as far as safety regulations will allow, to its original style.

It was built in 1788 by actor-manager Samuel Butler as part of a local theatre circuit and it prospered for many years under his direction and that of his descendants. When it eventually closed down it managed to escape the fate of most of its contemporaries which have long since disappeared. It was used over the years as a store-room, a furniture repository and an auction room until, in the early part of this century, its importance was realised and, through the efforts of a group of enthusiasts, it was restored to its original style and character.

The theatre has been in use for some time now and actors and audience alike have a special affection for its intimate atmosphere. Now it is also open to visitors and a unique theatre museum has been opened in two adjacent buildings. Here a series of galleries follow the fortunes of this theatre from its original construction to its restoration. One section contains model theatres of different ages and also on display is the oldest complete set of painted scenery in the country.

From the museum, visitors tour the theatre, treading the same boards as Edmund Kean, Macready and many other great performers, past and present. Standing on the stage, with its large proscenium and side doors, one can see just how close the audience is to the performers—particularly the occupants of the boxes who are on eye level. The tour continues to the old dressing rooms, where many of the performers would live while their season here lasted, and then into the auditorium: the pit stalls, originally furnished with bare wooden benches; the boxes, already mentioned, and the gallery, traditionally the cheapest place to be and consequently known for rowdiness—those at the front would use the kicking board to register their approval or disapproval of a performance and the gallery here was actually closed down at one time by the local magistrate because of immorality!

The survival of this little theatre is fortunate indeed and long may it echo to cries of 'Encore'.

The Magnificent Seven

Harewood House

(West Yorkshire) 1759 Home of the Earl and Countess of Harewood; also Harewood Bird Garden. Junction A61/A659, 7m. north of Leeds. 5m. A1 Wetherby.
Tel: Harewood (0532) 886 225.

Beaulieu

(Hampshire) Palace House (1538) home of Lord and Lady Montagu of Beaulieu; Ruins of 13th century Beaulieu Abbey; The National Motor Museum.
Tel: Beaulieu (0590) 612345.

There is something special about each of these Historic Houses — all situated in beautiful parklands, and most still owned and lived in by families who have owned them for centuries. These tangible links with the English heritage which can be experienced in the magnificent buildings and wonderfully varied collections, are enhanced by the many extra attractions offered to our visitors. Whether you decide to spend an hour or a full day with us, your visit will be a memorable and enriching experience.

For further information please telephone individual houses.

Blenheim Palace

(Oxfordshire) Home of the 11th Duke of Marlborough, birthplace of Sir Winston Churchill. A gift from the nation to the victor of Blenheim.
Tel: Woodstock (0993) 811325.

Broadlands

(Hampshire) The home of Lord Mountbatten and Lord Palmerston. Architecture and landscape by 'Capability' Brown. Special Exhibition "Mountbatten of Burma" and audio visual show. Located A31 Romsey.
Tel: Romsey (0794) 516878.

Warwick Castle

(Warwickshire) Magnificent medieval fortress. State Rooms. Armoury. Dungeon. Torture Chamber. Ghost Tower. Clock Tower and Barbican. Guy's Tower. Peacock Gardens.
Tel: Warwick (0926) 495421.

Castle Howard

(North Yorkshire) 18th century palace, the first creation of Sir John Vanbrugh. Unique collection of pictures, furniture, tapestries, porcelain and historic costumes. 15 miles from York, off A64.
Tel: Coneysthorpe (065 384) 333.

Woburn Abbey

(Bedfordshire) Home of the Dukes of Bedford. Only one hour by road from London, Oxford, Cambridge, Stratford, Birmingham and Leicester.
Tel: Woburn (052525) 666 or 246.

Vale & Downland Museum
·
WANTAGE

It is an extremely pleasing trend that many local museums are paying more attention to presentation than they once did and this museum in the Oxfordshire market town of Wantage is a prime example. The displays are related to the town and to the area known as the Vale of The White Horse (the white horse being the famous prehistoric figure cut out of a hillside at nearby Uffington) and, despite being so localised, the museum is distinguished by its design and by the imaginative way each section is set out.

The frontage of the museum is a converted cloth-merchant's house dating from the 17th century and a fine example of local vernacular architecture. Visitors have no notion as they approach the museum that this frontage hides a modern extension which, although only a few years old, utilises one of the oldest architectural devices in the form of huge wooden crucks spanning two floors. The natural wood, exposed brickwork and flagstone floors do not pretend to be ancient, but they do make an appreciative contribution to the character of the museum.

The gallery is arranged in chronological order, from the geology of the Vale up to the present day and has large sections on local trades and businesses. The walls are adorned with a fascinating collection of aged bills, receipts, tax demands etc which were discovered in a chimney recess of a local farmhouse. The White Horse, known in the 13th century as the second-best marvel in Britain (after Stonehenge), has a special section and so does Alfred the Great who was born in Wantage in 849AD. There are also reproduction rooms relating to prominent local families—the Ormond Room of the 18th century and a Vicarage room c1850. Transport items include a display relating to the old tramway and an annexe room full of old farm carts, a threshing machine and an early example of a fire engine. Part of the old building which fronts the museum has been converted to house a reconstruction of a Downland farm kitchen with large fireplace, cooking utensils, scrubbed tables, laundry and dairy items.

As well as taking the visitors through all the ages in and around Wantage, the museum also includes an area for temporary exhibitions on local subjects, a small brass rubbing section and a vast amount of local information on what to see and where to go. The shop includes lots of information sheets, work sheets for children, local history books etc. It is the kind of museum that not only gives a good insight into the area for visitors, but is also a place where local people will come to time and time again.

Prison & Police Museum
•
RIPON

This unusual museum is housed in a building long associated with law and order. It was in 1686 that the Mayor and the Ripon Liberty Magistrates ordered the erection of a House of Correction to bring Rogues, Vagabonds and Sturdy Beggars to work and correction in Stammergate (now St Marygate). In subsequent years the establishment became a general prison and a police station. The original House of Correction is now a private residence but the cell block has been converted to house the Museum.

Even before entering the museum, visitors must pass the old City Stocks and once inside, the atmosphere of an old prison is recreated with a reconstruction of a charge room of the 1900s; an empty cell designed to give visitors an impression of solitary confinement and a series of cells depicting all kinds of punishments including pillory, hanging and transportation. The Victorian era is represented by a display on hard labour, with a treadwheel to accommodate ten men and a crank which solitary confinement prisoners were expected to turn 10,000 times a day.

The Police section contains items from the 17th century to the present day, beginning with references to the Ripon Wakeman, responsible for the safety of the City during the night. The present day displays illustrate all aspects of the work of the police including computer technology, firearms and fingerprinting.

•

Maritime Heritage Centre
•
BRISTOL

Bristol has an illustrious nautical history which goes back a long way and on the very quay from which John Cabot departed in March 1497 to discover mainland America, a new museum has been opened to honour this heritage. The Bristol Maritime Heritage centre is housed in a modern building which was opened by Her Majesty The Queen in the summer of 1985 and relates the story of ships and shipbuilding in Bristol with the help of many beautifully constructed ship models, plans and paintings. At the centre of the museum is a section of an iron hull which contains a steam drag-boat engine of 1843 and a small area with seating where an excellent video, presented by the museum's curator, is shown at regular intervals.

The well-designed displays, with clear explanatory panels, trace the fortunes of the Bristol docks right from the time when the first wooden ships were built here using oak from the Forest of Dean. It was from Bristol that the majority of the early pioneers embarked on their voyages to colonise the New World and it was in Bristol that the revolutionary new ship designs of Isambard Kingdom Brunel came to fruition. It is ironic that such a contribution to the shape of the shipbuilding industry in general should have marked the beginning of the end for Bristol as a major port. As ships became larger it became more and more apparent that they could no longer navigate the winding stretch of the River Avon which was prone to silting up. A series of accidents seriously damaged the reputation of the port and eventually many of the maritime businesses either closed down or moved to the estuary at Avonmouth and Portishead.

Some work still continued at the City docks, particularly during the wars when a flourish of naval shipbuilding brought prosperity back to Bristol for a short while, and today there is still some repair work carried out there. Generally, though, the whole area went into a decline until, in recent years, a massive restoration programme was instigated to turn the dock area into a thriving place, with new housing, offices and leisure facilities. This museum is just one of many along the quayside and is particularly relevant to the area.

THE GREAT HOUSES OF THE

VICTORIA & ALBERT MUSEUM

**Apsley House,
The Wellington Museum,**
*at Hyde Park Corner
(Piccadilly Line)*
The Iron Duke's palatial home, known as "Number One, London", given to the nation and now restored to its original splendour.

Ham House,
*near Richmond, Surrey
(65 or 71 buses, or British
Rail to Richmond)*
Owned by the National Trust, administered by the V & A. Originally built in 1610, it was enlarged in the reign of Charles II with its present splendidly baroque interior. In 1678 John Evelyn said its parks and gardens "must needs be admired".

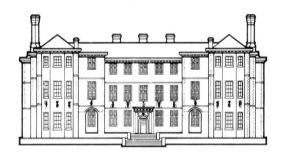

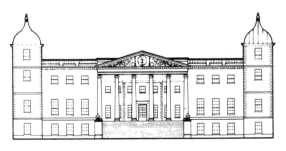

Osterley Park House,
*Osterley, Middlesex
(Piccadilly Line)*
Elizabethan Mansion transformed by Robert Adam into a neo-classical 18th century villa containing the famous Osterley State Bed, now completely restored. Set in its own landscape park. National Trust owned, V & A administered.

FOR DETAILS OF OPENING TIMES AND ADMISSION PRICES SEE GAZETTEER ENTRIES

Blakes Lock Museum
·
READING

Another local museum worthy of note is in the Berkshire town of Reading, always been best known locally for the 'Three Bs'—beer, biscuits and bulbs. As in any prosperous town, a large number of other trades and industries have also made their mark over the years and the town's newest museum is devoted to the most notable of these. It is housed in a former Victorian pumping house beside the Kennet and Avon Canal, a building worthy of preservation in its own right.

One of the most prized possessions in the museum is a complete printers workshop, donated by Parnells, formerly of London Street. Here visitors can see the presses, typefaces, ink containers and furniture of a typical jobbing printer of the late 19th/early 20th centuries. Another unusual reproduction room is that of an old barbers shop complete with old fashioned sinks and barbers chairs, an old oil stove and all the brushes, razors, shaving mugs etc. Old signs on the walls include one which extolls the virtues of a dry shampoo ('prevents catching cold'). There is

also a reconstructed bakery—formerly Huggins of Crown Street—complete with a cast-iron oven made in nearby Wokingham, an old dough trough and a variety of baking tins, pansions and scales.

Smaller exhibits include a number of shop fronts containing such things as the contents of a sweet shop, a toy shop, a shoemakers, a photographers and an extensive collection of old ironmongery, including tools and household items. Old Reading Chemists shops are represented too, with all the usual old jars, bottles and the old drawered cabinet where medicines were kept. Reading Doctor, E. M. Ruddock, wrote a book on homeopathic medicine in 1868 and a copy of this lies alongside a homeopathic medicine cabinet. Reading Sauce was nationally famous in its day, before being eclipsed by Lea and Perrins' Worcester variety, and was made in Duke Street by Charles Cocks. Mineral water was another thriving industry and a local dairy is also represented.

Being so close to the canal, and the Rivers Thames and Kennet, there is naturally a display on those waterways. Trading wharfs were in existence at least as far back as the time of the Abbey and parts of 12th and 14th century timber wharfs were discovered during

recent excavations. Displays include boat-building, with a set of tools, patterns etc set out as in a traditional workshop; angling and commercial fishing, particularly eel fishing; wharfs, locks and bridges and a colourful collection of canal art, with brightly painted buckets, kettles, teapots and other items used by the narrow-boat people.

●　　　●　　　●

Sussex Farm Heritage Centre
●
HERSTMONCEUX

Think of the countryside of years gone by and undoubtedly the first image will be that of a Shire horse plodding steadily across a field. It might seem a romantic image now, but these magnificent creatures, weighing almost a ton, dominated the landscape for many centuries because of their phenomenal strength and stamina. In these days of computerised farming, when huge tractors come complete with stereo systems and cows are milked on auto-mated roundabouts, there is nothing we like more than to see how things were done in the old days. A perfect place to do this is the Sussex

Farm Heritage Centre at Herstmonceux—a working farm run in the time-honoured way, where the only horse-power is on four legs. A team of the finest, award-winning Shire horses can be seen, both working and at close quarters and there is other livestock on show including several rare breeds. An impressive collection of rare and historic agricultural machinery and farm equipment is also on display, most of it still used around the farm. Horse-drawn vehicles range from a simple brewery dray to the complex threshing machine, still a vital piece of equipment for the production of thatching straw.

The farm is in a lovely part of the Weald and facilities include plenty of parking, picnic sites, light refreshments and souvenirs.

Take a trip to the 18th century

Spitbank Fort
•
PORTSMOUTH

In the 1860's, when Napoleon III was threatening our shores, Victorian engineers constructed a massive fort of granite and iron at the entrance to Portsmouth harbour as part of a network of coastal defences. Divers were sent down 35 feet to the sea bed to position solid stone foundations and upon them a circular wall, 15 feet thick at basement level, was built. As we all know, the expected invasion did not materialise, but a tour of Spitbank Fort will show just how determined the Victorians were to prevent it. Visitors can explore a maze of passages and over 50 rooms on two levels—the gun floor and the basement. Replicas of the massive 38 ton guns can be seen, together with the original shell and cartridge hoists which are still in working order. The fort had a fresh water supply from 402 ft-deep well and this too is still in working order, as are the forge and the Victorian cooking ranges which were still in use during World War II.

The fort was purchased from the Government in 1980 in a badly vandalised state and, although restoration work still continues, enough work has been done to enable visitors to appreciate its value. It's position at Spithead, where the Queen traditionally reviews her fleet, affords panoramic views of the Solent—a particularly busy piece of water with both commercial and pleasure craft always around. To reach the fort visitors must take a short boat ride either from Gosport pontoon or from Clarence Pier, Southsea (inside the fun-fair).

• • •

M U S E U M

O F   T H E

Y E A R

F or many years the AA has produced this guide and it has always included a large number of museums—from the vast national collections to the smallest of village museums. After taking an interest in them all for so long, we felt that it was time to make our own Museum of the Year award. Of course, choosing one museum from so many is no easy task and so we decided to confine our search to those museums that have opened during the last ten years. We also looked particularly at places which would appeal to all age groups, where people with a wide range of interests would be happy to spend some time. The list of candidates was impressive and we discovered some interesting new ways of presenting historical facts and artefacts. Here we announce the winner and give some space to the runners-up.

Winner

Black Country Museum

DUDLEY

I n our search for an AA Museum of the Year we can truthfully say that we considered museums from all parts of Britain. For our winner we came eventually to this gem in the heart of the West Midlands. Here, on a formerly derelict industrial site, a living and working museum has been created to represent a real Black Country community.

A village street scene – perfect for turn-of-the-century period film-makers

Some fascinating goods are on display at Gregory's General Store

There are quite a number of museums which urge us to 'step back in time', but there are few which can achieve this so convincingly as the Black Country Museum, for here is not just another collection of reconstructed buildings—these are real streets with shops, homes and industries. Each building—and they have all been brought from local areas—is not only furnished and equipped, but is also occupied by a costumed guide who will talk with authority and good humour about their particular environment. The shopkeeper of the general store—Gregory's Store c1883—will go through all the goods on the shelves, explaining what they are or what they were used for. There is everything here, from blue bags to lace-up corsets; flat irons to bullseyes.

Poorer dwellings line this village street

A display of meat, poultry and game takes up one window of Gregory's shop

Between these shops is the home of a chainmaker of the 1880s—very comfortable by the standards of that era—and the lady of the house will show visitors around, particularly concentrating on the room at the back where the family would spend most of their time (the front parlour was always kept for special occasions).

A little further along the street a chemists shop is a replica, rather than a reconstruction, but the entire contents of the original shop were donated to the museum, including its old wooden counter, cabinets, all the old bottles, an ingenious wooden pill maker and a pestle and mortar. In an adjacent room is a photographer's studio, complete with old camera, costumes and sepia tinted photographs.

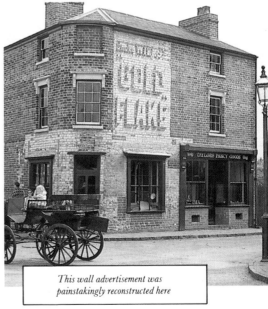

This wall advertisement was painstakingly reconstructed here

Pills and potions and photography

Out into the back garden you will see the 'brew'us' which contained laundry equipment and a bread oven, the outside toilet and the chainmaker's workshop. In the next street the houses show how the poorer folk lived with sparse furnishings and few home comforts.

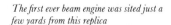
The first ever beam engine was sited just a few yards from this replica

Spiritual guidance was provided in this austere little Methodist Chapel

No community would be complete without its place of worship and its pub and these two institutions face each other across the corner of the street. The Methodist Chapel was first built at Netherton in 1837 and played an important part in the life of the community. The pub, the Bottle and Glass Inn, was built before 1836 in Brierley Hill. Today it is still licensed and operates as any other pub, so that during opening hours visitors may also become customers.

There are a number of workshops in operation at the museum: a glass engraver can be visited and he will talk about his craft as he works, displaying a number of items for sale; the chainmaker can be seen carrying out this difficult and dangerous work at his forge; there is also a mid-Victorian bakery with two coal-fired bread ovens and always the tempting aroma of freshly-baked bread.

An authentic old pub – and still licensed too

Coal mining was a major industry within the Black Country

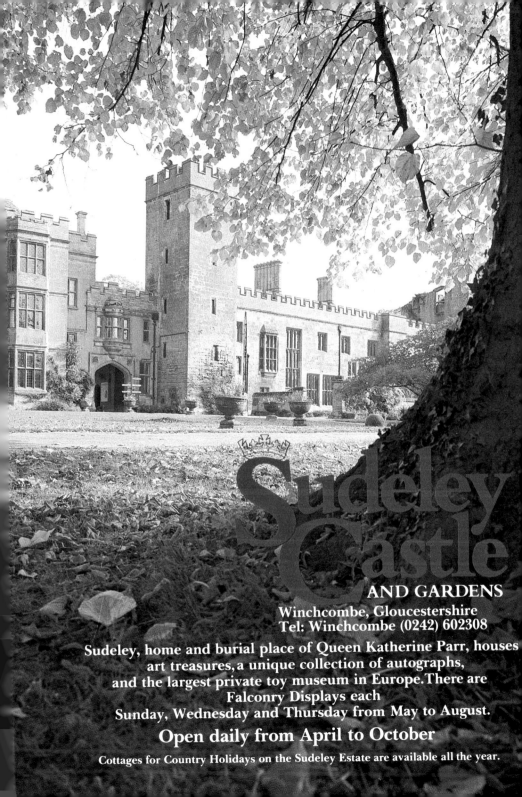

Free transport from the entrance to the village site in a 1920 tramcar

with helter-skelter, carousel, swing-boats and cake-walk.

Roll up for all the fun of the fair

One of the first exhibits visitors see on entering the museum is a replica of an engine house with a Newcomen beam engine. Nearby is the Racecourse Colliery, with its timber head frame and miners' hovel, representing a major industry hereabouts—in fact, when the site was cleared for the museum over forty filled-in mine shafts were discovered. The 1920 tramcar which transports visitors from the entrance to the village passes close by here and its terminus is opposite a reconstruction of an old fairground—a particularly colourful exhibit complete

Canals played a major part in local industry and transport, and they too are represented in the village. A canal bridge of 1879 is made mainly of cast and wrought iron; there is a boat dock, complete with narrowboat 'Diamond'; a lifting bridge of 1920 and a working

The entrance to the famous Dudley Tunnel leading to old lime workings

A real fairground atmosphere here, with traditional rides and sideshows

repair yard. By far the most important aspect of the canal exhibits here is the Dudley Tunnel, built in 1779–1792 and one of the great engineering feats of the 18th century. Today the Dudley Canal Trust run trips through the tunnel using the world's first electric narrow boat.

Visitors enter the village over this reconstructed metal bridge

Guides in traditional dress invite visitors to try their luck here

There are lime kilns at the museum too, built by Lord Ward in 1842 to extract lime for mortar, fertilizer and whitewash.

The winding gear of the Racecourse Mine

Just as the museum is a working one, it is also a constantly developing one and there are even more plans for the future. More buildings are awaiting reconstruction, stacked carefully in crates with every brick numbered. Much credit is due to the skill of the re-builders here—witness the building which still has its painted advertisement on an outside wall—and equal credit must go to the lively staff and volunteer guides who interpret the significance of the museum so well.

Just part of the museum site with the boatyard in front of the village

London Toy and Model Museum

BAYSWATER, W2

If this museum sounds too specialised to fit into our criteria for this award, think again. Here, in this leafy residential area off Bayswater Road, we have a museum which certainly appeals to children and model-makers, but which is also fascinating to anyone who has ever owned a teddy bear or a train set.

Several galleries are arranged on two floors and they contain displays of all kinds of toys and models, including thousands of model soldiers—Roman legionnaires to Commandos. There are also tin toys, including early car models and the largest known clockwork paddle steamer, toy animals of all shapes and

Famous names in a shopfront display

sizes and a small, but representative collection of dolls. One gallery depicts a nursery of c1860 and another takes the form of replica shops of two of Britain's best loved toy and model companies— Meccano and Bassett-Lowke. Naturally, there are lots of railway and vehicle displays, including some push-button working models, and the Tiatsa miniature vehicle collection of 15,000 items, is shown to visitors 2000 pieces at a time. Appropriately, as the museum is just 5 minutes from Paddington station, it also houses the Paddington Bear archives including Michael Bond's original manuscripts.

The gardens are among the museum's greatest assets and lots of activities for children take place here, including rides on a miniature steam railway, a small fairground carousel, a playbus and a Comet 4B flight simulator. Children may bring non-petrol driven boats for sailing on the boating pond and once a month the open track is available for them to bring their gauge 0 & 1 clockwork and steam locomotives.

The annual Teddy Bears' Picnic takes place in the museum's delightful garden

Cardiff Castle

1,900 YEARS OF HISTORY - Open all year

Contact: Information Office, City Hall, Cardiff. (0222) 31033

Runner-up

Boat Museum

ELLESMERE PORT

n important part of our national heritage is linked to the age of the canals, when most of the goods we now see thundering down our motorways were silently hauled along a network of inland waterways. An entire culture developed around the boat people—their dress, their songs, their lifestyle and their art—and all this was in danger of disappearing for ever. Fortunately, sufficient people cared enough to make sure that this did not happen and this superb collection was opened to the public in 1976.

A corner of the main exhibition hall showing different types of cargo

No better site for the museum could have been found than this huge basin on the Shropshire Union Canal, adjacent to both the River Mersey and the Manchester Ship Canal. Not only is there enough dock space for the floating exhibits, there are locks, wharfs and all the old buildings which once kept the waterborn traffic going. Warehouses, offices, company housing, workshops and mills were all grouped around the basin and many have now been restored to their former use or converted to provide exhibition space or visitor facilities.

We are all familiar with the narrowboats which are now used increasingly for holidays or pleasure trips, but here we can see them as they were originally—workboats upon which the boatman, his wife and his children would live in terribly cramped quarters. We can see the tiny cabins where everything the family owned would have to be tidily kept and where a stove would burn even through the summer so that meals could be cooked. The Wideboats or Barges are at least twice as wide as the narrowboats and there are several examples of these on show. There are also icebreakers, a weedcutter—essential for keeping the waterways navigable—and tugs. Larger craft include a 300 ton Weaver Packet, a steam Clyde Puffer and a concrete barge built during the Second World War to economise on the use of steel. A number of craft can always be seen undergoing restoration.

The Island Warehouse contains the main exhibition area of the museum and includes a number of boats, including a dug-out canoe, coracles, a Starvationer—one of the early narrowboats so named because its ribs can be seen—and the centrepiece, 'Friendship', which is perhaps the most famous of all narrowboats. Here too is the Lecture Theatre, refreshments, the shop and the archives.

With an art form all of their own the boats are meticulously maintained

Visitors can inspect many of these colourful craft at close quarters

Among other buildings on the site are Porters Row cottages which have been restored to show the living conditions of their former residents at different periods of the dock development. The Hydraulic Pumping Station contains restored steam engines which are regularly demonstrated. Other buildings have been converted to house further displays, including the story of the Manchester Ship Canal and the use of horses on the canals, and there is an Education and Conference Centre. Guided tours, boat trips and lots of special events complete the services offered by this outstanding museum.

WILTON HOUSE

S·A·L·I·S·B·U·R·Y
W·I·L·T·S·H·I·R·E

FOR THOSE WHO APPRECIATE
THE BEST OF BRITAIN'S HERITAGE

OPEN 25TH MARCH – 12TH OCTOBER, 1986

TUESDAYS – SATURDAYS INCLUSIVE
& BANK HOLIDAYS 11 A.M. – 6 P.M. SUNDAYS 1 – 6 P.M.
LAST ADMISSION TO HOUSE & GROUNDS 5.15 P.M.

GUIDED TOURS DAILY EXCEPT ON SUNDAYS
ENQUIRIES TELEPHONE: (0722) 743115

$$\boxed{\textit{Runner-up}}$$

Big Pit Mining Museum

BLAENAVON

It is impossible for anyone who has never worked in a coal mine to understand just what the job is like and how inhospitable the working environment is—even today, when new technology has only taken away some of the sheer physical effort of hacking coal from the ground. This pit, located in the South Wales Coalfield and a working mine until 1980, now gives visitors an opportunity to go underground and experience some of the working conditions of the miners for themselves.

Coal, 300 million years old and an essential ingredient in our industrial development

All kitted up with the traditional helmet, complete with lamp, and a small canister of emergency air, parties are taken down the 300 ft mine shaft and into the original seams. Usually the guide is an ex-miner and his commentary will really bring to life the day-to-day activities of a working mine. He will certainly recall mining in recent years, and will also be able to talk about the old days when pit-ponies were still in use (not as long ago as one might imagine). In fact, the underground stables where these sturdy creatures were kept are part of the tour, and the ponies' names can still be seen on their stalls. Originally kept underground for the whole of their working lives, the ponies were eventually awarded an annual two weeks holiday on the surface.

Visitors also tour the narrow tunnels, just wide enough for the tracks which carried the coal trucks to and from the workings. At regular intervals niches have been cut into the walls. At the warning of an approaching truck, any miner still in the tunnel had to dive into one of the recesses to avoid certain death. Accidents were not uncommon, both from the trucks and from the whiplashes of the cables which drew them along. Dangers still exist and

This recently-closed colliery is still intact and a fine reminder of our industrial heritage

rigorous precautions are taken to avoid any mishaps in the mines—anything that might cause sparks, such as watches or cigarette lighters, must be left behind on the surface. Visitors are also advised to bring warm clothing and sturdy shoes—the temperature underground is constantly low and the tour lasts for about one hour.

Once the tour underground is completed there are further exhibits to be seen on the surface, including a reconstructed miner's cottage, the locker rooms, and the blacksmith's workshop with its five forges and all the associated tools of the trade.

The pithead railway with its steam and diesel engines can also be seen and there is an exhibition hall illustrating the history of the Big Pit. The entire site provides a tremendous insight into what is still a hot, dirty and sometimes hazardous way to earn a living.

$\mathscr{Runner}\text{-}\mathscr{up}$

Scottish Agricultural Museum

INGLISTON

ithin what can only be described as an unprepossessing building on the outskirts of Edinburgh, we found this fascinating museum on the story of Scottish Agriculture. The emphasis here is on the hardships and privations endured by Scots who tried to make a living from the land. Reconstructed homesteads include a typical bothy showing the comfortless conditions in which the unmarried farm labourers would live; the fisherman's cottage—tiny and sparsely furnished; the herdsman's cottage which was the most comfortable of all. A cruck-framed croft was also in the process of reconstruction at the time of our visit.

Not many home comforts beside this hearth

The first display in the museum consists of enlarged photographs of 18th and 19th century gravestones upon which are carved motifs and implements relating to the dead person's trade. The ground floor displays then proceed to take you through the farming year—from ploughing, harrowing and sowing to harvesting, threshing, winnowing and milling. Exhibits include many different implements, backed by excellent old photographs and informative captions which explain how people worked on the land. The crofter's life and the fisherman's life are also depicted in the same way and the museum is particularly strong in material from the Hebrides and other islands. The traditional dress of the different kinds of farmworker is illustrated and there are sections dealing with thatching and peat-cutting.

The upstairs gallery is devoted to animal husbandry. The shepherd's life is also included together with types of sheep, spinning and natural vegetable dyes. The interpretation of the subject is admirably achieved here, conveying a powerful impression of agricultural daily life, and particular attention is paid to gaining the interest of young visitors.

GRANADA

Your welcome to the motorways for fast and friendly service 24 hours a day 365 days a year

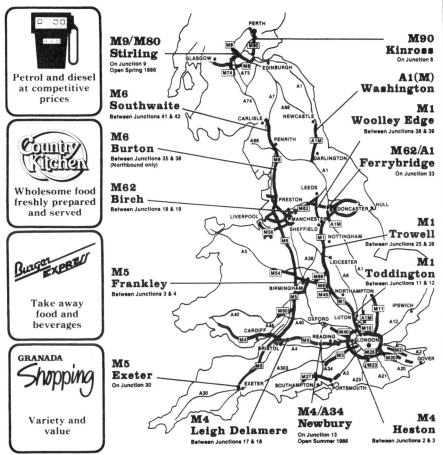

Petrol and diesel at competitive prices

Country Kitchen

Wholesome food freshly prepared and served

Burger EXPRESS

Take away food and beverages

GRANADA Shopping

Variety and value

M9/M80 Stirling
On Junction 9
Open Spring 1986

M6 Southwaite
Between Junctions 41 & 42

M6 Burton
Between Junctions 35 & 36
(Northbound only)

M62 Birch
Between Junctions 18 & 19

M5 Frankley
Between Junctions 3 & 4

M5 Exeter
On Junction 30

M4 Leigh Delamere
Between Junctions 17 & 18

M4/A34 Newbury
On Junction 13
Open Summer 1986

M90 Kinross
On Junction 6

A1(M) Washington

M1 Woolley Edge
Between Junctions 38 & 39

M62/A1 Ferrybridge
On Junction 33

M1 Trowell
Between Junctions 25 & 26

M1 Toddington
Between Junctions 11 & 12

M4 Heston
Between Junctions 2 & 3

Granada Motorway Service Areas offer a wide range of light refreshments, snacks, take-away food and full meals to suit all tastes and pockets. Shopping and petrol facilities are also available.

Choose Granada–you are very welcome

Great Castles and Historic Attractions in Wales.

Wales is a land rich in heritage, with romantic medieval castles, fascinating houses and some of the finest abbeys, churches and other historic attractions to be found in Europe.

When on your travels through Wales don't miss majestic Caernarfon Castle, or Beaumaris Castle in Anglesey, rightly considered to be one of the most beautiful castles in Wales. On the hills to the North of Cardiff is the lovely Castell Coch which resembles a fairy tale castle from the pages of a Hans Christian Andersen story. Set in probably the most romantic valley in Wales, and well worth a visit, is serene Tintern Abbey.

These are just some of the historic attractions in the care of Cadw: Welsh Historic Monuments.

heritage IN WALES

Join the 'Heritage in Wales' membership scheme and you can visit the historic attractions in the care of Cadw FREE of charge.

Heritage in Wales spans 6,000 years of history! You will find hours, weeks and years of enjoyment delving into Wales' past.

When you become a member of Heritage in Wales you'll receive a twice yearly newspaper; free organised lectures and site visits, discounts on Cadw gifts plus a free map and car sticker.

If you would like to know more about the historic attractions in the care of Cadw and the 'Heritage in Wales' membership scheme, write to the address below giving your name and address and we will forward a full colour Heritage in Wales brochure and application form.

Cadw
WELSH HISTORIC MONUMENTS

Cadw: Welsh Historic Monuments Marketing Dept (AA86) Brunel House
2 Fitzalan Road, CARDIFF CF2 1UY Tel: (0222) 465511

Gazetteer

The gazetteer gives locations and details of AA-listed establishments in **England, Wales and Scotland, Channel Islands and Isle of Man.** Details for islands are shown under individual placenames; the gazetteer text also gives appropriate cross-references. A useful first point of reference is to consult the location maps which show where AA-listed establishments are situated.
(There is no map for the Isles of Scilly.)

ABBOTSBURY
Dorset
Map **3** SY58

Abbotsbury Gardens Beach Rd
☎ (0305) 871387

20 acres of rare and tender plants growing in Mediterranean-type climate, unique on mainland Britain. Plants for sale.

Open 16 Mar–19 Oct, daily 10–6.

£1.50 (ch 50p, pen £1) Parties.

P ⚏ ৬ garden centre

Abbotsbury Swannery New Barn Rd
☎ (0305) 871242

Famous breeding ground for the largest catch of mute swans in the British Isles

and a home or port of call for a great many species of wild birds.

Open 11 May–14 Sep daily, 9.30–4.30.

Admission fee payable.

P (400 yds) ৬ ✖

ABERCRAF (ABERCRAVE)
Powys
Map **3** SN81

Dan-yr-Ogof Showcaves (3 m N on A4067)
☎ (0639) 730284 or 730693

The largest showcave complex in Western Europe, containing some of the largest stalactites and stalagmites in the country. Guided tours of passages. Children's model Dinosaur Park. Britain's first Archaeological Showcave. Dry ski-slope.

Open Etr–Oct daily from 10; for winter opening please telephone.

£2.65 (ch & pen £1.65) School Party 15 + £1.25.

P (30 yds) ⚏ ৬ (ground floor only) shop & information centre

ABERDEEN
Grampian *Aberdeenshire*
Map **15** NJ90

Aberdeen Art Gallery and Museums
Schoolhill
☎ (0224) 646333

Scottish art from 16th century to present day, with outstanding collection of 20th-century paintings. Water colours, print-room, and art library; contemporary sculpture and decorative arts; special exhibitions and events throughout the year.

Open Mon–Sat 10–5 (8pm Thu) Sun 2–5. (Closed Xmas and 1 & 2 Jan).

Free.

P (300 yds) ⚏ ৬ shop ✖ (ex guide dogs)

Cruickshank Botanic Garden
University of Aberdeen
☎ (0224) 40241 ext 5250 or 5247

Developed at the end of the 19th century, the 10 acres include rock and water gardens, a heather garden, collections of spring bulbs, gentians and Alpine plants. There is also an extensive collection of trees and shrubs.

Open all year Mon–Fri 9–4.30; also Sat & Sun May–Sep 2–4.30.

Free.

P (100 yds) ৬

James Dun's House 61 Schoolhill
☎ (0224) 646333

18th-century house used as a museum with changing exhibitions.

Open Mon–Sat 10–5 (Closed Xmas and 1 & 2 Jan).

Free.

P (400 yds) shop ✖ (ex guide dogs)

Aberdeen Maritime Museum Provost Ross's House, Shiprow
☎ (0224) 572215. For group bookings (0224) 646333

This new museum, housed in Aberdeen's oldest surviving building which is a National Trust of Scotland property, highlights Aberdeen's maritime history in dramatic and graphic fashion. Trust Visitor Centre shop.

Museum open Mon–Sat 10–5 (Closed Xmas and 1 & 2 Jan). Visitor Centre; May, Sep & 2–21 Dec, Mon–Sat 10–4 (5pm Jun, Jul & Aug)

Free.

P 50 yds) ♿ (ground floor only) shop ✖ (ex guide dogs)

Provost Skene's House Guestrow
☎ (0224) 641086

A 17th-century house restored as a museum of local history and social life. Furnishings, panelling and plaster ceilings of 17th and 18th century.

Open Mon–Sat 10–5. (Closed Xmas and 1 & 2 Jan).

Free

P (30 yds) ⚲ ♿ (ground floor only) shop ✖ (ex guide dogs)

ABERDOUR
Fife *Fife*
Map **11** NT18

see also **Incholm Abbey** under **Queensferry (South)**

Aberdour Castle

A 14th- to 17th-century stronghold. Fine dovecote and gardens.

Open Apr–Sep, Sun 2–7, Wed–Sat 9.30–7; Oct–Mar, Sun 2–4, Wed–Sat 9.30–4.

Aberdeen
—
Aberystwyth

(Closed Thu pm & Fri)
✳ 50p (ch & pen 25p)
⚠ (AM)

ABERGAVENNY
Gwent
Map **3** SO21

Abergavenny Castle & Museum
☎ (0873) 4282

Antiquities, rural craft tools, Welsh kitchen, saddler's shop, costumes and exhibits of local history. The castle remains date from 12th- to 14th-century and include walls, towers and gateway.

Museum open Mar–Oct, Mon–Sat 11–1, 2–5, Sun 2–5; Nov–Feb, Mon–Sat only 11–1, 2–4. Castle open daily 8–dusk.

✳ 45p (ch & pen 25p). Local residents free. Castle free.

P (200 yds) ⚠ (for disabled only) ♿ (ground floor & gardens only) shop ✖

ABERGWILI
Dyfed
Map **2** SN42

Carmarthen Museum Old Bishop's Palace
☎ Carmarthen (0267) 231691

Local prehistoric, geology and natural history. Roman and medieval displays, military history and costume. Folklife. Cheese and butter making, local pottery and temporary exhibitions. Egyptian exhibition 7 Jun–13 Sep, includes objects loaned by the British Museum.

Open Mon–Sat, 10–4.30. (Closed Xmas–New Year).

✳ 50p (ch, pen, students & unemployed 25p) Parties 10+.

⚠ ⛽ ♿ (ground floor only) shop ✖

ABERLADY
Lothian *East Lothian*
Map **12** NT47

Myreton Motor Museum
☎ (08757) 288

A comprehensive collection of cars and motorcycles from 1896, cycles from 1863 and commercial vehicles. Latest addition is a rapidly expanding collection of historic British military vehicles.

Open daily 10–6 (summer); 10–5 (winter).

✳ 75p (ch 16 25p).

⚠ ♿ (ground floor only) ✖ ⓥ

ABERYSTWYTH
Dyfed
Map **6** SN58

National Library of Wales Penglais Hill
☎ (0970) 3816

One of Britain's six copyright libraries, housed in imposing building of 1911–16, with later additions. Large number of books in all languages, musical publications, prints, drawings, and old deeds; specialises in Welsh and Celtic literature. Exhibitions of pictures.

Library & reading rooms open Mon–Fri 9.30–6, Sat until 5pm. (Closed BHs.). Exhibition Gallery only, open Whit & Aug BH.

Free.

⚠ ⚲ ♿ shop ✖

Vale of Rheidol Narrow Gauge Steam Railway
☎ (0970) 612378

Only steam railway operated by British Rail, with 3 engines and 16 passenger coaches (1ft 11¾in gauge). Opened in 1902. Runs between Aberystwyth and Devil's Bridge (11¾m) passing through some of the finest scenery in Wales. One of the 'Great Little Trains of Wales'. Events planned for GWR 150 year celebration.

Operates 24 Mar–24 Oct. Journey time (each direction) one hour. (Vista car & 1st class seating now available). Telephone for details of times of trains.

Fares: Standard £3.20 (ch £1.75). Economy £2.70 (ch £1.50).

⚠ ⚲ ♿ shop

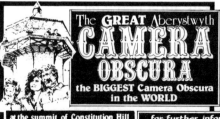

ABINGDON
Oxfordshire
Map **4** SU49

Abingdon Museum County Hall Market Pl
☎ (0235) 23703

Built 1678 by Christopher Kempster, one of Wren's master-masons; described as the grandest Market-House in England. Local history, archaeology, charters and town trades from clothmaking to MG car company. Temporary exhibitions programme.

Open daily, 2–5. (Closed BH).

10p (ch 5p).

P (500 yds) shop ✖

ACTON BURNELL
Shropshire
Map **7** SJ50

Acton Burnell Castle

Ruined 13th-century fortified manor house where the first English Parliament is said to have met in 1283.

Open at all reasonable times.

Free.

(AM)

ACTON SCOTT
Shropshire
Map **7** SO48

Acton Scott Working Farm Museum
Wenlock Lodge
(3m S of Church Stretton off A49)
☎ Marshbrook (06946) 306/7

Farm, at centre of a 1200-acre estate, which demonstrates agricultural practice as it was at the turn of the century. Rare breeds of farm animals are stocked and work is done by hand or horse. Visitors may participate in some of the farm work and craft demonstrations take place at weekends.

Open Apr–Oct, Mon–Sat 10–5; Sun & BH 10–6. (Last admission 30 mins before closing time.) Details not confirmed for 1986.

✻ £1.20 (ch 60p, pen free). Party.

⚠ ⚼ ⏟ ᴋ (ground floor only) shop ✖ Ⓥ

ADLINGTON
Cheshire
Map **7** SJ98

Adlington Hall W of Adlington Sta.
☎ Prestbury (0625) 829206

Tudor banqueting hall with Elizabethan black and white portion 18th-century additions, containing 'Bernard Smith' organ, restored in 1959 and associated with Handel. Gardens include yew walk and lime avenue.

Open Good Fri–Sep, Sun & BH 2–5.30 (also Wed & Sat during Aug); parties on weekdays by arrangement.

£1.50 (ch 75p). Party 25 + £1.

⚠ ⚼ ᴋ (ground floor only) shop Ⓥ

ALCESTER
Warwickshire
Map **4** SP05

Ragley Hall (2m SW)
☎ (0789) 762090

17th-century home of the Seymour family, with splendid great hall by James Gibbs. Fine gardens. Park includes adventure wood and country trail. Newfoundland Club Centenary 2 & 3 Aug 1986.

House and gardens open 29 Mar–28 Sep Tue–Thu, Sat & Sun 1.30–5.30, except Tue–Thu (Jun–Aug) 12–5. BH Mons 12–5.30. Park 11–6 daily (ex Mon & Fri) (Jul & Aug open daily).

House, garden & park ✻ £2 (ch £1 & pen £1.50). Party 30 + . Park £1 (ch 50p).

⚠ ⚼ (licensed) ⏟ ᴋ shop ✖ Ⓥ

ALDBOROUGH
North Yorkshire
Map **8** SE46

Roman Town

Remains of northernmost Roman town (though not northernmost military station). Positions of boundary walls, two

---

tessellated pavements and small museum.

Open, see end of gazetteer.

✻ 50p (ch 16 & pen 25p). Free during winter.

(AM)

ALDEBURGH
Suffolk
Map **5** TM45

Moot Hall Museum
☎ (072 885) 2158

Restored, two-storey, early 16th-century timber-framed building. Council chamber on upper floor, reached by external staircase, contains old maps and prints, objects of local interest.

Open Etr–Jun Sat & Sun 2.30–5, Jul–Sep daily 2.30–5.

25p (accompanied ch free).

P (limited) ✖

ALDERSHOT
Hampshire
Map **4** SU85

Airborne Forces Museum Browning Barracks, Queens Av
☎ (0252) 24431 ext 619

One of the Army's finest museums the exhibition includes briefing models for WWII operations. A post-war display including the Falklands 1982 together with captured enemy arms, vehicles, dioramas of actions, parachutes, equipment, photographs and many scale models. A medal display includes VC and GC's. Airborne Forces Day Parade and Display held first Sat in Jul.

Open daily (closed Xmas day) Mon–Fri 9–12.30, 2–4.30; Sat & Sun 10–12.30 & 2–4.30.

50p (ch, pen & members or ex-members of Airborne Forces 25p) Party 20 + .

⚠ shop ✖

Royal Corps of Transport Museum
Buller Barracks
☎ (0252) 24431 ext 2417

Uniforms and badges of Royal Corps of Transport and predecessors. In addition →

---

models and photographs of vehicles used from 1795 to present day.

Open Mon–Fri 9–12.30, 2–4.30, 'At Home Day' 12 Jul Corps Sunday 13 Jul. (Closed BH).

Free.

&. &. shop

ALFORD
Grampian *Aberdeenshire*
Map **15** NJ51

Alford Valley Railway
☎ (0336) 2107

Narrow-gauge passenger railway in 2 sections Alford–Haughton Park, Haughton Park–Murray Park approx 1½ miles each. Steam on peak weekends. Diesel traction. Railway Spring Fair 19 & 20 Apr 1986. Alford cavalcade 20 Jul.

Open Apr, May & Sep weekends and party bookings weekday from 11–5, Jun–Aug daily from 11 (30 min service).

80p return fare (ch 50p).

&. ⊞ &. shop

Grampian Transport Museum
☎ (0336) 2292

A road and rail museum with strong local themes. Large collection of vintage vehicles including horse drawn, steam, cars and lorries. Alford cavalcade vintage vehicle rally 19 & 20 Jul.

Open Apr–Sep, daily 10.30–5.

Transport Museum £1 (ch & pen 50p). Railway Museum 30p (ch 10p). Both £1.10 (ch & pen 55p).

&. ⊞ &. (ground floor and gardens only) shop & garden centre

ALFORD
Lincolnshire
Map **9** TF47

Alford Manor House Folk Museum
West St
☎ (05212) 2278

c1540 Museum includes period shops, school room, maid's bedroom, dairy, agricultural and transport galleries. Weekend craft market spring & late summer BHs.

Open May–Sep, Mon–Fri. 10.30–1, 2–4.30. 30p (ch 15p).

P (100 yds) ⊒ shop

ALFRISTON
East Sussex
Map **5** TQ50

Clergy House
☎ (0323) 870001

A mid 14th-century half-timbered thatched priests' house. There is a Medieval Hall, exhibition room, a further two rooms and garden.

Open Etr–Oct daily 11–6 (or dusk if earlier). Last admission ½hr before closing. Shop only also open Nov–Xmas.

70p. Party.

shop (open until Xmas) (NT)

Drusillas Zoo Park
☎ (0323) 870234

One of the best small zoos in the south with a good, varied collection of small mammals, rare breeds of farm stock; penguins, flamingo lagoon and newly opened Japanese garden. Adventure playground, railway, pottery and leather-craft shop. Butterfly house, cottage bakery and English vineyard (tours and tastings). English Wine Fair 1st weekend in Sep. Antique Fair 3rd Wed in each month May–Sep.

Open 22 Mar–2 Nov, daily 11–5.30. In winter zoo open daily until dusk (ex Xmas).

£2.25 (incl zoo, playland & railway ride) ch 3–13; Adults £2.25 & pen £1.50 (incl zoo & railway ride). Grounds free.

&. ⊒ (licensed) ⊞ &. shop & garden centre ✖ (in zoo or playland)

ALLINGTON
Kent
Map **5** TQ75

Allington Castle (The Order of Carmelites)
☎ Maidstone (0622) 54080

A 13th-century moated castle, with later alterations, standing on the banks of the River Medway. It retains castellated curtain walls, gatehouse and great hall.

Open daily (ex Xmas day) 2–4. Mammoth medieval market 14 Jun. Bonfire, fireworks & crafts 1 Nov. Xmas craft market Sun 7 Dec.

£1 (ch 50p).

&. &. (ground floor & gardens only) shop ⓥ

ALLOWAY
Strathclyde *Ayrshire*
Map **10** NS31

Burns' Cottage
☎ (0292) 41215

Thatched cottage, built in 1757, now museum, birthplace of Robert Burns in 1759.

Open Apr–mid Oct, Mon–Sat 10–5; Mar–May & Sep & Oct, Sun 2–7; Jun–Aug 10–7.

✱ 80p (ch & pen 40p).

P (100 yds) ⊒ (Etr–Oct) &. shop

Also **Burns' Monument**
☎ (0292) 41321

Built in 1823 to a fine design by Thomas Hamilton Junior with sculptures of characters in Burns' poems by a self-taught artist, James Thom.

Open as for **Burns' Cottage.**

Admission included in entrance to Burns Cottage.

P (100 yds) shop

Land O'Burn's Centre Murdoch's Loan
☎ (0292) 43700

Robert Burns Interpretation Centre. Audio-visual, multi-screen presentation showing the life of Robert Burns. Burns Festival 7–15 Jun. Exhibition area. Landscaped gardens.

Open daily 10–5; Jun & Sep 10–6, Jul & Aug 10–9 (10–6 Sat & Sun).

Admission fee payable.

&. &. shop

ALNWICK CASTLE
(Home of the Duke of Northumberland)

Including the Keep, Guard Chamber, Library and other principal apartments, Dungeon, State Coach and Museum of British and Roman Antiquities. Pictures by Titian, Canaletto, Van Dyck and other famous Artists, fine furniture, Meissen china and various historical heirlooms.

OPEN TO VISITORS
3rd May to 3rd October 1986 (Daily except Saturdays)
(Open Saturdays Bank Holiday Weekends only)
1 p.m. to 5 p.m. (No Admission after 4.30 p.m.)
Admission: Adults - £1.70, O.A.P.'s £1.00, Children under 16 — 80p
(Organised Party Rates: Adults £1.40, Children 60p)

FREE PARKING
Enquiries to The Supervisor, Estate Office
Alnwick Castle, Alnwick. (*Tel. Alnwick 602722 or 602207*)

ALNWICK
Northumberland
Map **12** NU11

Alnwick Castle
☎ (0665) 602722 or 602207

Norman border stronghold of Percy family, restored by Salvin. Keep, armoury, museums and main apartments.

Open 3 May–3 Oct, Sun–Fri & BH Sats 1–5 (no admission after 4.30 pm).

£1.70 (ch 16 80p pen £1). Party.

⚹ shop ✖

ALRESFORD
Hampshire
Map **4** SU53

Mid Hants Railway (Watercress Line)
Alresford Station
☎ (096273) 3810 or 4200

Steam railway now running on ten miles of the old Winchester to Alton line between Alresford & Alton. The train travels through beautiful Hampshire countryside with views of hills and watercress beds, after which the railway is named. At Ropley a variety of steam locomotives are in various stages of restoration. A special Wine & Dine train 'Watercress Belle' operates alternate Saturday evenings during season. Booking essential.

Open 8 Mar–26 Oct, Sat, Sun & BH's; mid wk running end May–last wk Jul; daily running last wk Jul–31 Aug. 'Santa Specials' wknds in Dec, booking essential. Leaflet available giving details, times of trains etc.

✹ Fares 1st class return £3.70 (ch £1.85); 1st class single £1.90 (ch 95p); 3rd class return £2.95 (ch £1.50); 3rd class single £1.50 (ch 75p); Pen £2.10 return, £1.10 single. Family ticket £8.50 (2 adults & up to 4 children for full return journey). Day rover 1st class £8, 3rd class £6.50. Dogs 25p.

⚹ ⚖ ⊞ ₺ shop ⓥ

ALSTON
Cumbria
Map **12** NY74

South Tynedale Railway The Railway Station
☎ (0498) 81696

A narrow-gauge railway, following the route of the former Alston to Haltwhistle branch along the beautiful South Tyne valley. At present the line runs between Alston and Gilderdale.

Open wknds Etr–Sep; daily Jul & Aug 11–4; other dates as advertised. Station open daily. Childrens day in May & Santa Specials in Dec, exact dates to be confirmed.

✹ 70p (ch 5–15 35p). Party.

⚹ ⚖ ⊞ ₺ (ex trains) shop

ALTHORP
Northamptonshire
Map **4** SP66

Althorp Hall

Elizabethan house redecorated 1790 by Henry Holland and entirely restored 1983. Magnificent collection of pictures, furniture and china. Home of the Spencer family since 1508. House not suitable for small children, frail or disabled. House and grounds may be closed without notice for security reasons. Coaches will be informed.

Open daily all year 2.30–5.30. Jul–Sep & BH 11–6. Wed Connoisseurs day throughout the year.

£2.50 (ch £1.25) Connoisseurs Day £3.50 Grounds & Lake only 50p (ch 25p).

⚹ ⚖ shop ✖ ⓥ

ALTON
Staffordshire
Map **7** SK04

Alton Towers
☎ Oakamoor (0538) 702200

Set in the former estate of the Earls of Shrewsbury, Alton Towers is Europe's premier leisure park with some of the world's most famous rides and shows. More than 80 attractions are imaginatively woven into the magnificent estate. Visitors can walk through the famous ruins and the gardens – reputed to rank among the finest in Europe, with its Pagoda Fountain, Chinese Temple and Rock Gardens.

Open Etr–Oct. 9 to 1 hr after attractions close. Attractions 10–5/6/7 pm. (Opening dates not confirmed for 1986)

✹ Adults & ch £4.99 (pen £1.99) ch 3 free. Party.

⚹ ⚖ ⊞ ₺ shop

ALTRINCHAM
Gt Manchester
Map **7** SJ78

Dunham Massey Hall (2m SW off B5160)
☎ 061-941 1025

A fine 18th-century house and park, home of the 10th and last Earl of Stamford until 1976. The house has an outstanding collection of 18th-century furniture, Huguenot silver and portraits of the Booth and Grey families, Earls of Warrington and Stamford, including Lady Jane Grey. The formal park still retains its herd of fallow deer.

Open 29 Mar–Oct, daily (ex Fri) including BH Mon, Garden, Restaurant & shop noon–5.30 (ex Sun & BH Mon 11–5.30). House only 1–5 (ex Sun & BH Mon 12–5). Last admission to House 4.30 pm.

House & Gardens, £2.50 (ch £1) family ticket £6. Car Park £1 refundable on house entry, in restaurant or shop. Parties by prior arrangement Mon–Thu only. Party 15+.

⚹ (charged) ⚖ (licensed) ₺ (ground floor & gardens, wheelchair available on request) shop ✖ (NT)

ALUM BAY
Isle of Wight
Map **4** SZ38

The Needles Old Battery West High Down (¾m SW)
☎ Isle of Wight (0983) 526445

A former Palmerstonian fort built in 1862, 250 ft above sea level. A 200 ft tunnel leads to a look out position which offers spectacular views of the Needles Rock and Lighthouse. Two of the original 12 ton gun barrels lie in the Parade Ground, whilst in the Powder Magazine an exhibition displays the history of the Needles Headland from the establishment of the Battery to the present day.

Open 24 Mar–28 Oct Sun–Thu but open Fri & Sat in Jul & Aug. Also open Good Fri, Etr Sat and BH Mons. 10.30–5 (last admission 4.45).

70 p (ch 40p).

P (1m at Alum Bay) Shop. Dogs must be kept under strict control because of cliffs (NT)

ALVINGHAM
Lincolnshire
Map **8** TF39

Water Mill Church Ln
☎ South Cockerington (050 782) 544

An 18th-century water cornmill restored as a working museum. There has been a mill on this site since the 11th century and it was once worked by the monks of Alvingham Priory. The present machinery was probably installed in 1782 and is powered by one of the few remaining breast wheels.

Open Jul & Aug Mon & Thu 2–5, 2nd & 4th Suns 2–5.30, BH Sun & Mon 11–5.30.

40p (ch 30p).

⚹ ⊞ shop ✖

AMBERLEY
West Sussex
Map **4** TQ01

Chalk Pits Museum Houghton Bridge (off B2139)
☎ Bury (079 881) 370

The museum is situated in a 36-acre former chalk quarry and limeworks, and shows the industrial past of the South-East. Working blacksmith, potter and printer. Cobbler's shop. Narrow-gauge railway.

Open Apr–Oct, Wed–Sun & BH Mon 10–6 (last admission 5).

£1.80 (ch 90p, pen £1.35). Family ticket (2 adults + 2 ch) £5.

⚹ ⚖ ⊞ ₺ shop

AMPFIELD
Hampshire
Map **4** SU42

Hillier Arboretum Jermyn's Lane →

☎ Braishfield (0794) 68787

The largest collection of trees and shrubs of its kind in the British Isles, set in 160 acres of attractive landscape. An all year round collection containing many rarities.

Open all year Mon–Fri 10–5; Sat, Sun & BH 1–6 Mar–2nd wknd Nov. Party 30 + .

£1 (ch 15 free).

🅰 ⌁ ♿ garden centre ✖

AMPTHILL
Bedfordshire
Map **4** TL03

Houghton House (N off A418)

Ruined 17th-century mansion with associations with the Countess of Pembroke, sister of Sir Philip Sidney.

Open at all reasonable times.

Free.

🅰 ♿ (grounds & ground floor only) (AM)

ANDOVER
Hampshire
Map **4** SU34

Andover Museum Church Close
☎ (0264) 66283

The museum is housed in a fine Georgian building; among its displays are locally manufactured agricultural machinery and an aquarium designed to display local fish found in the Test Valley. There is a new natural history gallery. Temporary exhibitions..

Open Tue–Sat 10–5.

Free.

🅰 ♿ (ground floor only) shop

Finkley Down Farm & Country Park
Finkley Down Farm
☎ (0264) 52195

A comprehensive selection of different breeds of farm animals and poultry, many rearing their young in a natural environment. The Pets Corner has tame, hand reared baby animals who can be stroked and petted. There is also a Countryside Museum, housed in a barn, and an adventure playground.

Open Etr–Sep, 10.30–6 (last admission 5).

Ampfield
Ardingly

✱ £1.20 (ch 3–16 & pen 75p).
🅰 ⌁ ⍾ ♿ shop Ⓥ

ANSTRUTHER
Fife *Fife*
Map **12** NO50

Scottish Fisheries Museum St Ayles, Harbour head
☎ (0333) 310628

A 14th- to 18th-century group of buildings around a cobbled courtyard, with displays of the history of fishing in Scotland. Boats. Marine aquarium. Library.

Open Nov–Mar daily (ex Tue) 2–5; Apr–Oct, Mon–Sat 10–5.30, Sun 2–5. Closed Xmas Day.

85p (ch 16, pen & unemployed 35p). Party.

P (100 yds) ⍾ ♿ (ground floor & courtyard only) shop ✖

ANSTY
West Sussex
Map **4** TQ22

Legh Manor
☎ Lewes (0273) 474379 (Sussex Archaeological Society)

A 16th-century house with features of great architectural interest. Access limited to Hall and three rooms. Garden laid out by Gertrude Jekyll.

Open Apr–Oct, 2nd and 3rd Weds and 2nd Sat in each month 2.30–5.30.

Admission fee payable.

🅰 ✖

APPLEDORE
Devon
Map **2** SS43

North Devon Maritime Museum Odun House, Odun Rd
☎ Bideford (02372) 74852

Exhibitions and displays on North Devon's maritime history. Also full size reconstruction of an Appledore kitchen c1900. Highly commended in National Heritage Museum of the Year awards in 1979.

Open Etr–Sep, daily 2–5.30, also Tue–Fri 11–1. Tape slide showing daily.

50p (ch 10p).

🅰 shop ✖

ARBROATH
Tayside *Angus*
Map **12** NO64

Arbroath Abbey
☎ (0241) 78756

Remains of a Tironensian Monastery founded in 1178 by William the Lion, King of Scotland. Abbot's House Museum. Scene of the signing of the 'Declaration of Arbroath' on 6 April 1320 in the presence of Robert the Bruce.

Open Apr–Sep 9.30–12.30 & 1.30–7; Oct–Mar 9.30–12.30 & 1.30–4.

50p (ch & pen 25p).

P (100 yds) shop (AM)

Arbroath Museum Signal Tower, Ladyloan
☎ (0241) 75598

Collection of local history from prehistoric times to the industrial revolution. Special features include the Bellrock Lighthouse, fishing and wildlife of Arbroath Cliffs.

Open Apr–Oct Mon–Sat 10.30–1, 2–5, Jul & Aug also Sun 2–5, Nov–Mar, Mon–Fri 2–5, Sat 10.30–1, 2–5.

Free.

🅰 ♿ (ground floor only) shop ✖ (ex guide dogs)

ARDINGLY
West Sussex
Map **4** TQ32

Wakehurst Place Garden 1½m N (garden administered by the Royal Botanic Gardens, Kew)
☎ (0444) 892701

The garden is noted for a fine collection of rare trees and flowering shrubs. A

picturesque water course links a series of ponds and lakes. There is an exhibition room and bookstall.

Open Nov–Jan 10–4; Feb & Oct 10–5; Mar 10–6; Apr–Sep 10–7. (Closed Xmas & New Years Day).

£1.50 (ch 60p). Party.

⚠ Ⓩ Book shop ✖ (ex guide dogs) (NT)

ARDMINISH

Isle of Gigha, Strathclyde *Argyll*
Map **10** NR64

Achamore Gardens

☏ Gigha (05835) 254

Unique garden of azaleas and rhododendrons created by the late Sir James Horlick Bt.

Open all year 10–sunset.

£1 (ch & pen 30p).

⚠ Ⓩ (licensed) ✠ ♿ shop & garden centre

ARDWELL

Dumfries and Galloway *Wigtownshire*
Map **10** NX14

Ardwell House Gardens

☏ (077686) 227

Country house gardens and grounds with flowering shrubs and woodland walks. House not open to public.

Open Mar–Oct 10–6.

✱ 50p (ch 25p).

⚠ ♿ (parts only) small garden centre

ARLINGTON

Devon
Map **2** SS64

Arlington Court (7m NE of Barnstaple, off A39)

☏ Shirwell (027182) 296

In large wooded estate with terraced garden and lake; the house, built in 1822, contains a fascinating collection of model ships, pewter and seashells. In the stables is a large collection of horse-drawn vehicles.

Open 28 Mar–Oct, Sun–Fri 11–6, last admission 5.30; open Sat before BH Mon. Gardens daily also all year, Nov–Mar during daylight hours.

£2.50. Gardens, grounds & stables £1.50. Party.

Ⓩ (licensed) ♿ shop (NT)

ARMADALE

Isle of Skye, Highland *Inverness-shire*
Map **13** NG60

Clan Donald Centre

☏ Ardvasar (04714) 227

Situated ½m N of Armadale Pier, Armadale Castle was built in 1815 as the home of Lord Macdonald. The main building is now a sculptured ruin. Picturesque woodland gardens overlook the Sound of Sleat. The north wing houses the museum of the Isles and audio-visual of 'The Sea

---

Ardingly
—
Arundel

Kingdom'. The recently restored stables houses the restaurant and the craft and book shop. Countryside ranger service available for guided woodland walks. Nature trail, children's play area. Clan Donald Archery Tournament Jul.

Open Etr–Oct, Mon–Sat 10–5; Sun Jun–Sep only, 1–5.

✱ £1.20 (ch, students & pen 60p).

⚠ Ⓩ (licensed) ✠ ♿ shop Ⓥ

ARNOL

Isle of Lewis, Western Isles
Ross & Cromarty
Map **13** NB34

Black House Museum

Good example of traditional Hebridean dwelling. Retains many of its original furnishings.

Open Apr–Sep, Mon–Sat 9.30–7, Oct–Mar 9.30–4.

✱ 50p (ch & pen 25p).

⚠ ♿ (ground floor & gardens only) (AM)

ARRAN, ISLE OF

Strathclyde *Bute*
Map **10**

see **Brodick**

ARRETON

Isle of Wight
Map **4** SZ58

Arreton Manor

☏ Newport (0983) 528134

An early 17th-century manor house with fine panelled rooms containing contemporary furniture. In the grounds is the Pomeroy Regency Dolls House and the National Wireless Museum; the former being a perfect example of miniature work and the latter a unique collection of vintage wireless receivers.

Open one wk before Etr to last wk Oct, Mon–Sat 10–6, Sun 2–6.

Admission fee payable.

⚠ Ⓩ shop

Haseley Manor

☏ Isle of Wight (0983) 865420

The oldest and largest manor open to the public on the Isle of Wight with parts of the south wing circa 1139. Rural life museum. Large pottery studio with demonstrations hourly. Pub in grounds. A play area for children includes a small lake with castle on an island and Noahs Ark Afloat.

Open all year, daily 10–6.

£1.50 (ch 7 £1 pen £1.35). Party.

⚠ Ⓩ (licensed) ✠ ♿ (ground floor only) shop

Robin Hill Adventure and Zoological Park Robin Hill

☏ Isle of Wight (0983) 527352

Over 100 interesting species of mammals, birds, reptiles and insects, in over 80 acres of down and woodland. Also large tropical Jungle House, 10-acre walk-through enclosure, colonies of monkeys, large Chelonian collection. Nature trail, water gardens, assault course, amusements and Freerideland with BMX bikes, archery, grass sledges and paddle boats.

Open Mar–Oct, daily 10–6.

✱ £1.75 (ch & pen £1.25) Parties 20 + .

⚠ Ⓩ (licensed) ✠ ♿ garden centre

ARUNDEL

West Sussex
Map **4** TQ00

Arundel Castle entrance at Lower Lodge in Mill Rd

☏ (0903) 883136 or 882173

Norman stronghold restored in 18th and 19th century in magnificent grounds. Fine portraits by Van Dyck, Gainsborough, Reynolds, etc, and furniture from 16th century. Also Fitzalan Chapel. Festival late Aug–early Sep.

Open 28 Mar–last Fri Oct, Sun–Fri 1–5 (12 noon Jun–Aug & BHs). Last admission 4p.m. (Closed Sat).

£2.50 (ch 5–15 £1.50 & pen £2). Party 20 + .

⚠ Ⓩ shop ✖

See advertisement on page 42

Arundel Toy and Military Museum

23 High St
☏ (0903) 883101 or 882908

Intriguing Henderson collection of old toys, games, dolls and small militaria, goss and curiosities collected worldwide and displayed in a Georgian cottage in the heart of the town. 'Britains' model exhibition Jun–Aug.

Open every weekend. 12–5, school & BH; Jun–Aug daily 10.30–5. Other times by arrangement.

75p (ch 15 students & pen 50p). Party 20 + .

P (50 yds) shop Ⓥ

Museum of Curiosity 6 High St

☏ (0903) 882420

The life work of the Victorian naturalist and taxidermist, Walter Potter, formerly housed at Bramber. First opened in 1861. Has a good collection of natural history and also the famous animal tableaux— Kittens' Wedding, Rabbits' Village School, Death of Cock Robin, Guinea Pigs' Cricket Match etc. Also curios, toys, dolls, from all over the world.

Open Etr–Oct 10.30–1 & 2.15–5.30; Nov–Etr most days & wknds 11–1 & 2.15–dusk.

75p (ch & pen 40p).

P shop

Wildfowl Trust Mill Road
☎ (0903) 883355

55 acres of well landscaped pens, lakes and paddocks with more than 1,000 ducks, geese and swans from all over the world. Hides overlook ponds, reed beds and a wader scrape which are sanctuaries for many wild birds. Also large viewing gallery, and education complex.

Open daily, 9.30–5.30. (Closed Xmas day).

£2 (ch 4 free, ch £1, pen £1.20). Party 20 +.

⚠ ⯑ ⅙ shop ✗ Ⓥ

ASHBURTON
Devon
Map **3** SX77

Ashburton Museum 1 West St
☎ (0364) 53278

Exhibits include local antiquities, weapons, American Indian antiques, geology specimens.

Open May–Sep, Tue, Thu, Fri, Sat 2.30–5.

Free.

P (150 yds) ✗

ASHBURY
Oxfordshire
Map **4** SU28

Ashdown House (2½m SE on B4000)

A 17th-century mansion situated amidst lovely downland, built of chalk blocks and rising to four storeys. Paintings from the Craven Collection.

Open (grounds, hall, staircase and roof only) Apr–Oct Weds & Sats 2–6.

£1.10.

(NT)

ASHBY-DE-LA-ZOUCH
Leicestershire
Map **8** SK31

Ashby-de-la-Zouch Castle

Mainly 14th-century but Hastings Tower added in 1474. Royalist stronghold in Civil War, later slighted.

Open at any reasonable time.

✳ 50p (ch 16 & pen 25p).

P ⅙ (grounds only) (AM)

Arundel
—
Ash Vale

ASHFORD
Kent
Map **5** TR04

Godinton Park (2½m NW)
☎ (0233) 20773

Gabled house, dating from 1628, with fine panelling and carving, portraits, furniture, and china. 18th- and 19th-century garden layout includes topiary work.

Open Etr, Sat, Sun, Mon & then Suns & BHs, or by appointment from Jun–Sep 2–5.

£1.20 (ch 16 60p). Party 20 +.

⚠ ⅙ (ground floor only) ✗ (in house)

Intelligence Corps Museum Templer Barracks
☎ (0233) 25251 ext 208

Items concerning the Corps from the two World Wars and other articles up to the present day.

Open Mon–Fri 10–noon, 2–4. (Closed BH)

Free.

⚠ ⅙ shop ✗

ASHINGTON
West Sussex
Map **4** TQ11

Holly Gate Cactus Garden Billingshurst Lane (B2133)
☎ Worthing (0903) 892930

Unique collection of over 20,000 plants, featuring many rare varieties from the more arid areas of the world such as U.S.A., Mexico, South America, Africa and the more tropical jungle cactus of Central and South America. The garden is attractively landscaped in over 10,000 sq ft of glasshouses.

Open all year daily, 9–5. (Closed 25 & 26 Dec).

50p (ch 30p). Party.

⚠ ⅙ garden centre

ASHLEWORTH
Gloucestershire
Map **3** SO82

Tithe Barn

A 15th-century building, 120ft long with porch bays and queen-post roof.

Open daily 9–6 or sunset.

20p.

✗ (NT)

ASHTON
Hereford and Worcester
Map **3** SO56

Berrington Hall (3m N Leominster)

Built 1778–81 by Henry Holland. Fine interior decoration, including painted and plaster ceilings, much of it unaltered, and recently restored stonework. 455 acre park, laid out by Capability Brown.

Open Apr & Oct, Sat, Sun & Etr Mon 2–5. May–Sep, Wed–Sun & BH Mon 2–6.

£1.50. Joint ticket with Croft Castle £2.50.

⯑ ✗ (NT)

ASHURST
Hampshire
Map **4** SU31

New Forest Butterfly Farm Longdown
☎ (042129) 2166

A large covered, heated glasshouse housing a tropical garden with free-flying butterflies from all over the world. Separate British butterfly section and outdoor dragonfly ponds. Other insects include tarantulas, scorpions, preying mantis, ants and locusts. Traditional wagon rides, drawn by Shire horse, through a secluded part of the estate.

Open Apr–Oct, daily 10–5.

✳ £1.80 (ch £1 & pen £1.30) excluding wagon rides. Party 15 +.

⚠ ⯑ ⊞ ⅙ (ex picnic area) shop & garden centre ✗

ASH VALE
Surrey
Map **4** SU85

Arundel Castle
Ancestral home of the Dukes of Norfolk

This beautiful castle has overlooked the town and river Arun for the past 700 years. Steeped in English history, the castle suffered some destruction at the hands of Cromwell's troops in the Civil War. Now fully restored, the State apartments and principal rooms contain many art treasures, paintings by Reynolds, Van Dyck and Gainsborough, with furniture from the 16th century.

Castle and grounds are open to visitors from 28th March to the last Friday in October, Sundays to Fridays from 1pm-5pm, and from 12 noon throughout June, July, August and all Bank Holidays. Last admission on any day is 4pm. The castle is not open Saturdays.
For full details apply to the Comptroller, Arundel Castle, Arundel, West Sussex, England. Telephone 0903 883136.

42

RAMC Historical Museum
Keogh Barracks
☎ Aldershot (0252) 24431 ext. Keogh 212

A collection of some 2,500 items, mainly of military interest but with many unusual items of general interest. Exhibits include a horsedrawn ambulance and a 1942 Austin K2 ambulance. There are three cases of items relating to the Falklands War and a display of a patient on an operating table.

Open Mon–Fri 8.30–4. (Closed Xmas, New Year & BH). Weekends & BH by appointment only.

Free.

P (100 yds) ঙ shop ✗

ASHWELL
Hertfordshire
Map **4** TL23

Village Museum Swan St

Early Tudor timber-framed house, once the tithe office of abbots of Westminster. Contains collection showing life of village from Stone Age to present day.

Open Suns & BH 2.30–5; Parties at any time by appointment in writing to the Friends of Ashwell Village Museum.

20p (ch 10p).

P (adjacent) ঙ (ground floor only) shop

ASTON MUNSLOW
Shropshire
Map **7** SO58

The White House Museum of Buildings & Continuous Family Life
☎ (058476) 661

Comprises a group of buildings from widely differing periods, dating from the 13th-century dovecote, and set amidst 6½ acres of trees, grass, hedges and gardens. Features are: the display of implements and tools once used on the estate, the Cider House, completely equipped for cider making and the Bake Oven. Guides available for Historical-Architectural tour covering the various periods through the ages.

Open Etr Sat–Oct, Sat, Wed & BH wknds.

✳ £2 (ch 15 50p) Garden & museum only £1.50. House only 75p

⚠ ⊞ shop & garden centre

ATCHAM
Shropshire
Map **7** SJ50

Attingham Park (3m SE of Shrewsbury)

The house was built between 1783 and 1785, designed by George Steuart, its fine interior contains Nash pictures and furnishings. Standing in over one thousand acres of park landscaped in 1797 by Humphry Repton.

Open 29 Mar–Sep, Sat–Wed 2–5.30. Oct, Sat & Sun only 2–5.30. BH Mon 11–5.30.

Ash Vale – Avebury

Pre-booked parties allowed daily ex Thu & Fri. Last admission 5 pm.

£1.80 (ch 90p). Gardens only 50p.

⚠ ⊞ ঙ shop ✗ (in house) (NT)

ATHELHAMPTON
Dorset
Map **3** SY79

Athelhampton (on A35 1m E of Puddletown)
☎ Puddletown (030584) 363

Family home for 500 years, one of finest medieval houses in Southern England. Ten acres of formal and landscaped gardens, with 15th-century dovecote. River gardens.

Open 26 Mar–12 Oct, Wed, Thu, Sun, BH & also Mon & Tue in Aug 2–6.

✳ House & gardens £2 (ch £1). Gardens only £1 (ch free). Plants & antiques for sale.

⚠ ⊞ ঙ (ground floor only) shop ✗

AUCHINDRAIN
Strathclyde *Argyll*
Map **10** NN00

Open-Air Museum
☎ Furnace (04995) 235

A folk life museum on ancient communal-tenancy farm. Original 18th- and 19th-century buildings being restored and furnished. Traditional crops and livestock, also a display centre.

Open Etr–Sep; Sun–Fri 11–4, Apr, May & Sep; daily 10–5, Jun , Jul & Aug (other times by appointment).

£1.50 (ch & pen £1).

⚠ ⊞ ঙ shop

AUCHTERARDER
Tayside *Perthshire*
Map **11** NN91

Strathallan Aero Park (4m NW off B8062)
☎ (07646) 2545

Impressive collection of vintage aircraft including a Lancaster, Lysander plus many other displays of a nostalgic nature.

Open Apr–Oct, daily 10–5. (Flying Days; during summer months). Parties in winter by arrangement.

✳ £1.50 (ch £1 under 5 free).

⚠ ⊞ ⊞ ঙ shop ✗ (ex in car park) ⓥ

AUDLEY END
Essex
Map **5** TL53

Audley End House

A 17th-century house built by Thomas Howard, Earl of Suffolk, with some work

---

by Robert Adam. Pictures and furnishings in state room. Miniature railway in grounds.

Open Apr–Sep, Sun, Tue–Sat & Mon BH 1–6. Grounds open mid-day.

✳ £1.80 (ch 16 & pen 90p).

⚠ (charge) ⊞ ঙ (ground floor & gardens only) (AM) ⓥ

AVEBURY
Wiltshire
Map **4** SU06

Avebury Manor
☎ (06723) 203

Dating from before the Conquest (Avebury Manor was built on the site of a Benedictine Cell) and standing beside the Great Stone Circle of Avebury, this early Elizabethan Manor house having been carefully restored is now a family home. Oak panelled rooms and coved plasterwork ceilings. State rooms visited by Queen Anne and Charles II. Much early oak and fine furniture in period setting. Portraits dated from 1532. The Queen Anne bedroom with imposing state bed, is of particular note; also the Cavalier bedroom (linked with tales of the supernatural and recounted by more than one visitor staying at the Manor). Surrounding gardens and parkland are equally intriguing. Topiary – old yew and box – pleasantly emphasise the historic atmosphere. Walled gardens, herb borders and wishing well, 16th century dovecote.

Open Apr–Sep, daily 11.30–6, Sun 1.30–6; Oct–Mar, Sat & Sun 1.30–5. (The above times are often extended in fine weather). Evening parties by appointment.

✳ £2 (ch £1, pen & NT members £1.75). Parties 30+.

⚠ ⊞ ⊞ ঙ (ground floor & gardens only) shop ✗

Avebury Museum (Alexander Keiller Museum)

Collection of finds from late Neolithic Age site and nearby Windmill Hill site. The whole village, as well as a circle of sarsen stones, is enclosed by banks and ditches.

Open any reasonable times.

✳ 50p (ch 16 & pen 25p).

⚠ ঙ (AM) (NT)

Great Barn Museum of Wiltshire Folk Life
☎ (06723) 555

Fine 17th-century thatched barn adjacent to the prehistoric stone circle. Inside the Great Barn, with its splendid roof structure, are displays on cheesemaking, thatching, blacksmithing, saddlery, sheep and shepherds, the wheelwright and other rural crafts. Regular craft demonstrations take place on Suns between Apr & Sep. Craft Fair Aug BH Mon & 'Four Counties Festival' of local history 6 & 7 Sep. A Tourist Information Centre is also housed in the Barn. →

Open Apr–Oct daily 10–5.30; Jan–Mar & Nov–Dec wknds only 2–4.30.

✻ 60p (ch & pen 30p). Family ticket (2 adults + 2 ch) £1.40.

P (300 yds) ⚠ (disabled only) & shop

AVINGTON
Hampshire
Map **4** SU53

Avington Park
☎ Itchen Abbas (096278) 202

17th-century mansion built largely of red brick with state rooms and fine ballroom. In wooded park in Itchen Valley.

Open May–Sep, Sat, Sun & BH 2.30–5.30. Last tour 5pm. Parties at other times by arrangement.

£1 (ch 10 50p).

⚠ 𝒯 (Sun & BH) & (ground floor only)

AXBRIDGE
Somerset
Map **3** ST45

King's Hunting Lodge The Square

Restored early Tudor house with old photographs and exhibits of local interest. Town stocks and constables' staves also on show.

Open Apr–Sep, daily 2–5.

Free.

⚠ (NT)

AYLESBURY
Buckinghamshire
Map **4** SP81

Bucks County Museum Church St
☎ (0296) 82158 or 88849

Housed in former grammar school built in 1720 and two 15th-century houses, which were completely altered in the mid 18th century. The displays relate to the geology, natural history, archaeology and history of the county and include costume, Rural Life Gallery and Aylesbury Gallery.

Open Mon–Fri 10–5, Sat 10–12.30, 1.30–5. (Closed Sun, Good Fri, Xmas & New Years day).

Free.

P (600 yds) shop ✻

AYLESFORD
Kent
Map **5** TQ75

Priory The Friars
☎ Maidstone (0622) 77272

Restored 13th- to 14th-century Carmelite house with fine cloisters, now conference centre and place of pilgrimage and retreat. Sculpture and ceramics by modern artists and pottery.

Open daily 9–dusk. Guided tours by arrangement. Shop, tea rooms and pottery open 10.30–12.45 & 2–4.30.

Donations.

⚠ 𝒯 & shop ✻

AYOT ST LAWRENCE
Hertfordshire
Map **4** TL11

Shaws Corner (at SW end of village)
☎ Stevenage (0438) 820307

The former home of George Bernard Shaw between 1906 and his death in 1950. Several of the rooms are as they were in his lifetime.

Open 30 Mar–Oct, Mon–Thu, 2–6; Sun & BH Mon noon–6 (last admission 5.30). (Closed Good Fri).

£1.30.

(NT) Ⓥ

AYR
Strathclyde *Ayrshire*
Map **10** NS32

Maclaurin Art Gallery & Rozelle House
Rozelle Park, Monument Rd
☎ Alloway (0292) 45447

Contemporary and traditional art, decorative and applied. Nature trail in surrounding park with open air sculpture; work by Henry Moore on display. Local history and art exhibitions displayed in mansion house. Small military museum.

Gallery open Mon–Sat 11–5, Sun (Apr–Oct only) 2–5. House open Apr–Oct, Mon–Sat 11–5, Sun 2–5 (Nov–Mar Sat only 2–5).

Free.

⚠ 𝒯 🍴 & (ground floor only) ✻

Tam O'Shanter Museum
☎ (0292) 269794

This is considered to be the point where Tam O'Shanter's memorable ride commenced. The house now contains items associated with Robert Burns.

Open Apr–Sep, Mon–Sat 9.30–5.30; Oct–Mar, Mon–Sat noon–4 also Sun, Jun, Jul & Aug 2.30–5.

Admission fee payable.

P (200 yds) shop ✻

AYSGARTH
North Yorkshire
Map **7** SE08

National Park Centre
☎ (09693) 424

Visitor centre with interpretative display, maps, walks, guides and local information available.

Open Apr–Oct daily mid mornings to late afternoons.

Free.

⚠ &

Yorkshire Carriage Museum (GW Shaw Collection), The Old Mill (1¾m E adjacent to bridge on unclass road N of A684)
☎ (09693) 652 & Richmond (0748) 3275

An old stone mill at Aysgarth Falls now houses over 50 horse-drawn vehicles including some splendid coaches, carriages and relics of the Era of Horse-Drawn Transport. Carriage drives & driving lessons can be arranged.

Open Etr–Oct daily 10.30–6 & later wknds & BHs.

60p (ch 30p & pen 50p).

P (200 yds) 𝒯 shop

AYTON, GREAT
North Yorkshire
Map **8** NZ51

Captain Cook Schoolroom Museum
High Street
☎ (0642) 722327

Exhibits relating to the explorer, including maps, books, pictures, etc.

Open Etr–Sep, daily 2–4.30. Oct wknds only 2–4.30. Other times by written appointment.

30p (ch 15p).

P shop ✻

BACONSTHORPE
Norfolk
Map **9** TG13

Baconsthorpe Castle

A late 15th-century moated and semi-fortified house, incorporating a gate-house, a range of curtain walls and towers.

Open any reasonable time.

Free.

⚠ & (AM)

BADDESLEY CLINTON
Warwickshire
Map **4** SP27

Baddesley Clinton
☎ Lapworth (05643) 3294

A medieval moated manor house with 120 acres, dating back to 1300, and little altered since 1634.

Open 22 Mar–Sep Wed–Sun & BH Mon 2–6. Oct, Sat & Sun 2–5. (Closed Good Fri).

✻ £1.70. Party by written appointment only. Entry to the house by timed numbered ticket when busy.

𝒯 shop no prams or pushchairs in the house (NT)

BAKEWELL
Derbyshire
Map **8** SK26

Magpie Mine (3m W)
☎ Matlock (0629) 3834

The surface remains are the best example in Britain of a 19th-century lead mine. Further information can be obtained from **Peak District Mining Museum, Matlock Bath,** *Derbyshire.*

Old House Museum Cunningham Pl, off Church Ln
☎ (062981) 3647

Early Tudor house with original wattle and daub interior walls and an open-timbered chamber. Exhibition of costumes, Victorian kitchen, farm utensils, toys, lacework, tools etc. Crafts exhibition Sat Jun 28.

Open 28 Mar–Oct, daily 2–5. Bookings for visits outside these hours to E T Goodwin, 32 Castle Mount Crescent, Bakewell, Derbyshire.

50p (ch of school age 25p).

P (500 yds) shop ✗

BALA
Gwynedd
Map **6** SH93

Cyffdy Farm Park Parc (3m SW)
☎ Llanuwchllyn (06784) 271

The rare breed centre of North Wales Animals include sheep, cattle, horses, pigs, goats, rabbits, poultry, waterfowl and llama. Hand milking to be seen daily. Collection of old farm machinery and country bygones. Farm trail, nature trail, fishing, pony hire, pets corner and children's playground. On certain days there is shearing, sheep dog handling, harp playing, donkey cart rides and trailer rides.

Open daily Mar–Oct. Partial winter opening by bookings only.

Admission fee payable.

🅐 ♨ ⏚ shop

BALERNO
Lothian *Midlothian*
Map **11** NT16

Malleny Garden off Bavelaw Rd

A delightful personal garden, with shrub roses and shaped yews.

Open May–Sep daily 10–sunset.

60p (ch 30p). Charge box.

🅐 (NTS)

BALLAUGH
Isle of Man
Map **6** SC39

Curraghs Wild Life Park
☎ Sulby (062489) 7323

Variety of British and foreign wildlife.

Open 5 Apr–29 Sep daily 9–5, Sun 10–6. Details not confirmed for 1986.

✳ £1 (ch 15 50p) Party 25+.

🅐 ♨ ⏚ shop ✗

BALLOCH
Strathclyde *Dunbartonshire*
Map **10** NS38

Balloch Castle Country Park
☎ Alexandria (0389) 58216

Situated on the shore of the loch, with large area of grassland suitable for picnics and surrounded by extensive woodlands. Views of the loch from the castle terrace (c1808). Walled garden. Nature trail. Countryside ranger service.

Open, Visitor Centre; Apr, May & Sep wknds 10–5. Jun–Aug daily 10–5. Country Park 8–dusk, garden 10–9 (4.30 winter). Details not confirmed for 1986.

Free.

🅐 ♨ ⏚

BALMACARA
Highland *Ross and Cromarty*
Map **14** NG82

Balmacara (Lochalsh House & Garden)
☎ (059986) 207

Magnificent stretch of West Highland scenery including Five Sisters of Kintail and Beinn Fhada. Natural history display in coach house and Lochalsh Woodland and Garden provides pleasant walks. Self-guided and guided walks from Balmacara on the Kyle to Plockton Peninsula. Ranger Naturalist Service.

Woodland and Garden open daily 9.30–sunset. Coach house open Etr–Oct, daily 10–6.

45p (ch 20p).

Kiosk Jun–Sep, Mon–Sat 10–1 & 2–6 (NTS)

BALMORAL
Grampian *Aberdeenshire*
Map **15** NO29

Balmoral Castle Grounds and Exhibition
☎ Crathie (03384) 334

The Highland residence of Her Majesty the Queen. Beautiful Deeside forest setting. Grounds, gardens and exhibition of paintings and works of art in the Castle Ballroom. Pony trekking & country walks.

Open May–Jul, Mon–Sat 10–5.

✳ £1.10, (ch free).

🅐 (for disabled only) P (100 yds from main gate) ♨ ⏚ (ground floor & gardens only) shop ✗ (in exhibition)

BALSALL COMMON
Warwickshire
Map **4** SP27

Berkswell Windmill
Windmill Ln
☎ Berkswell (0676) 33403

Also known as Balsall Windmill. A fine example of a Warwickshire tower mill complete in both machinery and fittings, including tools.

Open Etr–Sep, Sun only 10.30–12.30 & 2.30–5.30. All other days by appointment.

30p (ch & pen 15p.)

🅐 (limited) ⏚ (ground floor only) shop ✗

BAMBURGH
Northumberland
Map **12** NU13

Bamburgh Castle
☎ (06684) 208

Restored Norman castle in splendid North Sea coast setting. Impressive hall, and armoury with large weapon collection, also loan collection of armour from HM Tower of London. Guide services.

Open Apr–Oct, daily from 1pm.

✳ £1.50 (ch 60p).

🅐 ♨ ⏚ (ground floor only) shop ✗

Grace Darling Museum Radcliffe Rd.
☎ Seahouses (0665) 720 037

Pictures, documents, and various relics of the heroine, including boat in which she →

---

and her father, keeper of Longstone Lighthouse, Farne Islands, rescued nine survivors from wrecked 'SS Forfarshire' in 1838.

Open Apr, May, & Sep–mid Oct daily 11–6 and Jun–Aug daily 11–7.

Free.

⚠ ઇ shop ✕

BANBURY
Oxfordshire
Map **4** SP44

Banbury Museum 8 Horsefair, Marlborough Rd
☎ (0295) 59855

This small museum exhibits items of local history and archaeology. Changing programme of temporary exhibitions and of local artist's work. Tourist information Centre.

Open Jan–Mar, Mon, Wed–Sat 10–4; Apr–Sep, Mon–Sat 10–5; Oct–Dec, Tue–Sat 10–4.30.

Free.

P (100 yds) ⚑ ઇ shop ✕

BANCHORY
Grampian *Kincardineshire*
Map **15** NO69

Banchory Museum Council Chambers
☎ Peterhead (0779) 77778

Exhibition of local history and bygones.

Open Jun–Sep daily (ex Thu) 2–5.20

Free.

⚠ (limited) shop ✕ (ex guide dogs)

BANFF
Grampian *Banffshire*
Map **15** NJ66

Banff Museum High Street
☎ Peterhead (0779) 77778

Exhibition of British birds set out as an aviary. Local history and costumes also on show.

Open Jun–Sep, daily (ex Thu) 2–5.20.

Free.

P (100 yds) ઇ (ground floor only) shop ✕ (ex guide dogs).

Duff House (½m S, access south of town)

Designed by William Adam for William Duff (later Earl Fife). The main block was roofed in 1739, but proposed wings were never built. Although incomplete it ranks among the finest works of Georgian Baroque architecture in Britain. An exhibition illustrating the history of the house can also be seen.

Open Apr–Sep, Mon–Sat 9.30–7, Sun 2–7. Key Keeper in winter.

✸ 50p (ch & pen 25p).

(AM)

BANGOR
Gwynedd
Map **6** SH57

Bangor Museum & Art Gallery
(University College of North Wales)
Ffordd Gwynedd
☎ (0248) 351151 ext 437

The museum portrays history of North Wales, collections of furniture, crafts, costumes, maps, ceramics, and both Roman and prehistoric antiquities. Exhibitions illustrating history of the Menai Bridges and Conwy Bridge. Attendant always on duty to deal with enquiries. Art Gallery stages exhibitions of sculpture and paintings each year changing at approximately monthly intervals. If there is an exhibition in gallery the Museum may be closed and if the Museum is open the gallery will generally be closed but from Apr–Sep both will normally be open.

Open all year Tue–Sat 12–4.30 ex as above. (Closed PH).

Free.

P ઇ (ground floor only) ✕

Penrhyn Castle (3m E at Landegai on A5122)
☎ (0248) 353084

A huge neo-Norman castle (c1820–1845) placed dramatically between Snowdonia and the Menai Strait. The castle contains 'Norman' furniture, panelling and plasterwork designed by the architect Thomas Hopper; fine pictures; industrial railway and doll museums. Woodland and Victorian walled garden.

Open: 28 Mar–26 Oct daily except Tue, 12–5 (last admission 4.30)

£2 (ch 75p). Garden only 90p (ch 30p) Family ticket £4.75. Parties 20+.

P ⚑ ઇ ✕ (ex guide dogs) (NT)

BANHAM
Norfolk
Map **5** TM08

Banham Classic Collection
Kenninghall Rd
☎ Quidenham (095387) 490

Adjoining Banham Zoo. A collection of varied and interesting classical cars and motor cycles in an imaginative setting. Over 40 vehicles. Adventure playground.

Open Apr–Oct 11–6.

Admission fee payable.

⚠ ઇ shop

Banham Zoo & Monkey Sanctuary
The Grove
☎ Quidenham (095387) 476

Situated in over 20 acres of grounds, this zoo specialises in monkeys and apes, but also includes black panthers, camels, otters, sealions, penguins, llamas, wallabies, cranes, flamingos, macaws, etc. Fruit, farm and dairy produce on sale in Grove Farm Barn opposite.

Open daily 10–6.30 (or dusk if earlier).
£2 (£1.35 Sat) (ch 5 £1 (70p Sat) pen £1.50 (£1 Sat)).

⚠ ⚑ (licensed) ⊓ ઇ shop & garden centre ✕ Ⓥ

BANNOCKBURN
Central *Stirlingshire*
Map **11** NS89

Bannockburn Monument
☎ (0786) 812664

The Borestone site, by tradition King Robert the Bruce's command post before the battle. He is commemorated by a bronze equestrian statue. Visitor centre with tourist information and historical exposition in sound and colour.

Rotunda & site always open. Visitor Centre etc. open Mar–Oct, daily 10–6.

10p, Audio visual 60p (ch 30p).

⚠ ⚑ ઇ (NTS)

BARCALDINE
Strathclyde *Argyll*
Map **10** NM94

Sea Life Centre Loch Creran
☎ Ledaig (063172) 386

Newest and most modern marine, aquatic life display in Europe. It contains the largest collection of native marine life in Britain. Operated by a fish farming company, it exhibits marine life in unique ways enabling a greater understanding of the underwater world. Seal display, tidepool touch tank and intertidal dump tank.

Open daily Apr–Oct 9–6; Jul & Aug. 9–8.

£1.60 (ch 90p, pen £1.20).

⚠ ⚑ ⊓ ઇ shop ✕

BARDON MILL
Northumberland
Map **12** NY76

Vindolanda (Chesterholm)
☎ (04984) 277

Remains of 3rd- and 4th-century Roman fort and frontier town. Replicas of Hadrian's turf wall and stone wall. Large museum. Also ornamental garden.

Open daily Nov–Feb 10–4; Mar & Oct 10–5; Apr 10–5.30; May, Jun & Sep 10–6; July & Aug 10–6.30. (Closed Xmas).

Admission fee payable.

⚠ ⚑ ⊓ ઇ (ground floor only) shop ✕

BARLASTON
Staffordshire
Map **7** SJ83

Wedgwood Museum & Visitor Centre
☎ (078139) 3218

Traditional skills in the production of Wedgwood ware can be seen in the craft demonstration area, and the museum contains a comprehensive collection of the works of Josiah Wedgwood from 1750. A film show is included, and shopping facilities are also available.

46

Open Mon–Fri 9–5, Sat, Apr–Oct 10–4. (Closed 2 wks Xmas & 1st wk Feb). £1 (ch, pen & students 50p). Family ticket (2 adults + 2ch) £2.

 ⚠ ⚐ ⚒ shop ✖

BARNARD CASTLE
Co Durham
Map **12** NZ01

Bowes Museum
☎ Teesdale (0833) 37139

Splendid French-style château, built in 1869 and situated in the countryside of upper Teesdale. Houses a collection of fine and decorative arts of international importance. Formal garden, children's room, local history, temporary exhibitions.

Open May–Sep, Mon–Sat 10–5.30, Sun 2–5; Nov–Feb closes 4pm; Mar, Apr & Oct closes 5pm. (Closed 20–26 Dec & New Years day).

✱ £1.20 (ch & pen 35p).

⚠ ⚐ (Etr–Sep) ⚏ ⚒ shop ✖ (ex in gardens)

The Castle
11th- to 13th-century ruin with circular three-storeyed keep.

Open †, see end of gazetteer.

✱ 50p (ch 16 & pen 25p).

⚒ (AM)

Barlaston
—
Barnsley

Egglestone Abbey (1m SE)
Picturesque remains of Premonstratensian Abbey on right bank of River Tees.

Open, any reasonable time.

Free.

P ⚒ (AM)

BARNSLEY
Gloucestershire
Map **4** SP00

Barnsley House Garden (on A433)
☎ Bibury (028574) 281

Old garden completely re-designed since 1962. Laburnum walk (early June), lime walk, knot garden, herb garden and borders with use of ground cover, kitchen garden laid out as decorative potager. Two 18th-century summerhouses, one Gothic, the other Classical.

Mon–Fri 10–6 & 1st Sun in May, Jun & Jul 2–6, by appointment other days. House not open.

£1.

⚠ ⚒ garden centre ✖ ⓥ

BARNSLEY
South Yorkshire
Map **8** SE30

Monk Bretton Priory (1½m E)
An important Cluniac house with considerable remains of the church and claustral buildings.

Open, see end of gazetteer.

✱ 30p (ch 16 & pen 15p).

⚠ ⚒ (AM)

Worsbrough Mill Museum Park Rd, Worsbrough
(2½m S of Barnsley on A61)
☎ (0226) 203961

A 17th-century water-powered corn mill and an adjoining 19th-century mill powered by a rare 1911 hot bulb oil engine set in the wooded valley of the river Dove within Worsbrough Country Park. There are frequent special exhibitions and displays relating to milling, agriculture and local history. Special events, including working machinery and demonstrations planned. Stone ground wholemeal flour usually available. Three day events BH's.

Open all year, Wed–Sun 10–6 (or dusk if earlier) (special arrangements may apply May Day BH, Xmas & New Years Day).

Donations 25p (ch 10p, pen free). Parties.

P (250 yds) ⚒ shop ✖ (in mill)

BARNSTAPLE
Devon
Map **2** SS53

Marwood Hill Gardens
☎ (0271) 42528

12 acres with many rare trees and shrubs. Formal rose garden, alpine plants, two small lakes and a large bog garden. Walled garden with collection of Clematis, Camellias, Eucalyptus. Plants for sale.

Open daily dawn–dusk.

50p.

P ☕ (Sun & BH also parties by arrangement)

St Anne's Chapel Museum
☎ (0271) 72511 (ext 272 for enquiries)

14th-century former chapel, now small but interesting local museum. Historical records of industry and local life.

Open Whit–Sep, Mon–Sat 10–1 & 2–5. (Closed Wed pm).

Admission fee payable.

P (100 yds) 🐕

BARRA, ISLE OF
Western Isles *Inverness-shire*
Map **13**

see **Castlebay**

BARR, GREAT
West Midlands
Map **7** SP09

Bishop Asbury Cottage Newton Rd
☎ 021-569 2308

The boyhood home of Francis Asbury, the founder of Methodism in America. A small, mid 17th century cottage containing furniture of Asbury's period.

Open Mon–Fri 2–4. Other times by arrangement.

Free.

⚠ 🐕

BARROW-IN-FURNESS
Cumbria
Map **7** SD26

Furness Abbey
(1½m NE on unclass road)

In some areas telephone numbers are likely to be changed by British Telecom during the currency of this publication. If any difficulty is experienced when making a reservation it is advisable to check with the operator.

Cistercian Abbey with extensive remains of the Church, sited in the 'Glen of Deadly Nightshade' near Barrow.

Open, see end of gazetteer.

✱ 60p (ch 16 & pen 25p).

⚠ ♿ (AM)

Furness Museum Ramsden Square
☎ (0229) 20650

Museum of Furness district with finds from late Stone Age sites. Also Vickers ship models and Furness bygones. Various monthly exhibitions.

Open Mon–Wed & Fri 10–5, Thu 10–1 & Sat 10–4. (Closed PH).

Free.

P 🐕

BARRY
South Glamorgan
Map **3** ST16

Welsh Hawking Centre Weycock Rd
☎ (0446) 734687

Over 200 birds of prey, including eagles, owls, hawks, falcons, buzzards which can be seen and photographed, if you wish, in the mews, on the weathered ground and in some of the breeding aviaries. Flying demonstrations of the birds given at regular intervals during the day. Many other birds and animals can be seen including lions, leopards, talking parrots and racoon.

Open daily 10.30–5 (1hr before dusk in winter). (Closed Xmas day).

£1.50 (ch & pen 75p).

⚠ ☕ ♿ shop 🐕 Ⓥ

BASILDON
Berkshire
Map **4** SU67

Basildon Park (2½m NW of Pangbourne on W side of A329)
☎ Pangbourne (07357) 3040

A classical 18th-century house, by John Carr of York, in a magnificent setting overlooking the Thames Valley. Includes the Octagon Room, Shell Room, pictures and furniture.

Open 29 Mar–Oct, Wed–Sat 2–6; Sun & BH Mon noon–6. Last admission 5.30. (Closed Good Fri).

House & grounds £1.80 Thu & Fri £1.30.

☕ shop (NT) Ⓥ

Child Beale Wildlife Trust
☎ Upper Basildon (0491) 671325 or Pangbourne (07357) 4121

Riverside walks, and lakes with ornamental pheasants, peacocks, wildfowl, flamingoes, cranes, Highland cattle and rare sheep. Children's playground and paddling pool. Craft centre. New information/education facility. River trips.

Open 29 Mar–28 Sep, daily (ex Fri) 10–6.

✱ Coach £25 (pre booked £20), (Small £8), car £3, Motor-cycle £1, Pedestrian 50p (ch 25p).

⚠ ⛩ ♿ shop 🐕 (ex in car park)

BASINGSTOKE
Hampshire
Map **4** SU65

See also **Sherborne St John**

Willis Museum and Art Gallery
Old Town Hall, Market Pl
☎ (0256) 465902

The museum has recently moved and is now housed in the handsome Old Town Hall. Temporary displays shows what the new museum will eventually look like. Exhibition gallery.

Open Tue–Sat, 10–5.

Free.

P (200 yds) shop

BATH
Avon
Map **3** ST76

American Museum Claverton Manor (2½m E)
☎ (0225) 60503

Built in 1820 by Sir Jeffrey Wyatville, overlooks Avon valley, and now museum of American decorative arts and gardens including American Aborotum. Winston Churchill delivered his first political speech in the grounds in 1897. Events planned include Indian weekend 15–16 June; Independence Day displays 4–6 July; American Civil War Weekend 20 & 21 Sep.

Open 28 Mar–2 Nov, daily (ex Mon) 2–5. BH Sun & Mon 11–5.

✱ £2 (ch & pen £1.60). Grounds only 50p. Party 30+.

⚠ ☕ ♿ (ground floor & gardens only) shop 🐕

Assembly Rooms Bennett St
☎ (0225) 61111

Designed in 1769 by John Wood the Younger, restored and redecorated in 1979. Associated with novels by Charles Dickens and Jane Austen.

Open as Museum of Costume, in basement, last admission ½ hr before closing.

⚠ (limited) ☕ ♿ (NT)

Also **Museum of Costume** (Assembly Rooms)
☎ (0225) 61111 ext 327

Housed in the Assembly Rooms. Based on the internationally famous collections built up by Doris Langley Moore OBE, the collections are amongst the largest and most comprehensive in the world. Also on display are toys and dolls and an important collection of jewellery. Modern fashions and the 'Dress of the Year'.

Fashions from the Regency to the 1960s are displayed in period rooms and settings, many based on well known scenes in Bath. Twenties Style Apr '86–Feb '87. Guided tours at regular intervals.

Open Mar–Oct, Mon–Sat 9.30–6, Sun 10–6; Nov–Feb, Mon–Sat 10–5, Sun 11–5. Last admission ½hr before closing.

✱ £1.25p (ch 5–16 75p). Party 20 +. Combined ticket with Roman Baths ✱ £2.30 (ch 5–16 £1.15). Party 20 +.

⚲ (licensed mid Jul–mid Sep) ᕯ shop ✖

Bath Carriage Museum Circus Mews
☎ (0225) 25175

Finest and most comprehensive collection of horse-drawn carriages in the country. Large exhibition of harnesses etc from the coaching era. Housed in Circus Mews, built in 1759 by John Wood the Younger. Carriage rides available daily throughout the season.

Open daily 9.30–5 (Sun 10–5) summer; 11–4 (Sun 11–5) winter.

Admission fee payable.

⚠ ᕯ shop

Bath Postal Museum 8 Broad St
☎ (0225) 60333

New display entitled 'The Moving Finger Writes' covering written communication throughout history. Films and audio-visual presentations available.

Open daily Mon–Sat 11–5; Sun 2–5. (Closed Xmas).

✱ 75p (ch, students & pen 50p).

ᕯ shop ✖ ⓥ

Beckford's Tower & Museum
Lansdown
☎ (0225) 336228

Built in 1827 by H. E. Goodridge for William Beckford of Fonthill, in a striking Neo-Classical style. Fine views from Belvedere. 156 steps. Small museum on 1st floor.

Open Apr–Oct, Sat & Sun only 2–5.

50p (ch 14 & pen 25p).

⚠ ⇶ shop

Burrows Toy Museum York St
☎ (0225) 61819

Museum on two floors, devoted entirely to toys. Constructional and mechanical toys, dolls houses and dolls, books, games and pastimes from the past two hundred years. Adjoining Roman Baths.

Open daily 10–5.30. (Closed 25 & 26 Dec).

90 p (ch 4–16 & pen 60p). Party.

P (limited) ᕯ (ground floor only) shop ✖

Camden Works Industrial Museum
Julian Rd
☎ (0225) 318348

Housing the Bowler collection, the entire stock-in-trade of a Victorian Brass Founder, General Engineer and Aerated Water manufacturer, displayed in settings that capture the atmosphere of the original premises. Also, 'Story of Bath

Stone' with replica of mine face before mechanisation. Temporary exhibitions.

Open Etr–Oct 2–5; Nov–Etr wknds 2–5. Parties at other times by arrangement.

£1 (ch & pen 50p). Family ticket £2.

P shop ✖

Holburne of Menstrie Museum
(University of Bath) Great Pulteney St
☎ (0225) 66669

Old Master paintings, silver, porcelain, glass, furniture and miniatures in an elegant 18th-century building. Crafts Study Centre with work by 20th-century craftsmen.

Open Mon–Sat 11–5, Sun 2.30–6. (Closed Xmas and Mons Nov–Etr & mid Dec–Jan).

£1 (ch, students & pen 50p). Family ticket £2.

⚠ ⚲ (licensed; Etr–Oct) shop ✖

Museum of Bookbinding Manvers St
☎ (0225) 66000

Museum shows the historical and contemporary practice of the craft; a reconstruction of a 19th-century bindery and examples of the art.

Open Mon–Fri 9–1 & 2.15–5.30.

75p. Family ticket £2.

P (100 yds) ✖

RPS National Centre of Photography
The Octagon, Milsom St
☎ (0225) 62841

The RPS National Centre of Photography has three galleries, a cinema/lecture theatre and museum plus excellent conference facilities. There is an active exhibition policy of showing the best of both contemporary and historical photography. Also library, rare books, equipment and prints from the world famous collection, open by appointment.

Open Mon–Sat 10–5.30, last admission 4.45.

£1 (ch 7, pen & students 60p; ch under 7 & disabled, Free)

P ⚲ ᕯ (ground floor only) shop ✖

No. 1 Royal Crescent
☎ (0225) 28126

Stone-built 18th century house in perhaps the best known of Bath's terraces and crescents: House restored to original condition and two floors furnished as they might have been in the 18th century. Kitchen museum.

Open Mar–Oct, Tue–Sat & BH Mon 11–5, Sun 2–5. (Closed Good Fri.)

£1.30 (ch, pen & students 60p). Parties by arrangement.

P shop ✖

Roman Baths & Pump Room Abbey Churchyard
☎ (0225) 61111 ext 327

Remains of Roman baths of 'Aquae Sulis', with museum devoted to the Roman history of Bath and containing important archaeological finds from the City. Britain's only hot water springs and largest Roman bathing complex. Excavations of Roman Temple Precinct under Pump Room, also open to view. Guided tours at regular intervals.

Open Mar–Jun & Sep–Oct daily 9–6, Sun 9–6; Jul & Aug 9–7, Sun 9–7; Nov–Feb Mon–Sat 9–5, Sun 10–5. Last admission ½hr before closing.

✱ £1.50 (ch 16 90p). Party 20 +. Combined ticket with Museum of Costume ✱ £2.30 (ch 16 £1.15).

⚲ (licensed) ᕯ (ground floor only) shop ✖

BATHGATE
Lothian West Lothian
Map **11** NS96

Cairnpapple Hill Sanctuary and Burial Cairn (2m N)
☎ 031-226 2570 (Scottish Development Dept.)

Monumental temple, and burial cairn of several dates in the prehistoric period, notably the second millennium BC.

Open see end of gazetteer. Closed Fri & Mon am. Closed winter.

✱ 50p (ch & pen 25p).

(AM)

BATLEY
West Yorkshire
Map **8** SE22

Art Gallery Market Place
☎ (0924) 473141

Permanent collection of British oil paintings, water colours, drawings and sculpture mid 19th century onwards. Temporary loan and special exhibitions throughout the year.

Open Mon–Fri 10–6; Sat 10–4.

Free.

shop ✖

Bagshaw Museum Wilton Park
☎ (0924) 472514

A 19th-century building housing museum of local history, archaeology, geology, ethnography, Oriental arts, natural history and folk life. (Best approached from Upper Batley Lane.)

Open Mon–Sat 10–5, Sun 1–5.

Free.

⚠ ᕯ (ground floor & gardens only) shop ✖

BATTLE
East Sussex
Map **5** TQ71

Battle and District Historical Society Museum Langton House, High St →

☎ (04246) 3899

Diorama of Battle of Hastings and reproduction of Bayeux Tapestry. Exhibits also show local history. Summer Arts Festival. Battle Festival Jun/Jul.

Open Etr–Sep, Mon–Sat 10–1 & 2–5, Sun 2.30–5.30.

20p (ch 5p).

P (200 yds) & (ground floor only) shop

BEACONSFIELD
Buckinghamshire
Map **4** SU99

Bekonscot Model Village New Town, 1m from A40.
☎ (04946) 2919

The oldest model village in the world. Official opening of miniature coalmine Sun 23 Mar 1986.

Etr–Oct, 10–5 daily; Limited display in Mar, daily 10–5.

£1 (ch 3–16 60p; pen, students & unemployed 80p). Party 13+.

⚠ ♁ & wheelchairs available shop ⓥ

BEAMINSTER
Dorset
Map **3** ST40

Mapperton Gardens (2m SE off A356 & B3163)
☎ (0308) 862441

Extensive terraced and hillside gardens with formal borders and specimen shrubs and trees. 18th-century stone fish ponds and summer-house. Orangery.

10 Mar–10 Oct, Mon–Fri 2–6.

£1 (ch 5–18 60p, under 5 free).

⚠ (50 yds) ♨ & (top levels only) ✖

Parnham
☎ (0308) 862204

Impressive Tudor mansion set in 14 acres of traditional gardens, formal terraces and woodlands. Home of John Makepeace, leading furniture designer, and his workshop (open to visitors). Completed pieces shown in house.

Open 28 Mar–29 Oct, Wed, Sun & BH 10–5.

Battle
—
Beauly

£2 (ch 10–15 £1, under 10 free).
⚠ ♨ (licensed) & (ground floor & gardens only) shop

BEAMISH
Co Durham
Map **12** NZ25

North of England Open-Air Museum (off A693 & A6076)
☎ Stanley (0207) 231811

England's first open-air museum. Beamish is about Northern people and their way of life. On a 200-acre site, buildings of all kinds have been rebuilt and furnished as they were around the turn of the century and grouped into areas. "The Town" with Co-operative shops, Georgian town houses, the Sun Inn and stables, printers workshop and town park; the "Railway Area" with country station, goods shed, signal box, weighbridge house, rolling stock and steam locomotives; "Home Farm" with livestock, poultry, exhibitions, old agricultural machinery and implements and a traditional farm house kitchen, pantry and bailiff's office; the "Colliery" with colliery buildings, guided tours down a "drift" mine and a row of fully furnished pit cottages. A tram, from the museum's large transport collection, carries visitors between "areas".

Open Good Fri–14 Sep daily 10–6; 16 Sep–Etr daily (ex Mon) 10–5. Last admission 4 pm. Good Fri–14 Sep £2.50 (ch & pen £1.50); 16 Sep–Etr £1.50 (ch & pen £1). Parties. N.B. Not all areas open in winter.

⚠ ♨ (licensed summer only) ♁ & shop ⓥ

BEARSDEN
Strathclyde *Dunbartonshire*
Map **11** NS57

Roman Bath-House Roman Rd

Considered to be the best surviving visible Roman building in Scotland the bath-house was discovered in 1973 during excavations for a construction site. It was originally built for use by the Roman garrison at Bearsden Fort, part of the Antonine Wall defences.

Open at all reasonable times.

Free.

(AM)

BEAULIEU
Hampshire
Map **4** SU30

Beaulieu Abbey, National Motor Museum and Palace House (on B3054)
☎ (0590) 612345

The National Motor Museum, presenting the story of motoring from 1895, with 250 historic exhibits. Beaulieu Abbey Ruins and Exhibition of Monastic Life. Palace House, once the Great Gatehouse of the Abbey, contains displays with costumed figures depicting generations of the Montagu family. Special features include Monorail, Veteran Bus Rides, Model Railway, Transporama and 'Wheels' a ride on which visitors travel in 'pods' along electric track viewing displays showing evolution of the motor car. Many special events throughout the year including country sports & Crafts Fair 29 June and Fireworks Fair 1 Nov.

House, Motor Museum, Abbey & gardens, May–Sep 10–6; Oct–Apr 10–5. (Closed Xmas day).

✷ £3.70 (ch & students £2.20; pen £2.60). Party 15+.

⚠ ♨ (licensed summer only) ♁ & (ground floor only) shop ✖ in buildings ⓥ

See also **BUCKLER'S HARD, Maritime Museum**

BEAULY
Highland *Inverness-shire*
Map **14** NH54

Beauly Priory
Founded in 1230, one of three houses of the Valliscaulian Order established in

THE NATIONAL MOTOR MUSEUM·PALACE HOUSE & GARDENS·ABBEY & EXHIBITION

Scotland. Only the church remains, a long narrow building comprising aisleless nave, transepts and chancel. This is the burial place of the Mackenzies of Kintail and contains the fine monument of Sir Kenneth Mackenzie.

Open, see end of gazetteer (Closed Mon & Tue am in winter).

✳ 50p (ch & pen 25p).

(AM)

BEAUMARIS
Gwynedd
Map **6** SH67

Beaumaris Castle
Moated castle begun in 1295 by Edward I and completed in 1323, perhaps finest concentrically planned stronghold in Britain. Retains original small dock for shipping.

Open †, see end of gazetteer.

✳ 90p (ch 16 & pen 45p) Party.

⚠ ⚓ shop (AM Cadw)

Beaumaris Gaol
☎ Llangefni (0248) 723262 ext 138

Built in 1829, it is a grim reminder of the harshness of justice in Victorian Britain. Visitors can see the prison cells, the unique tread mill, and the condemned man's final walk to the scaffold. Courthouse also open to the public.

Open May–Sep, daily 11–6.

✳ 70p (ch & pen 35p)

P (100 yds) ⚓ (ground floor only) shop

Museum of Childhood 1 Castle St
☎ (0248) 712498

The eight rooms of exhibits, many of which are rare and valuable, illustrate the habits and interests of children and families spanning 150 years. They include children's saving boxes; dolls; educational toys and games; pottery and glassware depicting and used by children; early clockwork toys, including trains, cars, and aeroplanes; music boxes; polyphons; magic lanterns and an art gallery full of paintings and prints of children, as well as early samplers and needlework pictures worked by children.

Beauly
—
Bedford

Also children's furniture – push toys & cycles.

Open all year daily 10–6, Sun 1–5. (Closed Xmas).

£1.25 (ch & pen 75p, ch under 5 free). Family ticket £3.50.

P (50 yds) ⚓ (ground floor only) shop ✈

The Tudor Rose 32 Castle St
☎ (0248) 810203

One of the few ancient monuments in Wales of the 15th century. A half-timbered building with a fine period hall at the rear. Upstairs are two rooms and a minstrel gallery which offers a view of the barrel-braced ceiling and the hall below. Hendrick Lek bought and restored the property in 1945 and there is a continually changing exhibition of both his and his son's paintings, drawings and prints.

Open Jul–mid Sep, daily 10.30–5.30 also Etr & Whit wknds (out of season by request).

30p (ch 14 & pen 15p).

P (300 yds) shop ✈

BECCLES
Suffolk
Map **5** TM49

Beccles & District Museum Newgate
☎ (0502) 712628

Local industrial, rural and domestic displays, which includes tools of the printing trade, a prominent industry in the town. A new addition is a needlework banner depicting scenes of the town.

Open Apr–Oct, Wed, Sat, Sun & BH 2.30–5; Nov–Mar, Sun only 2.30–5.

Free.

P (100 yds) ✈

BEDALE
North Yorkshire
Map **8** SE28

Bedale Hall on A684 (1½m W of A1 at Leeming Bar)
☎ (0677) 23123

Georgian ballroom and museum room.

Open May–Sep, Tue 10–4, other times by appointment.

Free.

⚠ ⚓ (ground floor only) ✈

BEDFORD
Bedfordshire
Map **4** TL04

Bedford Museum Castle Lane
☎ (0234) 53323

A local history and natural history museum with 19th-century room sets, displays on agriculture, Bedfordshire geology, archaeology, birds and Mammals, and fossils and minerals. Also a programme of temporary exhibitions.

Open all year, Tue–Sat 11–5 & Sun 2–5. (Closed Mon ex BH Mon afternoons, Good Fri & Xmas).

Free

P (50 yds) ⚓ (lift available on request) shop ✈

Bunyan Museum Mill St
☎ (0234) 58870 & 58627

In the Bunyan Meeting House, dating from 1850, situated on the site of the barn where John Bunyan preached. Contains relics and a world-famous collection of over 400 editions of his works, including Pilgrim's Progress in over 165 languages.

Open Apr–Sep, Tue–Sat 2–4.

Admission fee payable.

P (100 yds) ⚓ ✈

Cecil Higgins Art Gallery Castle Close
☎ (0234) 211222

Sothebys Award for Best Fine Arts Gallery 1981. New extension contains outstanding collections of ceramics, glass, and English water-colours. Late Victorian style room settings in adjoining house including room decorated in the style of William Burges, and containing furniture designed mainly by him. Thomas Lester Lace on display. Cadbury's →

Built in 1829 Beaumaris Gaol is a grim reminder of the harshness of justice in Victorian Britain. Visitors can see the prison cells, the punishment cell, the unique treadwheel, the condemned cell and the condemned man's final walk to the scaffold. There is an exhibition of documents illustrating prison life in the nineteenth century.
Open daily 11am to 6pm —
Spring Bank Holiday to September
Also Beaumaris Court House
Open 11.30am to 5.30pm from May to September.

children's art exhibition 4 Jul–9 Aug. Special arrangements for group visits, evening parties and children's parties.

Open Tue–Fri 12.30–5, Sat 11–5, Sun 2–5 (Closed Mon, Good Fri & Xmas).

20p (ch & pen free).

P (50 yds) ⚱ (by arrangement) ⅋ shop ✸

BEDWYN, GREAT
Wiltshire
Map **4** SU26

Bedwyn Stone Museum
☎ Marlborough (0672) 870234

An open air museum that explains the ancient secrets of the freemason and how the carvings trace the behaviour of man in a language vastly different to that taught in school. Finest known sequence of carvings are to be found in the church adjacent.

Open all year.

Free.

⅋ garden centre

Crofton Beam Engines (1½m SW)
☎ Goring (0491) 874072 (steaming weekends) Marlborough (0672) 870300

The oldest working steam engine in the world, a Boulton and Watt of 1812 and also a Harvey's of Hayle of 1845, both are coal fired and pump water into the Kennet and Avon Canal with a lift of 40 feet.

Bedford
—
Bekesbourne

Public trips on narrow boat 'Jubilee' telephone Malmesbury (0666) 860423.

Operating in steam Etr, May, Spring & Aug BH wknds (Sat–Mon) also 26 & 27 Jun (educational for schools), 28 & 29 Jun and 27 & 28 Sep 10.30–1 & 2–5. Open but not in steam Sun Apr–Oct 11–5. Other times by arrangement.

When operating £1.50 (ch & pen 75p). Other times donations accepted.

⚠ ⚱ ⊞ shop

BEER
Devon
Map **3** SY28

Pecorama Underleys
☎ Seaton (0297) 21542

Situated high on a hillside at the back of the village, with good views across the bay. A steam-operated passenger carrying line which runs through the Pleasure Park with interesting scenic features and an exciting tunnel. The garden includes an aviary, putting green, crazy golf and children's corner. The main building houses an exhibition of railway modelling in various small gauges

---

displayed in typical locations around the house and garden. Souvenir and model railway shops. Snacks at Beer Victoria Station Buffet. Main meals in Orion Pullman Car.

Open Mon–Fri 10–5.30, Sat 10–1. Outside activities Etr, May Day; Spring BH wknd–early Oct & Sun during School hols & Aug BH.

✳ Exhibition 60p (ch 35p). Garden 60p (ch 30p). Railway 40p (ch 30p). Bargain ticket for all three £1.45 (ch 4–14 80p).

⚠ ⚱ (licensed) ⊞ shop

BEESTON
Cheshire
Map **7** SJ55

Beeston Castle (off A49)
The 13th-century stronghold, built by Earl of Chester, in an almost inaccessible position on steep hill.

Open, see end of gazetteer.

✳ 80p (ch 40p).

⚠ (AM)

BEKESBOURNE
Kent
Map **5** TR15

Howletts Zoo Park (off A257)
☎ Canterbury (0227) 721 286

Famous collection of wild animals, including breeding groups of gorillas,

---

tigers, small cats, free-running deer and antelope, also snow leopards, tapirs, and elephants.

Open daily 10–5. (Closed Xmas day). Prices not confirmed for 1986.

⚠ ☕ ⛼ ♿ shop ✖

BELTON
Lincolnshire
Map **8** SK93

Belton House Park and Gardens on A607

Splendid 17th-century house in rolling parkland; fine furniture, paintings, display of Speaker Cust's silver and Brownlow family silver-gilt; 19th-century gardens and orangery; children's playground.

Open 29 Mar–Oct, Wed–Sun & BH Mon (closed Good Fri) House open 1–5.30 (last admission 5pm); Grounds open 12–5.30.

£2.20 (ch £1.10) Party 20+.

P (250 yds) ☕ shop (NT)

BELTRING
Kent
Map **5** TQ64

Whitbread Hop Farm
☎ Maidstone (0622) 872068/872408

This, the largest group of Victorian oast and galleried barns in the world, is situated amidst picturesque countryside and hop gardens. These house the award winning museums, one on rural crafts, the other devoted to hop farming through the ages. In addition to these there are displays of farming machinery, carts and bygones. Other facilities include nature trails, coarse fishing, working craft centre, pets and children's play area and home for the famous Whitbread shire horses.

Open 26 Mar–late Oct 10–5.30. (Closed Mon ex BH).

£1.50 (ch 75p). Party.

⚠ ☕ ⛼ ♿ shop

BELVOIR
Leicestershire
Map **8** SK83

Belvoir Castle Between A52 & A607
☎ Grantham (0476) 870262

Home of the Duke of Rutland. Palatial early 19th-century reconstruction by James Wyatt, on hilltop overlooking Vale of Belvoir, with notable objets d'art, armoury and museums of 17th/21st Lancers. Many special events on Sundays at no extra charge; Medieval Jousting, Car Rallies etc.

Open 22 Mar–4 Oct, Tue–Thu & Sat 12–6, Sun 12–7, BH Mon only 11–7; Oct, Sun only 2–6 (last admission ¾ hr before closing time). (Closed 9–12 Jul).

£2.20 (ch £1.20). Party 30+.

⚠ ☕ ⛼ ♿ (ground floor and garden only) shop & garden centre ✖ Ⓥ

BEMBRIDGE
Isle of Wight
Map **4** SZ68

Bembridge Windmill (off B3390)

Last windmill on island, built about 1700 and in use until 1913. Stone-built tower mill with wooden cap and machinery.

Open 24 Mar–Sep, daily 10–5. Last admission 15 mins before closing.

60p (ch 30p).

(NT)

Maritime Museum Providence House, Sherborne St
☎ Isle of Wight (0983) 872223

Six galleries designed to interest the whole family. Included is a unique collection of salvage and shipwreck stories, early diving equipment and ship models.

Open Apr–Sep, daily 10–5.30. Party 10+.

85p (ch 50p, pen 60p, ch under 5 free).

⚠ ♿ (ground floor only) shop ✖ Ⓥ

BENINGBROUGH
North Yorkshire
Map **8** SE55

Beningbrough Hall off A19. Entrance at Newton Lodge

Built about 1716, this attractive house stands in a wooded park. The principal rooms have 100 pictures from the National Portrait Gallery. The Victorian laundry is open and exhibitions describe domestic life of the period. There are also gardens and an adventure playground.

Open 29 Mar–Oct, Tue–Thu, Sat & Sun 12–6 & BH Mon 12–6. Garden open from 11am. (Closed Good Fri).

House & garden £1.90. Garden & exhibitions £1.40.

P ☕ (from 11 am) shop (NT)

BENMORE
Strathclyde *Argyll*
Map **10** NS18

Younger Botanic Garden
☎ Sandbanks (036985) 261

Woodland and garden on a grand scale, featuring conifers, rhododendrons, azaleas, and many other shrubs.

Open Apr–Oct, daily 10–6.

20p (ch & pen 10p).

⚠ ☕ ⛼ ♿ shop ✖

BENTHALL
Shropshire
Map **7** SJ60

Benthall Hall on B4375

16th-century house with fine panelling and carved oak staircase, interior was improved in the 17th century. Garden contains shrubs and plants.

Open Etr Sat–Sep, Tue, Wed & Sat; BH ground floor rooms only 2–6.

✱ House £1.50. Garden only 60p.

(NT)

BERKELEY
Gloucestershire
Map **3** ST69

Berkeley Castle on B4509 (1½m W of A38)
☎ Dursley (0453) 810332

Home of Berkeleys for over 800 years, splendid 12th-century and later castle in which Edward II was murdered in 1327. →

Keep, dungeon, great hall, state apartments and medieval kitchens shown. Elizabethan terraced gardens include bowling alley and nearby is an extensive deer park. Butterfly house due to open May '86.

Open Apr daily 2–5; May–Aug weekdays 11–5, Sun 2–5; Sep daily 2–5; Oct Sun only 2–4.30; BH Mon 11–5. (Closed Mon except BH).

£2 (ch £1, pen £1.80). Party 25 + .

⚠ ⟁ ⊞ shop ✘

Jenner Museum The Chantry
☎ Dursley (0453) 810631

Commemorates Edward Jenner (1749–1823), who discovered smallpox vaccine. The museum is the house he lived in most of his life, 'that of a fascinating country doctor', which is situated in one acre of grounds with garden.

Open Apr–Sep daily 11–5.15, Sun 12–5.15 (Closed Mon ex BH Mon).

50p (ch & pen 20p) Parties.

⚠ & shop ✘

BERKHAMSTED
Hertfordshire
Map **4** SP90

Berkhamsted Castle

Remains of an 11th-century motte and bailey castle with later circular Keep. Former home of Black Prince and prison of King John of France.

Open all reasonable times.

Free.

& (AM)

BERNEY ARMS WINDMILL
Norfolk
Map **5** TG40

Access by boat from Great Yarmouth or by rail to Berney Arms station; road to mill unsuitable for cars. Tall, late 19th-century marsh windmill in lonely part of Halvergate Marshes, near confluence of Rivers Yare and Waveney.

Open † see end of gazetteer.

✻ 50p (ch 16 & pen 25p).

(AM)

Berkeley – Beverley

BERWICK-UPON-TWEED
Northumberland
Map **12** NT95

Castle & Town Walls
☎ (0289) 307881

Remains of 12th-century stronghold incorporating three towers and west wall. Medieval town walls reconstructed during Elizabethan period.

Open, any reasonable time.

Free.

(AM)

Museum & Art Gallery The Barracks
☎ (0289) 306332 ext 253

Local history, archaeology, natural history, fine art and decorative art including an important collection donated by Sir William Burrell.

Open 15 May–15 Oct 9.30–6.30; 16 Oct–14 Mar 9.30–4.

£1 (ch & pen 50p) includes entry to Museum of the King's Own Scottish Borderers.

P (100 yds) & ⚠ & shop

Museum of the King's Own Scottish Borderers The Barracks
☎ (0289) 304493

Designed by Vanbrugh in 1717, said to be the oldest barracks in Britain.

Open Mon–Sat 9.30–4.30, Sun 12–4.30.

£1 (ch & pen 50p) includes entry to Museum & Art Gallery.

P (100 yds) & (ground floor & gardens only) shop ✘

BETTYHILL
Highland *Sutherland*
Map **14** NC76

Strathnaver Museum
☎ (06412) 330

Fine stone-built, white harled building, formerly a church, in an area of

outstanding beauty. It contains a magnificent pitch pine canopied pulpit dated 1774, a fine collection of home-made furnishings, domestic and farm implements and Gaelic books. The churchyard contains a carved stone known as the Farr Stone dating back to the 10th century.

Open Jun–Sep, Mon–Sat 2–5. (Under revision). Other times by arrangement with the custodians.

50p (ch 30p). Party.

P 60 yds) & (ground floor & gardens only) ✘

BETWS-Y-COED
Gwynedd
Map **6** SH75

Conwy Valley Railway Museum Old Goods Yard
☎ (06902) 568

Two large museum buildings display railway items of both narrow and standard gauge with North Wales connections. Operating model railway layouts and steam-hauled miniature railway in 4½ acre grounds.

Open daily, Etr–Oct, 10–5.30. Spring & Autumn 11–4.

85p (ch 45p, pen 65p). Train ride 50p.

⚠ ⊞ & shop

BEVERLEY
Humberside
Map **8** TA03

Art Gallery, Museum & Heritage Centre
Champney Rd
☎ Hull (0482) 882255

Local antiquities, Victorian bygones and china, pictures by F W Elwell of Beverley and others, and bust of Sir Winston Churchill by Bryant Baker of New York. Various solo Art Exhibitions. Heritage Centre recently established.

Open Mon–Wed & Fri 9.30–12.30, 2–5, Thu 9.30–12, Sat 9.30–4.

Free.

⚠ shop ✘

54

The Guildhall Register Sq.
☎ Hull (0482) 882255

Formerly the Guild House established in 1500 and rebuilt in 1762; now used as a Magistrate's Court and the Mayor's Parlour. Exhibits include civil regalia, ancient charters, 15th–17th century furniture and pewter work. Guide service available.

Open Etr–Sep, Tue & BH 10–5. Other times by prior arrangement.

Free.

P (250 yds) & (ground floor only)

Lairgate Hall
☎ Hull (0482) 882255

Dates from 1710–80, now used as council offices. Interesting late 18th-century stucco ceiling, marble mantelpiece. Chinese room with hand-painted wallpaper.

Open Mon–Thu, 8.45–5.30, Fri 9–4.

Free.

& & ✕

Museum of Army Transport
Flemingate
☎ Hull (0482) 860445

A unique collection of road, rail, sea and air transport used by the British Army. There are 50 vehicles on display, most in picturesque tableaux, together with a Land Rover rigged for parachute-dropping, some locomotives, a Blackburn Beverley transport and a Beaver aircraft.

Open daily 10–5. (Closed Xmas day).

£1 (ch 16 & pen 50p). Party 20 + .

& ⚲ ⊞ shop ✕

BEWDLEY
Hereford and Worcester
Map 7 SO77

Bewdley Museum The Shambles, Load St
☎ (0299) 403573

A folk museum, situated in a row of 18th-century butchers shops. The crafts and industries of the Bewdley area are illustrated, including displays on charcoal burning, basket making and coopering. Craftsmen's workshops within the museum and demonstrations are often held. The recently opened brass foundry can be visited.

Open Mar–Nov, Mon–Sat 10–5.30, Sun 2–5.30.

30p (ch & pen 10p).

P (50 yds) & (ground floor only) shop

Lax Lane Craft Centre Lax Ln
☎ (0299) 402854

A brass rubbing centre where you can choose from a selection of exact replicas moulded from original medieval and Tudor brasses. Experienced staff will demonstrate how to tackle brass-rubbing.

Open Apr–Sep Mon–Fri 11–4, Sat, Sun & BH Mon 2–5. Details not confirmed for

1986. A charge is made for every rubbing which includes the cost of materials.

& & shop

Severn Valley Railway For details see gazetteer entry under Bridgnorth.

West Midland Safari & Leisure Park
Spring Grove (on A456 to Kidderminster)
☎ (0299) 402114

200-acre wildlife and leisure park. All-inclusive price includes animal reserves, pets corner, sea lion show, amusement park rides, splash cats, rowing boats, canoes, picnic and leisure areas, the 'Rio Grande' railway, pirate ship ride, and rollercoaster.

Open Apr–Oct daily 10–5.

✳ £3.50 (ch & pen £2.50). Parties 20 + .

& ⚲ (licensed) ⊞ & shop & garden centre ⓥ

BEXHILL-ON-SEA
East Sussex
Map 5 TQ70

Bexhill Manor Costume Museum Old Manor Gdns Old Town
☎ (0424) 215361

Set in small gardens, the museum contains a display of costumes, 1740–1960 accessories, toys and dolls.

Open Etr–Sep, Tue–Fri & BH 10.30–1 & 2.30–5.30, Sat & Sun 2.30–5.30. (Closed Mon, ex BH Mon).

50p (ch & students, 25p, pen 40p).

P (50–100 yds) & shop

BEXLEY
Gt London
(London plan 4 pages 174/175)

Hall Place (Near Junction of A2 & A233)
London Plan 4: **23**D6
☎ Crayford (0322) 526574

15th–16th century mansion Grade I listed building and ancient monument with contrasting elevations of chequered flint and brick. Ornamental gardens, with topiary in form of 'Queen's Beasts', roses, rock, water, herb, and peat gardens, conservatory houses and recreation facilities.

Open House Mon–Sat 10–5, Sun 2–6 (summer); Mon–Sat 10–5, Sun 2–dusk (winter); Gardens Mon–Fri 7.30–dusk, Sat & Sun 9–dusk.

Free.

& ⚲ (weather permitting) & (gardens only) ✕

BIBURY
Gloucestershire
Map 4 SP10

Arlington Mill (on A433)
☎ (028574) 368/533

17th-century corn mill on site of River Coln mentioned in Domesday Book. Now a museum with working machinery, agricultural implements and bygones.

Open daily Mar–Oct 10.30–7 (dusk in winter); Nov–Feb wknds only 10.30–dusk.

✳ £1 (ch 50p, pen 70p).

P (20 yds) ⊞ shop ✕

BICKENHILL
West Midlands
Map 7 SP28

National Motorcycle Museum Coventry Rd
(Nr junction 6 of M42, off A45, not far from National Exhibition Centre)
☎ 021-704 2784

British motorcycles built during the Golden Age of Motorcycling are on display. Spanning 80 years, the immaculately restored machines are the products of around 100 different factories.

Open daily (ex Xmas Day) 10–6.

£2.50 (ch 14 & pen £1.75). P 20 + .

& ⚲ & shop ✕ ⓥ

BICKLEIGH
Devon
Map 3 SS90

Bickleigh Castle off A396. Take A3072 from Bickleigh Bridge & follow signs
☎ (08845) 363

Medieval romantic home of the heirs of the Earls of Devon. Great Hall. Armoury. Guard Room. Stuart farmhouse. Elizabethan bedroom. 11th-century Chapel. Moated Gardens. Tower Exhibition showing castle's connection with Tudor Maritime history and the development of ships to present day. Museum of 18th–20th-century objects and toys. Display of World War II spy and POW escape gadgets – the most complete collection known.

Open Etr wk, then Wed, Sun & BH Mon to 25 May; 26 May–5 Oct daily (ex Sat) 2–5.

£1.80 (ch 16 90p pen & students £1.50). Party 20 + by prior arrangement.

& ⚲ & (ground floor & garden only) shop ✕ ⓥ

Bickleigh Mill Craft Centre & Farm
☎ (08845) 419

A picturesque old working watermill adapted to the production of craftwork (pottery, spinning, leatherwork, jewellery, making corn dollies etc). One of the largest and most comprehensive working craft centres in the West Country. Farm with rare breeds of animals and poultry where cows and goats are milked by hand and the farm worked by Shire horses complete with museum. Additional Fish Farm opened in 1981. A British Tourist Authority Award Winner. →

Open Jan–Mar Sat & Sun 10–5; Apr–Dec daily 10–6. (5pm Nov & Dec).

✱ £2 (ch £1) Party.

▲ ☕ (licensed) ⛉ ♿ (ground floor and gardens only) shop Ⓥ

BICTON
Devon
Map **3** SY08

Bicton Park, Gardens, Woodland Railway, Theme Halls & Countryside Collection (on A376 N of Budleigh Salterton)
☏ Colaton Raleigh (0395) 68465

Over 60 acres of historic gardens and pinetum. World of tomorrow features space station and SR2 leisure simulator. World of yesterday has original 'Penny in the Slot' machines, magic lantern shows and countryside collection with agricultural artefacts. World of leisure includes crazy golf, adventure playground, assault course and putting green. Summer Extravaganza 30–31 July; charity day 'Help the Aged' 16 August.

Open 24 Mar–Oct daily 10–6; See local press for winter opening.

£2.20 (ch £2, only one child in each family charged for; pen £2, Weds only £1). Prices from 1 July £2.50 (ch £2.30, only one child in family charged for; pen £2).

▲ ☕ (licensed) ⛉ ♿ shop & garden centre

BIDDENDEN
Kent
Map **5** TQ83

Baby Carriage Collection Bettenham Manor
☏ (0580) 291343

A unique collection of 400 baby carriages (prams) of a bygone era. Exhibits portray the history of the pram up to the present day and include 18th-century stickwagons, perambulators and mailcarts, Edwardian bassinettes, Victorias and large coachbuilt prams of the twenties. The museum, in a Kentish oast house, adjoins a 15th-century moated manor house of historical and architectural interest and is set in a 15-acre garden.

Open all year (ex Xmas day) by appointment only.

Free.

▲ ⛉ ♿ (ground floor & gardens only) ✘

Biddenden Vineyards Little Whatmans ($1\frac{1}{2}$m S off A262)
☏ (0580) 291726

The present vineyard was established in 1969 and has now reached eighteen acres. The varieties planted are mainly of German origin all of which produce fruity fragrant wines. Harvesting usually commences on 20th October when visitors can see the presses in operation. Visitors are welcome to stroll around the vines at leisure and to call at the shop for tasting of the wines, and cider etc.

Shop open Mon–Sat 11–5 (2pm Nov–Apr) Sun 12–5 (Closed Nov–Apr).

Free. Parties by arrangement.

▲ shop

BIDFORD-ON-AVON
Warwickshire
Map **4** SP15

Dorsington Manor Gardens (8m W of Stratford-upon-Avon on unclass road off B4085)
☏ (0789) 772442

Unique collection of domestic ducks, geese, hens and turkeys, over a hundred breeds in all, in grounds covering some 27 acres. Adventure playground, model railway, garden centre, nature trail and caravan & camping site.

Open Apr–Sep, daily 11.30–6.

✱ £1.50 (ch 75p, pen £1.30)

▲ ☕ (licensed) ⛉ ♿ shop

BIGGAR

Strathclyde *Lanarkshire*
Map **11** NT03

Gladstone Court Museum entrance by
113 High St
☎ (0899) 21050

*Interesting museum which portrays an
old-world village street, housed in
century-old coachhouse with modern
extension. On display are reconstructed
old shops, complete with fascinating
signs and adverts, a bank, telephone
exchange, photographer's booth, etc.
Albion Motors section. Blackwood Murray
run mid Aug. Commemorative run for
vintage and veteran vehicles held
annually in mid Aug. H.Q. Albion Owners
Club and Albion Commercial motor
archive. Museum shop.*

Open Etr–Oct, daily 10–12.30, 2–5; Sun
2–5.

✱ 80p (ch 40p, ch 8 free). Reduced price
for joint ticket with Greenhill Covenanters
House.

🅰 & shop ✖

Greenhill Covenanters House Burn
Braes
☎ (0899) 21050

*17th-century farmhouse brought stone by
stone 10 miles from Wiston and re-erected
at Biggar. Contains relics of the
covenanting period, history of Scotland
between the Union of the Crowns and the
Union of Parliaments. Rare breeds of
sheep, pigs and poultry.*

Open Etr–mid Oct, daily 2–5, other times
by arrangement.

✱ 60p (ch 30p, ch 8 free). Reduced price
for joint ticket with Gladstone Court.

🅰 & (ground floor and gardens only) ✖

BIGNOR

West Sussex
Map **4** SU91

Roman Villa & Museum (between A29 &
A285)
☎ Sutton (07987) 259

*Occupied in the 2nd and 4th century, first
discovered in 1811; preserves some of the
finest mosaic pavements in Britain.*

Open Mar & Oct 10–5; Apr–Sep 10–6.
(Closed Mon ex BH); Jun–Sep open daily.

£1 (ch 50p, pen 70p). Party.

🅰 ⬛ ⊞ & shop ✖

BIRCHAM, GREAT

Norfolk
Map **9** TF73

The Mill (½m W off unclassified
Snettisham rd)
☎ Syderstone (048523) 393

*A windmill and small bakehouse museum
in pleasant countryside. The tower mill of
five floors, above which is the cap, was
built in 1846 and used for milling until the
1930s.*

Biggar
Birmingham

Open Sun; Wed & BH fr Etr, 20 May–Sep,
daily, 10–6.

80p (ch 45p, pen 70p).

🅰 ⬛ shop ⓥ

BIRCHINGTON

Kent
Map **5** TR36

Powell-Cotton Museum Quex Park (1m
SE of village off B2048)
☎ Thanet (0843) 42168

*Museum includes natural history
dioramas, ethnography, weapons,
archaeology, oriental fine arts and
porcelain from Africa and Asia. Also on
view are furnished rooms in Quex house
and the gardens.*

Museum open Thu all year (more
frequently in summer incl BH). House &
Garden open summer 2.15–6.

Admission fee payable.

🅰 ⬛ & (ground floor & gardens only)
shop ✖

BIRKENHEAD

Merseyside
Map **7** SJ38

Birkenhead Priory Priory St
☎ 051-652 4177

*Founded in 1150, the Priory provided
accommodation for a prior and 16
Benedictine monks. Most of the buildings
were neglected after the Dissolution and
only the ruins remain.*

Open May–Sep, Tue–Sat, 10–1, 2–4; Oct–
Apr, Tue–Sat 10–1.

Free.

🅰 & (ground floor only)

Williamson Art Gallery & Museum
Slatey Rd
☎ 051-652 4177

*Exhibits include: major collection of work
by English water-colourists and Liverpool
school of painters; sculpture; decorative
arts; ceramics (English, Continental,
Oriental wares); glass, silver and furniture.
Also a large collection of paintings by P.
Wilson Steer, as well as approximately 25
special exhibitions throughout the year. A
local history and maritime museum
containing model ships, adjoins.*

Open Mon–Sat, 10–5; Thu, 10–9;
Sun 2–5. (Closed Xmas & BH).

Free

🅰 & shop ✖

BIRMINGHAM

West Midlands
Map **7** SP08

Aston Hall Trinity Rd, Aston
☎ 021-327 0062

*Jacobean mansion built by Sir Thomas
Holte, now in the care of the City Museum.
Panelled long gallery, balustraded
staircase and magnificent plaster friezes
and ceilings.*

Open Mid Feb–mid dec. Mon–Sat 10–5.
Sun 2–5.

✱ 80p (ch & pen 40p). Educational parties
booked in advance admitted free.

🅰 shop ✖ (ex guide drogs)

Birmingham Botanical Gardens
Westbourne Rd, Edgbaston
☎ 021-454 1860

*A wide range of plants from the tropics
and rain forest areas. Rare and valuable
trees and alpine specimens. Among the
features are the Tropical House, Warm
Temperate House or "Palm House" and
Cool Temperate House. The Outdoor
Gardens contain over 150 varieties of
trees, the Chronological Border including
plants from Roman times to the present
day and the Rose Garden. Of interest are
the aviaries of tropical birds, rock pools,
bog garden and a new garden for the
disabled.*

Open Mon–Sat 9–until dusk. Sun 10–until
dusk (Closed Xmas day).

✱ £1.25 (ch 5, pen & students 60p). Party.

🅰 ⬛ ⊞ & (most parts) shop & garden
centre ✖

Birmingham Nature Centre
Pershore Rd, Edgbaston
(At SW entrance to Cannon Hill Park,
opposite Pebble Mill Rd)
☎ 021-472 7775

*The Nature Centre displays living animals
of the British Isles and Europe in both
outdoor and indoor enclosures.
Conditions have been created to
resemble natural habitats also to attract
wild birds and butterflies etc.*

Open daily, 10–5.30, during summer
months, closes at 4 in the winter months.
(Closed Xmas & New Years day).

✱ 40p (ch & pen 20p) Educational parties
booked in advance admitted free.

🅰 & ✖ (ex guide dogs)

Birmingham Railway Museum
670 Warwick Rd, Tyseley
☎ 021-707 4696

*A working railway museum with a fully
equipped workshop displaying the steam
locomotive in its true environment. The
ever-expanding museum collection now
totals 11 steam locos and 33 historic
carriages, wagons and other vehicles. A
new feature on steam days is a regular
steam-hauled passenger train service
departing from the museum's own replica
GWR station platform.*

Open daily 10–5. (Closed Xmas). Steam
events first Sun in month & BH Apr–Dec.

Admission fee payable. (Higher charges
on steam days).

🅰 ⬛ & (ground floor only) shop

See advertisement on page 58

Blakesley Hall Blakesley Rd, Yardley (6m SE)
☎ 021-783 2193

A timber-framed yeoman's farmhouse, built c 1575, and furnished in close detail according to an inventory of 1684. Displays on timber building, late 17th and 18th-century pottery, the history of the house and 16th–17th century interior fittings crafts and the ancient parish of Yardley.

Open Mon–Sat, 10–5, Sun 2–5. (Closed Good Fri, Xmas & New Years day).

✳ 50p (ch & pen 25p). Educational parties booked in advance admitted free.

P (20 yds) shop ✘ (ex guide dogs)

City Museum & Art Gallery
Chamberlain Sq
☎ 021-235 2834

Fine and Applied Arts, Natural History, Archaeology and Local History exhibits. There is a fine collection of paintings from the fourteenth century to the present day, including a most important collection of Pre-Raphaelite work. Applied Arts include Costume, Silver, Ceramics and Textiles; there are Prehistoric, Egyptian, Greek and Roman antiquities, local history exhibits, an important coin collection and the famous Pinto Collection of wooden items. There are frequent lectures, temporary exhibitions, demonstrations and holiday activities for children.

Birmingham

Open Mon–Sat, 10–5, Sun 2–5. (Closed Good Fri, Xmas & New Years day).

Free.

P (20 yds) ⚲ ⅙ shop ✘ (ex guide dogs)

Museum of Science & Industry
Newhall St (close to Post Office Tower)
☎ 021-236 1022

Displays from the Industrial Revolution up to the present. Engineering hall was formerly a Victorian plating works and contains machine tools, electrical equipment, working steam, gas and hot air engines. Locomotive hall. Transport section. Science section. Pen room. Music room. In the aircraft section are a World War II Spitfire and Hurricane, and collection of aircraft engines. New James Watt Building contains oldest working steam engine in the world, dated 1779. Steam weekends Mar and Oct, Traction Engine Rally in May. Engines steamed 1st and 3rd Wed each month.

Open Mon–Sat 10–5, Sun 2–5. (Closed Xmas & New Years day).

Free.

P (100 yds) ⅙ shop ✘ (ex guide dogs)

Sarehole Mill Cole Bank Rd, Hall Green
☎ 021-777 6612

18th-century water mill, restored to working order and containing displays illustrating various aspects of milling, blade-grinding and English rural pursuits.

Open Etr–late Nov, Mon–Sat 10–5, Sun 2–5.

✳ 50p (ch & pen 25p). Educational parties booked in advance admitted free.

P (20 yds) shop ✘ (ex guide dogs)

Selly Manor & Minworth Greaves
Sycamore Rd, Bournville off A38
☎ 021-472 0199

Two 13th- and early 14th-century half-timbered houses re-erected in Bournville. Collection of old furniture etc. Herb garden.

Open mid Jan–mid Dec, Tue–Fri 10–5 (ex BH). Parties & guided tours by arrangement with the curator.

Free.

P ⅙ (ground floor only)✘

Weoley Castle Alwold Rd
☎ 021-427 4270

Remains of a fortified 13th-century manor house, with small site museum displaying finds from excavations.

Open Etr–late Oct, Tue–Fri 2–5.

✳ 20p (ch & pen 10p). Educational parties booked in advance admitted free.

P (30 yds) ✘ (ex guide dogs)

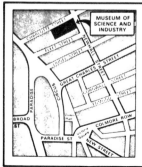

BISHOP AUCKLAND
County Durham
Map **8** NZ22

Auckland Castle
☎ (0388) 604823

Historic home of the Bishops of Durham since the 12th-century. The remarkable chapel dated from medieval times and survives complete with 17th-century fittings and its colourful timber roof. The State Rooms include the Gothick Throne Room lined with portraits of past bishops. The surrounding deer park includes an unusual 18th-century castellated deercote.

Open 11 May–24 Sep, Sun, Mon & Wed 2–5. Parties by arrangement.

75p (ch 30p, pen 50p).

P (limited) ঙ (ground floor only) shop ✖

BISHOP'S STORTFORD
Hertfordshire
Map **5** TL42

Rhodes Memorial Museum & Commonwealth Centre South Rd
☎ (0279) 51746

Early 19th-century house with exhibits illustrating life of Cecil Rhodes, also aspects of his life and work in Africa .

Open Mon–Sat 10–4, Tue 10–12 only. (Closed 1st 2wks Aug & BH).

50p (ch accompanied by adult free, in school groups 10p).

&

BISHOP'S WALTHAM
Hampshire
Map **4** SU51

Bishop's Waltham Palace (on A333)

Dates from 12th century and consists of state apartments around cloister court, with great hall and four-storeyed tower. Surrendered to Parliamentary forces in 1644 during Civil War.

Open see end of gazetteer.

✱ 50p (ch 16 & pen 25p).

& ঙ (grounds only) (AM)

BLACKBURN
Lancashire
Map **7** SD62

Lewis Museum of Textile Machinery
☎ (0254) 667130

Noted for series of period rooms portraying continuous development of textile industry from 18th century onwards. The gallery on the first floor has changing exhibitions.

Open Mon–Sat 10–5. (Closed Sun, Good Fri, Xmas, New Years day & some BH). (Booking 3 weeks in advance will enable a party to see machinery in operation.)

Free.

P (200 yds) shop ✖ (ex guide dogs)

Museum & Art Gallery Library St
☎ (0254) 667130

Local history, militaria, coins, ceramics, fine books and manuscripts, paintings, icons, watercolours and Japanese prints. Time tunnel and children's corner.

Open Mon–Sat 10–5. (Closed Sun, Good Fri, Xmas, New Years day & some BH).

Free.

P (200 yds) ঙ (ground floor only) shop ✖ (ex guide dogs)

BLACKGANG
Isle of Wight
Map **4** SZ47

Blackgang Chine Fantasy Theme Park
☎ Isle of Wight (0983) 730330

Opened as scenic gardens in 1843, covering some 20 acres, the grounds are floodlit on summer evenings. Attractions include water gardens, model village, maze, Dinosaur park, cowboy town and other amusements.

Open Apr, 1–23 May & Oct daily 10–5, 24 May–24 Sep daily 10–10 (floodlit).

✱ 1.20 (ch 3–13 75p). Sawmill & Quay 75p (ch 45p). Combined ticket to chine, sawmill & quay £1.70 (ch 3–13 95p).

& ╨ (licensed) ⅄ ঙ shop

Blackgang Sawmill & St. Catherines Quay
☎ Isle of Wight (0983) 730330

Exhibition of woodland skills and traditional trades, telling the story of wood. Situated in an attractive setting. Also maritime heritage, a history of local and maritime affairs including engines in steam.

Open Etr, May, Jun & Sep–2nd wk Oct 10–5. Whit wk & Jul–Aug 10–10.

✱ 75p (ch 3–13 45p). Combined ticket with Chine £1.70 (ch 3–13 95p).

& ╨ ঙ (ground floor & gardens only shop

BLACKMOOR GATE
Devon
Map **3** SS64

Exmoor Bird Gardens (off B3226)
☎ Parracombe (05983) 352

Tropical bird garden set in 7 acres of peaceful North Devon Countryside. Contains stream, waterfall and lake with penguins, waterfowl and swans. Aviaries with tropical birds, pheasants and rare breeds of poultry. Some small animals including wallabies, llama, ponies and goats. Also pets corner and children's adventure playground.

Open Etr–Oct 10–6.

£1.50 (ch 16 75p).

& ╨ ⅄ ✖ ⓥ

BLACKPOOL
Lancashire
Map **7** SD33

Grundy Art Gallery Queen St
☎ (0253) 23977

Established 1911, this gallery exhibits a permanent collection of paintings by 19th- and 20th-century artists. Also touring exhibitions, one man shows and group exhibitions.

Open Mon–Sat, 10–5. (Closed BH).

Free.

P (10 yds) ✖ ⅋

Tower Buildings & Circus
☎ (0253) 22242

The tower stands 518ft high. The buildings at its base contain family entertainment and the magnificent Ballroom with bar and dancing from 10am–11pm. Good Time Emporium Cabaret lounge, children's daytime entertainment, adventure playground (5–12 yrs), Tiny tots soft play area, Undersea World, Dome of Discovery, amusement arcades & Tower top lift ride. Also world famous Tower Circus.

Open Etr–Oct, Mon–Sun 9.30–11pm. Also open winter wknds.

Admission fee payable.

P (200 yds) ╨ ঙ shop

Zoological Gardens East Park Drive
☎ (0253) 65027

Over 500 large and small mammals and birds in 32 acres of landscaped gardens. Miniature railway.

Open daily, summer 10–6; winter 10–5 or dusk. (Closed Xmas day).

✱ £1.60 (ch & pen 80p). Educational service. Zoo bus service in season to and from Blackpool town centre 1¼m.

& (charge) ╨ (licensed) ⅄ ঙ shop ✖

BLAENAU FFESTINIOG
Gwynedd
Map **6** SH64

Gloddfa Ganol Slate Mine
☎ (0766) 830664

Explore the extensive underground workings of the world's largest slate mine. See the massive machinery and watch the splitting of the slate. Mining, railway and Wildlife Museums. Quarrymens Cottages. Land Rover conducted tours. Craft shop.

Open Etr–Oct, daily 10–5.30.

£2 (ch £1.20)

& ╨ (licensed) ⅄ ঙ shop & garden centre ⓥ

Llechwedd Slate Caverns
☎ (0766) 830306

Two exciting mine tours into the underground world of the Victorian Slate Miner. The miners underground tramway carries visitors into parts of the mine where early mining conditions have been recreated, whilst the Deep Mine can be →

59

explored on foot as the saga unfolds of the men who mined the huge chambers. Music, light and sound enhance the atmosphere of long ago.

Open 24 Mar–Oct daily 10–6 (last mine tour 5.15pm).

Either tour £2.15 (ch £1.35 pen £1.70).

 ⚓ 🍸 (licensed) 🚻 ♿ (Miners tramway suitable) shop 🗡 (on underground tours) Ⓥ

BLAENAVON
Gwent
Map **3** SO20

Big Pit Mining Museum
☎ (0495) 790311

Closed as a working mine in 1980, it has re-opened as a tourist attraction. At the bottom of the 300ft shaft, visitors, equipped with safety helmets and cap lamps, experience what life was really like for generations of South Wales miners. On the surface among the items to be seen are the former pithead baths and changing rooms where there's an exhibition of the history of Big Pit with a reconstructed miner's cottage of 40 years ago. It is recommended that stout shoes and warm clothing are worn.

Open Apr–Oct daily (ex Mon); Nov–Mar by arrangement. Details not confirmed for 1986.

✱ Underground tour & surface ticket £3 (ch £2). Surface only ticket £1.25 (ch 75p).

⚓ 🚻 ♿ (but not underground) shop 🗡 (underground)

BLAIR ATHOLL
Tayside *Perthshire*
Map **14** NN86

Atholl Country Collection The Old School
☎ (079681) 232

A collection of artefacts and photographs portraying local life and trades in Blair Atholl from approximately 1850 onwards. Displays include a crofter's kitchen, dress, communications, smiddy, sheep, byre with a real stuffed Highland cow and a gamekeeper's corner. There is a Kiddies Kirst where everything can be lifted up and examined.

Blaenau Ffestiniog
—
Boat of Garten

Open every afternoon 1.30–5.30 during summer season, also weekday mornings from 9.30 during Jul & Aug, or by arrangement.

50p (ch 25p).

⚓ 🚻 ♿ shop 🗡 Ⓥ

Blair Castle
☎ (079681) 207

13th-century in origin, altered in the 18th century and later given a castellated exterior. In 32 rooms Scottish life between the 16th- and 20th-century is presented with Renaissance style furnishings, paintings, Jacobite relics and arms. Lace, tapestries and Masonic regalia. Nature trails, deer park and pony trekking. Caravan Park. Numerous events throughout the year.

Open Etr week, each Sun & Mon in Apr, then daily from 20 Apr–12 Oct; Mon–Sat 10–6, Sun 2–6, Sun in Jul & Aug 12–6; (no admission after 5pm).

£2 (ch £1.20, pen £1.50) Family ticket £6.50. Party

⚓ 🍸 (licensed) 🚻 ♿ (ground floor & garden only) shop 🗡 (in house)

BLAIR DRUMMOND
Central *Perthshire*
Map **11** NS79

Blair Drummond Safari & Leisure Park
(Exit 10 off M9, A84 between Doune & Stirling)
☎ Doune (0786) 841456

Features wild animals in natural surroundings, including lions and tigers reserve. Also pets corner, boat safari, Astra glide and amusement area. Cinema 180.

Open 20 Mar–6 Oct daily, 10–4.30 (last admission).

£3 (ch & pen £2). Cinema 180 50p. Party 15+.

⚓ 🍸 🚻 ♿ (ex Cinema 180) shop 🗡 (kennels at entrance) Ⓥ

BLANDFORD FORUM
Dorset
Map **3** ST80

Royal Signals Museum Blandford Camp
☎ (0258) 52581 ext 248

Museum of history of army communications: paintings, uniforms, medals and badges.

Open Mon–Fri 9–5. (Closed BH).

Free.

⚓ 🗡

BLANTYRE
Strathclyde *Lanarkshire*
Map **11** NS65

David Livingstone Centre with 'The Livingstone Memorial'
☎ (0698) 823140

The birthplace of David Livingstone in 1813 containing personal relics, tableaux and working models. The 'Africa Pavilion' with exhibition describing life in modern Africa and Shuttle Row (Social History) Museum. Gardens.

Open daily, Mon–Sat 10–6, Sun 2–6. Last admission 5.15.

✱ £1 (ch & pen 50p)

⚓ 🍸 🚻 ♿ (ground floor & gardens only) shop Ⓥ

BLICKLING
Norfolk
Map **9** TG12

Blickling Hall on B1354

An early 17th-century red-brick house with notable garden containing early 19th-century orangery, parkland and lake. The house has some fine furniture, pictures, tapestries and a notable Jacobean plaster ceiling in the gallery.

Open 29 Mar–25 Oct, Tue, Wed, Fri, Sat, Sun & BH Mon. 1–5.

£2 (ch 70p). Gardens only £1.40. Party 15+.

🍸 (from noon) 🗡 (NT)

BOAT OF GARTEN
Highland *Inverness-shire*
Map **14** NH91

Strathspey Railway The Station
☎ (047983) 692

*Steam railway covering the five miles from
Boat of Garten to Aviemore, a twenty
minute journey; trains can also be
boarded at Aviemore. Timetables
available from station and Tourist
Information Office.*

Open 28–31 Mar then 6–27 Apr & 5–19
Oct Sun only; 3 May–29 Sep Sat, Sun &
Mon; 1 Jul–28 Aug Tue, Wed & Thu.
Evening diner trains each Sat Jun–Aug.

Basic return fare £2.20 (ch 5 free 15 half
fare). Family fares. party.

⚠ ⚏ (on train) & shop ⓥ

BODIAM
East Sussex
Map **5** TQ72

Bodiam Castle off A229
☎ Staplecross (058083) 436

*Picturesque moated structure, built in
1385 and dismantled 1643, with
gatehouse and 37 fireplaces inside.*

Open Etr–Oct, daily 10–6, Nov–Mar, Mon–
Sat. 10–sunset. Last admission ½hr before
closing. (Closed 25–28 Dec).

£1.10 (ch 17 50p). Parties (Mon–Fri).

⚠ (fee) ⚏ (licensed) & (ground floor
only) shop (NT)

BODMIN
Cornwall
Map **2** SX06

**Duke of Cornwall's Light Infantry
Regimental Museum** The Keep, Victoria
Barracks
☎ (0208) 2810

*The museum was started at the Depot in
1925 and contains an Armoury, Medals
display, Uniforms room and the Main
Gallery which displays pictures and relics
devoted to the major campaigns of the
Regiment from 1702 to 1945.*

Open Mon–Fri, 8–4.45 (ex BH).

50p (ch 16 free).

⚠ shop

Pencarrow House Washaway (4m N on
unclass road off A389)
☎ St Mabyn (020884) 369

*Gerogian mansion c. 1770 containing
impressive Inner Hall with marbled pillars
and cantilever staircase. Music room with
Rococo ceiling and many fine 18th-
century paintings, together with English,
French and Oriental furniture and china.
50 acres of woodland gardens with
signed trails. Children's play area.*

Open Etr–Sep, Mon–Thu & Sun, 1.30–5;
BH Mon & Jun–10 Sep, 11–5 (last tour of
house 5pm); Gardens daily during the
season.

✱ House and gardens £1.75 (ch 90p).
Parties 30+. Gardens only 50p (ch 25p).

⚠ ⚏ 🪑 & (ground floor & gardens only)
plant & craft shop ⓥ

Boat of Garten
—
Bothwell

BOLDRE
Hampshire
Map **4** SZ39

Spinners School Lane
☎ Lymington (0590) 73347

*Gardens entirely made by owners;
azaleas, rhododendrons, camellias,
magnolias etc. interplanted with primulas,
blue poppies and other choice woodland
and ground cover plants. Rare plants and
shrubs for sale. Nursery open all year.*

Open 20 Apr–1 Sep, daily (ex Mon) 10–6.
Other times by arrangement.

75p (ch under 5 free).

⚠ plants for sale ✱ (NGS)

BOLSOVER
Derbyshire
Map **8** SK47

Bolsover Castle on A632

*Originally Norman, re-built and enlarged in
1613. Fine fireplaces and ornate panelling
and range of buildings including
remarkable 170ft-long Riding School and
Gallery.*†

Open †, see end of gazetteer.

✱ 60p (ch 16 & pen 30p).

⚠ & (ex Keep) (AM)

BOLTON
Gt Manchester
Map **7** SD71

Tonge Moor Textile Museum Tonge
Moor Library, Tonge Moor Rd
☎ (0204) 22311 ext 379

*Includes Arkwright's waterframe (1768),
Compton's spinning mule (1779) and
Hargreave's spinning jenny.*

Open Mon & Thu 9.30–7.30, Tue & Fri
9.30–5.30, Sat 9.30–12.30. (Closed Sun &
Wed).

Free.

P (25 yds) & ✱ 🏫

BO'NESS
Central *West Lothian*
Map **11** NS98

Kinneil House
*Situated in a public park, and preserving
16th- and 17th-century wall paintings.*

Open, see end of gazetteer. (Closed Tue
afternoon & Fri).

✱ 50p (ch & pen 25p).

⚠ (AM)

Kinneil Museum & Roman Fortlet
☎ (0506) 824318

*Situated in the renovated 17th-century
stable block of Kinneil House. The ground
floor illustrates the industrial history of
Bo'ness. On the upper floor there is an*

---

*Interpretive display on the history and
environment of the Kinneil Estate. Kinneil
Roman fortlet is open for viewing near the
museum.*

Open May–Oct, Mon–Sat 10–12.30, 1.30–
5; Nov–Apr, Sat only 10–5.

Free.

⚠ shop ✱

BOOKHAM GREAT
Surrey
Map **4** TQ15

Polesden Lacey (1m S)

*Situated in beautiful grounds and housing
the Greville collection of pictures,
tapestries and furnishings.*

House open 1–27 Mar & Nov, Sat & Sun 2–
5 or sunset; 28 Mar–Oct, Wed–Sun 2–6.
BH Mon & preceeding Sun 11–6. Last
admission ½hr before closing time.
Gardens open daily 11–sunset.

Gardens only £1. House £1 extra.

⚏ (licensed) (Only open from 11am when
house open) ✱ (in house & some
gardens) (NT)

BOROUGH GREEN
Kent
Map **5** TQ65

Great Comp Gardens (off B2016)
☎ (0732) 882669

*7-acre garden replanned and maintained
by owners for many years. Trees, shrubs,
heathers, herbaceous plants and fine
lawns and paths.
The early 17th-century house is not open
to the public.*

Open Apr–Oct, daily, 11–6.

£1.20 (ch 5 60p).

⚠ ⚏ (Sun & BH only) & garden centre ✱
(NGS) ⓥ

BOSCOBEL
Shropshire
Map **7** SJ80

Boscobel House off A5

*House, c 1600, which preserves place
where Charles II hid in 1651. Descendant
of Royal Oak in grounds.*

Open †, see end of gazetteer.

✱ 60p (ch 16 & pen 30p).

⚠ & (gardens only) (AM)

Whiteladies Priory (St Leonards Priory)

*Remains of Augustinian nunnery, dating
from 1158. Largely destroyed in the Civil
War. Guide book available at* **Boscobel
House**.

Open any reasonable time.

Free.

(AM)

BOTHWELL
Strathclyde *Lanarkshire*
Map **11** NS75

Bothwell Castle entrance at Uddington
Cross by traffic lights. →

An impressive, ruined 13th- to 15th-century stronghold.

Open, see end of gazetteer (Closed Thu afternoon & Fri).

50p (ch & pen 25p)

⚨ (AM)

BOUGHTON MONCHELSEA
Kent
Map **5** TQ74

Boughton Monchelsea Place
(off A229)
☎ Maidstone (0622) 43120

Castellated Elizabethan and Regency manor house still inhabited, with breathtaking views of its 18th-century deer park and the Kentish Weald. Records preserved since 1570. Display of dresses and collection of old vehicles.

Open Good Fri–5 Oct, Sat, Sun, BH & Wed in Jul & Aug, 2.15–6.

House & gardens £1.30 (ch 14 65p, pen £1). Gardens only 60p (ch 35p, pen 50p). Party.

⚨ ⚏ shop ✗ (in house) Ⓥ

BOURNEMOUTH
Dorset
Map **4** SZ09

Big Four Railway Museum & Model Centre Dalkeith Hall, Dalkeith Steps, rear of 81A Old Christchurch Rd
☎ (0202) 27995

Contains over one thousand railway items, including one of the largest collections of locomotive nameplates, work plates etc. in the country. Also a large display of model locomotives.

Open daily 10–5. (Closed Sun & BH).

60p (ch 16 40p). Family £1.50.

P (30 yds) shop

Russell-Cotes Art Gallery and Museum East Cliff
☎ (0202) 21009

Built in 1894 as East Cliff Hall, contains period rooms, section on Oriental art and Henry Irving theatrical collection. Freshwater aquarium.

Bothwell
—
Bovington Camp

Open Mon–Sat 10.30–5.30. Last admission 5pm.

✳ 50p (ch 10p, ch 5 free).

P (200 yds) ⚏ shop ✗

BOURTON-ON-THE-WATER
Gloucestershire
Map **4** SP12

Birdland Zoo Gardens (on A429)
☎ Cotswold (0451) 20689 & 20480

Four-acre garden with over 1200 species of foreign and exotic birds.

Open daily Mar–Nov, 10–6; Dec, Jan & Feb 10.30–4 (Closed Xmas day).

£1.50 (ch 14 75p, pen 95p). Party 20+.

P (300 yds) ⚏ (summer only) ⚸ shop Ⓥ

Cotswolds Motor Museum
☎ Cotswold (0451) 21255

Cars and motorcycles from the vintage years up to the 1950s; also large collection of 500 old advertising signs together with 5,000 interesting items from the motoring years. All housed in an 18th-century water mill on the River Windrush.

Open Feb–Nov, daily 10–6.

70p (ch 14 30p, ch 4 free). Family ticket £2. Party.

P (50 yds) ⚸ shop

Model Village Old New Inn
☎ Cotswold (0451) 20467

Built to scale of one-ninth original. Includes miniature replica of River Windrush, working model waterwheel, churches and shops.

Open daily, 9–6.30 (summer); 9–dusk (winter). (Closed Xmas day).

80p (ch 60p, pen 70p). Party 20+.

⚨ ⚏ (licensed) 🍴 ⚸ shop

Village Life Exhibition The Old Mill
☎ Cotswold (0451) 21255

A complete Edwardian village shop is

---

exhibited, including the bedroom above it, bathroom and kitchen. Also on display is a blacksmith's Forge, model of the old mill, photographs and toys plus many other artefacts.

Open Feb–Nov, daily 10–6.

50p (ch 25p). Family ticket £1.50.

P shop

BOVEY TRACEY
Devon
Map **3** SX87

Parke Rare Breeds Farm
☎ (0626) 833909

In the wooded valley of the River Bovey, over 200 acres of parkland forms a beautiful approach to Dartmoor. A series of lovely walks through woodland beside the river and along the route of the old railway track. The Rare Breeds Farm established to preserve genetically pure stock, as many breeds have become extinct due to changing requirements and patterns of modern agriculture. A collection of rare and traditional breeds include goats, cattle, sheep, pigs and poultry in farm buildings and paddocks. There is also a pets corner and children's play area.

Open Good Fri–Oct, daily 10–6 (last admission 5.30pm).

£1.40 (ch 3–14 £1 pen £1.20). Party.

⚨ ⚏ 🍴 ⚸ shop ✗ (NT) Ⓥ

BOVINGTON CAMP
Dorset
Map **3** SY88

The Tank Museum (Royal Armoured Corps & Royal Tank Regiment) (off A352)
☎ Bindon Abbey (0929) 462721 ext 463 & 463953

Over 160 examples of armoured fighting vehicles (wheeled and tracked) dating from 1915 onwards. Separate displays of armament, power plant and associated equipments, videos and working models. Military model fair 24–26 May. RAC open day Sun 27 Jul.

Open, daily 10–5. (Closed 2 wks Xmas & New Year).

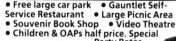

£1.60 (ch & pen 75p). Family ticket £3.
Parties.

⚠ ⚏ (licensed) ⟰ ♿ shop ✈

BOWES
Co Durham
Map **12** NY91

Bowes Castle on A66

*Norman keep built between 1171 and
1187, in angle of Roman fort of 'Lavatrae'.*

Open any reasonable time.

Free.

(AM)

BOWNESS-ON-WINDERMERE
Cumbria
Map **7** SD49 (see also **WINDERMERE**)

Belle Isle
☎ Windermere (09662) 3353

*Beautiful 38-acre island situated in the
middle of Lake Windermere. The unique
house was the first completely round
house built in England and contains
portraits of the Curwen family and
furniture specially designed by Gillow of
Lancaster. Nature trail. Children's
playground.*
Motor launch runs continuously from far
end of Bowness promenade.

Open May–Sep, Sun–Thu 10.15–5.

Charge for boat to island.

Guided tour of house 11.15, 12.30, 2.30
& 4.

£2 (ch £1) (includes return boat trip,
admission to 'Below Stairs' Museum &
guided tour of house). Party. Guided tour
of house only 60p.

P (on mainland) ⚏ (licensed) ⟰ shop

BRADFORD
West Yorkshire
Map **7** SE13

Bolling Hall Bolling Hall Rd
☎ (0274) 723057

*House dates from 15th century and
contains fine furnishings including rare
Chippendale bed, heraldic glass and
'ghost room'.*

Open Apr–Sep, Tue–Sun & BH Mon.
(Closed Good Fri & Xmas day). 10–6. Oct–
Mar, Tue–Sun 10–5.

Free.

⚠ shop ✈

Cartwright Hall Lister Park
☎ (0274) 493313

*Contains permanent collections of
European and British paintings, sculpture,
drawings, modern prints and ceramics.
Also includes varied and imaginative
exhibition programme.*

Open Apr–Sep, Tue–Sun & BH Mon.
(Closed Good Fri & Xmas). 10–6. Oct–
Mar, Tue–Sun 10–5.

Free.

P (100 yds) ⚏ ♿ shop ✈

Bovington Camp
—
Brading

Industrial Museum Moorside Road,
Eccleshill
☎ (0274) 631756

*Features the growth of the worsted textile
industry and other exhibits relevant to the
era.*

Open Tue–Sun & BH Mon 10–5. (Closed
Good Fri & Xmas).

Free.

⚠ ⚏ ♿ shop ✈

**National Museum of Photography, Film
& Television** Prince's Way
☎ (0274) 727488

*Incorporates displays, concepts, galleries
that explore photography in all its many
forms including press, medical/scientific,
moving pictures, exhibitions and studios.
Displays and talk-over tapes make for
realism and visitor participation. In
addition the only IMAX Cinema in Britain is
housed in the museum.*

Open Tue–Sun, 11–6. (Closed Mon ex
BH).

Museum free, IMAX Cinema £1.50 (ch 16
75p; pen, student & holders of UB40 £1).

P (25 yds & 100 yds) ⟰ ♿ shop ✈ (ex
guide dogs)

BRADFORD-ON-AVON
Wiltshire
Map **3** ST86

Barton Tithe Barn

*14th-century building, once property of
Shaftesbury Abbey, since presented to
Wiltshire Archaeological Society.*

Open any reasonable time.

Free.

♿ (AM)

Great Chalfield Manor (2½m NE)

*15th-century house, with great hall
restored in 1920's; small 13th-century
church adjacent.*

Open Apr–Oct, Tue–Thu 12–1 & 2–5.

£1.50.

⚠ ✈ (NT)

BRADGATE PARK & SWITHLAND
WOOD ESTATE
Leicestershire
Map **8** SK51

(6½m NE of Leicester off B5327)
☎ Leicester (0533) 871313 ext 645 (The
Ranger)

*850-acre country park. Natural parkland,
woods, herds of red and fallow deer, with
Old John Tower (1786). Ruins of Bradgate
House, completed c 1510 by son of 1st
Marquis of Dorset. The birthplace of Lady
Jane Grey (1537–54). Swithland Wood –
140 acres of ancient woodland.*

Open all year to pedestrians during
daylight hours. Ruins open Apr–Oct, Wed,
Thu & Sat, 2.30–5; Sun 10–12.30. Parties
by arrangement Apr–Oct.

Free (ex car park 20p).

Registered disabled or permit holders
issued by Bradgate Park Trust may drive
through the park, Apr–Oct, Thu 2.30–7.30;
Sun 9–11 am.

Also **Marion's Cottage** (visitor centre)
Newtown Linford.

*Typical Charnwood Forest cottage
offering selection of gifts, publications
etc. Information Centre and Exhibition.*

Open Apr–Oct, Wed, Thu, Sat & Sun 2–6;
Nov–Mar, Sat & Sun 2–5. Also BH Mon &
Tue. Parties by arrangement.

Free (ex car parks 20p).

⚠ ⟰ ♿ shop

BRADING
Isle of Wight
Map **4** SZ68

Lilliput Doll & Toy Museum High St
☎ Isle of Wight (0983) 407231

*Containing nationally recognised
comprehensive private collection with
over 1,000 exhibits. Doll collectors' shop
and hospital. Specialist doll shop.*

Open daily (ex 15 Jan–15 Mar) 10–5
(winter) 9.30–10 (summer).

60p (ch & pen 50p under 5 free).

P (100 yds) ♿ shop

Morton Manor
☎ Isle of Wight (0983) 406168

*Built in 1680 and exhibiting period
furniture of the 18th & 19th-century.
Beautiful terraced landscaped gardens
with ornamental ponds, sunken garden,
vineyard, winery & wine making museum.
Wines for sale.*

Open Etr–Oct daily, 10–5.30. (Closed
Sat).

£1.35 (ch 60p, pen £1.20). Party 15 + .

⚠ ⚏ (licensed) ♿ shop & plants for sale
Ⓥ

Nunwell House
☎ Isle of Wight (0983) 407240

*Impressive country house in beautiful
garden setting. Displays fine furniture in
lovely rooms including one in which King
Charles I spent his last night of freedom.
There are interesting collections of
militaria and also literary connections.
Small concerts will be held in the music
room during summer months, telephone
for details.*

Open 25 May–25 Sep, Sun–Thu 1.30–
5.30. (Closed Fri & Sat). Organised parties
at other times by appointment.

£1.20 (ch 16 60p).

⚠ ⚏ (Jul & Sep) ⟰ shop ✈ Ⓥ

Osborn-smith's Wax Museum (on
A3055)
☎ Isle of Wight (0983) 407286 →

63

House of Mystery and Intrigue. This popular Wax Museum is set in the Ancient Rectory Mansion, part dating before 1066 AD. Chamber of Horrors.

Open daily, 10–10 May–Sep; 10–5 Oct–Apr.

✱ £1.30 (ch 14 90p). party 20+. Combined ticket with Animal World available.

⚠ ⧉ (ground floor & gardens only).

Also **Osborn-smith's Animal World**

A fine collection of preserved animals, birds and reptiles from all over the world displayed in large colourful dioramas depicting their natural surroundings.

Open daily 10–10 May–Sep; 10–5 Oct–Apr.

✱ £1.10 (ch 14 80p). Party 20+. Combined ticket with Wax Museum available.

⚠ ⧉ ✖ (ex guide dogs)

BRAEMAR
Grampian *Aberdeenshire*
Map **15** NO19

Braemar Castle
☎ (03383) 219 or 224 (Nov–Apr)

Picturesque castle near River Dee. Built 1628 and burned 1689, purchased by Farquharson of Invercauld in 1732. Largely rebuilt as garrison post by Hanoverian Government after 1745 rising. Furnished residence of great charm with many items of historic interest.

Open May–6 Oct, daily 10–6

£1.10 (ch 13 55p). Party 30+.

⚠ shop ✖ (in castle)

BRAMBER
West Sussex
Map **4** TQ11

Bramber Castle

Former home of the Dukes of Norfolk this ruined Norman stronghold lies on a South Downs ridge with good views.

Open daily.

Free.

(NT)

House of Pipes
☎ Steyning (0903) 812122

Museum with 35,000 exhibits covering 150 countries and 1,500 years, believed to be the only 'smokiana' exhibition in the world. It is a fascinating study of social history in everyday life, set in a 19th-century shopping arcade.

Open daily 9–7.30. (Closed 25 Dec).

45p (ch 4–14 15p).

⚠ ⧉ ⧉ shop

BRAMHALL
Greater Manchester
Map **7** SJ88

Bramall Hall, Bramhall Park
☎ 061-485 3708

Set in landscaped park; a large timber

Brading
—
Brentford

framed hall dating from the 14th century, it is reputed to be one of the finest black and white houses in England. Unique medieval wall-paintings, windows and period furniture. Home of the Davenport family for 500 years the estate is now owned by the Metropolitan Borough of Stockport.

Open Tue–Sun & BH; Apr–Sep, 12–5; Oct–Mar, 12–4. (Closed Dec) Schools & parties by appointment only.

80p (ch 40p).

⚠ ⧉ ⧉ (ground floor & gardens only) shop ✖ Ⓥ

BRAMHAM
West Yorkshire
Map **8** SE44

Bramham Park (on A1 4m S of Wetherby)
☎ Boston Spa (0937) 844265

Queen Anne House containing fine furniture, pictures and porcelain, and is the house of Mr & Mrs George Lane Fox, descendants of the builder Robert Benson. The gardens contain ornamental ponds, cascades, temples and avenues. Horse trials 3 day international event 29 May–1 June.

Gardens open Etr & Spring BH wknds 1.15–5.30; House & gardens 8 Jun then Tue, Wed & Thu–29 Aug including BH wknd.

£1.20 (ch 5 60p, pen £1). Grounds only 80p (ch 5 40p, pen 70p). Party 20+.

⚠ ⧉ (gardens only) Ⓥ

BRAMPTON
Cumbria
Map **12** NY56

Lanercost Priory (2½m NE)

Once a house of Augustinian Canons, founded about 1166 by William de Vaux. Remains of quire and transepts.

Open Apr–Sep, Mon–Sat 9.30–6.30, Sun 2–6.30.

✱ 40p (ch 16 & pen 20p).

⚠ ⧉ (AM)

BRASTED
Kent
Map **5** TQ45

Emmett's Garden

Four-acre hillside shrub garden, formal garden and bluebell wood.

Open Etr–Oct, Sun & Tue–Fri 2–6 (last admission 5pm).

£1 (ch 50p).

⚠ (NT)

BREAMORE
Hampshire
Map **4** SU11

Breamore House, Countryside & Carriage Museums (on A338)
☎ Downton (0725) 22270

Elizabethan manor house (1583) with fine collection of paintings, china and tapestries. Countryside Museum displays rural arts and agricultural machinery; the Carriage Museum displays old coaches.

Open 28 Mar–Sep Tue–Thu, Sat, Sun & all BH, 2–5.30.

Combined ticket £2.50 (ch £1.30); Party & pen rates available. Breamore House £2 (ch £1), Countryside Museum £1.50 (ch 80p), Carriage Museum £1 (ch 50p).

⚠ ⧉ ⧉ (ground floor, museums & gardens only) shop ✖ Ⓥ

BRECON
Powys
Map **3** SO02

Brecknock Museum Captain's Walk
☎ (0874) 4121

Archaeological and local historical exhibits, folk life, decorative arts and natural history.

Open Mon–Sat (incl BH) 10–5.

Free.

⚠ ⧉ shop

24th Regiment Museum The Barracks, The Watton
☎ (0874) 3111 ext 310

Museum of South Wales Borderers and Monmouthshire Regiment, granted Freedom of the Borough in 1948. Regiment was raised in 1689 and has been awarded 23 VCs, of which 16 are displayed. Four rooms devoted to relics, weapons, photographs and medals. Special Zulu War display.

Open Apr–Sep daily; Oct–Mar, Mon–Fri 9–1 & 2–5. (Closed Xmas).

30p.

⚠ ⧉ shop ✖

BREDWARDINE
Hereford & Worcester
Map **3** SO34

Brobury House Gallery & Gardens
☎ Moccas (09817) 229

The gardens feature 8 acres of fine old trees, rhododendrons and lawns which sweep down to the River Wye affording magnificent views. Inside the gallery you will find literally thousands of original, old etchings and engravings from the 16th to the 20th centuries and a large selection of watercolours, mainly 19th century.

Gardens open Jun–Sep, Mon–Sat 9–4.30. Gallery open all year, Mon–Sat 9–4.30 (4pm winter).

Garden £1 (ch 16 50p). Gallery free.

⚠ ⧉ Ⓥ

BRENTFORD Gt London (London plan 4 page 174/175)

Kew Bridge Engines Trust, The
Pumping Station, Kew Bridge Rd
(entrance in Green Dragon Lane) London
plan 4: **30** B3
☎ 01-568 4757

*London's living steam museum containing
model engines, steam engines and six
beam engines, five working, plus traction
engines and a musuem of London's water
supply, step back into the 19th century
and see a site which worked from 1820–
1945; old workshop, forges etc. Various
events throughout year.*

Open all year daily 11–5. Engines in steam
Sat, Sun & BH Mon. (Closed Xmas wk).

Weekdays £1 (ch 50p); Sat & Sun £1.40
(ch & pen 80p) family ticket £4.

⚠ ⚖ & (ground floor only) shop ⓥ

Musical Museum 368 High St (7m W of
London, off A315) London plan 4: **40** B3
☎ 01-560 8108

*A unique collection of working musical
instruments from small musical boxes to
huge orchestrations. Instruments are
played during tours of one hour, when
silence must be maintained. Evening
concert's fortnightly.*

Open Apr–Oct, Sat & Sun 2–5 (1½ hr tour).

£1.50 (ch & pen 75p). Party.

P (50 yds) ⊞ shop ✖

BRESSINGHAM
Norfolk
Map **5** TM07

**Bressingham Gardens & Live Steam
Museum** (on A1066)
☎ (037988) 386

*There are three steam-hauled trains: a
9½-inch gauge, a 15-inch gauge running
through 2 miles of the wooded Waveney
Valley and a 2ft-gauge through two miles
of Europe's largest hardy plant nursery.
Also collection of 40 road and rail engines,
mostly restored to working order.
Exhibition hall. Steam roundabout. 6 acres
of informal gardens.*

Open 30 & 31 Mar; Suns 4 May–28 Sep &
BH Mons 11.30–6; Thu 22 May–11 Sep &
Weds in Aug 11.30–5.30.

✱ £1.20 (ch 50p, pen £1).

⚠ ⚖ ⊞ & (ground floor & gardens only)
shop & garden centre

BRIDGEND
Mid Glamorgan
Map **3** SS97

Newcastle

*Small ruined 12th-century and later
stronghold, with rectangular tower, richly
carved Norman gateway to S side, and
massive curtain walls enclosing polygonal
courtyard.*

Open Apr–Sep, weekdays 10–7, Sun 2–7;
Oct–Mar, weekdays 10–dusk, Sun 2–dusk.

Free.

⚠ (AM Cadw)

Brontford
—
Brighton

BRIDGNORTH
Shropshire
Map **7** SO79

Midland Motor Museum Stanmore Hall
(1½m on A458 Stourbridge Rd)
☎ (07462) 61761

*A collection of over 90 very well restored
sports and sports racing cars and racing
motor cycles, housed in the converted
stable of Stanmore Hall and surrounded
by beautiful grounds. Nature trail.
Camping Park.*

Open all year Jun–Aug 10–6; Sep, Oct &
Mar–May 10–5 (Sun & BH closes at 6);
Nov–Feb 10–5. (Closed 25 Dec).

£2.20 (ch £1.05, pen £1.75) family ticket (2
adults & up to 5 ch) £6. Motor Museum £2.
Party 20 +.

⚠ ⚖ (licensed) ⊞ & shop

Severn Valley Railway
☎ Bewdley (0299) 403816

*The leading Standard Gauge Steam
Railway, with one of the largest
collections of locomotives and rolling
stock in the country. Services from
Kidderminster, Bewdley to Bridgnorth
through 16 miles of picturesque scenery
along the river Severn. Special steam
Gala in Apr, Jun & Sep. Saturday evening
'Wine & Dine' and 'Sunday Luncheon'
trains are a speciality.*

Open weekends Mar–Oct & daily mid
May–early Sep & BH. Santa Steam
Specials late Nov–Dec wknds only.

✱ £1,90–£6.10 (ch £1–£3.10, pen £1.30–
£4.10) return fare (depending on length of
journey).

⚠ ⚖ ⊞ & shop

BRIDLINGTON
Humberside
Map **8** TA16

Sewerby Hall, Park & Zoo
☎ (0262) 678255

*Georgian house dating from 1714–20 and
1808, now Art Gallery and Museum of
history and archaeology. Amy Johnson
Trophy Room. Gardens of botanical
interest, especially the Old English Walled
Garden. Miniature Zoo and Aviary in
gardens.*

Park & grounds open all year 9–dusk.
From Spring BH–mid Sep games facilities
are available to public. Art gallery &
museum Etr–last Sun in Sep.

✱ 60p (ch 30p) Spring BH–mid Sep; Out
of season Park free, Zoo 10p.
Concessions for school parties. Art
Gallery & Museum free.

⚠ ⚖ (Cafeteria & Licensed bar open Etr
& weekends to Spring BH then daily to

---

end of Sep.) ⊞ & (ground floor &
gardens only) shop & garden centre

BRIDPORT
Dorset
Map **3** SY49

Museum & Art Gallery South St
☎ (0308) 22116

*Housed in a Tudor building, local trade
exhibits include an old 'Jumper' net loom
in use since 1830. Also exhibits of
archaeology, geology, social and natural
history. The art gallery contains paintings
from the collection of the donor of the
building, Cap A P Codd.*

Open daily 10.30–1; Jun–Sep also 2.30–
4.30.

20p (ch 12 10p).

P (250 yds) & (ground floor only) ✖

BRIGHOUSE
West Yorkshire
Map **7** SE12

Brighouse Art Gallery Halifax Rd
☎ (0484) 719222

*Temporary exhibitions throughout the
year of local artists work and of modern
works.*

Open Mon–Sat 10–5, Sun 2.30–5.
(Closed Sun, Oct–Mar; Xmas & New
Year's day).

Free.

P & ✖

BRIGHTON
East Sussex
Map **4** TQ30

Aquarium & Dolphinarium
Marine Pde & Madeira Dr
☎ (0273) 604233

*Britain's largest aquarium with marine,
tropical and freshwater fish, notable for its
spectacular Gothic Underground
Galleries which house seals, sealions and
a wide range of fish. Dolphinarium has a
show of dolphins performing their act.
Flight simulator and children's
playground.*

Open all year daily (ex Xmas day) from
10am. Last admission 5.15.

Admission fee payable.

P ⚖ ⊞ & shop ✖ ⓥ

Booth Museum of Natural History
194 Dyke Rd
☎ (0273) 552586

*Contains British birds mounted in natural
settings, butterfly gallery, also vertebrate
evolution and 'Unnatural History' displays.
Geology gallery. Temporary exhibitions;
classroom available for use.*

Open Mon–Sat (ex Thu) 10–5, Sun 2–5.
(Closed Good Fri, Xmas & New Years
day).

Free.

P (street opposite) & shop ✖

HMS Cavalier Brighton Marina
☎ (0273) 699919

Launched in 1944 HMS Cavalier is the only surviving destroyer to have seen active service in WWII. After 28 years service with the fleet, she was placed in reserve until, in 1977, she was bought by the HMS Cavalier Trust to prevent her going to the scrapyard. Preserved with all her weapons, radar, sonar radios and control arrangements intact, she offers a unique opportunity to see how the sailor lived and fought in these famous small ships.

Open daily 10.30–5.30 (or dusk if earlier).

✳ Pedestrians £1.60 (ch 14 & pen 90p). Car Visitors £1.30 (ch 14 & pen 70p) plus Marina car parking fee. Party 20 + .

♿ ⚇ (Licensed – in Marina) shop ✖

Museum & Art Gallery Church St
☎ (0273) 603005

The collections include Old Master Paintings, watercolours, Sussex archaeology, folklife and local history, ethnography and musical instruments. Also the Willett Collection of pottery and porcelain, and display of 20th-century fine and applied art, including Art Nouveau, Art Deco and 19th & 20th-century costume. Also various special exhibitions.

Open Tue–Sat 10–5.45, Sun 2–5. (Closed Mon, Good Fri, Xmas & New Years day).

Free.

P ⚇ (Tue–Sat) ♿ (ground floor only) shop ✖

Preston Manor Preston Park (off A23)
☎ (0273) 603005 ext 59

Georgian house with additions in 1905. Houses a notable collection of furniture, silver, portraits and family memorabilia.

Open Wed–Sat 10–5; Tue & Sun 10–1 & 2–5. (Closed Mon ex BH Mon, Good Fri & Xmas). Details not confirmed for 1986.

✳ 85p (ch 5–15 50p, pen 70p); Family ticket (2 + up to 4 ch) £2. Party 20 + ; joint admission with Royal Pavilion £2.35. Gardens free.

♿ shop ✖

Brighton – Bristol

Royal Pavilion Old Steine
☎ (0273) 603005

Marine Palace of the Prince Regent (George IV). Henry Holland's neoclassical villa (1787), transformed by John Nash with an Indian-style exterior and fantastic Chinoiserie internal decorations in course of restoration. Furniture includes original pieces lent by H M the Queen: Guided tours available. The Pavilion is undergoing an extensive structural restoration programme which may cause the closure of certain rooms and obscure the exterior of the building.

Open daily Jun–Sep 10–6, Oct–May 10–5. (Closed Xmas).

✳ £1.85 (ch 16 80p, pen, students, & unemployed £1.25) family ticket (2 + up to 4 ch £5). Party 20 + . Admission prices vary according to season.

♿ ⚇ ♿ (ground floor only) shop ✖

BRILL
Buckinghamshire
Map **4** SP61

Brill Windmill (off B4011)
☎ Aylesbury (0296) 22171

One of the oldest post mills in England, with parts c 1680. Worked until 1916 and now owned by the Burckinghamshire County Council.

Open Apr–Sep, Sun 2.30–5.30 & other times by appointment.

30p (ch 14 10p).

P (30 yds) ✖

BRIMHAM
North Yorkshire
Map **8** SE26

Brimham Rocks off B6265

Grotesquely shaped rocks on heath moorland at height of 950ft. Described in Victorian guide-books as 'a place wrecked with grim and hideous forms

defying all description and definition'. Old shooting lodge converted into information point and shop.

Always Accessible.

Shop & Information Centre Open: Jun–Sep, daily 11–5. (Closed Good Fri). 29 Mar–May also Oct: Sat, Sun & BH Mon & Tue 11–5.

Cars 80p.

♿ ⚇ shop (NT)

BRINKBURN
Northumberland
Map **12** NZ19

Priory Church off B6344

Well-restored Augustinian priory church, founded in 1135 in bend of River Coquet. Roof replaced in 1858, but remaining medieval fittings include font, double piscina and some grave slabs.

Open Apr–Sep. † see end of gazetteer.

✳ 50p (ch 16 & pen 25p).

♿ (AM)

BRISTOL
Avon
Map **3** ST57

Blaise Castle House Museum Henbury (4m NW of city, off B4957)
☎ (0272) 506789

18th-century mansion, now social history museum, situated in extensive grounds.

Open Sat–Wed 10–1 & 2–5. (Closed Xmas day–28 Dec & New Year's day).

Free.

♿ ♿ (ground floor only) shop ✖

Bristol Industrial Museum Prince's Wharf, Prince St
☎ (0272) 299771 ext 290

A converted dockside transit shed in the heart of Bristol 400 yds from SS Great Britain. Display of vehicles, horse-drawn and motorised from the Bristol area, locally built aircraft, aero-engines; railway exhibits include full-size industrial locomotive Henbury, steamed around once a month. Various kinds of machinery illustrating local trade and manufacturing.

Preston Manor
Preston Park, Brighton BN1 6SD

There has been a house on the site of Preston Manor since about 1250, but the present form of the house dates from 1738, with extensive additions in 1905. Preston Manor today presents the appearance of a comfortable Edwardian country house, with a notable collection of furniture, portraits, silver and family memorabilia.

The house is open from Tuesday to Sunday from 10.00 am to 5.00 pm; closed for lunch on Tuesday and Sunday only from 1.00—2.00 pm. Closed Good Friday, Christmas Day, Boxing Day. Open on Bank Holidays.

Admission (1984 prices): Adults 80p, OAP's 65p, Children 45p, Party of 20 + 75p. Joint admission with the Royal Pavillion £2.35.

Newly opened, display of history of the port of Bristol.

Open Sat–Wed 10–1 & 2–5. (Closed Xmas day–28 Dec & New Year's day).

Free.

P (½m) ⅊ (ground floor only) shop ✸

Cabot Tower Brandon Hill
☎ (0272) 266031 ext 537

More than 100ft high and dating from 1897–8, commemorates 400th anniversary of Cabot's discovery of North America on 24th June 1497. Fine viewpoint. Cabot Day 24 Jun.

Open all year, daily dawn–dusk.

10p.

P (500 yds)

City Museum & Art Gallery Queen's Rd
☎ (0272) 299771

Regional and world-wide collections, representing ancient history, natural sciences, fine and applied arts.

Open Mon–Sat 10–5. (Closed Good Fri, May Day, Spring BH Mon & Tue, 25–28 Dec & New Year's day).

Free.

P (400 yds) ⅊ shop ✸

John Wesley's Chapel (The New Room) Broadmead
☎ (0272) 24740

The oldest Methodist Chapel in the world built 1739, rebuilt 1748, in each case by John Wesley. Both chapel and living rooms above are preserved in their original form. Wesley day celebrations 21 May.

Open daily. (Closed Sun, Wed & BH) 10–4.

Free.

⅊ ⅊ (ground floor & gardens only) shop ✸

Maritime Heritage Centre Gas Ferry Road
☎ (0272) 20680

Important collection illustrating 200 years of Bristol shipbuilding.

Open daily (ex Xmas Eve and Xmas Day) 10–5 (winter); 10–6 (summer).

Free.

⚠ ⅊ ✸

National Lifeboat Museum Princes Wharf, Wapping Rd
☎ (0272) 213389

The only representative collection of Lifeboat history in Britain. 10 full size craft dating from the last century, also models, photographs and other artefacts.

Open 6 Apr–29 Sep 10.30–4.30.

50p (ch 30p). Subject to review.

P ⅊ (ground floor only) shop

Red Lodge Park Row
☎ (0272) 299771 ext 236

16th-century house altered, in the early 18th century, with fine oak carvings and furnishings of both periods.

Open Mon–Sat 10–1, 2–5. (Closed Good Fr, May Day, Spring BH Mon & Tue, Xmas & New Year's day).

Free.

P (50 yds) ✸

SS Great Britain Great Western Dock, Gas Ferry Rd off Cumberland Rd
☎ (0272) 20680

Designed by I K Brunel, she was the first iron, screw-propelled ocean-going ship, launched in 1843. Now being restored.

Open daily 10–6 (summer) 10–5 (winter). (Closed Xmas eve & day).

£1.50 (ch 5–16 & pen 70p).

⚠ ⅊ (licensed) ⅊ (ground floor only) shop ✸

St Nicholas Church Museum
St Nicholas Street
☎ (0272) 299771 ext 243

The history of Bristol from its beginning until the Reformation including Bristol church art and silver. Brass rubbing centre.

Open Mon–Sat 10–5. (Closed Good Fri, May Day, Spring BH Mon & Tue, 25–28 Dec & New Year's day).

Free.

P (200 yds) ⅊ (ground floor only) shop ✸

The Georgian House 7 Gt George St
☎ (0272) 299771 ext 237

Georgian house with 18th-century furniture and fittings.

Open Mon–Sat, 10–1, 2–5. (Closed Good Fri, May Day, Spring BH Mon & Tue, Xmas & New Year's day).

Free.

P (meters) ✸

Zoological Gardens Clifton Down
☎ (0272) 738951

Extensive gardens and varied collection of mammals, birds, reptiles and fish.

Open Mon–Sat (ex Xmas day) from 9am, & from 10am Sun. Closing times vary with season.

✱ £2.70 (ch 14 £1.30).

⚠ ⅊ (licensed) ⅊ ⅊ shop ✸

BRIXHAM
Devon
Map **3** SX95

Brixham Museum Bolton Cross
☎ (08045) 3203

Maritime museum illustrating the fishing history of Brixham and incorporating HM Coastguard National Museum.

Open Etr–mid Oct, daily, 10–5.30. Sun 11–1 & 2–5.30.

60p (ch 30p, pen 20p). Family ticket £1.50.

P (100 yds) shop ✸

BROADSTAIRS
Kent
Map **5** TR36

Bleak House Dickens & Maritime Museum Fort Rd
☎ Thanet (0843) 62224

Seaside residence of Charles Dickens, where he wrote the greater part of 'David Copperfield'. Special exhibitions of relics salvaged from the Goodwin Sands and the "Golden Age of Smuggling".

Open Etr–Jun & Oct–mid Nov 10–6. Jul–Sep 10–9. →

75p (ch 12 40p, pen 65p).

P (Eastern Esplanade) & (ground floor & garden only) shop

Crampton Tower Museum High St
(adjacent to railway station)
☎ Thanet (0843) 62078

Museum commemorating Thomas Russel Crampton, the notable Victorian engineer. The museum contains models, graphic and various items connected with railways in the area together with souvenirs of the Thanet Electric Tramways. The mechanics workshop contains the old Broadstairs–Canterbury stage coach.

Open 4 May–14 Sep, Sun, Mon, Tue & Fri 2.30–5.

30p (ch 15p).

P (200 yds) shop ✘

Dickens House Museum
Victoria Pde
☎ Thanet (0843) 62853

Immortalised by Charles Dickens in 'David Copperfield' as the home of Betsy Trotwood. Exhibits Dickens letters and former possessions, local and Dickensian prints, costumes and Victoriana. The parlour is refurbished as described in 'David Copperfield'.

Open Apr–Oct, daily, 2.30–5.30 & Jul–Sep, Tue & Wed evenings 7–9.

40p (ch 20p).

Parties by arrangement.

P (100 yds) shop ✘ (ex guide dogs)

BROADWAY
Hereford and Worcester
Map **4** SP03

Broadway Tower Country Park
☎ (0386) 852390

Historic tower built in 1799 by the 6th Earl of Coventry, with exhibitions on three floors, an observation room and telescope, giving magnificent views over twelve counties. Rare and interesting animals. Adventure playground, nature walks and a barbeque.

Open Apr–1st wknd Oct, 10–6.

✻ £1.35 (ch & pen 70p). Family ticket £3.90. Party.

⚠ ⚖ (licensed) ⴲ & (ground floor) shop

Snowshill Manor (3m S)
☎ (0386) 852410

Cotswold manor house filled with collections of fine craftmanship, including toys, clocks, Japanese armour and bicycles. Small formal garden.

Etr Sat–Mon, Apr & Oct Sat & Sun 11–1 & 2–5. May–Sep, Wed–Sun & BH Mon 11–1 & 2–6.

Parties by written appointment.

£2.30.

⚠ (NT)

Broadstairs
—
Brook

BROCKHAMPTON
Hereford and Worcester
Map **3** SO65

Lower Brockhampton (2m E of Bromyard, entrance by Bromyard Lodge).

On high ground on the north side of the A44. Half-timbered 14th-century house with rare 15th-century gatehouse.

Medieval hall open Etr Sat–Oct, Wed–Sat & BH Mon 10–1 & 2–6. Sun 10–1.

75p (ch 35p).

(NT)

BRODICK
Isle of Arran, Strathclyde *Bute*
Map **10** NS03

Brodick Castle, Garden and Country Park
☎ Brodick (0770) 2202

Parts date from the 13th century, the castle has later additions and was the former stronghold of the Dukes of Hamilton. It contains an impressive art collection and has an outstanding garden. Ranger/naturalist service.

Castle open 28 Mar–Apr (all Etr wknd) then Mon, Wed & Sat 1–5. May–Sep Mon–Sat 10–5, Sun 12–5. Last visitors 4.40 pm. Gardens, country park & Goatfell open daily 9.30–sunset.

House & Gardens £1.40 (ch 70p). Garden only 80p (ch 40p). Party.

⚖ Etr, then May–Sep, Mon–Sat 10–5; Sun 12–5. (NTS)

Isle of Arran Heritage Museum
Rosaburn
☎ Brodick (0770) 2636

A collection of traditional buildings, Smithy, Cottage finished in late 19th and early 20th century style. Stable block with displays of local social history, archaeology and geology.

Open mid May–Sep, Mon–Fri 10.30–1 & 2–4.30.

60p (ch 30p).

⚠ ⚖ ⴲ (ground floor & gardens only) shop ✘

BRODIE CASTLE
Grampian *Morayshire*
Map **14** NH95

(4½m W of Forres, off A96)
☎ Brodie (03094) 371

Largely rebuilt after being burnt down in 1645 and with additions of the 18th and 19th centuries. Contents include furniture, porcelain and paintings. There is a short woodland walk and bird observation hide.

Open 28–31 Mar then May–Sep, Mon–Sat 11–6, Sun 2–6 (last admission 5.15). Grounds open all year, 9.30–sunset.

£1.40 (ch 70p). Party.
Grounds – Admission by donation.
(NTS)

BROKERSWOOD
Wiltshire
Map **3** ST85

Woodland Heritage Museum & Woodland Park (off A361)
☎ Westbury (0373) 822238

80 acres of natural woodlands, with nature walks, lake, wildfowl etc and a woodland visitor centre specialising in wildlife & forestry exhibits. Guided walks. Collection of bird eggs of the world can be inspected on prior application. Woodland visitor centre has an audio-visual theatre showing large selection of natural history films & videos.

Park open daily 10–sunset. Museum open Mon–Fri 9–6 Sat & Sun 10.30–6 closed 1–2 each day. In winter museum closes at 5 on weekdays.

✻ 95p (ch 3 free with each adult).

⚠ ⚖ ⴲ & shop ⓥ

BROMLEY CROSS
Gt Manchester
Map **7** SD71

Turton Tower Turton (1½m N off B6391)
☎ Bolton (0204) 852203

A pele tower c. 1420 with Elizabethan and later additions. Period furniture, weapons and local history.

Open Sat–Wed, 12–6. (Closed Thu, Fri, Xmas & New Year). Details not confirmed for 1986.

✻ 60p (ch 30p).

⚠ ⴲ shop

BROMSGROVE
Hereford and Worcester
Map **7** SO97

Avoncroft Museum of Buildings
Redditch Rd, Stoke Heath
☎ (0527) 31886 & 31363

Buildings of historic and architectural interest have been re-erected on a 15-acre site. They include a working windmill and blacksmiths' shop, a cockpit theatre, merchant's house, a 1946 prefab, a Georgian ice house, an 18th-century dovecote and earth closet.

Open Jun–Aug daily 11–5.30; Apr–May & Sep–Oct daily 11–5.30 (Closed Mon ex BH); Mar–Nov 11–4.30. (Closed Mon & Fri ex BH).

£1.75 (ch 80p pen £1) family ticket (2+2 ch) £4.50. Party.

⚠ ⚖ ⴲ & (ground floor & gardens) shop ⓥ

BROOK
Kent
Map **5** TR04

Wye College Museum of Agriculture
(4m ENE of Ashford on unclass rd)
☎ Wye (0233) 812401

68

An exhibition of old farm implements and machinery housed in a fine 14th-century tithe barn. Display of hop cultivation in old oast house.

Open May–Sep, Wed 2–5 & Sats in Aug.

Free.

Parties by arrangement in writing to: *Hon. Curator, Museum, Wye College, Wye, Ashford, Kent TN25 5AH.*

⚠ ⚿ (ground floor only) ❧

BROOMY HILL
Hereford and Worcester
Map **3** SO43

Herefordshire Waterworks Museum
☎ Hereford (0432) 274104

The Museum is housed in a Victorian Pumping Station of 1856, near the banks of the River Wye. Two steam pumping engines, built in 1895 and 1906, have been restored to working order. There is a horse-drawn fire engine, pumps and gauges for visitors to work.

Open daily 15 Jul–31 Aug 2–5 & 1st Sun in Apr, May, Jul & Sep. Engines in steam on BH & preceding Sun. Details not confirmed for 1986.

✼ 80p (ch 6–12 & pen 40p) Family £2.20.

Party enquiries to: *The Secretary H R Penhale, 87 Ledbury Rd, Hereford HR1 1RQ.*

⚠ Ⓟ ⚿ (ground floor only) shop Ⓥ

BROUGH
Cumbria
Map **12** NY71

Brough Castle (on A66)

Dates from the 12th to 13th century, repaired in 17th century. Stands on site of Roman 'Verterae'.

Open, see end of gazetteer.

✼ 50p (ch & pen 25p).

⚠ (AM)

BROUGHAM
Cumbria
Mpa **12** NY52

Brougham Castle (off A66)

12th- to 14th-century castle, repaired in late 17th century.

Open †, see end of gazetteer.

✼50p (ch 16 & pen 25p).

⚠ ⚿ (ex Keep) (AM)

BROUGHTON
Borders *Peeblesshire*
Map **11** NT13

Broughton Place
☎ (08994) 234

Built on the site of a much older house and designed by Sir Basil Spence in 1938 in the style of a 17th-century Scottish tower house. The drawing room and main hall are open to the public and contain paintings and crafts by living British artists for sale. The gardens, which are

---

Brook
—
Buckfastleigh

open for part of the Summer, afford fine views of the Tweeddale hills.

Gallery open Apr–Sep daily (ex Wed) 10.30–6.

Gallery free. Garden, donation.

⚠ ⚿ shop ❧

John Buchan Centre
☎ Biggar (0899) 21050

The Centre tells the story of the author of 'The 39 steps' who was also Governor-General of Canada. Broughton village was his mother's birthplace and John Buchan's much loved holiday home. The display of books, photographs & other memorabilia includes references to his sister Anne, still remembered as 'O. Douglas'.

Open Etr–mid Oct, daily 2–5. Details not confirmed for 1986.

✼ 50p (ch 20p).

⚠ ⚿

BROUGHTON
Oxfordshire
Map **4** SP43

Broughton Castle (2m W of Banbury on B4035)
☎ Banbury (0295) 62624

Originally owned by William of Wykeham later passing into hands of first Lord Saye and Sele, early 14th- and mid 16th-century house with moat and gatehouse. Period furniture, paintings and Civil War relics.

Open 18 May–14 Sep, Wed & Sun, also Thu Jul & Aug; BH Sun/Mon 2–5.

£1.70 (ch 90p pen £1.30) Party 20 + .

⚠ (200 yds) Ⓟ ♏ ⚿ (ground floor only) shop Ⓥ

BROWNSEA ISLAND
Poole Harbour Dorset
Map **4** SZ08

Five hundred acres of heath and woodland with nature reserve, two lakes, mile of bathing beach and fine views of Dorset coastline. First scout camp held here by Lord Baden-Powell in 1907.

Open 29 Mar–28 Sep, daily 10–8 or dusk, by boat from Poole Quay or Sandbanks.

80p (ch 40p).

⚠ Ⓟ ♏ ⚿ ❧ (NT)

BRUAR
Tayside *Perthshire*
Map **14** NN86

Clan Donnachaidh (Robertson) Museum
☎ Calvine (079683) 264

Documents, books and pictures associated with the Clan Donnachaidh,

---

one of whose early chiefs fought for King Robert the Bruce. Craft display.

Open Etr–mid Oct, Mon–Sat 10–1 & 2–5.30, Sun 2–5.30. Other times by arrangement

Free.

⚠ ⚿ shop

BRYMPTON
Somerset
Map **3** ST51

Brympton d'Evercy
☎ West Coker (093586) 2528

Tudor and Stuart mansion in superb setting, state rooms; Zanussi Collection of antique domestic appliances, also Priest House Country Life Museum. Extensive gardens and vineyard. Special exhibitions throughout the season including the Royal Photographic Society International exhibition in May. Parish church alongside.

Open Etr & 3 May–Sep, daily (ex Thu & Fri) 2–6.

£2.20 (ch £1.10) discount for pen & NT members on Weds. Party.

⚠ (50 yds) Ⓟ ⚿ (ground floor only) shop & plants for sale ❧ Ⓥ

BRYN-CELLI-DDU
Gwynedd
Map **6** SH57

Bryn-Celli-Ddu Burial Chamber (3m W of Menai Bridge off A4080)

Excavated in 1865, and again 1925–29, prehistoric circular cairn covering passage grave with polygonal chamber.

Accessible at all reasonable times.

Free.

(AM Cadw)

BUCKDEN
Cambridgeshire
Map **4** TL16

Buckden Palace (off A1)
☎ Huntingdon (0480) 810344

Remains of ancient palace, once residence of Bishops of Lincoln. Fine Tudor tower and inner gatehouse of red brick, dating probably from c. 1490 and modern house in grounds.

Open Jul–Sep, Sun 3–7; exterior always viewable.

⚠ ⚿ (ground floor only) shop

BUCKFASTLEIGH
Devon
Map **3** SX76

Buckfast Butterfly Farm
☎ (0364) 42916

Visitors can wander freely under cover around a specifically designed tropical landscaped garden where living butterflies and moths from many parts of the world can be seen and photographed free flying. →

69

Open 22 Mar–Oct daily 10–6.
£1.75 (ch 90p, pen £1.50). Party 10 + .
🅰 ⚌ ⊞ ♿ shop ✕

Dart Valley Railway
☎ (0364) 42338

Steam-locomotive-hauled trains run
between Buckfastleigh and Totnes
Riverside. Store of ex Great Western
rolling stock, including a number of
locomotives. **Note** now open at Totnes
British Rail.

Open Etr, BH's & Jun–mid Sep, daily.
Other dates early & late season telephone
for details. Details not confirmed for 1986.
Museum and river walks.

✴ Admission to station & steam centre
80p (ch & pen 40p).
Dart Valley Railway train fare additional to
admission charge £2 (ch 15 £1.40, pen
£1.90). Party.
🅰 ⚌ ⊞ ♿ shop

BUCKIE
Grampian *Banffshire*
Map **15** NJ46

Buckie Museum & Peter Anson Gallery
☎ Forres (0309) 73701

*Maritime museum with displays relating to
the fishing industry including exhibits on
coopering, navigation, lifeboats and
fishing methods. Selections from the*

Buckfastleigh
—
Buckler's Hard

*Peter Anson watercolour collection of
fishing vessels are on display.*

Open all year (ex PH's) Mon–Fri, 10–8; Sat
10–noon.

Free.

🅰 ♿ shop ✕

BUCKLAND
Gloucestershire
Map **4** SP03

Buckland Rectory (off A46)
☎ Broadway (0386) 852479

*England's oldest parsonage, associated
with John Wesley; medieval house with
15th-century great hall which has an open
timber roof and contemporary glass. Also
earlier half-timbered house and spiral
stone staircase.*

Open May–Sep, Mon 11–4, Aug Mon & Fri
11–4.

Free.

🅰 ♿ (ground floor & gardens only)

BUCKLAND ABBEY
Devon
Map **2** SX46

Buckland Abbey (3m W of Yelverton off
A386)
☎ Plymouth (0752) 668000

*Originally owned by the Grenvilles, the
house was sold to Sir Francis Drake in
1581. Now a naval and Devon folk
museum including the legendary Drake's
Drum. Gardens and large medieval tithe
barn.*

Open Good Fri–Sep, Mon–Sat & BH 11–6,
Sun 2–6; Oct–Wed before Etr, Wed, Sat &
Sun 2–5, last admissions ½hr before
closing.

£1.40 (ch 65p). Party.

⚌ shop (NT)

BUCKLER'S HARD
Hampshire
Map **4** SZ49

**Buckler's Hard Village & Maritime
Museum** (off B3054)
☎ (059063) 203

*Historic ship building village on banks of
Beaulieu River where wooden warships,
including vessels for Nelson's fleet were
once built from New Forest oak. 18th-
century homes of a shipwright and
labourer, also a master-shipbuilder's
office, and a typical Inn scene have been
created in original buildings with
costumed figures. Buckler's Hard village
festival 20 Jul.*

Open Ctr Spring DI I 10 C, Spring DI I Sep 10–9; Oct–Etr 10–4.30. (Closed Xmas day).

✳ £1.30 (ch 70p & pen £1) Parties 15+.

⚠ ⅃ (licensed) ⌕ shop ✻ (in buildings)

BUDLEIGH SALTERTON
Devon
Map **3** SY08

Fairlynch Arts Centre & Museum
Fore St
☎ (03954) 2666

In an early 19th-century house, museum with exhibits of mainly local interest. Costume display, local environment and history exhibition, smugglers cellar, reference library. New exhibitions of general interest annually.

Open Etr–Oct, 2.30–5; Jul & Aug also mornings 10.30–12.30. (Closed Sun mornings). Details not confirmed for 1986.

✳ 40p (ch 10, pen & students 10p).

Honiton Lace making demonstrations most Sat & Sun afternoons.

P (100 yds) ⅃ (ground floor only) shop ✻

BUILDWAS
Shropshire
Map **7** SJ60

Buildwas Abbey

A beautiful ruined Savignac Abbey, founded in 1135, standing in a

---

Buckler's Hard
—
Burford

picturesque setting. Vaulted Chapter House dates from end of 12th century or early 13th century.

Open, see end of gazetteer.

✳ 50p (ch 16 & pen 25p).

(AM)

BUNGAY
Suffolk
Map **5** TM38

Otter Trust Earsham
☎ (0986) 3470

A 23-acre site bounded by the River Waveney, including three lakes. World's largest collection of otters in semi-natural conditions for captive breeding for release and research purposes. Mobile Interpretative Centre and a fine collection of waterfowl on the lakes. The Trust's main aim is to help save the world's otters from extinction.

Open Apr–Oct, daily 10.30–6 (or dusk if earlier).

✳ £1.50 (ch 16 70p).

⚠ ⅃ ⌕ & shop ✻ Ⓥ

DURFORD
Oxfordshire
Map **4** SP21

Cotswold Wildlife Park (2m S off A40 & A361)
☎ (099382) 3006

Landscaped open-plan zoological park with exotic mammals, tropical birds etc. Also large reptile collection, aquarium and insect house. Woodland walks, formal gardens, adventure playground, train and pony rides.

Open daily (ex Xmas day) 10–6 or dusk if earlier.

✳ £2 (ch 4 & pen £1.20). Party 20+.

⚠ ⅃ (licensed) ⌕ & shop

Tolsey Museum High St
☎ Clanfield (036781) 294

History of Burford shown in charters from the 14th century, silver maces, seals, craft, industrial and social products. 18th-century dolls house furnished in Regency style by local artists and craftsmen.

Open 28 Mar–2 Nov, daily 2.30–5.30.

✳ 20p (ch 5p & pen & students 10p).

P (10 yds) shop

BURFORD
Shropshire
Map **7** SO56

Burford House Gardens (off A456)
☎ Tenbury Wells (0584) 810777 →

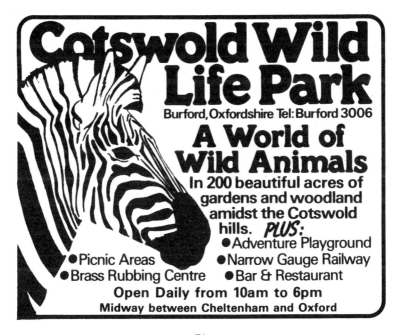

71

Surrounding the provincial Georgian House (1723) the artistically designed gardens contain many rare and unusual plants including shrubs and herbaceous plants, clematis and species roses. The famous nursery of Treasures of Tenbury which adjoins the garden holds the National Collection of Clematis of which many are featured in the gardens. Exhibition on history of Burford and the development of the genus clematis. (House not open).

Open 29 Mar–26 Oct Mon–Sat 11–5 Sun 2–5. Winter opening by arrangement.

£1.50 (ch 50p) Party 25 + .

△ ⚲ & garden centre ✗ (in gardens)

BURGH CASTLE
Norfolk
Map 5 TG40

The Castle (off A143)

Massive walls from former 3rd-century Roman fort, guarded by six pear-shaped bastions.

Accessible any reasonable time.

Free.

(AM)

BURGHCLERE
Hampshire
Map 4 SU46

Sandham Memorial Chapel (off A34)

Built in 1926–27 and presented to the NT in 1947. The walls are covered with paintings by Stanley Spencer and depict war scenes from the Salonika Front in the 1914–18 War.

Open daily 10.30–1 & 2–6 or dusk if earlier. (Closed Good Fri, Xmas day & New Year's day).

50p.

✗ (NT)

BURGHEAD
Grampian Moray
Map 15 NJ16

Burghead Museum 16–18 Grant St
☎ Forres (0309) 73701

Local history & temporary exhibitions.

Open Tue 1.30–5, Thu 5–8.30, Sat 10– noon.

Free.

P (street) & ✗

BURGH-LE-MARSH
Lincolnshire
Map 9 TF56

Gunby Hall (2½m NW off A158)

Red-brick house c1700 with oak staircase, wainscoted rooms and Reynolds portraits. (Ground floor only open). Formal gardens and herbaceous borders.

House & garden open Apr–Sep, Thu 2–6. Tue, Wed & Fri by prior written appointment only with J. Wrisdale, Gunby Hall, Gunby, Spilsby, Lincs.

Burford
—
Burwash

✱ £1.20 (ch 60p)

Garden only 80p (ch 40p).

△ ✗ (NT)

Newton Flag Gallery & Workshop The Bishop Tozer's Chapel, Middlemarsh Rd
☎ Skegness (0754) 68401

A unique family business manufacturing flags and banners in an old chapel on a "cottage industry" basis and flags can be seen being made in the workshops. A selection of royal banners and standards, civic, National, regimental and historical flags are on display.

Open Mon–Fri 10–4.

Admission fee payable.

△ shop ✗

BURNHAM MARKET
Norfolk
Map 9 TF84

Carmelite Friary (¼m NE on unclass road)
☎ Norwich (0603) 611122 ext 481

Gatehouse and remains of Carmelite Friary founded in 1241 with some original windows and interesting flint and stone panelling. The adjoining farmhouse incorporates a 14th-century doorway and a large buttress.

Open all year, Gatehouse and remains of Carmelite Friary accessible at all times.

Free.

P.

BURNLEY
Lancashire
Map 7 SD83

Towneley Hall Art Gallery & Museum & Museum of Local Crafts & Industries
☎ (0282) 24213

14th-century house with later modifications. Collection of oil paintings, early English water colours, period furniture, ivories, 18th-century glassware, archaeology and natural history. Nature trails. Loan Exhibitions Apr–Sep.

Open Mon–Fr 10–5.30 (5.15 winter), Sun 12–5. (Closed Sat & Xmas).

Free.

△ ⚲ (in grounds) ⟊ & (ground floor only) shop & garden centre ✗

BURTON AGNES
Humberside
Map 8 TA16

Burton Agnes Hall on A166
☎ (026289) 324

Built in 1598, magnificent Elizabethan house with five centuries of furniture, pictures, china and tapestries. Old

---

gatehouse. Woodland gardens and herbaceous borders on view.

Open 28 Mar–Oct daily, 11–5.

£1.25 (ch & pen 90p).

P (200 yds) ⚲ ⟊ & (ground floor & gardens only) shop ✗ (in hall) Ⓥ

Norman Manor House

Dates from 1170 and preserves original Norman piers and groined roof of a lower chamber. Upper room and an old donkey wheel.

Open see end of gazetteer.

Free.

△ (AM)

BURTON COURT
Hereford and Worcester
Map 3 SO45

(7m W of Leominster off B4457, between A44/A4112)
☎ Pembridge (05447) 231

14th–18th-century house with original 14th-century great hall and other interesting work. Notable collection of Chinese and European costumes and model fairground exhibition.

Open Spring BH–mid Sep Wed, Thu, Sat, Sun & BH Mon, 2.30–6.

75p (ch 35p).

⚲ & ✗ (ex guide dogs) Ⓥ

BURTON UPON TRENT
Staffordshire
Map 8 SK22

The Bass Museum of Brewing History
Horninglow St
☎ (0283) 45301

The museum is housed in the Company's Joiner's Shop, built in 1866 and traces the history of the Brewing Industry from earliest times to present day. Shire horse stables, vintage vehicles and model of Burton upon Trent as it was in 1921, complete with trains. Fine collection of drinking glasses. Steam festival May BH.

Open Mon–Fri 10.30–4.30; Sat & Sun, 11– 4.30. (Closed Xmas & New Year's day).

£1 (ch & pen 50p). Disabled free. Party.

△ ⚲ (licensed) ⟊ & (ground floor & outside exhibits only) shop ✗

BURWASH
East Sussex
Map 5 TQ62

Bateman's (1m SW)
☎ (0435) 882302

A lovely 17th-century house, the home of Rudyard Kipling from 1902 to 1936. The study remains as it was during his time here. Attractive gardens and recently restored water-mill. No indoor photography permitted.

Open Etr–Oct, Sat–Wed, 11–6 (last admission 5.30).

£2 (ch £1).

△ ⚲ shop ✗ (NT)

BURY
Gt Manchester
Map **7** SD81

Bury Art Gallery & Museum Moss St
☏ 061-761 4021

Contains a fine collection of 19th-century British paintings including works by Turner, Constable and Landseer. The museum outlines the social history of the town. Temporary exhibitions.

Open Mon–Fri, 10–6, Sat 10–5. (Closed Sun & BH).

Free.

P (30 yds) & shop ✖

Regimental Museum The Lancashire Fusiliers Wellington Barracks, Bolton Rd
☏ 061-764 2208

Covers the history of XX The Lancashire Fusiliers from 1688 to the present day. Among the many exhibits is a special VC section, this Regiment won more VCs than any other in the British Army in 1914–18 war.

Open Mon–Wed, Fri & Sat 9–12.15 & 12.45–5. (Closed BH).

10p (ch 15 5p).

▲ & (ground floor & gardens only) ✖

Transport Museum East Lancashire Railway Preservation Society
☏ 061-764 7790

Preserved buses, lorries, a fire engine and a steam roller are among the road displays. Whilst the railway exhibits include steam age items and mainline diesels, carriages and a steam operated crane. Steam-hauled brake-van rides last Sun in each month Mar–Sep and BH Mon during these months.

Open Sat, Sun & BH Mons, Mar–Sep 10–5.

40p (ch 20p) Family £1.

▲ ⬙ (Sun & BH Mons) shop

BURY ST EDMUNDS
Suffolk
Map **5** TL86

Angel Corner & The Gershom-Parkington Collection Angel Hill
☏ (0284) 63233 ext 227

Bury
—
Bwlchgwyn

Queen Anne house containing Gershom–Parkington fine collection of clocks and watches.

Open Mon–Sat, 10–1, 2–5 (4pm Nov–Feb). (Closed Sun, Good Fri, Etr Sat, May BH, Xmas & New Year).

Free. (Donation).

P (adj & 10 yds) ✖ (NT)

Moyse's Hall Museum Cornhill
☏ (0284) 63233 ext 236

A rare 12th-century house, now a museum of Suffolk local history, archaeology and natural history.

Open all year, Mon–Sat 10–1 & 2–5 (4pm Nov–Feb). (Closed Sun; winter BH & May Day).

40p (ch & pen 20p, ch accompanied by adult, free). Party.

P (100 yds) & (ground floor only) shop

Suffolk Regiment Museum The Keep, Gibraltar Barracks, Out Risbygate
☏ (0284) 2394

Exhibits include uniforms, weapons, medals, campaign souvenirs, documents and photographs. 'Minden Day' 29 Jul '86.

Open all year, Mon–Fri 10–12 & 2–4.

Free.

▲ shop ✖

BUSCOT
Oxfordshire
Map **4** SU29

Buscot Park (off A417)

An 18th-century house with a fine collection of paintings and notable water garden layout. No indoor photography.

Open Apr–Sep, Wed–Fri inc Good Fri, 2nd & 4th wknd in each month. 2–6 (last admission to house 5.30).

£1.60 (grounds only 80p).

✖ (NT)

BUTE, ISLE OF
Strathclyde *Bute*
Map **10** see **Rothesay**

BUXTON
Derbyshire
Map **7** SK07

Buxton Micrarium The Crescent
☏ (0298) 78662

The first exhibition of its kind: a unique opportunity to explore the world of nature using special push-button remote-controlled microscopes.

Open 22 Mar–9 Nov, daily 10–5.

£1.30 (ch 70p, pen £1). Party.

P & shop ✖ ⓥ

Poole's Cavern (Buxton Country Park) Green Ln
☏ (0298) 6978

Natural limestone cavern in 100 acres of woodland. Includes a visitor centre with video show and Roman exhibition.

Open Good Fri–9 Nov 10–5 daily.

✳ £1.30 (ch 75p, pen £1.10).

▲ ⬙ ⊞ & (cavern accessible) shop ✖ (in cavern)

BWLCHGWYN
Clwyd
Map **7** SJ25

Geological & Folk Museum of North Wales Milestone Visitor Centre, Old Silica Quarry (on A525)
☏ Wrexham (0978) 757573

An exhibition of the geology combined with an illustration of the development of Man in North Wales. A Rock Garden contains many large specimens of different rock types of the area. The Geological Trail is a 1½ hour walk displaying many excellent geological features.

Open Mon–Fri 10–4. Sat & Sun (summer only) 11–5.

Free admission to site & Gardens; Museum & trail 50p (ch 30p). Party.

▲ ⬙ (licensed) ⊞ & (ground floor & Rock Garden) shop & plants for sale

73

BYLAND ABBEY
North Yorkshire
Map **8** SE57
(2m W of village of Ampleforth)

Considerable remains of the church and monastic buildings dating from late 12th- and early 13th-century. Well preserved glazed tiles.

Open, see end of gazetteer.

✱ 50p (ch 16 & pen 25p).

&. (AM)

CADBURY
Devon
Map **3** SS90

Fursdon House
☎ Exeter (0392) 860860

Fursdon has been the home of the Fursdon family since 1259. Re-modelled in 1732, the house contains family furniture and portraits displayed in a Jacobean panelled dining room, Georgian hall and Regency library. Also on display is a unique family costume collection containing rare 18th-century examples as well as everyday items used by the family over the past few hundred years.

Open Etr Sun & Mon; then May–Sep Thu, Sun & BHs 2–5.30 also Weds Jul & Aug.

(Admission to house by guided tour only at 2.30, 3.30 & 4.30).
House & grounds £1.70 (ch 85p, under 10 free).
Grounds only (including woodland walks) 80p (ch 10–16 40p). Party 20+.

&. ⵏ &. (ground floor only) shop ✖ Ⓥ

CADEBY
Leicestershire
Map **4** SK40

Cadeby Light Railway In grounds of
Cadeby Rectory
☎ Market Bosworth (0455) 290462

Probably the smallest of Britain's narrow gauge railways. Engine normally running is a 1919 steam saddle tank locomotive. Other exhibits include a 1927 Foster Traction Engine and two steam rollers from 1903 onwards. Exhibition model railway in 4mm scale representing the Great Western Railway in South Devon of about 1935. Brass Rubbing Centre in Cadeby Church (50 facsimiles). Steam traction engine rally 16 & 17 Aug.

Open all year on second Sat of each month also 1st Sat Nov & Boxing Day 2–5.30.

Free.

P (100 yds) ⵏ &. (ground floor only) shop

CAERLAVEROCK
Dumfries and Galloway *Dumfriesshire*
Map **11** NY06

Caerlaverock Castle

A famous medieval stronghold, mainly 13th- to 15th-century.

Open, see end of gazetteer.

✱ 50p (ch & pen 25p).

&. (AM)

Wildfowl Trust Eastpark Farm
☎ Glencaple (038777) 200

An exciting wild refuge of over 1,000 acres on the north Solway shore. Outstanding hide facilities, observation towers and an observatory provide impressive views of the magnificent flocks of Barnacle and Pink-footed geese and the huge numbers of Wigeon, Pintail and wading birds that spend most of the winter in the refuge.

Open 16 Sep–Apr (ex 24 & 25 Dec).
Guided tours 11 & 2 daily.
£1.50 (ch 80p, ch 4 free, pen £1.20). Party 20+.

&. ✖

CAERLEON
Gwent
Map **3** ST39

Amphitheatre Barracks & Fortress Baths (on A449)

Roman amphitheatre with accommodation for 6000 people from legionary fortress dated AD 80–100. Excavated from 1849 onwards.

Open †, see end of gazetteer.

✱ 50p (ch 16 & pen 25p). Party.

&. shop (AM Cadw)

CAERNARFON
Gwynedd
Map **6** SH46

Caernarfon Castle

Begun by Edward I in 1283 and completed in 1323 it includes polygonal angle towers, notable Eagle Tower and extensive town walls. Birthplace of Edward II, first Prince of Wales, and site of investiture in 1969 of present Prince of Wales.

Open †, see end of gazetteer.

✱ £1.60 (ch & pen 80p). Party.

&. shop (AM Cadw)

Segontium Roman Fort and Museum
☎ (0286) 5625

Branch archaeological gallery of the National Museum of Wales. Remains of Roman fort of 'Segontium', and museum of excavated relics.

Open Mon–Sat 9.30–6. Sun 2–6. Closed at 4pm Nov–Feb and 5.30pm wkdays, 5pm Suns Mar, Apr & Oct. (Closed 24–26 Dec, 1 Jan, Good Fri & May Day).

Free.

P shop ✖ (AM Cadw)

CAERPHILLY
Mid Glamorgan
Map **3** ST18

Caerphilly Castle (on A469)

A concentrically planned castle, begin in 1268 by Gilbert de Clare and completed in 1326. The largest in Wales with extensive land and water defences.

Open †, see end of gazetteer.

✱ 80p (ch & pen 40p).

&. shop (AM Cadw)

CAERWENT
Gwent
Map **3** ST49

Roman Town (beside A48)

Complete circuit of town wall (in use from 1st to 4th-centuries) together with excavated areas of houses, shops and temple.

Accessible at any time.

Free.

(AM Cadw)

CAIRNDOW
Strathclyde *Argyll*
Map **10** NN11

Strone House
☎ (04996) 284

A garden featuring rhododendrons, azaleas, conifers and daffodils, also the tallest tree in Britain measuring 190 ft.

Open Apr–Sep, dawn–dusk.

Admission fee payable

&. ⵏ

CAISTER-ON-SEA
Norfolk
Map **9** TG51

Caister Castle, Motor Museum, Tower and Grounds
☎ Wymondham (057284) 251

The Motor Museum exhibits vehicles from 1893 to the present day and the grounds include the substantial remains of the moated castle, a 98 ft tower and the 1951 Festival of Britain Tree Walk, removed from Battersea Park.

Museum & grounds open mid May–Sep, Mon–Fri & Sun 10.30–5.

Admission fee payable. Party.

&. ⵏ &. shop

Roman Town

South gateway, town wall built of flint with brick bonding courses, part of what may have been a seaman's hostel.

Open any reasonable time.

Free.

(AM)

CALBOURNE
Isle of Wight
Map **4** SZ48

74

Watermill and Rural Museum (On B3401)
☎ (098378) 227

A 17th-century mill with water-wheel and mill-stones still in working order.

Open Etr–Oct, daily 10–6.

✱ £1 (ch 50p, pen 80p).

🅐 🛗 🍴 shop

CALDICOT
Gwent
Map **3** ST48

Caldicot Castle, Museum and Countryside Park (On B4245)
☎ (0291) 420241

A Norman castle with interesting features including a local history museum. The Tower Gallery houses monthly art exhibitions. The Countryside Park includes an adventure playground and barbecue site.

Open Mar–Oct, Mon–Fri 11–12.30 & 1.30–5, Sat 10–1 & 1.30–5 & Sun 1.30–5. Details not confirmed for 1986. Park open all year.

45p (ch & pen 25p). Pre-booked educational parties free. Countryside Park free.

🅐 🍴 ♿ (Park only) shop

See advertisement on page 203

CALLANDER
Central *Perthshire*
Map **11** NN60

Calbourne
—
Calstock

Kilmahog Woollen Mill
☎ (0877) 30268

A former woollen mill, famous for hand-woven blankets and tweed. An old water wheel has been preserved in working order. Showroom open for sale of woollens, tweeds and tartans.

Open mid Mar–mid Nov daily 9–5 & mid Nov–mid Mar daily 10–4. (Closed Jan).

Free.

🅐 🛗 shop

CALLANISH
Isle of Lewis, Western Isles *Ross & Cromarty*
Map **13** NB23

Callanish Standing Stones
Unique collection of megaliths comprising an avenue 27ft in width, with 19 standing stones, terminating in a 37ft-wide circle containing 13 additional stones. Other stones, burial cairns and circles in the near vicinity.

Accessible at all times.

Free.

🅐 (AM)

CALNE
Wiltshire
Map **3** ST96

Bowood House & Gardens (2m W off A4)
☎ (0249) 812102

Georgian house dating from 1754. Rooms on view include Robert Adam's famous Library and the Laboratory where Dr Joseph Priestley discovered oxygen gas in 1774. Superb exhibitions of paintings, watercolours, sculpture, costume, etc. Capability Brown's Pleasure Gardens cover 100 acres and a massive children's adventure playground. Rolls-Royce Wessex Region Rally Sun 17 Aug.

Open Apr–Sep, daily 11–6, including BH. Rhododendron Walks (separate entrance off A342) open mid May–mid Jun 11–6. Details not confirmed for 1986.

House and grounds ✱ £2 (ch £1, pen £1.50). Rhododendron Gardens 80p (ch 50p).

🅐 🛗 (licensed) 🍴 ♿ (ground floor of house only) shop & garden centre 🐾

CALSTOCK
Cornwall
Map **2** SX46

Cotehele House (2m W on W bank of Tamar, 8m SW of Tavistock off A390)

Granite house 1485–1627, formerly home →

of Earls of Mount Edgcumbe, contains 17th- and early 18th-century armour, furniture and tapestry. Beautiful gardens on different levels with medieval dovecot. There is a restored manorial watermill in valley below, a small shipping museum and a restored sailing barge 'Shamrock' can be seen from the quay.

Open Apr–Oct, daily 11–6 or dusk, last admission 5.30; Nov–Mar garden only open during daylight hours.

✳ House, garden & mill £2-60, garden grounds & mill £1.50.

⚏ (NT)

CAMBO
Northumberland
Map **12** NZ08

Wallington House Garden & Grounds
☎ Scots Gap (067 074) 283
(1m S on B6342)
17th- and 18th-century house with rococo plasterwork and a central hall added in the 19th century, situated in a great moorland estate of over twelve thousand acres rising to an altitude of over one thousand feet. Magnificent fuschias in conservatory in walled garden.

House open Good Fri–6 Apr daily. 7 Apr–end Apr Wed, Sat & Sun 2–6 May–Sep, Wed–Mon, 2–6; Oct, Wed, Sat & Sun, 2–5. Grounds open all year.

✳ House & Grounds £2.40. Grounds only £1. Party.

🅰 ⚏ ⌱ 🕭 🕱 (in house) (NT)

CAMBRIDGE
Cambridgeshire
Map **5** TL45

Ancient university city on the River Cam. Many of the colleges line the East bank, overlooking the Backs; sweeping lawns set with willow trees, on the opposite side of river transformed from rough marshland by Richard Bently (Master of Trinity College from 1669 to 1734). The colleges are open to the public on most days during daylight though there are some restrictions during term time.

Cambridge and County Folk Museum
2–3 Castle St
☎ (0223) 355159
The former White Horse Inn, now houses 11 rooms of exhibits including a large collection of domestic, agricultural and trade exhibits relating to the county. 50th Anniversary of Museum Festival Jul–Sep.

Open Tue–Sat 10.30–5 & Sun 2.30–4.30.

50p (ch & pen 20p).

P (200 yds) 🕭 (ground floor & gardens only) shop 🕱

Fitzwilliam Museum Trumpington St
☎ (0223) 69501

Houses an extensive art and archaeological collection including Egyptian, Greek and Roman antiquities,

---

European paintings, manuscripts, Renaissance objets d'art and armour plus special exhibitions throughout year.

Open Tue–Sat 10–5, Sun 2.15–5 plus Etr Mon, Spring & Summer BH. (Closed Good Fri, May Day & 24 Dec–1 Jan).

Free.

P (600 yds) ⚏ (Tue–Sat 10.30–4) 🕭 shop 🕱 (ex guide dogs)

Museum of Archaeology
Downing St
☎ (0223) 359714

New archaeology gallery covering man's development from the earliest times to Civilization throughout the world, and local archaeology up to the 19th-century.

Open Mon–Fri 2–4, Sat 10–12.30. (Closed 24 Dec–2 Jan & 1 wk Etr).

Free.

P (160 yds) 🕭 (ground floor only) 🕱 ⌗

Scott Polar Research Institute
Lensfield Rd
☎ (0223) 66499

Contains relics and equipment relating to Arctic and Antarctic expeditions with special emphasis on those of Captain Scott. Includes Eskimo and general polar art collections and information on current scientific exploration.

Open Mon–Sat 2.30–4. (Closed some BHs).

Free.

🅰 shop 🕱

University Botanic Garden
1 Brookside, Bateman St
☎ (0223) 350101

Originally founded in 1762 and now covering 40 acres with fine botanical collections.

Open Mon–Sat 8–6.30 (dusk in winter). Sun, for non-keyholders May–Sep 2.30–6.30. For keyholders open all year 10–6.30. Glasshouses 11–12.30 & 2–4.

Free (For Sunday keys – particulars from Director).

P (100 yds) 🕀 🕭 shop 🕱 (ex guide dogs)

CAMELFORD
Cornwall
Map **2** SX18

North Cornwall Museum and Gallery
The Clease
☎ (0840) 212954

Museum of rural life with sections on agriculture, slate and granite quarrying, blacksmith's and wheelwright's tools, cobbling, the dairy and domestic scenes

---

including a collection of bonnets. The gallery holds various exhibitions.

Open Apr–Sep, Mon–Sat 10–30–5. (Closed Sun).

75p (ch 25p, pen & students 50p).

P 🕭 (ground floor only) 🕱 (ex guide dogs)

CANFORD CLIFFS
Dorset
Map **4** SZ08

Compton Acres Gardens Canford Cliffs
Rd (on B3065)
☎ (0202) 708036

Rock and water gardens covering 15 acres, with examples of Japanese, Roman and Italian gardens with fine views over Poole Harbour and Purbeck Hills.

Open Apr–Oct daily 10.30–6.30.

✳ £1.40 (ch 70p, pen £1). Party 30+.

🅰 ⚏ 🕭 shop & garden centre 🕱 ⓥ

CANONS ASHBY
Northamptonshire
Map **4** SP55

Canons Ashby House
☎ Blakesley (0327) 860044

An exceptional, small manor house with restored gardens, small park and church—part of the original 13th-century Augustinian Priory.

Open 29 Mar–Oct Wed–Sun & BH Mon 1–5.30 or sunset if earlier (last admission 5) (Closed Good Fri).

£2 (ch £1). Donation box for church. Parties booked in advance.

🅰 🕱 (ex guide dogs) (NT)

CANTERBURY
Kent
Map **5** TR15

Blean Bird Garden Honey Hill, Blean (3m NW on A290).
☎ Canterbury (0227) 471666

Exotic tropical birds can be seen living free in a natural environment amongst the trees. The garden has the largest breeding collection of Macaws, Cockatoos and Parrakeets in England, also Owls, Soft bills, Peacocks and Pheasants. Pets corner tropical house & woodland walk.

Open Apr–Oct 10–6.

£1.50 (ch 75p). Party 20+.

🅰 ⚏ 🕀 🕭 shop 🕱 ⓥ

Howe Barracks (Queens Regimental Museum)
☎ (0227) 457411 ext 259

Contains exhibits of all the former county regiments of Kent, Surrey, Sussex and Middlesex from which the Queen's Regiment was formed on 31 Dec 1966.

Open all year Mon–Fri 10–12.30 & 2–4.

Free.

🅰 shop 🕱

Museum of Canterbury Poor Priests'
Hospital, Stour St
☎ (0227) 452747

*This new museum of Canterbury's
heritage is due to open in Spring 1986 in
the medieval Poor Priests' Hospital, which
has been fully restored. The displays take
the form of a time walk through
Canterbury's history from the first town
under the Romans to the present. Early
treasures of the city will be displayed here
– Roman cavalry swords, and silver spoon
hoard; pagan Anglo-Saxon gold; Viking
finds; and displays will feature a
reconstruction of Becket's tomb; a
medieval street with pilgrim badge shop;
Christopher Marlowe; the Pilgrim Fathers;
the city in the Civil War; and Stephenson's
Locomotive 'Invicta', among many others.*

Open Apr–Sep Mon–Sat 11–1 & 2–4.
Reduced opening hours between Oct–
Mar. Details not confirmed for 1986.

✱ 50p (ch 25p).

P & (ground floor & gardens only) shop
✗

Roman Pavement Butchery Ln
☎ (0227) 452747

*Canterbury's underground museum
preserves, below the streets in the Roman
levels, the remains of a Roman town
house with its mosaic pavements and
hypocaust. Archaeological finds from
other parts of the Roman city are on show.*

Open Apr–Sep. Mon–Sat 10–1 & 2–5;
Oct–Mar, Mon–Sat 2–4.

✱ 30p (ch 12p)

P shop ✗

**Royal Museum, Art Gallery and Buffs
Regimental Museum** High St
☎ (0227) 452747

*The archaeology of east Kent, Anglo
Saxon glass and jewellery, English and
Continental porcelain, paintings include
works by local artist Sidney Cooper,
engravings and photographs; collections
of medals, uniforms, weapons and
trophies of the Royal East Kent Regiment.
Canterbury festival exhibitions Sep/Oct
plus monthly changing exhibitions.*

Canterbury
Cardiff

Open Mon–Sat 10–5.
Free.
P shop ✗

St Augustine's Abbey
*Founded by St Augustine on land given
by King Ethelbert in 598; foundations of a
7th-century church. Remains of 11th-
century round church underlie extensive
ruins of medieval Benedictine abbey.*

Open † see end of gazetteer.

✱ 50p (ch 16 & pen 25p)

(AM)

West Gate Museum St Peter's St
☎ (0227) 452747

*A 14th-century gateway, the last of the
city's gates to survive and now housing
displays and material relating to the
gatehouse in the city wall systems and its
use as a gaol. The battlements offer a
panoramic view of the city.*

Open all year Mon–Sat; Apr–Sep 10–1 &
2–5; Oct–Mar 2–4 only.

✱ 30p (ch 12p).

P shop ✗

CAPEL BANGOR
Dyfed
Map **6** SN68

**Rheidol Power Station & Information
Centre** Cwm Rheidol
☎ (097084) 667

*A guided tour of the power station,
located in a secluded valley, is
complimented by a fish farm, nature trail
and lakeside picnic area.*

Tours of the Power Station Etr–Oct, daily
11–4.30.

✱ 80p (ch 16 40p, pen 60p)

⚠ ⚤ ⟊ & (ex basement) shop

See advertisement under Aberystwyth

CAPESTHORNE
Cheshire
Map **7** SJ87

Capesthorne Hall (On A34 between
Congleton and Wimslow)
☎ Chelford (0625) 861221 or 861439

*The home of the Bromley-Davenport
Family, built in 1722, containing
interesting furniture, pictures, silver and
Americana. Children's play area, angling
in season & caravan park. Numerous
events throughout the year.*

Open Etr–Sep Tue, Wed, Thu, Sat & Sun;
May & Jun Wed, Sat & Sun; Apr Sun only.
Also open all BHs. Park & Garden 12–6,
Hall 2–5. (Opening dates to be confirmed
for 1985.)

Hall, Park & Garden £1.75 (ch 85p), Park,
Garden & Chapel £1 (ch 50p). Parties
20+.

⚠ ⚤ (licensed) ⟊ & (ground floor &
gardens only) shop

CARDIFF
South Glamorgan
Map **3** ST17

Cardiff Castle Castle St
☎ (0222) 822083

*Roman and Norman with 12th-century
keep, and 1861 additions including state
apartments and curtain walls built on
visible remains of Roman Wall.*

Open daily (ex Xmas & New Year BHs).
Conducted tours Mar, Apr & Oct, Mon–
Sat 10–12.30 & 2–4 (castle closes 5) Sun
10–12 & 2–4, May–Sep, daily 10–12.40 &
2–5 (castle closes 6); Nov–Feb daily 11–3
(castle closes 4). Only short tours when
functions in progress. Conducted tour
Jul–Sep ✱ £2 (ch & pen £1), rest of year
£1.60 (ch & pen 80p). Short tour and
Military Museum (when appropriate) £1.30
(ch & pen 70p). Green, Roman Wall,
Norman Keep and Military Museum
£1.05p (ch & pen 55p). Party 20+.

P (¼ mile) & (grounds only) shop ✗ (ex
grounds)

**National Museum of Wales (Main
Building)** Cathays Park
☎ (0222) 397951 →

Collections and exhibitions in archaeology, geology, botany, zoology, industry and art.

Open Tue–Sat 10–5, Sun 2.30–5. (Closed 24–26 Dec, New Years day, Good Fri & May Day).

Free.

P ⚑ ⬇ & shop ✖

Welsh Industrial and Maritime Museum Bute St
☎ (0222) 481919

A branch museum of the National Museum of Wales. Working exhibits tell the story of motive power and the roles played by a variety of machines over two centuries of intense industrial production and progress in Wales. Collection of boats, road and railway vehicles.

Open Tue–Sat 10–5. Sun 2.30–5. (Closed Good Fri, May Day, 24–26 Dec & New Year's day).

Free.

P & book shop ✖

CARDIGAN
Dyfed
Map **2** SN14

Cardigan Wildlife Park
☎ (0239) 614449

An unusual variety of Park and Sanctuary with a diverse range of mammals, birds and plants. Other features include fishing on the River Teifi, nature walks and disused slate quarries.

Open all year 10–sunset (last admission 5.30pm).

£1.50 (ch & pen 75p). Party 12+.

⚠ ⬇ (seasonal) ⏟ & (ex some trails) shop ✖

CARDONESS CASTLE
Dumfries and Galloway
Kirkcudbrightshire
Map **11** NX55

(1m SW of Gatehouse of Fleet off A75)

A 15th-century stronghold overlooking the Water of Fleet, once the home of the McCullochs of Galloway.

Cardiff
—
Carloway

Open Apr–Sep, Mon–Sat 9.30–7, Sun 2–7. Oct–Mar, Mon–Sat 9.30–4, Sun 2–4.

✱ 50p (ch & pen 25p).

⚠ (AM)

CARISBROOKE
Isle of Wight
Map **4** SZ48

Carisbrooke Castle (on B3401)

12th-century and later building, once the prison of Charles I, now houses the Isle of Wight Museum.

Open † see end of gazetteer.

✱ £1.50 (ch 16 & pen 75p). Reductions in winter.

⚠ (charge) ⬇ (Apr–Sep) & (grounds & lower levels only) (AM) ⓥ

CARLISLE
Cumbria
Map **12** NY45

Carlisle Castle

Restored castle and dungeons built by William II in 1092, but dating mainly from 12th century.

Open † see end of gazetteer.

✱ £1 (ch 16 & pen 50p). Winter 50p (ch 16 & pen 25p)

⚠ & (exterior of building only) (AM) ⓥ

The Border Regiment & King's Own Royal Border Regiment Museum
Queen Mary's Tower, The Castle.
☎ (0228) 32774

300 years of the Regiment's history depicted in trophies, weaponry, models, silver and pictures, together with the story of Cumbria's part time soldiers.

Open daily, 15 Mar–15 Oct 9.30–6.30, 16 Oct–14 Mar, 9.30–4 (Sun 2–4).

£1 (ch & pen 50p). Prices include entry to Carlisle Castle.

⚠ & (ground floor only) shop ✖

The Guildhall Greenmarket
☎ (0228) 34781

Renovated, half timbered early 15th-century Guildhall with exposed timberwork and wattle and daub walls. Once the meeting place of Carlisle's eight trade guilds and retains much of the atmosphere of the period. Displays feature many items relating to these guilds, and other reminders of life in medieval Carlisle.

Open mid May–mid Sep, afternoons only, telephone for details.

Free.

P (300 yds) shop ✖

Museum and Art Gallery Castle St
☎ (0228) 34781

At Tullie House – a fine Jacobean House (1689), with Victorian extensions are comprehensive collections featuring the Archaeology and Natural History of Cumbria, English porcelain, costume, toys and musical instruments. Also temporary exhibitions in the Art Gallery.

Open; Apr–Sep, Mon–Fri 9–6.45 (5 winter), Sat 9–5 also Sun (Jun–Aug only) 2.30–5; Oct–Mar, Mon–Sat 9–5.

Free.

P (200 yds) & (ground floor only) shop ✖

The Prior's Tower Cathedral grounds
☎ (0228) 35169 & 21834

The 13th-century tower has a first-floor room decorated by Prior Senhouse c1510 with remarkable painted ceiling of 45 panels. On second floor Priors bedroom houses museum covering 850 years of Cathedral history.

Open Mon–Sat 2–5 (May–Sep 10–9) Suns by appointment.

40p (ch 14 20p)

P (150 yds) ⬇ (licensed) ⏟ shop ✖ (ex guide dogs)

CARLOWAY
Isle of Lewis, Western Isles Ross & Cromarty
Map **13** NB24

CARLISLE MUSEUMS & ART GALLERY

TULLIE HOUSE MUSEUM, Castle St.
Attractive Town House (1689) with comprehensive collections including British paintings (19/20 C), English Porcelain, Costume, Prehistoric and Roman Archaeology, British Birds and local Geology including minerals. Extensive temporary exhibition programme. Sales Counter. Free leaflet. Tel 0228-34781 Admission Free.

GUILDHALL MUSEUM, Greenmarket
Newly renovated half-timbered house (C 1405) with displays on Guild and local history including medieval objects. Sales Counter. Free leaflet. Tel as above

Dun Carloway Broch

Well preserved broch of late prehistoric, about 30ft in height, one of the finest in the Western Isles.

Open see end of gazetteer.

Free.

⚠ (AM)

CARLTON
North Yorkshire
Map **8** SE62

Carlton Towers
☎ Goole (0405) 861662

The Duke of Norfolk's Yorkshire home, Carlton Towers was built in 1614 on property owned by the Duke's ancestors since the Norman Conquest. It was remodelled in the 18th- and 19th-centuries and now presents a mainly Victorian appearance. The elaborate state rooms are by John Francis Bentley, architect of Westminster Cathedral. Interesting paintings, furniture, silver and heraldry. Exhibitions of family uniforms and coronation robes. Viewing of the Priest's hiding hole.

Open Etr Sat–Tue; May Day Sun & Mon; Spring BH. Sat–Tue; Aug BH. Sat–Tue; May–Sep Suns only. 1–5 (last admission 4.30pm).

£1.50 (ch 5 free, ch £1, pen £1.20).

⚠ ⟐ shop ✗ (ex guide dogs) ⓥ

CARNASSERIE CASTLE
Strathclyde Argyll
Map **10** NM80

(1½m N of Kilmartin off A816)

Built in the 16th century by John Carswell, first Protestant Bishop of the Isles. It was taken and partly destroyed in Argyll's rebellion of 1685, and consists of a towerhouse with a courtyard built onto it.

Open, see end of gazetteer.

Free.

(AM)

CARNFORTH
Lancashire
Map **7** SD47

Carloway
—
Castle Acre

Steamtown Railway Museum
☎ (0524) 734220

Housed in the old BR/LMS Engine Shed are over 30 Main line and Industrial locos including Flying Scotsman & Sir Nigel Gresley plus 2 Continental locos. Steam Cavalcade of locos on Sun 31 Aug. Passenger rides daily Jul & Aug Sun Etr–Oct.

Open daily (ex 25 Dec) 9–5 Etr–Sep, 10–4 Oct–Etr.

✳ £1.80 (ch & pen 90p) incl steam ride, Etr–Sep; £1 (ch 50p) Oct–Etr. Handicapped admitted free.

⚠ ⟐ ♫ ♿ shop

CARRADALE
Strathclyde Argyll
Map **10** NR83

Carradale House (Off B879)
☎ (05833) 234

Overlooks the lovely Kilbrennan Sound. Beautiful gardens with flowering shrubs, mainly rhododendrons. Best visited between Apr and Jun. Plants, vegetables and shrubs for sale.

Open Apr–Sep 10–5.30.

20p (ch free).

⚠

CARRAWBROUGH
Northumberland
Map **12** NY87

Roman Wall (Mithraic Temple) (on B6318)

Remains of Mithraic temple measuring only 35ft by 15ft, dating from 3rd-century but with later alterations. On line of Roman Wall near fort of 'Procolitia'. Excavations in 1950 revealed three dedicatory altars to Mithras and figure of the Mother Goddess.

Open any reasonable time.

Free.

⚠ (AM)

CARRBRIDGE
Highland Inverness-shire
Map **14** NH92

Landmark Visitor Centre
☎ (047984) 614

Europe's first 'visitor centre', with an exhibition on the history of Strathspey, a multi-screen theatre showing in sound and vision 'The Highlander', the story of the break up of Europe's last tribal society. Evening fim shows, Treetop trail, giant woodland maze, sculpture park, balancing trail, adventure play area, pine forest nature centre, craft and bookshop.

Open Summer, 9.30am–9.30pm; winter, 9.30am–5pm.

£1.75 (ch 90p), Highlander Show & Exhibition 80p (ch 45p), Trails £1.20 (ch 75p).

⚠ ⟐ (licensed) ♫ ♿ shop & garden centre

CARREG CENNEN CASTLE
Dyfed
Map **3** SN61
(3m SE of Llandeilo)

Spectacularly sited hill-side ruin, originally native Welsh stronghold, rebuilt in late 13th-century. Remarkable passage lit by loopholes cut into side of cliff.

Open †, see end of gazetteer.

✳ 60p (ch & pen 30p)

⚠ shop (AM Cadw)

CASTLE ACRE
Norfolk
Map **9** TF81

Earthworks of former castle, slight remains of keep and 13th-century Bailey from fortified borough. Admission free at any reasonable time. Remains of late 11th-century priory, including 12th-century church noted for its arcaded west front. 11th Prior's Loding and early 16th-century gatehouse. →

Priory open † see end of gazetteer.

✻ 50p (ch 16 & pen 25p).

🏛 ♿ (ground floor & grounds only) (AM)

CASTLE ASHBY
Northamptonshire
Map **4** SP85

Castle Ashby House
☎ Yardley Hastings (060129) 234

Elizabethan House built in 1574 with Inigo Jones (1635) front: Set in a magnificent position its interior contains 17th-century ceilings, staircases and panelling and a valuable collection of pictures. A lettered stone parapet (1624) surrounds house, and the grounds and terraces date largely from 1860.

Gardens & aboretum open all year daily 10–6. House also open on certain days, contact house for further details.

Gardens & arboretum 50p (ch 25p). For admission prices to house, contact Castle Ashby House for details.

🏛 (100 yds) ♿ (gardens only)

CASTLEBAY
Isle of Barra, Western Isles *Inverness-shire*
Map **13** NL69

Kisimul Castle Accessible by boat from Castlebay.
☎ (08714) 225 or 336

The historic home of the Macneils of Barra, facing Castlebay, was once a 15th-century island stronghold.

Open May–Sep Wed & Sat from 2pm. Details not confirmed for 1986.

Castle ✻ 70p (ch 25p). Boat trip to Castle 80p (ch 25p).

P 🍴

CASTLE BOLTON
West Yorkshire
Map **7** SE09

Castle Bolton
☎ Wensleydale (0969) 23408

Set in pretty Wensleydale and dating from 1379–97 this was once a former stronghold of the Scropes, prison of Mary Queen of Scots, 1568–69 and besieged

Castle Acre
—
Castle Hedingham

and taken in 1645 by Parliament Forces. Also part restored to original state this century.

Open daily (ex Mon) during daylight hours.

Admission fee payable.

🏛 🍷 (licensed) 🚽 shop 🍴

CASTLE CARY
Somerset
Map **3** ST63

Hadspen House Gardens (2m SE off A371)
☎ (0963) 50200

A sheltered south sloping garden of eight acres, containing modern planting of rare species in an 18th-century setting.

Tue-Sat (ex Jan) 10–5, plus Apr–Oct Sun & BH 2–5.

£1 (ch 50p). Party 15 +.

🏛 🍷 (on Sun & BH) ♿ garden centre 🍴

CASTLE DONINGTON
Leicestershire
Map **8** SK42

The Donington Collection
Donington Park
☎ Derby (0332) 810048

The world's largest collection of single seater Grand Prix racing cars and a display of racing motor cycles. Also, Donington Park International Motor Sport Centre, which has a full programme of car and motorcycle racing from Mar–Oct.

Open daily 10–5 last entry 4.15. (Closed Xmas week).

Admission fee payable.

🏛 🍷 (licensed) 🚽 ♿ 🍴

CASTLE DOUGLAS
Dumfries and Galloway
Kirkcudbrightshire
Map **11** NX76

Threave Castle
(Follow A75 SW to Bridge of Dee (3m) then take unclass road to N)

Stands on an islet in the Rover Dee. This lonely castle, erected by Archibald the Grim in the late 14th-century, is four storeys in height with round towers guarding the outer wall. It was dismantled in 1640. Access to the island by rowing boat.

Open Apr–Sep, Mon–Sat 9.30–7, Sun 2–7; Oct, Mon–Sat 9.30–4, Sun 2–4.

✻ Ferry charge 50p (ch 25p).

(AM)

Threave Garden (1m W of Castle Douglas)
☎ (0556) 2575

Fine garden, noted for a splendid springtime display of over 200 varieties of daffodil. Walled garden and glasshouses. This house is NTS School of Gardening.

Open daily 9–sunset. Walled garden & glasshouses 9–5. Visitor Centre & shop 28 Mar–Oct, daily 9–6.

£1.20 (ch 60p). Party.

🍷 (Etr–Sep, daily 10–5) ♿ (NTS)

CASTLE HEDINGHAM
Essex
Map **5** TL73

Colne Valley Railway and Museum
Access to site is on A604 between Castle Hedingham and Great Yeldham.
☎ Hedingham (0787) 61174

The original Colne Valley and Halstead railway buildings have been rebuilt on the site, with stock including six steam locomotives and items of rolling stock. Locomotives in steam to be seen as advertised below. 5 acre wooded, riverside picnic/nature area.

Open Feb–Xmas, daily 10–5 to view static exhibits. Steam days every 1st & 3rd Sun of the month & BH Suns & Mons between Etr–Oct, 12–5. Railbus rides available on other days subject to demand.

Steam days £2 (ch £1) includes free rides. Non-steam days £1 (ch 50p).

🏛 🍷 🚽 ♿ (ground floor only) shop 🍴 Ⓥ

Hedingham Castle

Situated in the lovely old village of Castle Hedingham, Essex, near the Suffolk border, is of great historical interest. Built in 1140 by Aubrey de Vere, son of one of William the Conqueror's leading nobles. The de Veres, an important medieval family, owned the castle for 550 years. The castle is in a splendid state of preservation, retaining four floors and roof. The Banqueting Hall with its minstrels' gallery possesses the finest Norman arch in England. The beautiful Tudor bridge built in 1496 spans the dry moat and replaces the original drawbridge. Families can enjoy the peace and quiet of these tranquil surroundings, and can picnic on the grass of the Inner Bailey.

Open from May-end October, daily 10am-5pm. Parties welcome all the year round by appointment with the Curator.
Telephone Hedingham (0787) 60261/60804.

Hedingham Castle
☎ Hedingham (0787) 60261/60804
A majestic Norman Castle, built in 1130, its banqueting hall, minstrels gallery, keep and other features are in fine state of preservation. Besieged by King John and once the home of the de Veres, Earls of Oxford.
Open May–Oct daily 10–5.
£1.50 (ch 70p).
⚠ ♨ shop ✻

CASTLE HOWARD
See MALTON

CASTLE KENNEDY
Dumfries and Galloway *Wigtownshire*
Map **10** NX15

Castle Kennedy Gardens (situated 3m E of Stranraer on A75)
☎ Stranraer (0776) 2024
17th-century and later gardens with a fine collection of flowers and shrubs, situated on a peninsula between two lochs. Also, there is a Plant Centre adjoining the gardens.
Open Apr–Sep daily 10–5.
£1 (ch 25p pen 80p).
⚠ ♨ ♫ shop & plant centre ⓥ

CASTLE RISING
Norfolk
Map **9** TF62

Castle Rising (off A149)
Fine Norman keep probably built by Earl of Arundel, within impressive earthworks.
Open † see end of gazetteer.
✳ 60p (ch 16 & pen 30p).
⚠ (charge) ⚹ (exterior only) (AM)

CASTLETON
Derbyshire
Map **7** SK18

Blue-John Cavern & Mine
☎ Hope Valley (0433) 20638
One of the finest examples of water-worn caves, measuring ⅓ mile long, with 200ft high chambers. Contains eight of the fourteen veins of Blue John Stone.
Open all year daily 9.30–6 (dusk in winter). (Closed 25 & 26 Dec & 1 Jan).
Admission fee payable.
P shop ⓥ

Peak Cavern (on A625)
☎ Hope Valley (0433) 20285
One of the most spectacular natural limestone caves in the district which has an electrically lit underground walk of about ⅓ mile. Grand Entrance Hall, where ropes have been made for over 500 years, and traces of a row of cottages can be seen.
Open 28 Mar–mid Sep, daily 10–5.
£1.10 (ch & pen 60p).
⚠ (300 yds) shop

Castle Hedingham
—
Cawdor

Peveril (or Peak) Castle
Ruined keep erected originally by Henry II; later portion has vanished.
Open † see end of gazetteer.
✳ 60p (ch 16 & pen 30p)
⚠ (AM)

Speedwell Cavern Winnats Pass
☎ Hope Valley (0433) 20512
Floodlit cavern with illuminated canal and bottomless pit. One mile underground boat trip.
Open daily 9.30–5.30. (Closed 25 & 26 Dec & 1 Jan).
£2 (ch 14 £1.50). Party
⚠ shop

CASTLETOWN
Isle of Man
Map **6** SC26

Castle Rushen
☎ (0624) 823326
14th-century stronghold with remains of the earlier structure, and State apartments. Also a Norman keep flanked by 14th-century towers, and a clock given by Queen Elizabeth I in 1597. The castle is available for hire for functions.
Open Jun–Sep, Mon–Sat 10–6, Oct–May, Mon–Fri 10–5, Sat 10–noon. Details not confirmed for 1986.
✳ 50p (ch & pen 25p).
P (20 yds) ♨ ⚹ (ground floor & gardens only) shop

Nautical Museum
☎ Douglas (0624) 75522
Includes 18th-century Manx yacht 'Peggy', an interesting Quayle Room and Cabin Room.
Open early May–late Sep, Mon–Sat 10–1 & 2–5, Sun 2–5. Details not confirmed for 1986.
✳ 25p (ch 10p).
P (50 yds) ⚹ (ground floor only) ✻ (ex guide dogs)

CÂTEL (CASTEL)
Guernsey *Channel Islands*
Map **16**

Le Friquet Butterfly Farm and Flower Centre Le Friquet Rd
☎ Guernsey (0481) 54378
European and exotic species of butterflies housed in a glass covered recreation of their natural habitat and seen in a free-flying environment. Established in 1977 to breed as well as exhibit butterflies. Flower centre, putting & croquet, & evening barbecues.
Open Etr–Oct 10–5.

Butterfly house ✳ 95p (ch 50p, pen 75p).
Insectarium 20p (ch & pen 10p).
⚠ ♨ (licensed) ⚹ shop & garden centre

CAUSEWAYHEAD
Central *Stirlingshire*
Map **11** NS89

Wallace Monument
☎ Stirling (0786) 72140
A 220ft high tower erected in 1869, in which Sir William Wallace's famous two-handed sword is preserved. No fewer than seven battlefields are visible from the summit in addition to a wide panoramic view towards the Highlands. There is a Hall of Heroes and an audio-visual system on the life of Wallace and 'The Forth Panorama'. Also a new sound and light show brings to life busts of some of Scotlands most famous sons.
Open Feb, Mar & Oct 10–5; Apr & Sep 10–6; May, Jun, Jul & Aug 10–7. Details not confirmed for 1986.
✳ 80p (ch 40p). Party 15 + .
P (10 mins walk) ♨ shop ✻
See advertisement under Stirling

CAVENDISH
Suffolk
Map **5** TL84

Cavendish Manor Vineyards and Nether Hall
☎ Glemsford (0787) 280221
A 15th-century manor house in scenic Stour Valley village surrounded by its own vineyards. The house and adjacent museum contains an extensive collection of paintings and rural bygones. Tours around the vineyards and wine tasting.
Open daily 11–5.
£1.50 (pen £1, ch 16 free).
⚠ ♫ shop

The Sue Ryder Foundation Museum
Sue Ryder Home
☎ Glemsford (0787) 280252
The museum depicts the work, background and history of the small, international Foundation which cares for the sick and disabled of all ages. Gardens of Home also open as well as the Chapel.
Open Mon–Sat 10–5.30, Sun 10–11am & 12.30–5.30. Details not confirmed for 1986.
40p (ch 12 20p). Parties by appointment.
⚠ ♨ ⚹ shop ✻ (ex guide dogs)

CAWDOR
Highland *Nairnshire*
Map **14** NH84

Cawdor Castle
☎ (06677) 615
Home of the Thanes of Cawdor since the 14th-century and home of the present Earl and Countess Cawdor. It has a draw-bridge, an ancient tower built around →

a tree, and a freshwater well inside the house. Nature trails, pitch and putt and putting green. Antique open days beginning of May and Sep. The site of the 'Cawdor Highland Games' in Aug.

Open May–5 Oct daily 10–5.30 (last admission 5pm).

✳ £1.80 (ch 5–15 90p, students £1.50, pen/disabled £1.30). Party 20 + . Gardens, grounds & nature trails only 85p.

⚠ ⯑ (licensed) ⛩ ♿ (ground floor & gardens only) shop ✸

CAWTHORNE
South Yorkshire
Map **8** SE20

Cannon Hall (on A635)
☎ Barnsley (0226) 790270

Built circa 1765, mainly by John Carr of York, the museum set in 70 acres of parkland is owned by Barnsley Metropolitan Borough Council. Also Regimental Museum of the 13th/18th Royal Hussars (Queen Mary's Own). The Harvey Collection of Dutch and Flemish paintings (formerly the National Loan Collection) is now on permanent display.

Open Mon–Sat 10.30–5 & Sun 2.30–5. (Closed Good Fri & 25–27 Dec).

Free.

⚠ ♿ (ground floor) ✸

Cawdor
—
Chalfont St Giles

CENARTH
Dyfed
Map **2** SN24

Cenarth Fishing Museum Cenarth Falls

Located on the River Teifi, this is Britain's first rod and line fishing museum. As well as a very large collection of fishing equipment on display there is poaching tackle and wildlife exhibits. Above the museum is an art gallery and video showing fishing films.

Open Etr–Oct, daily.

Admission fee payable.

P

CERES
Fife
Map **11** NO31

Fife Folk Museum The Weigh House
☎ (033482) 380

A regional, rural folk collection displayed in the historic Weigh House, Cottages, new extension; and terraced garden near Ceres Green.

Open Apr–Oct, Mon, Wed–Sat 2–5, Sun 2.30–5.30. Details not confirmed for 1986.

✳ 50p (ch 20p). Party.

P (200 yds) ♿ (ground floor & gardens only) ✸

CERRIGYDRUDION
Clwyd
Map **6** SH94

Llyn Brenig Information Centre & Estate
☎ (049082) 463

A 2,400 acre estate with a unique archaeological trail and 'round-the lake' walk of ten miles for which a completion certificate is available. Nature trail, and Nature Reserve includes a number of rare plants and birds. Access to bird hide, best viewing Dec–Feb. There are special fishing platforms and an open day for disabled anglers. The Centre includes a bi-lingual exhibition on geology, archaeology, history and natural history.

Open Apr–17 Oct daily 8–6; Nov–Mar Mon–Fri 8–4. (Access in the winter may be limited by snow; cross-country skiing is then available).

Free (except for canoeing, fishing & sailing).

⚠ ⯑ (wknds Apr–Jun & Sep, daily Jul–Aug) ♿ Souvenir & fishing tackle shop (Apr–17 Oct)

CHALFONT ST GILES
Buckinghamshire
Map **4** SU99

Chiltern Open Air Museum Newlands Park, Gorelands Ln (off B4442)
☎ (02407) 71117

An open air museum of buildings and associated artefacts reflecting 500 years of life in the Chiltern area. Situated in 45 acres of parkland with nature trail.

Open Etr–Sep, Wed, Sun & BH Mon 2–6. (Last admission 5pm).

£1.20 (ch 14 60p & pen 90p). Party 30 +.

  ⚬ ♨ ⚬ shop

Milton's Cottage Dean Way
☎ (02407) 2313

Half timbered 16th-century cottage with a charming garden, the only existing home in which John Milton lived and worked. Here he completed 'Paradise Lost' and commenced 'Paradise Regained', and there are ninety-three rare books on display including 1st editions of the above mentioned works.

Open Feb–Oct, Tue–Sat 10–1 & 2–6, Sun 2–6. Also open Spring & Summer BH.

80p (ch 15 30p). Party 20 +.

P (50 yds) ⚬ shop ✗

CHANNEL ISLANDS
Map **16**
Refer to Guernsey or Jersey for details.

CHARD
Dorset
Map **3** ST30

Forde Abbey
☎ South Chard (0460) 20231

12th-century Cistercian monastery with notable gatehouse, enlarged by Abbot Chard, and converted to a house by Cromwell's Attorney General in the 17th century. Inhabited by the present family since 1864, it contains a set of five famous Mortlake tapestries. The grounds cover some 20 acres, with water and rock gardens.

Open May–Sep, Wed, Sun & BH 2–6. £2 (ch 70p) gardens only £1.20. Party. ⚬ ♨ ⚬ (ground floor & gardens only) shop and garden centre ⓥ

CHARLECOTE
Warwickshire
Map **4** SP25

Charlecote Park (on B4086)

Fine restored Elizabethan house (1558), built originally for Lucy family, with picturesque gatehouse Museum, video, carriages and Victorian kitchen. In the Great Hall, Shakespeare was said to have been brought before Sir Thomas Lucy for poaching in 250-acre deer park.

Open Etr Sat–Tue 11–5. Apr & Oct, Sat & Sun 2–5. May–Sep, Sun, Tue, Wed, Fri, Sat & BH Mon 11–6.

£2.20. Family ticket £6. Evening parties by prior arrangement on 2nd Thu in month.

⚬ shop (NT)

Chalfont St Giles
Cheddar

CHARLWOOD
Surrey
Map **4** TQ24

Gatwick Zoo & Aviaries Russ Hill
☎ Crawley (0293) 862312

The zoo extends to almost ten acres and contains hundreds of birds and animals. A particular feature is a large monkey island which contains both Spider and Squirrel Monkeys. The other small animals and birds are to be seen in large natural settings and nearly all breed each year.

Open Etr–Oct, daily 10.30–6 (or dusk). £2 (ch 3–14 £1, pen £1.50). Party 20 +.

⚬ ♨ ⚬ shop ✗ ⓥ

CHARTWELL
Kent
Map **5** TQ45

(2m SE of Westerham)
☎ Edenbridge (0732) 866368

Former home of Sir Winston Churchill, now Churchill Memorial with many relics of the famous statesman.

Open 1–26 Mar & Nov Wed & Sat 11–4; 29 Mar–Oct Tue–Thu 12–5. Sat. Sun & BH Mon 11–5. Garden & studio, Apr–Oct same times.

House & garden £2.40 (ch £1.20). Studio 40p. Gardens only £1 (ch 50p). Entrance by numbered ticket at times in summer to avoid delay, waiting time can be spent in the gardens.

⚬ ♨ (licensed) (10.30–5.30 on open days) shop (NT)

CHATHAM
Kent
Map **5** TQ76

Chatham Historic Dockyard Visitor Centre Pembroke Gate, Dock Rd
☎ Medway (0634) 812551

Guided tours can be taken around the buildings of this historic dockyard whose history spans some 400 years. The Visitor Centre is situated in the Old Galvanising Shop where people are introduced to the dockyard, its buildings and its history, by an audio visual programme and an exhibition.

Open Wed–Sun, 10–6 (4.30pm 4 Nov–29 Mar). (Opening dates to be confirmed for 1986).

✱ Admission & guided tour £2.25 (ch & pen £1.25). Admission only £1 (ch & pen 50p) Party.

⚬ ♨ ⚬ (ground floor only) shop

Fort Amherst Barrier Rd, off Dock Rd
☎ Medway (0634) 47747

The only surviving Napoleonic Fortress in the country, Fort Amherst is currently

---

undergoing the largest restoration project in the United Kingdom after lying dormant much of the time since the turn of the century. Constructed from 1756–1820 to protect the Royal Naval Dockyard from landward attack, the Fort comprises massive ditches, gun positions, impressive bastions and a complex network of tunnels. Restored barracks with a working & firing gun battery. A series of events are arranged throughout the year including Napoleonic living history and battles 30 & 31 Aug.

Open Jul–Sep daily 12–5. Apr–Jun Suns only 12–5.

£1 (ch 50p, pen 80p). Party.

⚬ ♨ ⚬ shop ✗ ⓥ

CHATSWORTH
Derbyshire
Map **8** SK27

(3½m E of Bakewell)
☎ Baslow (024688) 2204

(Chatsworth House Trust)

17th-century palatial home of the Duke and Duchess of Devonshire, which contains one of the richest collections of fine and decorative art in private hands. Farming and Forestry Exhibition. New adventure playground. Guided tours available at extra cost. Numerous events throughout the year including Horse Trials 3–5 Oct.

House and Garden open 23 Mar–26 Oct daily 11.30–4.30.

House & Garden £3.20 (ch £1.50, pen £2.50) family ticket £8. Garden only £1.50 (ch 75p).

⚬ ♨ (licensed) ⚬ (garden only) shop & garden centre ✗ (ex garden) ⓥ

See advertisement on page 84

CHAWTON
Hampshire
Map **4** SU73

Jane Austen's House
☎ Alton (0420) 83262

Situated in the village street, it is now a museum, and visitors are allowed to picnic in the garden.

Open daily Apr–Oct 11–4.30 also Nov, Dec & Mar Wed–Sun, Jan & Feb Sat & Sun. (Closed Xmas).

85p (ch 14 35p). Party 15 +.

⚬ ⚬ (ground floor) shop ✗

See advertisement on page 84

CHEDDAR
Somerset
Map **3** ST45

Cheddar Caves Museum The Cliffs
☎ (0934) 742343

A natural museum on archaeology, and zoology containing Paleolithic to Pleistocene finds. A burial of the last phase of the Ice Age, together with flint and bone implements of this period found →

83

in Gough's Cave are preserved in the museum. Evidence of Iron Age and Romano-British occupation has also been found.

Open Etr–Sep daily 10–5.30.

✱ 30p (ch & pen 20p).

⚠ shop ✖

Cheddar Caves
☎ (0934) 742343

Gough's Cave is the most beautiful show cave in Britain. There are no security screens to hinder viewing either in Gough's or Cox's caves. Fantasy Grotto also has installed an exhibition of holograms. Adventure caving expeditions depart four times daily, participants are supplied with helmets, lamps and boilersuits, minimum age 12 yrs.

Open Etr–Sep 10–5.30; Gough's Cave rest of year (ex Xmas) 11–4.30.

Gough's Cave £1.40 (ch 70p, pen £1); Cox's Cave 80p (ch 40p, pen 60p); Fantasy Grotto (incl. Hologram exhibition) 50p (ch & pen 30p); Jacob's Ladder 30p (ch & pen 20p); Exhibition & Museum 30p (ch & pen 20p). Combined ticket £2.50 (ch & pen £1.30). Adventure caving £2.95.

⚠ shop ✖ (in museum).

CHEDDLETON
Staffordshire
Map **7** SJ95

Cheddar
Cheltenham

Flint Mill beside Caldon Canal, Leek Rd
☎ Barlaston (078139) 2561

Two mills are preserved here with their low-breast wheels, one in working order. The original 17th-century south watermill ground corn but the 18th-century north mill was built to grind flint for the pottery industry. Museum collection includes examples of motive power (100 HP Robey steam engine and model Newcomen engine) and transport (restored 70ft horse-drawn narrow boat 'Vienna' moored on the Caldon Canal) and a haystack boiler of about 1770.

Open Sat & Sun afternoons.

Free.

⚠ ♿ (ground floor only)

CHEDWORTH
Gloucestershire
Map **4** SP01

Roman Villa Yanworth, off A429

Located in Chedworth Woods, dating from AD180–350, and with mosaic pavements. One of the best preserved Roman-British villas.

Open Mar–Oct, Tue–Sun & BH Mon 11–6. Feb & Nov–9 Dec, Wed–Sun 11–4 (or sunset).

£1.50.

no picnics shop ✖ (NT)

CHELMSFORD
Essex
Map **5** TL70

Chelmsford and Essex Museum
Oaklands Park, Moulsham St
☎ (0245) 353066, Essex Regiment Museum (0245) 260614

Prehistoric and Roman Essex, coins, costumes, paintings, British birds and mammals, glass, ceramics, geology and local industries display. Also Victorian room, Tunstill collection of glass and temporary exhibition programme. Incorporates Essex Regiment Museum brought here from Warley.

Open Mon–Sat 10–5, Sun 2–5. (Closed Good Fri, 25–26 Dec & 1 Jan plus other days as may be advertised).

Free.

⚠ ♿ (ground floor only) shop ✖

CHELTENHAM
Gloucestershire
Map **3** SO92

Art Gallery & Museum Clarence St
☎ (0242) 37431

Contains nationally important Arts and Crafts Movement collection; notable 17th-century Dutch and 17th–20th century British paintings. Also a large collection of English and Oriental ceramics, pewter, social history and archaeological material relating to the area. Temporary exhibitions throughout the year.

Open Mon–Sat 10–5.30 (Closed Suns & BH).

Free.

P (500 yds) & shop ✗

Gustav Holst Museum 4 Clarence Rd Pittville
☎ (0242) 524846

The composer's birthplace containing rooms with period furnishings and working Victorian kitchen. Holst personalia and reference collection.

Open Tue–Fri noon–5.30, Sat 11–5.30. (Closed BH).

Free.

P (300 yds) shop ✗

Pittville Pump Room and Museum
Pittville Park
☎ (0242) 521621 & 512740 (museum only)

Probably finest building in town, and masterpiece of 19th-century Greek revival, bought by borough in 1890. Notable colonnaded façades, portico, pillared and balconied hall. Pump Room

Cheltenham
—
Chertsey

restored and spa fountain repositioned in 1960. Now used for receptions, concerts, dances and other functions. Also **Museum** with 'Cheltenham's Gallery of Fashion': visual presentation of the town from the late 18th century. Temporary exhibitions throughout the year.

Open Apr–Oct Tue–Sun 10.30–5; Nov–Mar Tue–Sat 10.30–5. (Closed Good Fri & Mons ex Etr, Spring & Aug BH).

Admission free (small admission charge for museum).

⚠ (free) & (ground floor & gardens only) shop ✗

CHEPSTOW
Gwent
Map **3** ST59

Chepstow Castle
Earliest documented masonry castle, begun 1067–71 by William Fitz-Osbern. It has a fortified Port Wall. It was dismantled in 1690.

Open † see end of gazetteer.

✱ 80p (ch 16 & pen 40p).

⚠ shop (AM Cadw)

Chepstow Museum Gwy House, Bridge St
☎ (02912) 5981

Exhibitions of the local history of Chepstow, the lower Wye Valley, and the surrounding area, newly displayed in a fine 18th-century house. Exhibition themes change monthly.

Open Mar–Oct, Mon–Sat 11–1 & 2–5, Sun 2–5.

50p (ch & pen 25p). Party.

P (opposite) & (ground floor only)

CHERTSEY
Surrey
Map **4** TQ06

Chertsey Museum 33 Windsor St
☎ (09328) 65764

A late Georgian house, The Cedars, containing Matthews collection of costumes and accessories, local history collection, including a 10th-century Viking sword, silver, glass, dolls and collection of Meissen porcelain figures. Also various exhibitions throughout the year and the 'Black Cherry Fair' in July.

Open Tue & Thu 2–5, Wed, Fri & Sat 10–1 & 2–5. (Closed Xmas).

Free.

P (road outside) ⚐ & (ground floor & garden only) bookshop

CHEDDLETON FLINT MILL
Staffordshire

Specialises in the history of pottery raw materials. Original buildings and equipment restored to running order, many items having been collected to show the related processes. Two of the working exhibits — Robey steam engine, model Newcomen engine. The restored narrow boat "Vienna" is moored permanently on the Caldon Canal at the wharf. Cheddleton Flint Mill Industrial Heritage Trust is a registered Charity.

PRINKNASH POTTERY, GLOUCESTER.

Set in beautiful Cotswold countryside, PRINKNASH provides facilities for all the family. Guided tours of POTTERY WORKS daily. GIFT SHOP open 9 am - 6 pm. Self service facilities in TEAROOM - Party bookings for lunches/teas welcome. Walled MONASTERY GARDEN with breathtaking view of Vale of Gloucester. Opening hours dependant on season. ABBEY CHURCH open 5 am - 8 pm.
Take A46 or M5 junction 13 (South) 11 (North)
PRINKNASH ABBEY, CRANHAM, GLOUCESTER Tel (0452) 812239.

Thorpe Park Staines Rd (1¾m N on A320)
☎ (09328) 62633

*500 acres of fun for all the family. Over 50
attractions included in the admission
price, though additional charges are
made for roller skate hire, watersport and
coin operated amusements. The
attractions include Space Station Zero,
family rollercoaster ride, Phantom
Fantasia ghost ride, Thorpe Farm, Cinema
180 and many more. Free transport
around the park by land train or waterbus.*

Open mid Mar–early Nov daily 10–6 (9pm
peak season). (Closed mid wk early & late
season). Telephone for further details.

£4.50 (ch 14 & pen £4, ch 3 free).
Handicapped £3.50 (attendants, free).
Party 20 +.

⚠ ⚑ (licensed) ⌁ ♿ shop ✕ (ex guide
dogs)

CHESSINGTON
(London plan 4 pages 174/175)

Chessington Zoo London plan 4: **4** B1
(on A243)
☎ Epsom (03727) 27227

*Situated in 65 acres of lovely Surrey
countryside, it has a large and varied
collection of animals and birds including
gorillas and chimpanzees, as well as a*

Chertsey
—
Chester

*children's zoo and Reptile House. During
the summer there is a funfair, miniature
railway and free circus.*

Open daily Nov–Mar 10–4; Apr–Oct 10–5.
(Closed Xmas day).

✳ £3.25 (ch 3–13 £1.85 & pen £2.25).
Party 15 +.

⚠ ⚑ (licensed) ⌁ ♿ shop ✕

CHESTER
Cheshire
Map **7** SJ46

Cheshire Military Museum The Castle
☎ (0244) 47203 (cavalry) & 27617
(infantry)

*Exhibits depicting the history of the
Cheshire Regiment, Cheshire Yeomanry,
5th Royal Inniskilling Dragoon Guards and
3rd Carabiniers.*

Open daily 9–5.

20p (ch 10p).

⚠ wknds only (charge) P (300 yds) shop

Chester Heritage Centre St Michael's
Church, Bridge St Row
☎ (0244) 317948 or 2144 ext 2108

*Exhibition of Chester's architectural
heritage, including 20-minute audio-visual
show and displays relating to the city's
history and the large-scale conservation
programme now in operation. Exhibitions
on range of historical and architectural
themes.*

Open Oct–Mar, Mon, Tue, Thu–Sun 1.30–
4.30; Apr–Sep, Mon, Tue, Thu–Sat 10–5,
Sun 2–5. BH 2–5.

50 p (ch & pen 25p). Parties 10 +.

P (150 yds) shop ✕

Chester Visitor Centre Vicars Lane
(opposite Roman Amphitheatre)
☎ (0244) 318916

*Over 2,000 years of Chester history told
by audio-visual film, a life size
reconstruction of the unique Chester
Rows during Victorian days, a Map and
Print Room showing the city's
development. A Brass Rubbing Centre
(cost includes materials), and a Craft
Shop specialising in British-made goods.*

Open daily 9am–9pm.

35p (ch & pen 20p).

P (150 yds) ⚑ (licensed) ⌁ ♿ (ground
floor only) shop

How much can you do in a day at

Thorpe Park

A MEMBER OF THE RMC GROUP

Thorpe Park is THE place for a great family day out. Our new "one ticket" system means that after paying the initial entrance fee, all rides and attractions are free!* Treasure Island ● Star Ride ● Phantom Fantasia ● Cinema 180 ● Water Gardens ● Children's Rides ● Thorpe Farm ● Roller Skating ● Waterbus Trips ● Mr. Rabbit Show ● Thorpe Belle ● Model World ● World War I Aeroplane Exhibit ● Cap'n Andy's Review ● Boating ● Magic Mill and lots more. Telephone Bookings and Enquiries Office for further details. *Except Watersports Skate Hire and Coin Operated Amusement

Thorpe Park, Staines Road, Chertsey, Surrey KT16 8PN.
Tel: Chertsey (09328) 62633.

Grosvenor Museum 27 Grosvenor St
☎ (0244) 21616 and 313858

One of the finest collections of Roman remains in Britain, including special Roman Army gallery and many inscribed and sculptured stones excavated in Chester. Natural History gallery and art gallery. Temporary exhibitions.

Open Mon–Sat 10.30–5, Sun 2–5. (Closed Good Fri & Xmas).

Free (Schools should book in advance).

P (200 yds) ♿ (ground floor only) shop

Zoo and Gardens
☎ (0244) 380280

One of Europe's finest zoological gardens with 3,500 animals in 110 acres of natural enclosures and superb landscaped gardens. Tropical House, Aquarium and Waterbus rides.

Open all year, daily (ex 25 Dec) 10–dusk. Last admission 3.30 (Winter), 5.30 (Summer). Gardens open until dusk.

✱ £2.70 (ch 3–15 & pen £1.30). Party. 20+.

(licensed) ♿ shop Ⓥ

CHESTERFIELD
Derbyshire
Map **8** SK37

Peacock Information and Heritage Centre Low Pavement
☎ (0246) 207777/8

A medieval timber framed building thought to have been a guildhall. First floor is now used as an exhibition room. Audio visual on history of Chesterfield available for showing on request. Special medieval market in July.

Open Mon–Sat. Information centre 9–5.30; Heritage centre noon–5.

Free.

P (100 yds) ♿ (ground floor only) shop

CHICHELEY
Buckinghamshire
Map **4** SP94

Chicheley Hall
☎ North Crawley (023065) 252

Built for Sir John Chester between 1719 and 1723. It is one of the finest and least altered 18th-century houses in the country. Fine Georgian craftsmanship: brickwork, stone and wood carving, joinery and plasterwork. Naval museum and collection of English sea pictures and furniture.

Open 28 Mar–28 Sep, Sun, Good Fri & BH Mons 2.30–6.

£1.80 (ch 90p). Party 20+

♿ (ground floor only) shop

CHICHESTER
West Sussex
Map **4** SU80

District Museum 29 Little London
☎ (0243) 784683

Housed in a former 18th-century corn store with displays of local history, archaeology and geology. Temporary Exhibitions programme.

Open all year, Tue–Sat 10–5.30.

Free.

P (100 yds) ♿ (ground floor only) shop (ex guide dogs)

Guildhall Museum Priory Park
☎ (0243) 784683

Branch of District Museum in medieval Greyfriars church, later used as City Guildhall, containing archaeological finds from district. The small public park contains mound of Norman Castle.

Open Jun–Sep, Tue–Sat 1–5.

Park open daily.

Free.

P (100 yds) ♿ shop

Mechanical Music and Doll Collection
Church Rd, Portfield
☎ (0243) 785421 →

Chester Zoo

It's an experience, an entertainment and an education. Set in 110 acres of beautifully laid out floral gardens. You and your family will have a really great day out — learning through pleasure. There's so much to see and do. Come along soon.

Chester Zoo

'GOOD ZOOS ARE GOOD NEWS'

Location: *Just off the A41 on the outskirts of Chester and well signposted.*

Open: *10am-dusk*

Barrel organs, dance organs, street pianos, music boxes, polyphons, phonographs can be seen and heard: all fully restored and playing music of a bygone age. Also magic lanterns, stereoscopic viewers and Victorian dolls.

Open Etr–Sep, daily 10–6; Oct–Etr, wknds only 10–5; Evening bookings by arrangement.

£1 (ch 75p pen 90p). Party 30+. (Admission includes guided tour & demonstrations).

🏛 ♿ shop ✖ Ⓥ

Pallant House Gallery 9 North Pallant
☎ (0243) 774557

A fine Queen Anne town house containing restored period rooms with antique furniture and an Edwardian kitchen. Permanent collections on display include the Walter Hussey Collection of paintings, drawings, prints and sculpture, the Geoffrey Freeman Collection of Bow Porcelain and collections of 18th-century English drinking glasses and enamels. There is also a programme of temporary exhibitions. A small garden is being planted in authentic 18th-century style.

Open all year Tue–Sat 10–5.30. (Closed Sun, Mon & BHs).

50p (accompanied ch 10p, students & pen 30p). Pre-booked school parties free.

P (50 yds) ♿ (ground floor & gardens only) shop ✖

St Mary's Hospital nr St Martin's Sq
☎ (0243) 783377

Refounded circa 1240, with interesting hall with wagon roof.

Open Apr–Sep Tue–Sat 11–12 & 2–5; 2–4 Oct–Mar. (Closed BH & Staff Hols).

10p.

P (200 yds) ♿ ✖

CHIDDINGSTONE
Kent
Map 5 TQ54

Chiddingstone Castle (off B2027)
☎ Penshurst (0892) 870347

17th-century house altered to Castle style in 1800, containing furniture, Royal

---

Chichester
—
Chippenham

Stewart and Jacobite paintings and relics, fine collection Japanese lacquer and swords, Egyptian and Oriental antiquities. Run by the trustees of the Denys Eyre Bower bequest. Fishing in lake £5 per day.

Open 28 Mar–Sep & Oct wknds, Wed–Sat 2–5.30, Sun & public hols 11.30–5.30. Also 17 Jun–16 Sep Tue 2–5.30 (advisable to check weekday times).

£1.50 (ch 5–15 85p under 5 free). Party 20+.

🏛 🍴 ⛱ ♿ (ground floor only) shop ✖

CHILHAM
Kent
Map 5 TR05

Chilham Castle
☎ (0227) 730319

Impressive hexagonal Jacobean manor house (not open) and Norman castle keep overlooking the River Stour. Extensive garden, woodland and lakeside walks. Petland for children. Special events include Horse Trials 11 May and Sports & country fair beginning Sep 1986.

Garden open 16 Mar–26 Oct daily 11–5.

✳ Weekdays (ex mon & Fri). Admission fee payable. Parties 12+.

🏛 🍴 (licensed) shop

CHILLINGHAM
Northumberland
Map 12 NU02

Chillingham Wild Cattle (Castle **not** open to public) off B6348
☎ Chatton (06685) 213 or 250

Park containing herd of some 50 remarkable wild white cattle.

Viewable Apr–Oct Mon, Wed, Sat & BH 10–12 & 2–5, Sun 2–5.

£1 (ch 35p) tickets available from keepers cottage.

🏛 ✖

CHILLINGTON HALL
Staffordshire
Map 7 SJ80
(6m NW of Wolverhampton)
☎ Brewood (0902) 850236

Home of the Giffards since 1178, present house, by Smith of Warwick and Sir John Soane, dates from 1724 and 1785, with grounds by Capability Brown. Fine saloon and association with Charles II's escape after Battle of Worcester in 1651. Extensive woodland walks.

Open 1 May–11 Sep, Thu 2.30–5.30 also 30 Mar, 4 & 25 May, and all Suns in Aug. Party by arrangement other days.

£1.20 (ch 16 60p) Grounds only 60p (ch 16 30p).

🏛 ♿ (ground floor & gardens only) Ⓥ

CHINGFORD
Gt London
(London plan 4 pages 174/175).

Queen Elizabeth's Hunting Lodge and Museum Epping Forest, Rangers Rd
London plan 4: **45** F5
☎ 01-529 6681

Picturesque Tudor building dating from c 1543 now housing museum relating to life of animals, birds and plants in Epping and Man's association with them.

Open all year Wed–Sun & BH Mon's, 2–6 (or dusk).

25p (accompanied ch free).

🏛 ♿ (ground floor only) shop ✖

CHIPPENHAM
Wilts
Map 3 ST97

Sheldon Manor
☎ (0249) 653120

Plantagenet Manor House with 13th-century porch and 15th-century detached Chapel. Beautiful terraced gardens, with water garden, ancient yew trees and hedges and a collection of old-fashioned roses.

Open 23 Mar–Oct, Sun, Thu & BHs, 12.30–6. (House opens 2pm).

✳ House & gardens £1.50 (ch 50p).

🏛 🍴 (licensed) ♿ (ground floor & gardens only) shop

CHILHAM CASTLE GARDENS
Near Canterbury, Kent
A Jacobean house (not open) and a mediaeval Castle Keep set in terraced gardens with many fine trees overlooking a lake.
Enjoy a day out in the gardens, visiting, Petland, seeing the birds of prey, looking round the Castle, and on Sundays watching mediaeval jousting.
Licensed restaurant and Gift Shop.
See Gazetteer entry for details.

CHIRK
Clwyd
Map **7** SJ23

Chirk Castle (off the A5, ½m W Chirk
village, 1½m driveway)
☎ (0691) 777701

Marcher fotress, completed in 1310,
commanding fine views over the
surrounding countryside. Elegant
staterooms with elaborate plasterwork,
superb Adam-style furniture, tapestries
and portraits. Formal gardens with
clipped yews and a variety of flowering
shrubs. Entrance gates by the Davies
Brothers, 1721. 18th century parkland.

Open 30 Mar–28 Sep Sun, Tue–Thu & BH;
4–26 Oct, Sat & Sun 12–5 (last admission
4.30).

£1.70 (ch 60p). Family ticket £4.25. Party
20+.

Ⓐ 🍷 (licensed) ﴾ (ground floor &
gardens only) shop ✗ (ex guide dogs)
(NT)

CHITTLEHAMPTON
Devon
Map **2** SS62

Cobbaton Combat Vehicle Museum
Cobbaton (2m NW)
☎ Chittlehamholt (07694) 414

World War II British and Canadian
vehicles, war documents and military
equipment are among exhibits in this
private collection; which also includes a
section on 'Mums War' and the home
front. A childrens 'mini assault course' is
available.

Open Apr–Oct daily 10–6. Winter by
appointment.

£1 (ch 50p).

Ⓐ ﴾ ﴿ shop

CHOLMONDELEY
Cheshire
Map **7** SJ55

Cholmondeley Castle Gardens (7m W
of Nantwich on A49)
☎ (082922) 383

Ornamental gardens, including an ancient
private chapel, which have a lakeside
picnic area and rare breeds of farm
animals. There is also a tearoom and
attractive gift shop with plants for sale.

Open Etr–Sep Sun & BH 12–6.

£1 (ch 50p).

Ⓐ 🍷 ﴿ shop

CHORLEY
Lancashire
Map **7** SD51

Astley Hall
☎ (02572) 62166

Timbered and richly plastered 16th-
century house in some 99 acres of park
and woodland. Fine furnishings, pottery
and pictures together with special
exhibitions.

Chirk
—
Clapham

Open daily Apr–Sep, 12–6; Oct–Mar Mon–
Fri 12–4, Sat 10–4 & Sun 11–4.

65p (accompanied ch 25p,
unaccompanied ch & pen 40p).

P (100 yds) 🍷 ﴿ (ground floor only) shop

CHRISTCHURCH
Dorset
Map **4** SZ19

**Christchurch Castle and Norman
House**

Rare example of ruined Norman house
c 1160; stands in bailey of 11th-century
house.

Open any reasonable time.

Free.

(AM)

Red House Museum and Art Gallery
Quay Rd
☎ (0202) 482860

Local history, archaeology, natural history,
Victoriana, dolls and costumes are
contained in this Georgian house.
Exhibition gallery showing touring
exhibitions.

Open all year Tue–Sat, 10–5 & Sun 2–5.
(Closed Mon & 25 Dec).

Admission fee payable.

P (100 yds) ﴿ (ground floor) shop ✗

Tucktonia Stour Rd
☎ (0202) 482710

Exhibits to 1/24th scale, including
buildings of London, Industrial Britain and
Cornish fishing village, which are
illuminated and animated. Also, there is a
leisure complex with features for all ages.

Open daily 10am–dusk (closed during
bad weather, details obtainable by
telephone).

Admission fee payable.

Ⓐ 🍷 ﴾ ﴿ shop ✗

CHURCH CROOKHAM
Hampshire
Map **4** SU85

Gurkha Museum Queen Elizabeth's
Barracks
☎ Fleet (02514) 3541 ext 63

Contains a record of the Gurkha's service
to the Crown from 1815.

Open Mon–Fri 9.30–4.30 Apr–Oct only Sat
9.30–4.30 & BH. Other times by request.

Free.

Ⓐ ﴿ shop ✗

CHYSAUSTER ANCIENT VILLAGE
Cornwall
Map **2** SW43

Eight dryatona maaanry houaoo loading
off a courtyard and incorporating
characteristic Cornish underground
chamber or 'fogou'. Adjoining dwellings
are byres. Inhabited between 1st and 3rd
century AD.

Open † see end of gazetteer.

✹ 50p (ch 16 & pen 25p).

Ⓐ (AM)

CILGERRAN
Dyfed
Map **2** SN24

Cardigan Wildlife Park
Entrance near village off A478
☎ Cardigan (0239) 614449

Park specialising in European animals,
particularly those of Wales, past and
present, in an unusually diverse area of 50
acres of natural habitats. Other features
include nature trails, wildlife sanctuary,
playground. Fishing.

Open all year, daily 10–5.30.

✹ £1.20 (ch & pen 60p). Parties 12+ on
application.

Ⓐ 🍷 (licensed) ﴾ shop ✗ Ⓥ

Cilgerran Castle off A484

In picturesque setting above the River
Teifi, Norman to 13th-century castle
reduced to ruins during the Civil War.

Open see end of gazetteer.

✹ 50p (ch 16 & pen 25p)
shop (AM Cadw)

CIRENCESTER
Gloucestershire
Map **4** SP00

Corinium Museum
☎ (0285) 5611

Contains one of the country's most
comprehensive collections of Roman
remains, mosaic floors, Romano-British
sculpture, items of everyday life and a
remarkable example of a five-letter square
palindrome. Special exhibitions
throughout the year.

Open Apr–Sep, Mon–Sat, 10–5.30; Sun 2–
5.30; Oct–Mar, Tue–Sat 10–5, Sun 2–5,
Open bank holidays. (Closed Xmas).

✹ 55p (ch 25p, pen & students 35p)
Party.

P (250 yds) ﴿ shop

See advertisement on page 90

CLAPHAM
North Yorkshire
Map **7** SD76

Yorkshire Dales National Park Centre
☎ (04685) 419

Visitor Centre with interpretative display
on 'The Limestone Dales'. Audio-visual
theatre. Maps walks, guides and local
information available. →

Open Apr–Oct daily mid morning–late afternoon.

Free.

⚐ ⌂

CLARE
Suffolk
Map **5** TL74

Ancient House Museum High St
☎ (0787) 277865

Traditionally the priest's house and now a museum of local history. Amongst the exhibits on display are photographs of local interest, domestic tools and artifacts, Victorian/Edwardian kitchen utensils, costumes and items of dress, tools and exhibits of local trades and crafts, and items of archaeological interest dating from pre-Roman times.

Open Etr–Oct Wed–Sat 2.30–4.30, Sun 11–12.30 & 2.30–4.30. BH as Sun.

40p (ch 20p, pen 30p).

P (50 & 500 yds) ⚐ shop ✖

CLAVA CAIRNS
Highland *Inverness-shire*
Map **14** NH74

(6m E of Inverness)

Situated on the south bank of the River Nairn, this group of burial cairns has three concentric rings of great stones.

Open all times.

Free.

(AM)

CLEARWELL
Gloucestershire
Map **3** SO50

Clearwell Caves Ancient Iron Mines
☎ Dean (0594) 23700

Exhibits of local mining and geology from Forest of Dean area, including several vintage stationary engines. Deep level trips for more adventurous.

Open Mar–Oct daily 10–5. Other times by arrangement.

£1 (ch & pen 50p). Educational parties at any times by prior arrangement with proprietor, Mr Ray Wright, The Bungalow,

Clapham
Clitheroe

Heywood Rd. Cinderford Glos. GL14 2QT.

⚐ ⌂ shop ✖ (ex guide dogs)

Clearwell Castle
☎ Dean (0594) 32320

A 'mock' Gothic castle reputed to be the oldest in Britain with a Regency interior. There are 8 acres of formal gardens on five different levels which are still being restored, and a Bird Park. Adventure playground and Bicycle museum.

Open Etr–Oct 11–5. (Closed Sat & Mon ex BH).

Admission fee payable.

⚐ ⌕ ⌂ shop (dogs on leads outside only).

CLEETHORPES
Humberside
Map **8** TA30

Lincolnshire Coast Light Railway
North Sea Lane Station, Humberston
☎ Grimsby (0472) 814493

Historic narrow-gauge passenger-carrying light railway. Steam and diesel locomotives.

Open Etr Sat, Sun & Mon 12–5; May Day Sat, Sun & Mon 12–5. Spring Bank Hol–Summer Bank Hol Suns 9–5. School summer hols daily 12–5. Diesel haulage except Sats in School Hols, & Spring & Summer BHs.

✳ 15p, 25p return (ch 15 10p return 15p, ch 5 free) except when steamhauled, then 20p single fare.

⚐ & shop

CLEVEDON
Avon
Map **3** ST47

Clevedon Court (off B3130)

14th-century manor house associated with Tennyson and Thackeray, with 14th-century chapel and terraced garden.

Open 29 Mar–Sep Wed, Thu & Sun & BH Mon 2.30–5.30, last admission 5pm.

£1.50.

⚐ ⌕ ✖ (NT)

Clevedon Craft Centre Moor Ln. (Turn off B3130 opposite Clevedon Court, cross M5)
☎ (0272) 872867 or 872149

Fourteen studios with craftpersons available for discussion. Commissioned work undertaken.

Open all year 10–5, some workshops closed Sun morning & Mon; closed Xmas.

Free.

⚐ ⌕ (Closed Mon) & shop

CLITHEROE
Lancashire
Map **7** SD74

Browsholme Hall Bashall Eaves (2¼m NW)
☎ Stonyhurst (025486) 330

Home of the Parker family since 1507. Tudor with Elizabethan front, Queen Anne Wing and Regency additions, Portraits, furniture, panelling and antiquities.

Open Etr & wk following Spring BH, Aug BH & preceding wk & Sat Jun–Aug (2–5). (Organised parties at other times contact Mrs Parker by telephone number as above).

£1.50 (ch 75p). Party.

⚐ & (ground floor only) shop ✖ (in grounds only on leads) Ⓥ

Clitheroe Castle Museum
☎ (0200) 24635

Contains important collection of carboniferous fossils and many items of local interest and is located in Castle House, a short distance from Clitheroe Castle. The castle itself is one of the oldest structures in Lancashire and has one of the smallest Norman keeps in England. The ground floor displays local history and archaeology, whilst the first floor is devoted to the geology of the area. A special feature is the newly restored Hacking Ferry boat. The grounds are also open to visitors and command

magnificent views over the Ribble Valley.
A series of events between May & Nov to celebrate the 800th anniversary of the Castle.

Open daily Etr—Oct 2–4.30 BH 11–4.30. 20p (ch free if accompanied). Party visits arranged.

P ⚓ ♿ (ground floor only) shop ✸

CLIVEDEN
Buckinghamshire
Map **4** SU98

(3m NE of Maidenhead)
☎ Burnham (06286) 5069

Extensive and historic gardens overlooking the Thames. Once the home of Nancy, Lady Astor.

Grounds open Mar–Dec daily 11–6 or sunset if earlier.

£2 (Mon–Wed (excluding BH) entry £1.50). House open 30 Mar–Oct, Thu & Sun 3–6 by timed ticket. 60p

⚓ (Apr–Oct) ✸ (in house) (NT)

CLOUDS HILL
Dorset
Map **3** SY89

Clouds Hill (4m SW of Bere Regis)

Former home of T E Lawrence (Lawrence of Arabia). Three rooms only.

Open 29 Mar–Sep, Wed–Fri, Sun & BH 2–5; Oct–Mar, Sun 1–4.

£1 No photography.

⚠ ✸ ⌗ (NT)

CLUN
Shropshire
Map **7** SO28

Clun Town Trust Museum
☎ (05884) 247

Situated in the town hall, the original court house to Clun Castle; court was moved to market square in 1780. Flint tools, maps of earthworks, etc, domestic and family relics, and exhibits of local geological and mineralogical interest.

Open Etr–Nov Tue–Sat 2–5 and BH wknds Sat, Mon & Tue 11–1 & 2–5. Other times by request, and parties by arrangement only. (School parties welcome) enquiries *Mrs F Hudson, Florida Villa.*

Free. (Donations).

P (300 yds & street parking).

COBHAM
Kent
Map **5** TQ66

Cobham Hall (off B2009)
☎ Shorne (047482) 3371

16th-century and later mansion with work by Inigo Jones and Wyatt, situated in large park with fine trees; now girls' public school.

Open Mar 26–31; Jul 16, 17 20, 23 & 24; Aug every Wed, Thu, Sun (ex last Sun in Aug) & Mon 25, 2–5.30 (last tour 5).

Clitheroe
—
Colchester

£1 (ch & pen 50p) Party 15 + .

⚠ ⚓ ♿ (ground floor & gardens only) shop Ⓥ

Owletts

17th-century house with contemporary staircase and ceiling.

Open Apr–Oct, Wed & Thu 2–5.

50p.

(NT)

COBHAM
Surrey
Map **4** TQ16

Painshill Park
☎ (0932) 64674

The gardens are still in the process of restoration and at present are able to be seen only by guided walk. In the 18th century this was one of the finest landscape gardens in the country. Even today, after the ravages of time, the gardens represent a unique part of our heritage and, when fully restored will be a valuable national asset.

Open to general public Apr–Oct, Wed at 2pm. Guided Tours by arrangement Thu, Sat & Sun 10am & 2pm. (Opening times subject to review).

✳ £1.50 (ch & pen £1).

⚠ ⚓ ✸

COCKERMOUTH
Cumbria
Map **11** NY13

Wordsworth House

Built 1745, birthplace in 1770 of William Wordsworth. Original staircase and fireplaces. Poet's childhood garden; displays.

Open 26 Mar–2 Nov daily (ex Thu) 11–5, Sun 2–5. (Last admission 4.30). Nov–23 Dec house closed but shop open Mon–Wed, Fri & Sat 10–5.

£1.30 (ch 65p) Party.

⚓ shop (NT)

COCKLEY CLEY
Norfolk
Map **5** TF70

Iceni Village and Museum
☎ Swaffham (0760) 21339 & East Harling (0953) 717649

Full-scale reconstruction on original site of Iceni encampment, showing how tribe lived 2,000 years ago. There is also a historical museum housed in a cottage, built in 1450, comprising of models and exhibits of local life from prehistoric times to present day. Agricultural and carriage

museum. Early Saxon church, circa 620, in grounds.

Open Etr–Sep, Sun 1.30–5.30. School parties by appointment.

✳ £1 (ch 50p).

⚠ ♿ shop

COGGESHALL
Essex
Map **5** TL82

Paycocke's

An early 16th-century house with notable panelling.

Open 29 Mar–12 Oct, Wed, Thu, Sun & BH Mon 2–5.30.

£1 (ch 50p).

✸ (NT)

COITY
Mid Glamorgan
Map **3** SS98

Coity Castle

12th- to 16th-century stronghold with hall chapel and remains of square keep.

Open, see end of gazetteer.

✳ 30p (ch 16 & pen 15p).

(AM Cadw)

COLBOST
Isle of Skye, Highland *Inverness-shire*
Map **13** NG24

The Skye Black House Folk Museum
(on B884)
☎ Glendale (047081) 291

Typical 19th-century house of the area containing implements and furniture of bygone days, with peat fire burning throughout the day. A replica of an illicit whisky still can be seen behind the museum.

Open Etr–Oct daily 10–7.

Admisssion fee payable.

P (15 yds)

COLCHESTER
Essex
Map **5** TL92

Beth Chatto Gardens, White Barn House (4m E on A133 at Elmstead Market)
☎ Wivenhoe (020622) 2007

The garden, begun only 25 years ago, has a variety of contrasting plantings. The dry garden, on gravel soil and full sun, contains plants adapted to drought. The shade garden has plants with fine foliage, as well as flowering plants. 5 large pools, full of fish, are surrounded by exotic bog plants. The adjoining nursery contains over 1,000 different plants.

Open Mar–Oct Mon–Sat 9–5; Nov–Mar Mon–Fri 9–4. (Closed BH & 2 weeks Xmas).

50p.

⚠ ♿ ✸ garden centre (NGS)

Bourne Mill

Dutch-gabled fishing lodge, dating from 1591, erected from materials from St John's Abbey.

Open 29 Mar–12 Oct wknds, BH Mons & Tues in Jul–Sep 2–5.30. Other times by appointment.

70p (ch 35p). No unaccompanied children.

(NT)

Colchester and Essex Museum The Castle, North of High St
☎ (0206) 712481

This massive 11th-century castle, built largely of Roman bricks around vaulted base of Roman temple, now houses an extensive collection of Roman and other antiquities.

Open Mon–Sat 10–5 (10–4pm Sats Oct–Mar) Sun (Apr–Sep only) 2.30–5. (Closed Good Fri, 25–27 Dec).

✻ 65p (ch 25p pen free); conducted tours of vaults and cells Sat Apr–Sep; weekdays Jul & Aug, tours 45p (ch 20p).

P (200 yds) ⅃ (ground floor) shop ✻

Colchester Zoo Stanway Hall (3m W of town off B1022)
☎ (0206) 330253 (for general enquiries) or 331292

Situated in a 40-acre park is this 14th- to 17th-century church, as well as the hall which was rebuilt in 16th century. The zoo includes a large collection of mammals, Reptile House, aquarium and birdland. Lakeside miniature railway and amusements.

Open daily 9.30–dusk. (Closed Xmas day).

✻ £1.90 (ch 3–14 90p).

A ⅃ ♯ ⅃ Ⓥ

Hollytrees Museum High St
☎ (0206) 712481

Fine Georgian house, dating from 1718, with collection of costume, toys etc.

Open Mon–Sat 10–1, 2–5 (4pm Sat Oct–Mar). (Closed Good Fri & 25–27 Dec.)

Free.

P (150 yds) shop ✻ ⅋

Colchester
—
Compton

Museum of Social History Holy Trinity Church, Trinity St
☎ (0206) 712481

Historical displays of country life and crafts, with some bicycles etc.

Open Mon–Sat 10–1 & 2–5 (4pm Sat, Oct–Mar). (Closed Good Fri & 25–27 Dec).

Free.

P (200 yds) ⅃ shop ✻ ⅋

Natural History Museum All Saints Church, High St
☎ (0206) 712481

Formerly 15th-century All Saints Church, with the flint tower. Features the Natural History of Essex with special reference to the Colchester area.

Open Mon–Sat 10–1 & 2–5 (4pm Sat Oct–Mar). (Closed Good Fri & 25–27 Dec).

Free.

P (200 yds) ⅃ shop ✻ ⅋

COLDSTREAM
Borders Berwickshire
Map **12** NT84

The Hirsel (½m W on A697)
☎ (0890) 2834

Starting from the Homestead Museum and Craftcentre at the Lake there are Nature Walks round the lake, along the Leet Valley and into the famous Rhododendron and Azalea Wood, Dundock.

Open daylight hours.

Admission by donation.

A ⅃ (Sun & Bh pm) ♯ ⅃ (most parts)

COLWYN BAY
Clwyd
Map **6** SH87

Welsh Mountain Zoo and Flagstaff Gardens
☎ (0492) 2938/3166

Set in a 37 acre estate overlooking Colwyn Bay with magnificent panoramic views. The animals are presented in natural settings, interspersed with the gardens and woodland. In addition to the lions, elephants, various species of deer, reptiles, tropical birds, birds of prey, parrots, penguins, sea lions, bears, chimpanzees and monkeys, the zoo provides a natural home for a variety of local wild life. Eagles are flown completely free during the Summer months, and Californian Sealions perform their tricks during feeding.

Open all year daily. Winter (Jan–Mar & Nov–Dec) 9–4; Spring & Autumn (Apr–May & Sep–Oct) 9–5; Summer (Jun–Aug) 9–8.

Free flights of eagles 12 noon & 3, sealion feeding displays 12.15 & 3.15; both take place daily between Apr & Sep.

Admission fee payable.

A ⅃ (licensed) ♯ shop ✻ (in zoo)

COMBE MARTIN
Devon
Map **2** SS54

The Combe Martin Motorcycle Collection Cross St
☎ (027188) 2346

The collection was formed in 1979 and contains early and late British motorcycles, displayed against a background of old petrol pumps, signs and garage equipment.

Open late May–mid Sep, daily 10–6.

60p (ch & pen 40p. ch under 7 free). Party 10+.

P ⅃ shop

COMPTON
Devon
Map **3** SX86

Compton Castle (off A380 near Marldon)

Restored 14th- to 16th-century house with courtyard, hall, chapel and old kitchen open to the public.

Open 28 Mar–Oct, Mon, Wed & Thu, 10–12.15 (last admission 11.45) & 2–5 (last admission 4.30).

Welsh Mountain Zoo and Flagstaff Gardens
Colwyn Bay, Clwyd

Situated overlooking Colwyn Bay with magnificient panoramic views. A 37 acre estate in which the animals are presented in natural settings, interspersed with gardens and woodland.
For opening times and admission charges see gazetteer entry.

£1.30 Party.
(NT)

COMPTON
Surrey
Map **4** SU94

Watts Picture Gallery Down Lane
☎ Guildford (0483) 810235
*Memorial gallery with a collection of about
150 paintings by G F Watts who is buried
by the nearby Watts Mortuary Chapel.*

Gallery open Fri–Wed 2pm–6pm Apr–Sep
& 2pm–4pm Oct–Mar, also 11am–1pm
Wed & Sat. Chapel open daily.

Free.

⚠ ᕕ (ground floor only) shop ✗

COMRIE
Tayside *Perthshire*
Map **11** NN72

Museum of Scottish Tartans A85 town
centre
☎ (0764) 70779
*The most comprehensive collection of
tartans and Highland dress in the world
including a specialised library. The
research collection has over 1500
specimens and a unique system which
records details of every known tartan.
There are demonstrations of spinning,
weaving and dyeing and research will be
done on request, charges according to
amount of work done.*

Open Summer: Mon–Sat 10–5, Sun 2–4.
Winter: Mon–Fri 10–4, Sat 10–1.

90p (ch & pen 50p). Family Ticket £2.

P (700 yds) shop ⓥ

CONISBROUGH
South Yorkshire
Map **8** SK59

Conisbrough Castle
*Unique example of circular six-buttressed
keep, built in the late 12th-century.
Curtain walls with solid round towers.*

Open † see end of gazetteer.

✱ 50p (ch 16 & pen 25p).

⚠ (AM)

Compton
—
Conwy

CONISTON
Cumbria
Map **7** SD39

Brantwood (2½m SE off B5285, on
unclass road east side of Coniston
Water.)
☎ (0966) 41396
*Former home of John Ruskin. One of the
most beautifully situated houses in the
Lake District with fine views across
Coniston Water. Large collection of
Ruskin paintings and other memorabilia.
Delightful nature trail through Brantwood
Estate.*

Open daily mid Mar–mid Nov 11–5.30 &
then Wed–Sun 11–4.30.

Admission fee payable.

⚠ ᨏ (licensed) ᕕ (ground floor only)
shop ✗

The Ruskin Museum The Institute
☎ (0966) 41387
*Exhibits of the life and work of John
Ruskin with personal relics, letters and
sketchbooks on display. There are
pictures by Ruskin and his immediate
circle and a collection of minerals,
including specimens given to the institute
in 1884. Also items of local history.*

Open Mar–Nov, daily 9.30–6 or dusk.
20p.

P 20 yds (roadside), 200 yds car park ✗

Steam Yacht Gondola Far End
☎ (0966) 41288
*Originally launched in 1859, the Steam
Yacht Gondola was in service on Coniston
Water until 1937. It re-entered service in
1980 and visitors can enjoy the unusual
pleasure of her silent progress and olde-
world comfort.*

Open Apr 4–May 24 & Sep 9–Oct 27 (4
trips daily). May 25–Sep 8 (5 trips daily).
Trips commence 11 at Coniston, on Sat
12.30. Piers at Coniston & Park-a-Moor.

Admission fee payable
(NT)

CONWY
Gwynedd
Map **6** SH77

Aberconwy Junction of Castle St and
High St
☎ (049263) 2246
*Medieval house that dates from the 14th
century, now housing the Conwy
Exhibition which depicts the life of the
borough from Roman times to the present
day.*

Open 28 Mar–29 Sep 11–5. (Closed Tue);
4–26 Oct Sat & Sun 11–5. (Last admission
4.45).

60p (ch 30p) Party 20 + .

shop ✗ (ex guide dogs) (NT)

Conwy Castle
*A magnificent linear plan fortress built
1283–89 by Edward I. Also extensive town
walls, originally with 22 towers, and old
and new road bridges.*

Open † see end of gazetteer.

✱ 90p (ch 16 & pen 45p).

⚠ shop (AM Cadw)

Conwy Visitor Centre Adjacent Vicarage
car park
☎ (049263) 6288
*Conwy's colourful past, illustrated on film
and in displays. Welsh craft and
bookshop, guided tours, evening film
shows and special events. There is a
newly opened 'brass rubbing centre'.*

Open Mar–Dec daily 10–5 (9.30am–9pm
Jun–Sep).

45p (ch 35p family £1) party 12 + 25p.

P (70 yds) ᕕ (ground floor only) shop

Plas Mawr High St
☎ (049263) 3413
*Considered to be the finest example of an
Elizabethan town mansion in Great Britain
and practically in the same condition as
when built between 1570 and 1580.*

Open Feb–Mar & Nov Wed–Sun 10–4;
Apr–Sep daily 10–6; Oct daily 10–4. Art
exhibitions Mar–Nov. →

BRANTWOOD

CONISTON
Home of John Ruskin 1872-1900
The most beautifully situated house in the Lake
District, containing fine displays of Ruskin
watercolours and drawings. Delightful nature
walks — 3 miles around the Brantwood estate.
Delicious teas and lunches in the Proserpina
Gallery. Excellent bookshop. OPEN ALL
YEAR.   Tel: Coniston (0966) 41396.

75p (ch 25p, ch 5 free, students & pen 40p) Party.

P outside car park (200 yds) shop

Smallest House The Quay
☎ (049263) 3484

The 'Guinness Book of Records' smallest house in Britain, with a mid-Victorian Welsh cottage interior.

Open Apr–mid Oct 10–6 (10–9.30/10 in Jul & Aug. In winter by arrangement.

20p (ch under 5 free).

P (100 yds) & (ground floor only) shop

CORBRIDGE
Northumberland
Map **12** NY96

Roman Station

Remains of Roman 'Corstopitum', c AD210, including granaries, portico columns and probable site of legion headquarters. Excavated finds in new museum on site.

Open see end of gazetteer.

✳ 80p (ch 16 & pen 40p).
⚠ & (AM)

CORBY, GREAT
Cumbria
Map **12** NY45

Corby Castle (on unclass rd from A69 at Warwick Bridge)
☎ Wetheral (0228) 60246

An early 19th-century mansion built round an ancient pele tower and 17th-century manor house and situated in wooded grounds by the River Eden.

Grounds open Apr–Sep, daily 2–5.

30p (ch free).
⚠ (free) ✕

CORFE CASTLE
Dorset
Map **3** SY98

Corfe Castle
☎ (0929) 480442

12th- to 16th-century stronghold in Purbeck Hills besieged in 1646 during Civil War and later slighted.

Conwy
—
Cosford RAF

Open Mar–Oct, daily 10–6. Nov–Feb weekends only 12–4 weather permitting. £1.20 (ch 16 60p). Party 15+ by arrangement.
⚠ ⚞ (NT)

Corfe Castle Museum
☎ (0929) 480248

Tiny rectangular building, partly rebuilt in brick after fire in 1680. Small museum with old village relics and dinosaur footprints 130 million years old. First floor accessible by staircase at one end, and Ancient Order of Marblers meet here each Shrove Tuesday (open by appointment only).

Open daily; Etr–Sep 8–7, Oct–Etr 8–5 (times are approximate).

Free.

P (400 yds)

CORGARFF
Grampian Aberdeenshire
Map **15** NJ20

Corgarff Castle

A 16th-century tower, which was besieged in 1571 and is associated with the Jacobite Risings of 1715 and 1745. It later became a military barracks.

Open Apr–Sep, Mon–Sat 9.30–7, Sun 2–7. Apply to Key Keeper in winter.

✳ 50p (ch 25p).
⚠ (AM)

CORRIS
Gwynedd
Map **6** SH70

Railway Museum in village, 300 yds from A487
☎ (065473) 343

Museum in century-old railway building with photographs of operation of Corris narrow-gauge railway from 1890–1948. Items connected with railway are

---

constantly added, and some old wagons are on show, half mile of track between museum and old engine shed at Maespoeth has now been re-instated. Passengers not carried. Children's playground nearby.

Open BH periods & Mon–Fri 15 Jul–6 Sep 10.30–5.30, and as advertised locally during holiday season. Details not confirmed for 1986.

Free.

⚠ shop

CORSHAM
Wiltshire
Map **3** ST86

Corsham Court
☎ (0249) 712214

Elizabethan manor with additions by Capability Brown and Nash, Georgian state rooms with furniture by Chippendale, Adam, Cobb and Johnson, famous Methuen collection of Old Masters, garden with flowering shrubs, herbaceous borders, Georgian bath house, peacocks and 15th-century gazebo.

Open 14 Jan–14 Dec, Tue–Thu, Sat, Sun & BH 2–4 Jun–Sep & BH to 6 (Open other times by appointment).

£2 (ch £1). Gardens only £1 (ch 50p). Party 20+.

⚠ & ✕ (in building)

COSFORD RAF
West Midlands
Map **7** SJ70

Aerospace Museum
☎ Albrighton (090722) 4872

One of the largest aviation collections in the U.K. including the Victor and Vulcan bombers, the Hastings, York, British Airways Airliners, the Belfast freighter and the last airworthy Britannia. The Research and Development collection includes the famous TSR2, Fairey Delta 2, Bristol 188 and many more important aircraft. British Airways exhibition hall and comprehensive missile display.

Open Apr–Oct, daily then Nov–Mar weekdays only 10–4.

CORSHAM COURT
WILTSHIRE

Visit the Stately Home of Lord Methuen, containing a very fine collection of paintings by Old Masters displayed in the magnificent Georgian State Rooms. The XVIII Century Furnishings by Chippendale compliment the many other treasures to be found in the charming and relaxed atmosphere of this beautiful mansion.
Corsham Court is signposted from the A4 Bath to Chippenham road (M4 Exit 17)

Entrance Fees and Times of Opening Above.

£1.50 (ch & pen 00p).

🅰 🔤 🖒 shop 🍴 (inside building)

COTON
Northamptonshire
Map **4** SP67

Coton Manor Gardens
☎ Northampton (0604) 740219

A beautiful old garden surrounding 17th-century stone manor house. Rare wildfowl, cranes and flamingos add greatly to the attraction of the lakes and water gardens, and there are also unusual plants for sale.

Open Apr–Oct Thu & Sun, also Wed Jul & Aug and BH Mon & Tue then Oct Sun only (2–6).

✱ £1.30 (ch 60p).

🅰 🔤 🖒 (gardens only) shop & garden centre

COTTESMORE
Leicestershire
Map **8** SK91

Rutland Railway Museum Cottesmore
Iron Ores Mining Siding, Ashwell Rd
☎ Leicester (0533) 676376

A collection of industrial rail stock which includes 0–4–0, and 0–6–0 steam saddle tank engines, diesel engines and 60 assorted wagons, as used in the coal-iron-ore and quarry sidings. A coach from the Wisbech Tramway and many other items of interest can be seen. The engines and rolling stock can be seen working on the mineral branch line which used to carry ironstone from the quarry to the main line at Ashwell.

Open Sat & Sun, 10.30–dusk. Steam days Etr Sun & Mon, May Day Sun & Mon, Whitsun Sun & Mon, Jul 5 & 6, 9 & 10 Aug & 27 & 28 Sep. Special weekend 9 & 10 Aug.

Steam Days 70p (ch & pen 30p). Summer Steam Rally 9–10 Aug £1 (ch 50p). Other days by donation.

🅰 🔤 (steam days) ⇞ 🖒 shop (steam days) 🍴

COUGHTON
Warwickshire
Map **4** SP06

Coughton Court

A 16th-century and later house with imposing gatehouse, two Elizabethan half-timbered wings and Jacobite relics.

Open Etr Sat–Thu 2–5. Apr & Oct, Sat & Sun 2–5. May–Sep, Wed–Sun & BH Mon 2–6.

£1.50.

🔤 shop 🍴 (NT)

COVENTRY
West Midlands
Map **4** SP37

Cosford RAF
Coxwold

Coventry Cathedral 7 Priory Row
☎ (0203) 27597

The present cathedral was designed by Sir Basil Spence and consecrated in May 1962. Contains outstanding modern works of art, including the Sutherland altar tapestry, the West Screen (a wall of glass engraved by John Hutton with saints and angels) and stained glass unequalled in modern times. Also there is the opportunity to enjoy the art of modern technology in the new 'Visitors Centre'.

Open daily 8.30–7.30pm (summer), 8.30–5.30 (winter) ex during services.

Tower 50p (ch 25p). Visitors Centre
✱ £1.25 (ch 6 free, ch 6–16, students & pen 75p) family £3.

P (100 yds) 🔤 (licensed) 🖒 shop 🍴

Coventry Toy Museum Much Park St
☎ (0203) 27560

Collection of toys dating from 1740 to 1951, including trains, dolls, dolls houses and games.

Open May–Dec daily 10–6.

✱ 50p (ch & pen 30p).

P ⇞ shop 🍴 Ⓥ

Herbert Art Gallery and Museum
Jordan Well
☎ (0203) 25555 ext 2315

Collections include social history, archaeology, folk life, industry, natural history, visual arts. Of special interest are the life collection of Graham Sutherland's studies for the 'Christ in Glory' tapestry in Coventry Cathedral, the Frederick Poke collection of fine 18th-century English furniture and silver. A permanent exhibition of Coventry's history, and the Natural History live animal display.

Open Mon–Sat 10–6, Sun 2–5 (Closed Good Fri & part Xmas).

Free.

P 🖒 shop 🍴

Lunt Roman Fort Coventry Rd, Baginton (on S side of city, off Stonebridge highway, A45).
☎ (0203) 25555 ext 2315

Reconstruction of Roman fort, which stood on this site AD60–80, with interpretive centre housed in reconstructed granary. Other features include gateway and gyrus.

Open end May–Sep, Tue, Wed & Fri–Sun noon–6.

✱ 20p (ch & pen 10p).

🅰 ⇞ shop 🍴 🖒

Museum of British Road Transport, St Agnes Ln, Hales St
☎ (0203) 25555 ext 2086

Portrays the large part that Coventry and the West Midlands area in general have played in the development of transport throughout the world. There are over 400 exhibits in displays of motor cars, commercial vehicles, motor cycles and cycles, together with associated relevant materials.

Open Apr–Sep daily, Mon–Fri 10–4 and Sat & Sun 10–5.30. During winter Fri 9.30–4 and Sat & Sun 10–5. Special arrangements for pre-booked parties during winter months.

✱ 90p (ch & pen 45p). Family £2.25.

P (adjacent) 🖒 shop 🍴

St Mary's Guild Hall between Bayley Lane and Earl St
☎ (0203) 25555 ext 2874

Medieval guildhall, with minstrels' gallery, restored hall with portraits and Flemish tapestries, and Caesar's watchtower.

Open Etr, then May–Oct, Mon–Sat 10–5, Sun 12–5 (subject to civic requirements–enquiry advised before visiting).

Free.

P (cars–25 yds) 🍴

COWES
Isle of Wight
Map **4** SZ49

Maritime Museum and Public Library
Beckford Rd
☎ (0983) 293341

Ship models, photographs, paintings, books etc, showing the island's maritime past.

Open Mon–Fri 9.30–6, Sat 9.30–4.30. (Closed BH's).

Free.

P shop 🍴

COXWELL, GREAT
Oxfordshire
Map **4** SU29

Great Coxwell Barn

Stone-built 13th-century barn, possibly finest in England, with fine roof timbers.

Open at all reasonable times.

Free.

(NT)

COXWOLD
North Yorkshire
Map **8** SE57

Shandy Hall
☎ (03476) 465

Medieval house, once the home of Laurence Sterne whose books, 'Tristram Shandy' and 'A Sentimental Journey' were written here between 1760 and 1768, now a museum dedicated to him.

Open Jun–Sep Wed 2–4.30 & Sun 2.30–4.30. At other times by appointment.

✱ £1 (ch accompanied 50p).

🅰 shop and garden centre 🍴

CRAIGIEVAR

Grampian *Aberdeenshire*
Map **15** NJ50

Craigievar Castle
☎ Lumphanan (033983) 635

Tower house, built 1610–1626, with notable Renaissance ceiling. Perhaps the most characteristic example of the true Scottish Baronial period.

Castle open May–Sep, daily 2–6. Last visitors 5.15. Ground open all year. 9.30–sunset.

£1.40 (ch 70p) includes audio-visual. Party.

Grounds – admission by donation. (NTS)

CRAIGNURE

Isle of Mull Strathclyde *Argyll*
Map **10** NM73

Mull & West Highland Narrow Gauge Railway Craignure (Old Pier) Station
☎ (06802) 494 (in season) & (06803) 389/472 (out of season)

Scotland's first passenger train on an island, opened in 1983. The 10¼ inch gauge line runs the 1¼ miles from Craignure to Torosay Castle with both steam and diesel trains operating.

Open Etr wk then 3 May–27 Sep. Ring for details of train times.

✳ £1 (ch 70p) return. 75p (ch 60p) single. Family return £2.70. Party 20+.
🅰 (Craignure only) ⬛ (Torosay Castle) &
(ground floor only) shop ⓥ

Torosay Castle and Gardens
☎ (06802) 421

The 19th-century house contains portraits and wildlife pictures, a superb collection of stags 'Heads' (antlers) and the huge head of a prehistoric elk, dug out of a bog in Co Monaghan. There is also a Victorian library and archive rooms. The terraced gardens and statue walk cover 11 acres and include a water garden, an avenue of Australian gum trees, a Japanese Garden and many Gulf Stream shrubs.

Open daily 10.30–5.30. May–Sep (last entry 5pm). Apr & Oct parties by appointment. Gardens dawn–dusk.

✳ Castle & Gardens £1.50 (pen & students £1.20 ch over 5 90p). Party. Gardens & Tea Room 80p (pen & students 60p ch over 5 40p).
🅰 ⬛ shop ✕ (in house)

CRANBORNE

Dorset
Map **4** SU01

Cranborne Manor Private Gardens and Garden Centre
☎ (07254) 248

Privately owned 17th-century gardens, having a preserved Elizabethan mount and knot gardens, herb and river gardens.

Gardens only open Apr–Oct first Sat & Sun in month BH & some other weeks

advertised locally Sat 9–5, Sun 2–5. Garden Centre open all year, Mon–Sat 9–5, Sun 2–5.

£1 (ch 20p).
🅰 🕂 & shop ✕

CRANHAM

Gloucestershire
Map **3** SO81

Prinknash Abbey (on A46 between Cheltenham and Painswick)
☎ Painswick (0452) 812239

Situated in a large park, this 14th-century and 16th-century house was the residence of Benedictines and guests of Gloucester Abbey until 1539. Again became a priory, and later an abbey, for Benedictine monks from Caldey in 1928.

Abbey Church open daily 5am–8.30pm Pottery Mon–Sat 10.30–4.30 also Sun pm (Pottery Shop 9–6).

✳ Viewing Gallery 30p (ch 14 10p). Guides available.
🅰 🕂 & shop & garden centre

See advertisement under Cheltenham.

Prinknash Bird Park
☎ Painswick (0452) 812727

Set in nine acres of beautiful parkland and lakes, with Mute Swans, Black Swans, geese and many varieties of waterfowl. The park also includes numerous White and Indian Blue Peacocks, fallow deer and Pygmy goats. Also there is the Golden Wood, stocked with ornamental pheasants, leading to the restored and reputedly haunted 16th century Monks fishpond which contains trout.

Open Etr–Oct.

£1.20 (ch 16 & pen 70p). Party 10+.
P (25 yds) & shop ✕ ⓥ

CRANMORE

Somerset
Map **3** ST64

East Somerset Railway
☎ (074988) 417

At Cranmore Railway Station is an exhibition of steam locomotives and rolling stock, with locomotive engine shed and workshops, steam-hauled passenger train service. Signal box art gallery. Museum, wildlife centre and childrens play area. Special events include Jazz concert and vintage vehicle rally. Santa trains in Dec.

Open daily Apr–Oct 10–5.30 (ex weekdays Apr, Sep & Oct until 4pm only); Nov–Mar weekends only 9–4. Details not confirmed for 1986.

80p (ch 40p). Steaming days incl train ride £1.80 (ch 90p).

🅰 ⬛ (& restaurant car on steaming days)
🕂 & (ground floor only) shop ⓥ

CRATHES

Grampian *Kincardineshire*
Map **15** NO79

Crathes Castle and Garden (3m E of Banchory on A93.)
☎ (033044) 525

A picturesque 16th-century building noted for its magnificent painted ceilings. It has a famous garden and the extensive grounds contain nature trails. Ranger/naturalist service.

Castle open Etr & May–Sep, Daily 11–6. Last admission 5.15. Garden & grounds open daily from 9.30–sunset.

✳ Castle £1.40 (ch 70p) Gardens 80p (ch 40p) Grounds: cars 70p, minibuses £1.65, coaches £5 (May–Sep only, other times by donation). Combined ticket £1.80 (ch 90p). Party.

Visitor Centre ⬛ & Shop (Etr & May–Sep daily 11–6). (NTS)

CREETOWN

Dumfries and Galloway
Kirkcudbrightshire
Map **11** NX45

Creetown Gem Rock Museum and Art Gallery
☎ (067182) 357

A beautiful collection of gemstones and minerals from around the world. Collected by the proprietors the outstanding specimens and gemstone objects d'art are guaranteed to interest any visitor whether expert or not. Three large exhibition halls and a gemstone workshop.

Open daily summer 9.30–6 (5pm winter). 70p (ch 5–15 30p, pen 50p).
🅰 (free) ⬛ & shop

CREGNEISH

Isle of Man
Map **6** SC16

Manx Open-Air Folk Museum
☎ Douglas (0624) 75522 or 25125

Comprises group of traditional Manx cottages (some thatched), including crofter-fisherman's home, farmstead, loom-shed with hand loom, lathe shed with treadle lathe, and smithy.

Open early May–mid Sep, Mon–Sat 10–1, 2–5, and Sun 2–5. Details not confirmed for 1986.

✳ 25p (ch 10p).
P (100 yds) ⬛ & (ground floor only) shop ✕ (ex guide dogs)

CRESWELL

Derbyshire
Map **8** SK57

Creswell Crags Visitor Centre off Crags Rd (1m E off B6042)
☎ Worksop (0909) 720378

Limestone Gorge which was once the home of early man. Picnic site and a visitor centre, which explains the archaeological significance of the site with an exhibition and audio-visual programme which shows what life was like for our ancestors.

Open Mar–Oct, Tue–Sun & BH Mons 10–5; Nov & Dec Suns only 10–5.

Free.

 ⚠ ⌜ shop

CREWKERNE
Somerset
Map **3** ST40

Clapton Court Gardens (3m S on B3165)
☎ (0460) 73220

One of Somerset's most beautiful gardens with rare and unusual shrubs and plants in 10 acre formal and woodland settings, and having an outstanding springtime display of bulbs and brilliant Autumn colours. Plant centre selling unusual plants. Fuchsias and pelargoniums a speciality.

Open all year Mon–Fri 10.30–5, Sun 2–5. Also Etr Sat & Sat in May only 2–5.

£1.20 (ch 14 30p pen £1). Party 20+ prebooked only.

⚠ ⌓ (Apr–Sep weekdays) ♿ (gardens only) plant centre ✖

CRICCIETH
Gwynedd
Map **6** SH43

Criccieth Castle
13th-century fortress, rebuilt with two baileys and notable gatehouse. Wide views over Snowdonia.

Open †, see end of gazetteer.

✱ 60p (ch 16 & pen 30).

Shop (AM Cadw)

CRICH
Derbyshire
Map **8** SK35

Tramway Museum Matlock Rd (off B5035)
☎ Ambergate (077385) 2565

Vintage tramcars from many parts of Britain, and from abroad. Many are in working order, and visitors may have unlimited rides along a 1m tramway with views over Derwent Valley. Tramway period street project with reconstructed, Georgian Assembly Rooms façade and Derby. Depots, exhibitions and displays.

Open Etr, then Sat, Sun & BHs until end Oct. Also open Mon–Thu, May–Sep, 10–5.30 weekdays, 10.30–6.30 weekends & Fri 25 Jul–Aug only.

£2 (ch £1).

⚠ ⌓ ⌜ ♿ shop Ⓒ

CRICHTON
Lothian *Midlothian*
Map **11** NT36

Creswell
—
Cromford

Crichton Castle
A 14th- to 16th-century castle, notable for the Earl of Bothwell's Italianate wing.

Open, see end of gazetteer. (Wknds only in winter months).

✱ 50p (ch & pen 25p).

(AM)

CRICKET ST THOMAS
Somerset
Map **3** ST30

Wild Life Park and Country Life Museum
☎ Winsham (046030) 755

An historic and beautiful park now devoted to a variety of birds and animals from many countries. The National Heavy Horse centre, agricultural museum & woodland railway. Film location for B.B.C. Television's 'To The Manor Born'. Various special events in summer.

Open daily Apr–Oct 10–6; Nov–Mar 10–5 or dusk whichever is earlier.

✱ £2.50 (ch 3–14 £1.50). Party 20+ by arrangement.

⚠ ⌓ (licensed) ⌜ ♿ shop garden centre

CRIEFF
Tayside *Perthshire*
Map **11** NN82

Glenturret Distillery The Hosh (1½m NW off A85)
☎ (0764) 2424

The oldest distillery in Scotland, established 1775, it produces the award winning malt whiskies eight, twelve, fifteen and eighteen years of age.

Open Mar–Oct, Mon–Fri 10–3.45. Jul & Aug Mon–Sat 9.45–4.15. Nov & Dec Mon–Fri 2–3.45.

Free guided tours and 'drams' to visitors. Heritage Centre 80p (ch under 12 free, 12–16 40p, pen 60p). Party 40+. Parties 15+ by arrangement.

⚠ ⌜ ♿ (ground floor & gardens only) shop ✖

Innerpeffray Library (4½m SE of B8062)
☎ (0764) 2819

Scotlands oldest Free Lending Library, founded in 1691. Housed in a late 18th century building it is of ancient and historical interest and contains many rare books.

Open Mon–Wed & Fri–Sat 10–12.45 & 2–4.45 Sun 2–4.

50p (ch 10p).

⚠ ✖

CROFT
Hereford and Worcester
Map **7** SO46

Croft Castle (Off B4362)
Restored, partly 14th-century mansion, with 16th- to 18th-century alterations, including Gothick staircase and ceilings. The 1,636-acre estate includes fine oaks, beeches and Spanish chestnuts lining the avenue. The Iron Age fort of Croft Ambrey is nearby.

Open Etr Sat–Mon 2–5 Apr & Oct, Sat & Sun 2–5; May–Sep, Wed–Sun & BH Mon 2–6.

£1.50 Joint ticket with Berrington Hall. £2.50.

Teas at Berrington Hall (NT)

CROMARTY
Highland *Ross and Cromarty*
Map **14** NH76

Hugh Miller's Cottage
☎ (03817) 245

The house is c1711 and was the birthplace in 1802 of Hugh Miller, the geologist.

Open 28 Mar–Sep, Mon–Sat 10 & 1–5; Jun–Sep also Sun 2–5.

65p (ch 30p).

(NTS)

CROMER
Norfolk
Map **9** TG24

Cromer Museum East Cottages, Tucker St
☎ (0263) 513543

Three 19th-century Fishermen's Cottages, one with period furnishings, also pictures and collections of Victorian Cromer. Collections illustrate the natural history, archaeology and geology of the area.

Open Mon 10–1 & 2–5, Tue–Sat 10–5, Sun 2–5. (Closed Good Fri, 25 & 26 Dec and 1 Jan).

24 May–Sep 20p (ch 5p students & UB40s 10p) Sep–23 May 10p (ch 5p students & UB40s 5p).

P (50 yds) shop ✖

Lifeboat Museum
☎ (0263) 512503

*Situated in No 2 boathouse at the bottom of The Gangway. Covers both local lifeboat history and general RNLI history. Also **Lifeboat Station** on pier.*

Open May–Sep daily 10–5.

Free.

P ♿ shop

CROMFORD
Derbyshire
Map **8** SK35

Arkwright's Cromford Mill
☎ Wirksworth (062982) 4297 →

Site of the world's first successful water powered cotton spinning mill. The Arkwright Society are gradually restoring mills, warehouses and the watercourses.

Open all year Wed–Fri, 10–4.30. Sat & Sun 11–5. Open BHs. Guided tours and evening parties by arrangement.

30p (ch & students 20p).

 ⚠ Ⓡ ✻ shop ⚿ (ground floor only)

CRYNANT
West Glamorgan
Map **3** SN70

Cefn Coed Museum
Blaenant Colliery on A4109
☏ (0639) 750556

Adjacent to a working colliery, the centre explains the history of coal mining in the Dulais Valley. An original steam winding engine has been retained, now operating by electrical power, and there is also a simulated underground mining gallery. There are nearby forest walks and picnic sites.

Open Apr–Oct daily 11–6, last admission 5.15 (Closed Nov–Mar ex by special arrangement).

70p (ch & pen 45p) (ch 5 & disabled Free). Party.

⚠ Ⓡ ✻ ⚿ shop

CULLODEN MOOR
Highland *Inverness-shire*
Map **14** NH74

Culloden Battlefield
☏ (0463) 790607

The Cairn, built in 1881, recalls the famous battle of 1746, when 'Bonnie' Prince Charles Edward Stuart's army was routed by the Duke of Cumberland's forces. Near the Graves of the Clans is the Well of the Dead, and also the Cumberland Stone. The battle fought around Old Leanach Farmhouse, now a museum. There is also a Trust Visitor Centre and exhibition.

Site always open. Visitors Centre 28 Mar–31 May & 1–26 Oct, daily 9.30–5.30. Jun–Sep, daily 9–7.30.

Admission to Visitor Centre & museum (includes audio-visual exhibition) £1.10 (ch 55p). Party 20+.

⚠ shop (NTS)

CULROSS
Fife *Fife*
Map **11** NS98

Culross Abbey
Cistercian monastery, founded by Malcolm, Earl of Fife in 1217. The choir is still used as the parish church and parts of the nave remain. Fine central tower, still complete.

Open, see end of gazetteer.

Free.

(AM)

Cromford
—
Cynonville

Culross Palace
Dated 1597 and 1611, and noted for the painted rooms and terraced gardens.

Open, see end of gazetteer.

✻ £1 (ch & pen 50p).

(AM) Ⓥ

CULZEAN CASTLE
Strathclyde *Ayrshire*
Map **10** NS21
(4m N of Kirkoswald)
☏ Kirkoswald (06556) 274

An 18th-century castle set in 560 acres (**see below**) and designed by Robert Adam. It contains fine plaster ceilings, a splendid oval central staircase, and a circular drawing room. There is a fine collection of family portraits and a guest flat here was presented to the late General Eisenhower.

Open 28 Mar–Sep, daily 10–6. Oct, daily 12–5 (last admission ½ hr before closing).

£1.70 (ch 85p). Party (ex Jul & Aug).

(NTS)

Culzean Country Park
☏ Kirkoswald (06556) 269

560 acres including the 1783 walled garden, camellia house, orangery, swan pond and aviary. The Robert Adam-designed Home Farm has been converted into a Reception and Interpretation centre. Ranger and Naturalist service.

Park open all year. Centre 28 Mar–Sep daily 10–6, Oct daily 10–4.

✻ Pedestrians Free. Cars £1.20, minibuses & caravans £2.50, coaches £7. Prices under review.

Ⓡ ⚿ (NTS)

CUPAR
Fife *Fife*
Map **11** NO31

Hill of Tarvit Mansion House and Garden (2m S off A916)
☏ (0334) 53127

A virtually rebuilt manor house with a notable collection of furniture, tapestries and paintings.

Open 28–31 Mar, Apr & Oct, Sat and Sun 2–6. May–Sep, daily 2–6. Last admission ½ hr before closing. Garden and grounds open all year 9.30–sunset.

House & Garden £1.40 (ch 70p). Party. Garden only 60p (ch 30p).

(NTS)

CUSWORTH
South Yorkshire
Map **8** SE50

Cusworth Hall Museum (2m NW Doncaster)
☏ Doncaster (0302) 782342

18th-century house with fine chimney pieces and chapel in south-west wing. Museum of South Yorkshire life, and sections of interest to children. Temporary exhibitions and many annual events. Also extensive grounds which are open all year, with fishing in ponds, cricket and football pitches. Children's study base, and research facilities.

Open Mon–Thu & Sat 11–5 (4pm Nov–Feb). Sun 1–5 (4pm Nov–Feb) (Closed Xmas).

Free.

⚠ (ex coaches) ⚿ (ground floor & gardens only) shop ✉

CWMCARN
Gwent
Map **3** ST29

Scenic Forest Drive
☏ Newbridge (0495) 244223 or Penhow (0633) 400205

Operated by Forestry Commission. A 7m scenic drive through mountain forest with spectacular views over the Bristol Channel and surrounding countryside; play areas, forest and mountain walks, barbecue facilities.

Open Good Fri–Aug daily 11–8 then Sep 11–6.

✻ £1 per car.

⚠ ✻ ⚿

CYMER ABBEY
Gwynedd
Map **6** SH71
(1m E of Llanelltyd)

Remains of the church of a small early 13th-century Cistercian monastery.

Accessible at all reasonable times.

✻ 30p (ch 16 & pen 15p).

⚠ (AM Cadw)

CYNONVILLE
West Glamorgan
Map **3** SS89

Welsh Miners Museum and Afan Argoed Country Park (on A4107)
☏ Cymmer (0639) 850564 or 850875

Set in the picturesque wooded Afan Valley and includes simulated coal faces, pit gear, and miners' equipment which illustrate the harsh realities of 'coal getting' and the effects it had on the communities of South Wales. The Countryside Park has forest walks and trails and also picnic areas. Countryside Centre adjoins the parking area.

Open daily Apr–Oct 10.30–6; Nov–Mar noon–5 wknds only (parties accepted weekdays by arrangement). Park open daily daylight hours.

20p (ch & pen 10p). Party.

⚠ Ⓡ ✻ ⚿ shop ✉

DACRE
Cumbria
Map **12** NY42

Dalemain
☎ Pooley Bridge (08536) 450 or 223

Originally a medieval pele tower, added to in Tudor times with the imposing Georgian façade completed in 1750. Splendid oak panelling, Chinese wallpaper, Tudor plasterwork, fine Queen Anne and 18th-century furniture. Rooms include the Victorian nursery and the housekeeper's work room. The tower contains the Westmorland and Cumberland Yeomanry Museum. Countryside Museum in 16th-century cobbled courtyard. Historic gardens, Adventure playground.

Open Etr–mid Oct Sun–Thu 11.15–5.15. Last entry 5 pm.

£1.90 (ch 5 free, ch 16 & pen £1) Family Ticket £5. Gardens only £1 (ch free). & free. Party.

⚠ (Free) ⬛ (licensed) 🍴 & (ground floor & gardens only) shop garden centre ✖ ⓥ

DALKEITH
Lothian *Midlothian*
Map **11** NT36

Dalkeith Park Buccleuch Estate
☎ 031-663 5684

The extensive grounds of Dalkeith House offer woodland and riverside walks. Nature trails and woodland adventure playground; a beautiful Adam bridge and an orangery.

Open end of Mar–Oct (wknds Nov) daily 11–6.

✻ 65p.

⚠ 🍴 ✖ before 1pm

DANBY
North Yorkshire
Map **8** NZ70

The Moors Centre Lodge Lane
☎ Castleton (0287) 60654

The former shooting lodge offers full information and countryside interpretation service to visitors to the North York Moors National Park. The grounds include

riverside meadow, woodland and terraced gardens, children's play area and brass rubbing centre. Slides shown daily, and also an exhibition about the North York Moors. Bookshop information desk.

Open 24 Mar–Oct daily 10–5, Nov–23 Mar Sun 12–4; (Guided walks Sun).

Free.

⚠ ⬛ 🍴 & (ground floor) shop ✖

DARLINGTON
Co Durham
Map **8** NZ21

Art Gallery Crown St
☎ (0325) 462034

Contains a permanent collection of pictures but also has temporary loan exhibitions throughout the year.

Open Mon–Fri 10–8, Sat 10–5.30 (Closed Sun & all weekend BH).

Free.

P (50 yds) & ✖

Darlington Museum Tubwell Row
☎ (0325) 463795

Local social and natural history, archaeology and bygones. Observation beehive and beekeeping exhibits, approx May–Sep, each year.

Open all year Mon–Wed & Fri 10–1 & 2–6; Thu 10–1; Sat 10–1 & 2–5.30 (Closed Good Fri, May Day, Xmas & New Year's Day).

Free.

P (50 yds) & (ground floor only) shop ✖ (ex Guide Dogs) ♿

Darlington Railway Museum
☎ (0325) 460532

Housed in North Road Station built in 1842, carefully restored and still in use. It contains exhibits and models connected with the Stockton and Darlington and the North Eastern Railway Companies,

including an early railway coach, circa 1845, a chaldron wagon and seven steam locomotives, one of which is the original 'Locomotion No 1' built by Robert Stephenson & Co in 1825, also the 'Derwent', built 1845.

Open daily Mon–Sat 10–4, Sun 2–4 (times may be extended in summer).

✻ 50p (ch 5–15 & pen 30p). Party.

⚠ & shop ✖

DARTINGTON
Devon
Map **3** SX76

Dartington Hall
☎ Totnes (0803) 862271 ext 58

Only the 14th-century banqueting hall of the house shown. Large gardens, with trees and shrubs, courtyard, and terraces.

Open daily. (Gardens and hall occasionally closed for special events.)

Admission by donation.

⚠ ⬛ & (gardens only) garden centre (NGS)

DARTMOUTH
Devon
Map **3** SX85

Bayard's Cove Castle

Low, circular ruined stronghold, built by townspeople in 1537, with gunposts as at Dartmouth Castle (**see below**).

Accessible at all reasonable times.

Free.

⚠ (AM)

Butterwalk Museum
☎ (08043) 2923

Half-timbered 17th-century house, part of restored colonnaded arcade, with small maritime and nautical museum which has over 150 ship models.

Open Nov–Mar 27, Mon–Sat 2.15–4; Etr–Oct, Mon–Sat 11–5.

✻ 30p (ch 5 free, ch 16 10p).

P (100 yds) shop

Dartmouth Castle

Tudor stronghold, dating from 1481, with some remains of earlier structure. Stands →

on the estuary of the River Dart facing Kingswear Castle on opposite shore, to which it was attached by chain in times of war. Timber-framed opening for the chain can still be seen.

Open † see end of gazetteer.

✱ 60p (ch 16 & pen 30p).

⚠ (AM)

Newcomen Memorial Engine
☎ (08043) 2923

In Royal Avenue Gardens by the River Dart, this building commemorates the 300th anniversary of Newcomen's birth (1663), and houses his atmospheric pressure steam pumping engine of 1725. Possibly the oldest of its type in the world, it may be seen working.

Open to view Etr–Oct, Mon–Fri 11–5 (closed Sat & Sun ex by arrangement).

✱ 30p (ch 5 free, ch 16 10p) 18 page booklet is available.

P (adjacent) &

DEAL
Kent
Map **5** TR35

Deal Castle

Built by Henry VIII, with massive central citadel, contains exhibits of Iron Age weapons, early pottery and relics of Deal's history.

Open † see end of gazetteer.

✱ 60p (ch 16 & pen 30p).

⚠ & (courtyard & ground floor only) (AM)

Maritime & Local History Museum
22 St George's Rd
☎ (03045) 5922

Exhibits include local boats, model sailing-ships, 'bygones', maps, old photographs etc. Annexe where land and sea finds are examined, treated and classified. Local booklets, postcards etc.

Open Spring BH–Sep daily 2–5.

Admission fee payable.

P (200 yds) & shop

Walmer Castle (1m S on coast)

Built in the 16th century, official residence of the Lord Warden of the Cinque Ports.

┌─────────────────┐
│   **Dartmouth**   │
│   —   │
│   **Denbigh**   │
└─────────────────┘

Open † see end of gazetteer but closed always between 1 & 2pm, also Mon except BH. Garden closed winter.

✱ Summer £1 (ch & pen 50p) Reductions in winter.

⚠ & (courtyard & ground floor only) (AM)

DEDDINGTON
Oxfordshire
Map **4** SP43

Deddington Castle

Mainly earthworks from outer bailey and inner ward. Excavations have revealed portions of a 13th-century chapel.

Open at any reasonable time.

Free.

(AM)

DEDHAM
Essex
Map **5** TM03

Castle House
☎ Colchester (0206) 322127

Former home and studio of the late Sir Alfred Munnings KCVO, PRA. Contains paintings, drawings, sketches, and other works.

Open 4 May–5 Oct Wed, Sun & BH Mons, Thu & Sat in Aug 2–5. Parties by arrangement.

£1 (ch 25p pen 50p).

⚠ & (ground floor only)

DEENE
Northamptonshire
Map **4** SP99

Deene Park
☎ Bulwick (078085) 361 or 223

Mainly 16th-century house of great architectural importance and historical interest. Large lake and park. Extensive gardens with old fashioned roses, rare trees and shrubs.

Open 30 & 31 Mar; 4, 5, 25 & 26 May; Suns Jun–Aug including 25 Aug. Park open fr 1; House 2–5.

✱ £2 (ch 14 £1).

⚠ ⚖ ⚘ & (ground floor & gardens only) shop ✖ Ⓥ

Kirby Hall (1½m W)

Fine, partially restored house, begun in 1572, but altered in mid 17th century for Sir Christopher Hatton, Lord Chancellor, by John Thorpe. The later portion is ascribed to Inigo Jones. Attractive garden layout.

Open † see end of gazetteer.

✱ 50p (ch & pen 25p).

⚠ & (grounds & ground floor only) (AM)

DEERHURST
Gloucestershire
Map **3** SO82

Odda's Chapel (off B4213 near River Severn)

Rare Saxon chapel, dating back to 1056 and erected originally by the Lord of the Manor. Attached to old house.

Open any reasonable time.

Free.

& (AM)

DENBIGH
Clwyd
Map **6** SJ06

Denbigh Castle

Built 1282–1333, with gatehouse preserved and fine viewpoint.

Open †, see end of gazetteer.

✱ 60p (ch 16 & pen 30p).

⚠ shop (AM Cadw)

Town Walls and Leicester's Church

Remains of walls include one of the gateways and ruined church, 'Leicester's Folly', which was planned to become cathedral of the diocese, in place of St Asaph's, after the Reformation.

Open, see end of gazetteer.

Key to both available from Denbigh Castle.

(AM Cadw)

THE SIR ALFRED MUNNINGS ART MUSEUM, CASTLE HOUSE, DEDHAM, ESSEX

A large Collection of Paintings, Sketches and other Works by Sir Alfred Munnings, KCVO, President of the Royal Academy 1944-1949, in his former home and studios.
Free Car Park.
See gazetteer entry — Castle House — for opening times and admission charges.

DERBY
Derbyshire
Map **8** SK33

Derby Museum & Art Gallery
☎ (0332) 31111 ext 405

Antiquities, social and natural history, militaria, Bonnie Prince Charlie room (1745 rebellion), toy theatre collection, and also temporary exhibitions. There are paintings by Joseph Wright of Derby (1734–1797), Derby porcelain and costumes. Many temporary exhibitions.

Open Tue–Sat 10–5. (Closed Sun, Mon & BH.)

Free.

P (100 yds) shop ✗ (ex guide dogs)

Industrial Museum Silk Mill, off Full St
☎ (0332) 31111 ext 740

Housed in an early 18th-century silk mill substantially rebuilt in 1910. The Rolls-Royce collection of aero-engines occupies the ground floor gallery, alongside the history of aviation from the Wright Brothers to the present day. 'An introduction to Derbyshire Industries' occupies the upper floor gallery. Temporary exhibitions.

Open Tue–Fri 10–5, Sat 10–4.45 (Closed BH).

P (200 yds) & shop ✗ (ex guide dogs)

DEREHAM
Norfolk
Map **9** TF91

Norfolk Rural Life Museum Beech House (2½m NW on unclass rd at Gressenhall)
☎ (0362) 860563

Illustrates the history of the county of Norfolk over the past 200 years, with particular emphasis on agriculture.

Open Etr–Sep Tue–Sat 10–5, Sun 2–5.30. Also BH Mons 10–5.

60p (ch 5p, students & UB40s 30p). Party 10+.

⚠ ⚟ (Sun pm only) & shop ✗

DEVIZES
Wiltshire
Map **4** SU06

Devizes Museum 41 Long St
☎ (0380) 77369

Exhibits from prehistoric, Roman and medieval periods in Wiltshire, also a new Natural History Gallery. New picture gallery with John Piper window.

Open all year, Tue–Sat 11–1 & 2–5. (4pm in winter).

75p (ch 5p, students & pen 50p).

P (20 yds) & (ground floor only) shop ✗

DIDCOT
Oxfordshire
Map **4** SU58

Derby
—
Dobwalls

Great Western Society Didcot Railway Centre (Access through main entrance of Didcot station)
☎ (0235) 817200

Largest collection of ex-Great Western rolling stock. Assembled in GWR engine shed and includes 20 steam locomotives, a diesel railcar, and a large selection of passenger and freight rolling stock. A typical GWR station has been recreated and original track relaid. 25th anniversary of Great Western Society 24th May–1 Jun.

Open Mar–Oct Sat, Sun & BH 11–5; 21 Jul–5 Sep Mon–Fri 11–4.30. Steam days first & last Sun of each month Mar–Oct, also BH, Sun & Wed in Aug, 9 Mar, 15 Jun & 27 Sep. GWR steam train in operation.

✱ £1–£2 depending on event (ch & pen half price). Special rates for family parties.

P ⚟ ⚟ shop ⚟

DINAS MAWDDWY
Gwynedd
Map **6** SH81

Meirion Mill
☎ Dinas Mawddwy (06504) 311

In the Dyfi Valley, at the southern end of the Snowdonia National Park, is this working woollen weaving mill and retail shop in rural estate. Pack-horse bridge (AM). Field-walk on track-bed of Old Mawddwy Railway. Gardens and children's playground. Dog exercise area.

Open Apr–Oct daily including BH; Winter, Mon–Fri (ex Xmas Day) 10–5 & some wknds.

Free (ex educational visits).

⚠ ⚟ ⚟ & shop

DINMORE
Hereford and Worcester
Map **3** SO45

Dinmore Manor
☎ Hereford (0432) 71322

12th- to 14th-century Chapel of the Knights Hospitallers of St John of Jerusalem, with cloisters and music room.

Chapel and gardens open all year, daily (ex 25 Dec), 10–6.

60p (ch & pen 30p).

⚠ & (ground floor & gardens only) ✗

see advertisement under Hereford.

DINTING VALE
Derbyshire
Map **7** SK09

Dinting Railway Centre (off A57 in Dinting Ln)
☎ Glossop (04574) 5596

One engine is always in steam on Suns & BHs between Mar–Oct, & Weds during Jul

---

& Aug. Steam weekends on 1 Jan, 28–31 Mar; 4 & 5, 25 & 26 May; and 24 & 25 Aug.

Open daily, 10.30–5. (Closed Xmas).

✱ 90p (ch 16 40p). Increased at BH & special events. Party.

⚠ ⚟ ⚟ & (ground floor only) shop

DIRLETON
Lothian
Map **12** NT58

Dirleton Castle
The oldest part of this romantic castle dates from 12th century. It was rebuilt and extended in the 14th and 16th centuries. Beside the castle lie the gardens established in the late 16th century.

Open see end of gazetteer.

£1 (ch & pen 50p). (AM).

Ⓥ

DISLEY
Cheshire
Map **7** SJ98

Lyme Park
Elizabethan in origin, enlarged by Leoni in 1726 and by Lewis Wyatt in 1817 with fine Palladian façade, Jacobean rooms and collection of pictures and furnishings. A park of more than thirteen hundred acres contains herd of deer.

Hall shown Apr–Sep, Tue–Sat 2–5, Sun & BH 1–6, Oct Tue & Sat 2–4.30, Sun 1–5. Last admission ½ hour before each closing time. Park & gardens open all year daily 8–sunset.

House 90p (ch 40p) subject to review.

⚠ (NT)

DOBWALLS
Cornwall
Map **2** SX26

Forest Railroad
☎ (0579) 20325

Very extensive miniature railway based on the era of steam on the American railroads. A mile ride modelled on the Cumbres Pass route of the Denver and Rio Grande railroad, and another spectacular mile of track based on the Sherman Hill route of the Union Pacific railroad. Nine superb scale locomotives including U.P. 'Big Boy'. Forest, tunnels, embankments, canyons and the steepest gradients on a miniature railway anywhere. Also Hall of Memories, children's play areas and radio-controlled boats.

Open daily Etr–early Oct 10–6 (last admission 5pm).

Admission fee payable to also include Thorburn's Edwardian Countryside, **see below**.

⚠ ⚟ ⚟ shop

Thorburn Museum and Gallery
☎ (0579) 20325

The unique world-renowned permanent memorial exhibition of paintings, →

---

sketches, prints, books, letters, photographs etc by Britain's greatest bird painter–Archibald Thorburn (1860–1935). Over 100 original paintings, many of major importance, are on display in the collection which is housed in a large converted barn.

Open daily, Good Fri–early Oct daily 10–6 (last admission 5pm).

Admission fee payable.

  🔥 ♿ shop

DODDINGTON
Lincolnshire
Map **8** SK87

Doddington Hall
☎ Lincoln (0522) 694308

Romantic Elizabethan mansion with Tudor gatehouse, walled rose garden and fine furniture, porcelain, textiles and pictures.

Open May–Sep, Wed & Sun 2–6, also Etr, May, Spring & Aug BH Mons. (Parties at other times by arrangement. School project.)

£1.90 (ch 95p). Garden 95p (ch 45p). Party.

♿ ⚱ (licensed) ♿ (ground floor & garden only) shop ✼ (in house)

DOLLAR
Central *Clackmannanshire*
Map **11** NS99

Castle Campbell and Dollar Glen
(1m N)

A 15th-century tower with 16th- and 17th-century additions, in a picturesque Ochil Hills setting above the Dollar Glen, providing splendid views.

Open 24 Mar–Sep, Mon–Sat (ex Thu pm) 9.30–7. Oct–Mar, Mon–Wed, Thu am & Sat 9.30–4.

✱ 50p (ch & pen 25p).

♿ Castle (AM) Glen (NTS)

DOLWYDDELAN
Gwynedd
Map **6** SH75

Dolwyddelan Castle

Restored rectangular keep of c1200, with 13th-century curtain walls, and fine views.

Dobwalls
—
Dorchester

Accessible at all reasonable times.

Free.

(AM Cadw)

DONCASTER
South Yorkshire
Map **8** SE50

Museum & Art Gallery Chequer Rd
☎ (0302) 734287

Prehistoric and Romano–British archaeology, British natural history, local history and costumes, British and European Art Collection, paintings, sculpture, ceramics, glass and silver. Temporary exhibitions.

Open all year (Closed Xmas Day & New Years Day). Mon–Thu & Sat 10–5, Sun 2–5.

Free.

♿ ⚱ (pre booked parties) ♿ (ground floor only) shop ✼

DONINGTON-LE-HEATH
Leicestershire
Map **8** SK41

Donington-le-Heath Manor House
(near Coalville)
☎ Coalville (0530) 31259

Medieval manor house of c1280 with very few alterations.

Open 26 Mar–28 Sep, Wed–Sun, also BH Mon & Tue, 2–6

Free.

♿ ⚱ ♿ (ground floor & gardens only) shop ✼

DORCHESTER
Dorset
Map **3** SY69

Dinosaur Museum Icen Way
☎ (0305) 69880

The only museum in Britain devoted entirely to dinosaurs and laid out in a way

---

that really brings the world of dinosaurs alive. The museum has actual size reconstructions, fossils, inter-active exhibits such as 'feelies' where the visitor is encouraged to decide what a dinosaur would have felt like, as well as computerized and mechanical displays.

Open all year daily 9.30–5.30 (Closed Xmas day & New Year's day).

£1.20 (ch 80p, pen 90p). Family ticket (2 + up to 3 ch) £3.30.

P (100 yds) ⚱ ♿ (ground floor only) shop ⓥ

Dorset County Museum High West St
☎ (0305) 62735

Fine collection of prehistoric and Roman antiquities, geology, natural history, rural crafts and relics of both Thomas Hardy and William Barnes. Hardy's reconstructed study can be seen. Temporary exhibitions.

Open Mon–Fri 10–5 & Sat 10–1 & 2–5. (Closed Sun, Good Fri, 24, 25 & 26 Dec & New Year's day.)

✱ 60p (ch 5–16 & pen 30p, ch 5 free).

P (400 yds) ♿ (ground floor only) shop

Dorset Military Museum The Keep
☎ (0305) 64066

Covers nearly 300 years of military history, with exhibits of Dorset Regiment, Dorset Militia and Volunteers, Queen's Own Dorset Yeomanry and Devonshire and Dorset Regiment (from 1958).

Open Mon–Fri 9–1 & 2–5; Sat 9–noon, Jul–Sep 9–1 & 2–5 on Sat. (Closed Xmas day & Boxing day).

40p (ch & pen 20p).

♿ shop

Hardy's Cottage (3m E off A35 near Higher Bockhampton)
☎ (0305) 62366

Thatched house, birthplace in 1840 of Thomas Hardy. Cottage open only by appointment with tenant.

Exterior viewable Apr–Oct, daily (ex Tue am). 11–6 (or sunset).

£1 Interior.

♿ ✼ (NT)

Old Crown Court
☎ (0305) 65211 ext 215

The court is contained in the Old Shire Hall, dating from 1796–97, and was the scene of the trial of the six Tolpuddle Martyrs in 1834 who were sentenced to transportation to Botany Bay in Australia for demanding a wage increase. The building is now a Tolpuddle Memorial.

Open all year Mon–Fri 10–1 & 2–4 Guided tours of cells 11 am & 3 pm. (Closed PHs). Other times only by arrangement at adjacent West Dorset District Council.

Free.

✲

Maiden Castle (1m SW)

Prehistoric earthworks the name being derived from Celtic 'Mai-Jun' (the stronghold by the plain). Huge, oval, triple-ramparted camp, with extensive plateau on summit. Complicated defensive system of ditches and ramparts.

Open at any reasonable time.

Free.

⚠ (AM)

DORNIE
Highland Ross and Cromarty
Map **14** NG82

Eilean Donan Castle
☎ (059985) 202

┌─────────────────┐
│   **Dorchester** │
│   —   │
│   **Dounby**   │
└─────────────────┘

Standing in a beautiful mountain setting at the meeting-point of Lochs Duich, Alsh and Long, connected to the mainland by a causeway. This Seaforth fortress, erected originally in 1220, was destroyed in 1719 after being held by Jacobite troops, and was restored in 1912.

Open Etr–Sep, daily 10–12.30 & 2–6.

£1.

⚠ shop ✲

DOUGLAS
Isle of Man
Map **6** SC37

Manx Museum
☎ (0624) 75522

Items illustrate Island's archaeology, history, natural history, folk life and art. Also National Reference Library.

Open all year, Mon–Sat 10–5 (Closed 25 & 26 Dec, 1 Jan, Good Fri & the morning of 5 Jul).

Free.

⚠ shop ✲ (ex guide dogs)

DOUNBY
Orkney
Map **16** HY22

The Brough of Birsay (6m NW)

Ruined Romanesque church consisting of nave, chancel and semicircular apse, with claustral buildings on north side. Adjacent to the ruins are remains of a Norse village. Crossing by foot except at high water (no boat).

Open, see end of gazetteer. (Closed Mon & Tue morning in winter).

✳ 50p (ch & pen 25p).

(AM)

Click Mill (NE of village, off B9057)

An example of one of the rare old Orcadian horizontal watermills, in working condition.

Open at all reasonable times.

Free.

(AM)

Skara Brae (4m SW)

A remarkable group of well-preserved Stone Age dwellings, engulfed in drift sand, including stone furniture and fireplace. The most remarkable survival of its kind in Britain.

Open, see end of gazetteer.

✳ £1 (ch & pen 50p).

(AM) ⓥ

DOUNE
Central *Perthshire*
Map **11** NN70

Doune Castle
☎ (0786) 841203

Restored 14th-century stronghold, with two fine towers, on the banks of the River Teith. Associations with Bonnie Prince Charlie and Sir Walter Scott.

Open Apr–Oct daily, 10–5 (ex Thu in Apr & Oct).

✱ £1 (ch & pen 50p).

⚠ shop (AM)

Doune Motor Museum (situated 9m NW of Stirling on A84)
☎ (0786) 841203

Approximately 40 cars on display. Motor racing hill climbs held in Apr, Jun and Sep.

Open Apr–Oct, daily, 10–5.

✱ £1.50 (ch 75p, pen 90p).

⚠ ⬚ (licensed) ⌇ ⌖ shop ✖ ⓥ

DOVER
Kent
Map **5** TR34

Dover Castle

Norman castle with keep (1181–87) containing 242ft deep well. Roman 'Pharos' or lighthouse and restored Saxon St Mary de Castro's church nearby.

Keep † grounds and underground passages open, see end of gazetteer.

✱ Admission to keep, summer £1.20 (ch 16 & pen 60p). Reductions in winter. Grounds free.

⚠ (10p) ⬚ (Apr–Sep) (AM) ⓥ

Dover Museum Ladywell
☎ (0304) 201066

The Museum, founded in 1836, contains exhibits of local history, archaeology, ceramics, coins, natural history and geology. Monthly programme of temporary exhibitions.

Open Mon, Tue & Thu–Sat 10–4.45.

Free.

P (25 yds) ⌖ shop ✖

Roman Painted House New St
☎ (0304) 203279

Large part of an exceptionally preserved Roman town house, 1,800 years old and containing the best preserved and oldest Roman wall paintings north of the Alps. Also substantially complete underfloor central heating system; part of late-Roman defences; extensive display panels on Roman Dover together with some recent finds. Free guided tours for parties.

Open Apr–Oct, Tue–Sun 10–5.

✱ 40p (ch & pen 20p).

⚠ ⌖ (ground floor & gardens only) shop ✖

Doune
—
Dryburgh

DOWNE
Gt London
Map **5** TQ46

Down House (Darwin Museum) Luxted Rd
☎ Farnborough (Kent) (0689) 59119

Home of Charles Darwin for 40 years and contains the Darwin Memorial. Gardens, also open.

Open Mar–Jan, Tue–Thu, Sat & Sun 1–6 (last visitor 5.30). Also open BH Mon. (Closed 24–27 Dec).

£1.20 (ch 5–16 30p & pen 60p).

⚠ ⌖ shop ✖

DRAYTON MANOR PARK & ZOO
Staffordshire
Map **4** SK10
(on A4091, 1m S of junction with A5 1½m S of Tamworth)
☎ Tamworth (0827) 287979

Family Leisure Park with 160 acres of Parkland and Lakes, open plan Zoo, amusement park with 25 rides, and wristbands for unlimited Rides or discount tickets. The rides include Looping Roller Coaster, Log Flume, Paratower, Cable Cars, Jungle Cruise, Pirate Ship, Flying Dutchman, and Dinosaurland etc.

Open Etr–Oct daily 10.30–6

✱ £1 (ch 16 60p) cars 30p. Party.

⚠ ⬚ (licensed) ⌖ shop garden centre ✖ (ex park)

DRE-FACH-FELINDRE
Dyfed
Map **2** SN33

Museum of the Woollen Industry
☎ Velindre (0559) 370929

A branch of the National Museum of Wales, it occupies part of a working mill, the Cambrian Mills. Its collection of textile machinery dates back to the 18th century and the exhibition traces the development of the industry.

Open Apr–Sep, Mon–Sat 10–5. (Closed May Day). Oct–Mar, Mon–Fri 10–5.

Free.

⚠ ⊞ ⌖ (ground floor only) shop

DREWSTEIGNTON
Devon
Map **3** SX79

Castle Drogo (2m NE of Chagford, turn off A382 at Sandy Park)
☎ Chagford (06473) 3306

A granite castle built between 1910 and 1930, one of the most remarkable works of Sir Edwin Lutyens. Standing at 900ft it overlooks the gorge of the River Teign.

Open 28 Mar–Oct, daily 11–6, last admissions 5.30.

£2.30 (gardens & grounds only £1.20). Party.

⬚ (licensed) ⌖ shop (NT)

DRUMCOLTRAN TOWER
Dumfries and Galloway
Kirkcudbrightshire
Map **11** NX86
(5m NE of Dalbeattie)

A 16th-century tower house, three-storeys in height and built to an oblong plan, with a projecting tower or wing.

Open, see end of gazetteer. Key with keeper.

Free.

(AM)

DRUMNADROCHIT
Highland *Inverness-shire*
Map **14** NH53

Official Loch Ness Monster Exhibition
Loch Ness Centre
☎ (04562) 573

Tells the story from 565 A.D. to present day. Includes a scale model of the loch, equipment used in the hunt, sonar display and models of various underwater investigations. Videos, audios and a display on the natural history of the loch. The Exhibition has doubled in size and now encompasses the International House of Heraldry and in summer a glass blowing exhibition.

Open Etr, then May–Oct daily. May–mid June & Sep–Oct 9.30–8.15. Mid June–Aug 9 am–9.30 pm. (Reduced hours in winter please telephone for details).

✱ £1.35 (students 95p, pen 80p, ch 10–16 yrs 65p, ch 5–9 yrs 45p). Family ticket £3.25 (max one couple & five children).

⚠ ⬚ (licensed) ⌖ (assistance required) shop ✖ (ex grounds)

Urquhart Castle

Historic, mainly 14th-century castle overlooking Loch Ness, destroyed before the 1715 Rising.

Open, see end of gazetteer.

✱ £1 (ch & pen 50p).

(AM)

DRYBURGH
Borders *Berwickshire*
Map **12** NT53

Dryburgh Abbey

One of the famous Border monasteries founded by David I. The ruins are of great beauty and occupy a lovely situation in a horseshoe bend of the River Tweed. Within the church are the graves of Sir Walter Scott and Earl Haig.

Open, see end of gazetteer.

✱ £1 (ch & pen 50p).

⚠ (AM)

DRYSL WYN
Dyfed
Map **2** SN52

Dryslwyn Castle
Ruined, 13th century, native Welsh stronghold on a lofty mound, important for its part in the struggles between the Welsh and English in the 13th century.

Accessible at any time.

Free.

 △ (AM Cadw)

DUDLEY
West Midlands
Map **7** SO99

Black Country Museum Tipton Rd (opposite Dudley Guest Hospital)
☎ 021-557 9643

An open-air museum of the region with buildings re-erected to form a village representing the way of life in this area. The village has a canal boat dock with a range of narrowboats on display. A chainmaker's house with its brewhouse has been re-erected, together with other buildings including a public house. Demonstrations of chainmaking and glass cutting are given in traditional workshops. Trips into the famous Dudley Tunnel start from the site daily. Also, a coal mine, chemist's shop, cottages, chapel and public house are on display. Transport across the site is provided by an electric tramway system.

Open Mar–Dec, daily 10–5 or dusk if earlier. (Closed Xmas).

✱ £1.75 (ch & pen £1). Party.

△ Ⓑ (licensed) ⏜ ♦ (ground floor only) shop

Dudley Zoological Gardens & Castle
☎ (0384) 52401

Situated in 40 acres of attractively wooded grounds with over 1000 animals. Also Children's Corner, miniature steam railway, a chair-lift and the ruins of Dudley Castle.

Open all year, daily Mon–Sat from 9 am, Sun from 10 am. (Last admission 4.30 pm in summer, 3.30 pm in winter.). Details not confirmed for 1986.

✱ £2.40 (ch 3–15 & pen £1.20). Party.

△ Ⓑ (licensed) ⏜ ♦ shop ✱

Museum & Art Gallery St James's Rd
☎ (0384) 55433 ext 5530

Includes the Brooke Robinson collection of fine and decorative art, Geological Gallery and a wide variety of temporary exhibitions throughout the year.

Open Mon–Sat 10–5. (Closed BHs).

Free.

P ♦ (ground floor only) ✱

DUFFTOWN
Grampian *Banffshire*
Map **15** NJ33

Dryslwyn
–
Dumfries

Balvenie Castle
Mainly 15th- and 16th-century, the ancient stronghold of the Comyns, preserving a remarkable iron 'yett'.

Open, see end of gazetteer. Open Apr–Sep only.

✱ 50p (ch & pen 25p).

△ (AM)

Dufftown Museum The Tower, The Square
☎ Forres (0309) 73701

Small local history museum featuring Mortlach-Kirk material. Temporary displays.

Open May–Sep, Mon–Sat 9.30–5.30 (6.30 in Jul & Aug) also Sun in Aug 2–6.30. Details not confirmed for 1986.

Free.

P ♦ shop ✱

Glenfiddich Distillery (N of town, off A941)
☎ (0340) 20373

Situated by Balvenie Castle in the heart of Speyside country, the distillery was founded in 1887 by Major William Grant. A visitor's reception centre houses a bar and a Scotch whisky museum. The theatre offers a programme in six languages covering the history of Scotland and Scotch whisky.

Open all year Mon–Fri 9.30–4.30 (Jun–Aug, Thu until 7.30 pm), also 11 May–13 Oct Sat 9.30–4.30, Sun 12–4.30. (Closed 23 Dec–5 Jan).

Free.

△ ⏜ ♦ (ground floor & gardens only) shop

DUFFUS
Grampian *Moray*
Map **15** NJ16

Duffus Castle (off B9012)
Motte and bailey castle, with 8-acre bailey surrounding rebuilt 15th-century hall and 14th-century tower, now broken into two halves.

Open all reasonable times.

Free.

△ (AM)

DUMBARTON
Strathclyde *Dunbartonshire*
Map **10** NS37

Dumbarton Castle
Ancient capital of the Britons of Strathclyde. Surviving military fortifications date to 17th- and 18th-centuries.

Open, see end of gazetteer.

✱ 50p (ch & pen 25p).
(AM)

DUMFRIES
Dumfries and Galloway *Dumfriesshire*
Map **11** NX97

Burns House Burns St
☎ (0387) 55297

Robert Burns died in this house in 1796. In the house are displayed memorials and personal relics of the poet.

Open all year, Mon–Sat 10–1 & 2–5; Apr–Sep Sun 2–5. (Closed Mon Oct–Mar).

30p (ch, pen & students 15p).

P (200 yds) shop

Burns Mausoleum St Michael's Churchyard
☎ (0387) 55297

Mausoleum in the form of a Grecian temple containing the tombs of the poet, Jean Armour, Burns' wife, and their five sons. A sculptured group depicts the Muse of Poetry throwing her cloak over Burns at the plough.

Open as Burns House by arrangement with Custodian.

P (200 yds)

Dumfries Museum and Camera Obscura The Observatory, Church St
☎ (0387) 53374

Large collection of local history, archaeology, geology, local birds and animals. The Old Bridge House branch museum (on the Old Bridge) contains period rooms portraying the local way of life in the past.

Open all year, Mon–Sat 10–1 & 2–5; Sun 2–5 Apr–Sep only. (Camera obscura and Old Bridge House open Apr–Sep only closed Mon).

Museum and Old Bridge House free. Camera Obscura 50p (ch 25p).

P ♦ shop

Lincluden College
Originally the site of a Benedictine nunnery, founded in 1164. It was suppressed at the end of the 14th century and in its place a college of eight secular canons under a provost was established. The present remains are those of the collegiate church, dating from the early 15th century and the provost's house, dating from the 16th century.

Open, see end of gazetteer. Closed Thu afternoon & Fri.

✱ 50p (ch & pen 25p).
(AM)

Old Town Mill Mill Rd
☎ (0387) 64808

Burns interpretation centre with exhibition of 'Robert Burns and Dumfries'.

Open all year Tue–Sat 10–8, also Apr–Sep Mon 10–8, Sun 2–5.

Free.

Shop

DUNBAR
Lothian *East Lothian*
Map **12** NT67

Tyninghame Gardens (1m N of A1
between Dunbar & East Linton)
☎ East Linton (0620) 860330

*Beautiful and varied gardens. A walled
garden, terraced gardens and a lovely
'secret' garden set around the ruins of the
Norman St Baldred's Church.*

Open Jun–Sep Mon–Fri 10.30–4.30.

✳ 70p (ch 25p, pen 40p).

🅰 ♿ ✻

DUNBEATH
Highland *Caithness*
Map **15** ND12

Laidhay Croft Museum
☎ Lybster (05932) 357

*Late 18th- to early 19th-century
Caithness-type longhouse with dwelling,
byre and stable under one roof and
detached winnowing barn. All thatched
and furnished in typical croft style.*

Open Etr–Sep daily 10–6.

50p (ch free).

🅰 ♿ (ex Byre & small bedroom)

DUNDEE
Tayside *Angus*
Map **11** NO43

Barrack Street Museum Barrack St
☎ (0382) 23141

*Museum of Natural History; Scottish
Wildlife of Lowlands and Highlands. Great
Tay Whale. Some changes in displays
may be caused by redevelopment.*

Open Mon–Sat 10–5.

Free.

P (250 yds) shop ✻

Broughty Castle Museum
Broughty Ferry (4m E)
☎ (0382) 76121 or 23141

*15th-century castle rebuilt as estuary fort
in 19th century. Displays of arms and
armour, seashore wildlife, Dundee's
former whaling industry and history of
former Burgh of Broughty Ferry.*

Open Mon–Thu & Sat 10–1 & 2–5. Sun 2–5
(Jul–Sep only).

Free.

🅰 🛗 shop ✻

Camperdown Park
☎ (0382) 23141 Ext 4413. Bookings
621993

*The park comprises about 400 acres
formed around the neo-Classical Manor
House. The parklands were extensively
planted with a wide variety of trees, the
most famous being the Camperdown Elm,
a weeping form of Wych Elm. Today the
recreational attractions include a golf
course, a Wildlife Centre with a large
collection of indigenous and domestic
animals, an extensive network of
footpaths and forest trails and a large*

Dunbar
—
Dungeness

*adventure play area. A restaurant and
function area is located in the manor
house.*

Open Apr–Sep, daily. Other times by
arrangement.

Free.

🅰 ♿ 🛗 ♿ (ground floor & gardens only)
✻

Claypotts Castle (junction of A92 and
B978)

*A fine example of a fortified residence of
the late 16th century; later it belonged to
John Graham of Claverhouse, 'Bonnie
Dundee' of the 1688/9 uprising.*

Open, see end of gazetteer. (Closed in
winter).

50p (ch & pen 25p).

(AM)

**Dundee Art Gallery and Museum
(McManus Gallery)** Albert Sq
☎ (0382) 23141

*Major Art Gallery with changing
exhibitions of local and national interest.
Important Scottish and Victorian
collections. Local history displays cover
Trade and Industry, Social and Civic
History. Restricted displays of
archaeology during redevelopment in
1986. McManus Galleries is one of
Dundee's finest Victorian buildings by
Gilbert Scott.*

Open Mon–Sat 10–5.

Free.

P (300 yds) ♿ shop ✻

Mills Observatory Balgay Park, Glamis
Rd
☎ (0382) 67138 or 23141

*Observatory, built in 1935, with fine
Victorian 10-inch Cooke refracting
telescope and other instruments. Gallery
displays on astronomy and space
exploration, and small planetarium.*

Open Apr–Sep Mon–Fri 10–5, Sat 2–5;
Oct–Mar, Mon–Fri 3–10, Sat 2–5.

Parties booked in advance.

Free.

🅰 🛗 shop ✻

DUNDRENNAN
Dumfries and Galloway
Kirkcudbrightshire
Map **11** NX74

Dundrennan Abbey

*The remains of Cistercian house founded
in 1142. Here Mary Queen of Scots spent
her last night on native soil before seeking
shelter in England.*

Open, see end of gazetteer.

✳ 50p (ch & pen 25p).

🅰 (AM)

DUNFERMLINE
Fife *Fife*
Map **11** NT08

Andrew Carnegie Birthplace Museum
Junction of Moodie St and Priory Ln
☎ (0383) 724302

*The cottage in which the great
philanthropist was born in 1835. New
displays tell the exciting story of the
weaver's son who gave away 350 million
dollars and how the Carnegie Trusts still
spend his money for the good of mankind.*

Open all year daily. Apr–Oct Mon–Sat 11–
5 (Wed 8 pm), Sun 2–5; Nov–Mar 2–4.

Free.

P ♿ (ground floor only) shop ✻ (ex guide
dogs)

Dunfermline Abbey Pittencrieff Park

*Benedictine house founded by Queen
Margaret. The foundations of her church
remain beneath the present Norman nave.
The site of the choir is now occupied by a
modern parish church, at the east end of
which are remains of St Margaret's shrine
dating from the 13th century. King Robert
the Bruce is buried in the choir and his
grave is marked by a modern brass.
Guest house was a royal palace where
Charles I was born.*

Open, see end of gazetteer.

Free.

(AM)

Dunfermline District Museum Viewfield
Terrace
☎ (0383) 721814

*Interesting and varied displays of local
history, domestic bygones and damask
linen. Periodic special exhibitions.*

Open all year, Mon–Sat 11–5. (Closed Sun
& BHs).

Free.

P ✻

Pittencrief House Museum Pittencrief
Park
☎ (0383) 722935 or 721814.

*Situated in a rugged glen, with lawns,
hothouses, and gardens, overlooked by
the ruined 11th-century Malcolm
Canmore's Tower. Fine 17th-century
mansion house, with galleries displaying
local history, costume and temporary
exhibitions.*

Open May–Aug Mon & Wed–Sun 11–5.

Free.

🅰 🛗 ✻

DUNGENESS
Kent
Map **5** TR01

'A' Nuclear Power Station
☎ Lydd (0679) 20461 ext 238

*Building open throughout the year for
organised group tours by pre-
arrangement any weekday and to the
general public on Wed, tours at 2 pm & 3
pm, 11 Jun–24 Sep. Ticket obtainable*

from the local South Eastern Electricity Board shops. Ch under 14 not admitted.

Free.

⚠ &. (by arrangement) ✕

DUNKELD
Tayside *Perthshire*
Map **11** NO04

Little Houses
☎ (03502) 460

Dating from after the Battle of Dunkeld in 1689. Trust display of photographs of the restoration scheme and an audio-visual show are in the Tourist Information Centre.

Open 28 Mar–May & Sep–23 Dec, Mon–Sat 10–1 & 2–4.30; Jun–Aug, Mon–Sat 10–6, Sun 2–5.

Free.

shop (NTS)

Loch of The Lowes Wild Life Reserve
☎ (03502) 337

Variety of wild life. Great crested grebes and other waterfowl in natural surroundings can be watched through high powered binoculars from observation hide. Exhibition and slide programme in visitor centre.

Open Apr–Sep daily 10–7 (Jun–Aug open until 8.30 pm) subject to review. Hide open all times. Special arrangements for parties booked in advance.

Free

⚠ &. (ground floor only) shop ✕

DUNS
Borders *Berwickshire*
Map **12** NT75

Jim Clark Room Newton St
☎ (03612) 82600

Contains motor racing trophies won by the famous driver Jim Clark, who was killed in Germany in 1968. Included are the two world Championship Trophies of 1963 and 1965 and other Grand Prix awards. Clark was the first Honorary Burgess of Duns and his parents gave the trophies to the town.

Dungeness
—
Durham

Open Etr–Sep Mon–Sat 10–1 & 2–6, Sun 2–6.

50p (ch 16 25p ch under 5 free). Parties during winter by special arrangement.

⚠ &.

Manderston (1¾m E off A6105)
☎ (0361) 83450

A fine Edwardian house with magnificent State Rooms and extensive domestic offices, all completed in 1905, to a high standard of workmanship. Also there is the only silver staircase in the world. Stables, marble dairy, gardens, woodland garden and lakeside walks.

Open 15 May–28 Sep, Sun & Thu 2–5.30. Also open BHs.

Admission fee payable. Party 20+ (by appointment at any time).

⚠ ⚲ &. (ground floor only) shop

DUNSTER
Somerset
Map **3** SS95

Dunster Castle
☎ (0643) 821314

Restored 11th-century and later castle, with rare portraits, hall leading to famous staircase, gallery containing leather hangings. Restored flour mill and sub-tropical terraced gardens.

Open 29 Mar–Sep, Sat–Wed 11–5; Oct Sat–Wed noon–4.

£2.20 (ch £1.10). Party 15+.

⚠ ⌁ (NT)

Old Dovecote
☎ (0643) 821395

12th-century dovecote, part of former priory, retaining a rare original potence (revolving ladder for reaching nesting boxes).

Open Etr–mid Oct daily, 10–dusk.

Charge for Leaflet.
P (¼ mile) ✕

DUNVEGAN
Isle of Skye Highland *Inverness-shire*
Map **13** NG24

Dunvegan Castle
☎ (047022) 206

Historic and romantic home of the Chief of Macleod since the 13th century. Pit dungeon and famous 'Fairy' flag.

Open Etr–mid Oct Mon–Sat. Late May–Sep 10.30–5; Etr–late May & during Oct 2–5 only.

✱ £1.80 (ch 90p). Gardens only 50p (ch 25p).

⚠ ⌁ &. (ground floor & gardens only) shop

DUNWICH
Suffolk
Map **5** TM47

Dunwich Museum St James Street
☎ Westleton (072873) 358

Contains the history and relics of the ancient city of Dunwich. Also flora and fauna of the area.

Open Apr–Oct, Sat & Sun 2–4.30. Also Tue & Thu, May–Sep & daily in Aug. (Subject to availability of volunteers).

Free.

⚠ shop ✕

DURHAM
Co Durham
Map **12** NZ24

Durham Castle
☎ (0385) 65481

Norman structure, utilised since 1832 by University of Durham.

Open all year for guided tours only. First three weeks of Apr & Jul–Sep Mon–Sat 10–12 & 2–4.30; rest of year Mon, Wed & Sat 2–4. Closed at times owing to university functions.

✱ 85p (ch 40p).

P (500 yds) ✕

107

Durham Light Infantry Museum & Arts Centre Aykley Heads

☎ (0385) 42214

History of famous regiment, including armaments, medals and uniforms in a modern setting. Also Arts centre on first floor. Exhibitions, films and family activities. Military Vehicle Rally Aug BH Sun & Mon.

Open Tue–Sat 10–5 & Sun 2–5. (Closed Mon ex BHs).

✳ 50p (ch, pen and UB40 20p).

⚠ ⚏ & shop ✖

Finchale Priory (3m NE)

Considerable remains of the 13th-century church of the Benedictine priory in picturesque position on banks of the River Wear.

Open † see end of gazetteer.

✳ 30p (ch & pen 15p). Free during winter.

⚠ & (AM)

Oriental Museum University of Durham, Elvet Hill

☎ (0385) 66711

Contains a wide range of artefacts from all periods of the Orient from Ancient Egypt to Japan. Also special temporary exhibitions.

Open Mon–Fri 9.30–1. Also at weekends Mar–Oct, Sat 9.30–1 & 2–5, Sun 2–5 only.

Durham
—
Dyrham

✳ 50p (ch & pen 30p).

⚠ & (ground floor only) shop ✖

St Aidan's College Grounds Windmill Hill

☎ (0385) 65011

The College was designed by Sir Basil Spence, and built in the early sixties. The spacious and well-stocked grounds, landscaped by Professor Brian Hackett, are at their best during July, when the shrub beds are in flower. Features include a laburnum walk and a reflecting pool, well stocked with acquatic plants and fish. From the garden there are fine views of Durham Cathedral.

Open all year, daily from 9–dusk.

Free, but donations to NGS.

⚠ ⚏ (by prior arrangement) & (ground floor only) ✖ (garden only)

DUXFORD
Cambridgeshire
Map **5** TL44

Duxford Airfield (off junction 10 of M11 on A505)
☎ Cambridge (0223) 833963

This former Battle of Britain fighter station with hangars dating from the First World War, now houses most of the Imperial War Museum's collections of military aircraft, armoured fighting vehicles and other large exhibits. There are more than ninety historic aircraft on the airfield, and also on display is the Duxford Aviation Society's civil aircraft collection including Concorde 01.

Open 15 Mar–2 Nov (ex Good Fri & May Day BH) 10.30–5.30 (last admission 4.45 pm or dusk).

£2.50 (ch 5–16 & pen £1.50). Admission not confirmed.

⚠ ⚏ licensed ⚑ & (ex aircraft) shop ✖ ⓥ

DYMCHURCH
Kent
Map **5** TR02

Martello Tower (No 24)

One of a series of circular towers designed to repel expected Napoleonic invasion in the early 19th century, with rooftop mounting for heavy gun.

Open see end of gazetteer (Apr–Sep only).

✳ 30p (ch 16 & pen 15p).

⚠ (AM)

DYRHAM
Avon
Map **3** ST77

Dyrham Park

17th-century mansion, designed partly by William Talman in 1698, with contemporary Dutch-style furnishings. Garden front of 1692 by Hauduroy.

House & garden open 29 Mar, May & Oct, Sat–Wed 2–6; Jun–Sep, Sat–Thu 2–6. Park open daily 12–6.

£2.20 (ch £1.10). Party 15+.

⚠ ⬚ ♿ (NT)

EASBY
North Yorkshire
Map 7 NZ10

Easby Abbey

Sited on banks of River Swale, a Premonstratensian Abbey dedicated to St Agatha, founded 1155. Considerable remains of monastic buildings.

Open, see end of gazetteer.

✳ 50p (ch 16 & pen 25p).

⚠ (AM)

EASDALE
Strathclyde *Argyll*
Map 10 NM71

An Cala Garden

Featuring cherry trees, azaleas, roses, water and rock gardens.

Open Apr–mid Sep, Mon & Thu 2–6.

40p (ch 10p accompanied).

⚠ ♿ (ex wild garden)

Easdale Island Folk Museum
☎ Balvicar (08523) 382

A pictorial history of life on the Slate Islands in the 19th century showing the industrial and domestic life of the villagers. Scenic walks to visit the sea-filled quarries devastated by the great storm of November 1881 when 240 men lost their livelihoods. Microfilms of records dating back to 1745. Regular passenger ferry service to the Island Museum from Easdale.

Open Apr–Oct, Mon–Sat 10.30–5.30, Sun 10.30–5.

60p (ch 25p).

P (on mainland) ⬚ (licensed) ♿

EASTBOURNE
East Sussex
Map 5 TV69

Coastal Defence Museum Tower 73 (The Wish Tower), King Edward's Pde
☎ (0323) 35809

One of the Martello Towers erected to combat threatened Napoleonic invasion in the early 19th century and now restored as a museum displaying defence methods and equipment of that period.

Open Etr–Oct daily 9.30–5.30. Details not confirmed for 1986.

Admission fee payable.

P (30 yds) ♿ shop 🍴

Eastbourne Redoubt Fortress Royal Parade
☎ (0323) 33952

Extensive fortification built in 1804 during Napoleonic Wars against the threat of invasion. Now the home of the Sussex Combined Services Museum and the Regimental Museum of the Royal Sussex Regiment. The Fort also contains an Aquarium/Grotto with marine and freshwater fish.

Open Etr–Oct daily; 9.30–5.30. Details not confirmed for 1986.

Admission fee payable.

P (10 yds) ⬚ ♿ ♿ (ground floor only) shop ⓥ

Lifeboat Museum Grand Pde
☎ (0323) 30717

The museum displays details of the work carried out by the various lifeboats which have been on station at Eastbourne. There are also displays illustrating the work of the RNLI, a selection of lifeboat models, the original sails and oars from the last sailing lifeboat at the station, various types of gear worn by lifeboat men, together with descriptions and accompanying photographs of notable rescues.

Open Jan–Mar wknds only, Apr–Dec daily, 9.30–6.

Free.

⚠ ♿ (ground floor only) shop

Towner Art Gallery & Local History Museum Manor Gardens, High St
☎ (0323) 21635 or 25112

Georgian manor house (1776) with later alterations set in pleasant gardens, containing collection of 19th- and 20th-century British works of art. Frequent temporary exhibitions. Museum has displays of Eastbourne history.

Open all year, Mon–Fri 10–5 & Sun 2–5. (Closed Mons in winter, Good Fri, Xmas day & New Year's day).

Free.

P ♿ (ground floor & gardens only) shop 🍴

EAST CLANDON
Surrey
Map 4 TQ05

Hatchlands
☎ Guildford (0483) 222787

A handsome 18th-century house with notable ceiling in the drawing room and a splendid example of Robert Adam's work in the library. Boscawen exhibition.

Open 30 Mar–mid Oct, Wed, Thu, Sun & BH Mons 2–6 (last entry 5.30).

£1.20 (ch 60p).

⚠ (limited) 🍴 (NT)
See also **Clandon Park** (NT)

EAST COKER
Somerset
Map 3 ST51

Coker Court
☎ West Coker (093586) 3146

Former home of Helyar Family and partly on view to the public. The Great Hall, built in the 15th century, has two tapestries on view and there are two Georgian rooms open.

Open Apr–Sep, Fri & BH 2.30–5.

50p.

🍴 🏰

EAST COWES
Isle of Wight
Map 4 SZ59

Barton Manor Vineyard and Gardens
☎ Cowes (0983) 292835

20-acre gardens, grounds and lake with 5-acre vineyard. Winery and Wine Bar.

Open daily May–12 Oct (plus Etr & Sat and Sun in Apr) 10.30–5.30.

✳ £1.50 (ch free, pen £1.25). Prices include guide leaflet.

⚠ ⬚ (licensed) ♿ shop 🍴

EAST FORTUNE
Lothian *East Lothian*
Map 12 NT57

Museum of Flight East Fortune Airfield
☎ 031-225 7534

National Museums of Scotland. The former airship base now displays the history of aircraft and rockets and has working exhibits which visitors may operate. Exhibits include a Supermarine Spitfire Mk 16, De Haviland Sea Venom, Hawker Sea Hawk and Comet (4c).

Open July & Aug daily 10–4, plus open days.

Free.

⚠ ♿ 🍴

EAST GRINSTEAD
West Sussex
Map 5 TQ33

Sackville College High St
☎ (0342) 21639

Early Jacobean almshouse, with hall and chapel, built round a quadrangular courtyard, and founded in 1609 by 2nd Earl of Dorset. Contains fine oak furniture.

Open May–Sep, daily 2–5.

75p (ch 25p).

⚠ 🍴

Standen (1½m S, signposted from B2110)

Designed in 1894 by Philip Webb with original William Morris textiles and wallpapers. There is also a beautiful hillside garden.

Open 29 Mar–Oct, Wed, Thu, Sat & Sun 2–6. →

Last admission 5.30 pm.
£1.70. Garden only 85p.
⚖ 🕱 (in house) (NT)

EAST LAMBROOK
Somerset
Map **3** ST41

**East Lambrook Manor Garden &
Margery Fish Nursery**
☎ South Petherton (0460) 40328

*Cottage style garden of the late Margery
Fish.*

Garden & Nursery open daily 9–1 & 2–5.
50p.

P (near entrance) shop & garden centre
🕱

EAST LINTON
Lothian *East Lothian*
Map **12** NT57

Hailes Castle (1m SW on unclass rd)

*An old castle or fortified manor house of
the Gourlays and Hepburns, with a 16th-
century chapel, dismantled in 1650.*

Open, see end of gazetteer.

✳ 50p (ch 25p).

⚠ (AM)

Preston Mill
☎ (0620) 860426

*This is the oldest working water-driven
meal mill to survive in Scotland. Conical
roof, projecting wind vane and red
pantiles.*

Open 28 Mar–Sep Mon–Sat 10–12.30 & 2–
5.30, Sun 2–5.30; Oct Mon–Sat 10–12.30
& 2–4.30, Sun 2–4.30; Nov–Mar, Sat 10–
12.30 & 2–4.30, Sun 2–4.30.

85p (ch 16 40p). Phantassie Doocot a
short walk away once held 500 birds.

(NTS)

EASTNOR
Hereford and Worcester
Map **3** SO73

Eastnor Castle
☎ Ledbury (0531) 2304

*Built by Sir Robert Smirke for the 1st Earl
Somers in the early 19th century, contains
fine furnishing, pictures, and armour.
Grounds have specimen trees.*

Open Sun, 19 May–Sep also Wed & Thu
Jul & Aug, also BH Mons. Other times by
appointment for parties only.

Admission fee payable.

⚠ ⚖ & (gardens only) shop

EASTON
Suffolk
Map **5** TM25

Easton Farm Park
☎ Wickham Market (0728) 746475

*Rare breeds of farm animals, Victorian
Dairy, pets paddock and adventure
playpit. Visitors can watch the cows being
milked each afternoon. Country bygones,*

East Grinstead
—
Edinburgh

*and picnic area. Also there is a working
blacksmith with a forge, and coarse
fishing.*

Open Etr–Sep daily 10.30–6.

✳ £1.60 (ch 3–16 90p pen £1.20). Party.

⚠ ⚖ & (ground floor only) shop

EASTWOOD
Nottinghamshire
Map **8** SK44

D. H. Lawrence Birthplace 8A Victoria
St
☎ Langley Mill (07737) 66611

*Birthplace of D. H. Lawrence in 1885;
restored and furnished in manner
depicting working class life in Victorian
times. A craft centre is adjacent to the
birthplace.*

Open Mon, Tue, Thu, Fri & Sun 1.30–4;
Wed, 9.30–noon; Sats 9.30–4; also BH.
(Closed 24 Dec–1 Jan).

Admission fee payable.

P (20 or 100 yds) shop 🕱

ECCLEFECHAN
Dumfries and Galloway *Dumfriesshire*
Map **11** NY17

Carlyle's Birthplace
☎ (05763) 666

*A characteristic late 18th-century Scottish
artisan's house, where Thomas Carlyle
was born in 1795. Collection of
manuscripts and personal relics.*

Open 28 Mar–Oct, Mon–Sat 10–6.

60p (ch 30p).

(NTS)

ECCLES
Gt Manchester
Map **7** SJ79

Monks Hall Museum Wellington Rd
☎ 061-789 4372

*16th-century building with later additions,
housing a small toy museum and material
of local interest including a Nasmyth
steam hammer. There are frequent
temporary exhibitions.*

Open Mon–Fri 10–5, Sun 2–5 (Closed
Good Fri, Xmas & New Year's day).

Free.

P (few yds in side st) & 🕱

EDINBURGH
Lothian *Midlothian*
Map **11** NT27

Camera Obscura Outlook Tower Visitor
Centre, Castle Hill
☎ 031-226 3709

*Guided tours of Edinburgh's unique
optical device, which was installed in*

---

*1850. Rooftop views over the city. Also,
displays of pinhole photography, and the
country's first exhibition of floating 3-D
laser images.*

Open daily Oct–Mar 10–5; Apr–Sep 9.30–
5.30.

✳ £1.25 (ch & pen 60p, students £1)
Party.

P (200 yds) & (ground floor only) shop

Canongate Tolbooth 163 Canongate
☎ 031-225 2424 ext 6638

*Dates from 1591 and shows a curious
projection clock. Also there is a Brass-
rubbing centre.*

Open Jun–Sep Mon–Sat 10–6, Sun 2–5
during festival. Oct–May 10–5.

Free.

P (in the Royal Mile) shop 🕱

City Art Centre 2 Market St
☎ 031-225 2424 ext 6650. After 5 pm &
weekends 031-225 1131

*The Art Centre houses the City's
permanent fine art collection comprising
3,000 paintings, drawings, prints and
sculptures mostly by Scottish artists,
dating from 17th century to the present.
There is also a diverse programme of
temporary exhibitions drawn from the UK
and abroad.*

Open Mon–Sat 10–5 (10–6 Jun–Sep) &
Sun 2–5 during Edinburgh Festival.
Free.

P (metered) ⚖ (licensed) & shop 🕱

Craigmillar Castle

*A 14th-century stronghold associated
with Mary, Queen of Scots. 16th- and
17th-century apartments survive.*

Open Apr–Sep Mon–Wed & Sat 9.30–7.
Sun 2–7. Oct–Mar closes 4 pm.

✳ 50p (ch & pen 25p).

⚠ (AM)

Edinburgh Castle

*An historic stronghold, famous for the
Crown Room, Banqueting Hall, Scottish
United Services Museum, St Margaret's
Chapel and the impressive Scottish
National War Memorial.*

Open 5 Jan–Mar 9.30–5.05 weekdays,
12.30–4.20 Sun; May–Oct 9.30–6
weekdays, 11–6 Sun; Nov–Dec 9.30–5.05
weekdays, 12.30–4.20 Sun. Last
admission ticket sold 45 mins before
closing time.

✳ £2 (ch & pen £1). Family £4. War
Memorial Free.

⚠ (AM)

Edinburgh Zoo The Scottish National
Zoological Park
☎ 031-334 9171

*Set in 80 acres of grounds, this zoo is one
of the finest in Europe, containing a
superb collection of mammals, birds and
reptiles. Also magnificent panoramic
views of Edinburgh and surrounding
countryside.*

Open all year. Mon–Sat 9–6, Suns 9.30–6 in summer, but closes 5 pm or dusk in winter.

✳ £2.40 (ch & pen £1.20). Party 10+ application to Booking's Officer, Zoological Park, Murrayfield, Edinburgh EH12 6TS.

⚠ 𝒯 (licensed) ⚞ ♿ (ground floor & gardens only) shop garden centre ✗

George Heriot's School Lauriston Place
☎ 031-229 7263

Dates from 1628 and was founded by George Heriot, the 'Jingling Geordie' of Sir Walter Scott's 'Fortunes of Nigel'.

Open 7 Jul–22 Aug Mon–Fri, 9.30–4.30.

Free.

P (200 yds) ♿ (ground floor only) ✗

Georgian House 7 Charlotte Sq
☎ 031-225 2160

Lower floors open as typical Georgian house, furnished as it might have been by first owners, showing domestic surroundings and reflecting social conditions of that age.

Open 28 Mar–Oct, Mon–Sat 10–5 & Sun 2–5; Nov, Sat 10–4.30 & Sun 2–4.30 (last admission ½ hr before closing).

£1.20 (ch 16 60p) (includes audio-visual shows).

(NTS)

Edinburgh

Gladstone's Land 483 Lawnmarket
☎ 031-226 5856

Built in 1620 and contains fine examples of tempera painting on the walls and ceilings and is furnished as a typical 17th-century home. Ground floor includes shop front and goods of the period.

Days and times of opening as **Georgian House.**

£1 (ch 16 50p).

(NTS)

Huntly House 142 Canongate
☎ 031-225 2424 ext 6689 (031-225 1131 after 5 pm & weekends)

Dating from 1570 and housing the City Museum of local history. Includes collections of silver, glass and pottery.

Open Mon–Sat, Jun–Sep 10–6, Oct–May 10–5. (During Festival period only Sun 2–5).

Free.

P (Meters) shop ✗

John Knox House Museum 45 High St
☎ 031-556 6961

15th-century house preserving old wooden galleries, which was built by the goldsmith to Mary, Queen of Scots. During recent renovation work, the original floor in the Oak Room was uncovered as well as a magnificent painted ceiling which dates back to the early 1600s. There is also a room which contains a model of the house, and paintings and prints showing the development of the house from 15th-century to the present day.

Open Mon–Sat 10–5; Oct–Mar 10–3.30. (Closed Xmas & New Year). Last admission 4.30, Winter 3.

£1 (ch & pen 70p). Party 20+.

P shop ✗

Lady Stair's House off Lawnmarket
☎ 031-225 2424 ext 6593 (031-225 1131 after 5 pm & weekends)

A restored town house dating from 1622, containing a museum of literary relics of Robert Burns, Sir Walter Scott and Robert Louis Stevenson.

Open Mon–Sat, Jun–Sep 10–6, Oct–May 10–5. (During Festival period only Sun 2–5).

Free.

P (Meters) shop ✗

Share This Heritage

Scotland has its own heritage of hydro electric power, a heritage which the North of Scotland Hydro-Electric Board invites you to share by seeing its Visitors' Centre in **Pitlochry Power Station**, by Loch Faskally. In its exhibition it features one of the Board's major developments, the Tummel Valley Scheme.
Two videos with a scale model of the valley, mimic diagrams and photographs illustrate both how the scheme operates and how

CRUACHAN

salmon share the rivers and lochs of the north of Scotland with the Board.
Open seven days a week 9.40am — 5.30pm from the beginning of April till the end of October. For further details please telephone **0796/3152.**
Over on the west coast, 18 miles from Oban, on the banks of Loch Awe, the Board has built a power station in the heart of a mountain, **Ben Cruachan.**
There is an attractive Visitors' Centre featuring an exhibition and a range of souvenirs.
Tours throughout the day take visitors down the near mile-long tunnel to see the underground power house, due to their popularity, especially during June, July and August, the tours are often fully booked so to avoid disappointment please come early.
Open seven days a week 9am — 4.30pm from the beginning of April till the end of October.
For further details please telephone 086 62 673.

Lauriston Castle Cramond Rd South, Davidson's Mains (on NW outskirts of Edinburgh, 1m E of Cramond)
☎ 031-336 2060

A late 16th-century mansion, with furniture and antiques, displaying English and French styles.

Open Apr–Oct daily ex Fri 11–1 & 2–5 (last tour approx 4.20); Nov–Mar Sat & Sun only 2–4 (last tour approx 3.20). Details not confirmed for 1986.

✴ 80p (ch 40p).

⚠ ♨ ✘

National Gallery of Scotland The Mound
☎ 031-556 8921

One of the most distinguished of the smaller galleries in Europe, containing collections of Old Masters, Impressionists and Scottish paintings including: Raphael's Bridgewater Madonna, Constable's Dedham Vale, and masterpieces by Titian, Valasquez, Raeburn, Van Gogh and Gauguin. Drawings, watercolours and original prints by Turner, Goya, Blake etc (shown on request Mon–Fri 10–12.30 & 2–4.30).

Open Mon–Sat 10–5, Sun 2–5; winter lunchtime closure (Oct–Mar) 12–1 West Gallery, 1–2 East Gallery and New Wing. (Mon–Sat 10–6, Sun 11–6 during Festival).

Free.

P (300 yds) ⚹ shop ✘

Edinburgh

Palace of Holyroodhouse at E end of Canongate
☎ 031-556 7371

Historic Royal Palace of 16th- and 17th-century, built by Sir William Bruce, and associated with Mary, Queen of Scots and Prince Charles Edward. Outstanding picture gallery and state apartments. Ruined 13th-century nave of former Abbey Church.

Open 4 Jan–4 May, 1 Jun–6 Jul, 8 Aug–24 Dec & 27–31 Dec. Historical Apartments only, 5–11 May, 28–31 May & 7–13 Jul & 5–7 Aug. Hours 4 Jan–22 Mar & 20 Oct–31 Dec 9.30–3.45 (Closed Sun); 23 Mar–19 Oct 9.30–5.15, Sun 10.30–4.30. (Subject to closure for State visits.)

£1.40 (ch & pen 70p). Historical Apartments only 70p (ch & pen 40p). School parties Free on application, between Nov–Apr, Mon–Fri. Reduction for students.

P (200 yds) ⚹ (ground & first floors only) shop ✘

Parliament House East of George IV Bridge
☎ 031-225 2595

Dates from 1639, but façade was replaced in 1829. The Hall has a fine hammer-beam roof. The Scottish Parliament met here before the Union of 1707. Now the seat of Supreme Law Courts of Scotland.

Open Mon–Fri 10–4.

Free.

⚠ ⚖ (Closed Mon & when courts recess) ⚹ (ground floor only) ✘ (ex guide dogs)

Register House (East end of Princes St)
☎ 031-556 6585

Designed by Robert Adam, it was founded in 1774. Headquarters of the Scottish Record Office and the repository for National Archives of Scotland. Changing historical exhibitions. Historical and Legal Search Rooms available to visitors.

Open all year Mon–Fri 9–4.45. (Closed certain PHs).

Free.

P (300 yds) ⚹ (ground floor only) ✘

Royal Botanic Garden Inverleith Row
☎ 031-552 7171 ext 260

Famous garden, noted especially for the rhododendron collection, rock garden, plant houses and exhibition hall.

Garden open all year (ex Xmas Day & New Year's day). Mar–Oct Mon–Sat 9–1 hr before sunset, Sun 11–1 hr before sunset; Oct–Mar Mon–Sat 9–sunset, Sun 11–

Edinburgh

A late 16th-century mansion situated on the outskirts of the city about 3¼ miles north-west of Princes Street. During its long history Lauriston has had many owners, the last private owners Mr and Mrs W R Reid left the Castle to the nation, with a view to the education of the public taste. It was a condition of the bequest that the Castle should be maintained much as it was in their lifetimes. William Reid collected many period and reproduction furniture, Derbyshire Blue John ornaments, Crossley wool 'mosaics', engravings and minor objet d'art. There is a free car park and a tearoom is located a short walk away in what was once the Lauriston Home Farm.

For admission charges and times of opening see gazetteer entry.

sunset. Plant houses & exhibition hall open Mon–Sat 10–5, Sun 11–5 (from 10 am during festival period).

Free.

P (Aboretum Rd) ⬡ Apr–Sep ♿ shop ✘

Royal Observatory Visitor Centre Blackford Hill
☎ 031-667 3321

The centre features the works of Scotland's National Observatory at home, overseas and in space. A wide range of different astronomical exhibits includes the latest discoveries in the exploration of the Universe. Educational exhibits about the tools of the astronomer and a collection of historical telescopes. Panoramic view of Edinburgh from the Visitor Centre balcony.

Open Mon–Fri 10–4; Sat & Sun noon–5. (Closed Xmas day & New Years day).

65p (ch & pen 35p). Party.

⚠ shop ✘

Royal Museum of Scotland Chambers St
☎ 031-225 7534

The most comprehensive display in Britain under one roof comprising the decorative arts of the world and ethnography, natural history, geology, technology and science. Lectures, gallery talks and films at advertised times.

Open Mon–Sat 10–5, Sun 2–5.

Free.

P (meters) ⬡ ♿ shop ✘

Royal Museum of Scotland (formerly Museum of Antiquities) 1 Queen St
☎ 031-557 3550 ext 279

Extensive collections and national treasures from earliest times to the present day, illustrating everyday life and history.

Open Mon–Sat 10–5 (6 pm during Festival) & Sun 2–5 (11–6 during Festival).

Free.

P (Meters) shop ✘

Scottish National Gallery of Modern Art Belford Rd
☎ 031-556 8921

Edinburgh
Elgin

New home of the national collection of 20th-century painting, sculpture and graphic art. Among many modern masters represented are Derain, Picasso, Giacometti, Magritte, Henry Moore, Barbara Hepworth, Lichtenstein and Scottish painting. Some sculpture is displayed. The gallery print room and library are also open to the public by appointment.

Open all year Mon–Sat 10–5 & Sun 2–5. (During Festival Mon–Sat 10–6, Sun 11–6).

Free.

⚠ ⬡ (licensed) ♿ shop ✘

Scottish National Portrait Gallery Queen St
☎ 031-556 8921

Striking red Victorian building containing portraits of men and women who have contributed to Scottish history. The collection includes such popular figures as Mary Queen of Scots, James VI and I, Burns, Sir Walter Scott and Ramsay MacDonald. Many other artists, statesmen, soldiers and scientists are portrayed in all media, including sculpture. Collections also illustrate the development of Highland dress. There is an extensive reference section of engravings, and photographs.

Open all year daily. Mon–Sat 10–5 & Sun 2–5. (During Festival Mon–Sat 10–6, Sun 11–6).

Free.

P (Meters) ♿ (telephone prior to visit) shop ✘

West Register House Charlotte Sq
☎ 031-556 6585

The former St George's Church, designed by Robert Reid in the Greco-Roman style in 1811. Now an auxiliary repository for the Scottish Record Office and housing its museum. Search Room available to visitors.

Open Mon–Fri 9–4.45 (ex PH)

Free.

P (meters) ♿ ✘ 🚌 (ex by arrangement)

EDNASTON
Derbyshire
Map **8** SK24

Ednaston Manor
☎ Ashbourne (0335) 60325

A Lutyens house with garden of botanical interest. Large collection of shrubs, shrub roses, clematis and unusual plants.

Open Etr–Sep, Mon–Fri 1–4.30 & Sun 2–5.30. House not open.

Free.

⚠ ⬡ (Suns only) garden centre ✘

EDZELL
Tayside Angus
Map **15** NO56

Edzell Castle

A 16th-century castle with remarkable walled garden dating from 1604.

Open, see end of gazetteer (but closed Tue & Thu am).

✳ 50p (ch & pen 25p).

P ♿ (exterior & garden only) (AM)

ELCOT
Berkshire
Map **4** SU36

Elcot Park Hotel
(5½m W Newbury off A4)
☎ Kintbury (0488) 58100

16-acre garden overlooking the Kennet Valley with extensive views. Mainly lawns and woodland laid out by Sir William Paxton in 1848. Magnificent display of daffodils, rhododendrons and other shrubs in Spring.

Open all year, daily 10–6.

Free (ex on NGS Suns).

⚠ ⬡ (Licensed restaurant) ♿ (NGS)

ELGIN
Grampian Moray
Map **15** NJ26

Elgin Cathedral North College St →

PALACE OF HOLYROODHOUSE

Visit Her Majesty The Queen's official residence in Scotland.

Guided tours of the State Apartments and the Historic Rooms including Mary Queen of Scots chambers.

Palace **closed** mid-May for Visit of the Lord High Commissioner and late-July for the Visit of The Queen.

Ticket Office Open:

Winter Time Weekdays: 9.30-3.45. Sundays Closed.
Summer Time Weekdays: 9.30-5.15. Sundays 10.30-4.30

PALACE OF HOLYROODHOUSE
Edinburgh, EH8 8DX.
(Tel. 031-556 7371)

Founded in 1224, but in 1390 was burned by Alexander Stewart, Earl of Buchan, the 'Wolf of Badenoch'. Much 13th-century work still remains; the nave and chapter house are 15th century.

Open, see end of gazetteer.

✳ 50p (ch 25p).

P (AM)

Elgin Museum 1 High St
☎ (0343) 3675

The museum conserves and displays the heritage of Elgin and Moray. It also contains a collection of unique fossil fish and reptiles.

Open Apr–Sep, Mon–Fri 10–4 & all year Sat 10–12.

25p (ch, pen & students 10p).

P (20 yds) ✖

Pluscarden Abbey (6m SW on unclass road)
☎ Dallas (034389) 257

The original monastery was founded by Alexander II in 1230. Restoration took place in the 14th and 19th centuries, and the Abbey has been re-occupied by the Benedictines since 1948.

Open daily, 8 am–8.30 pm.

Free.

🅰 ♿ (ground floor only) shop

ELLESMERE PORT
Cheshire
Map **7** SJ37

Boat Museum Dockyard Rd
☎ 051-355 5017

The museum is situated in an historic dock complex at the junction of the Shropshire Union and Manchester Ship Canals. These docks were one of the most important transhipment areas for cargoes from sea-going vessels to the smaller boats of the inland waterways system. The Museum has a collection of over 50 craft ranging from a small weedcutter to a 300 ton coaster. Other features include exhibitions on canals, horses, the town and energy, restored warehouses and workshops, an Education Centre, and a trip boat. Four of the original steam engines which once drove the hydraulic power system remain and two have been restored and are in steam on the first Sunday of each month and Bank Holidays. Visitors may go aboard some of the craft.

Open Apr–Oct daily 10–5; Nov–Mar daily 10–4 (ex Fri). (Closed 24–26 Dec).

✳ £1.80 (ch 16 & pen 85p, students £1.20). Boat trip 80p (ch & pen 50p).

🅰 🕃 ♿ shop ⓥ

ELLISLAND FARM
Dumfries and Galloway *Dumfriesshire*
Map **11** NX98
(6m NW of Dumfries off A76)
☎ Auldgirth (038774) 426

In this farm on the west bank of the Nith,

Elgin
Enfield

Robert Burns lived from 1788 to 1791 and composed Tam O'Shanter and other poems and songs. Material associated with the poet is on display.

No restriction on time of visiting, but visitors are advised to telephone in advance.

Free.

🅰 (limited) ♿ (ground floor & gardens only) ✖

ELSHAM
Humberside
Map **8** TA01

Elsham Hall Country Park Brigg
☎ Barnetby (0652) 688698

With domestic animals, bird garden, carp feeding, nature trails, and quizzes. Arboretum, adventure playground and butterfly garden, and pony trekking (by appointment). Craft shop & Wrawby Moor art gallery. Sculptures, and blacksmith (craftsmen at work when advertised).

Open 29 Sep–Etr Sun 11–4; 24 Mar–28 Sep weekdays 11–5.30, Sun & BH 11–6.30. (Closed Good Fri & Xmas day).

✳ £1.30 (ch 70p). Party 20 + . Parties by appointment.

🅰 🕃 (licensed) 🕂 ♿ shop & plant centre

ELSTOW
Bedfordshire
Map **4** TL04

Moot Hall (1½m SW of Bedford on A6)
☎ Bedford (0234) 66889

A 15th-century market hall with a 17th-century collection portraying the life and times of John Bunyan.

Open all year, daily (ex Mon, but including summer BHs). Tue–Sat 10–1 & 2–5 (dusk in winter); Sun 2–5.30 (dusk in winter) Details not confirmed for 1986.

Admission fee payable.

🅰 🕂 ♿ (ground floor only)

ELTON
Cambridgeshire
Map **4** TL09

Elton Hall (on A605, 8m W Peterborough)
☎ (08324) 223

A collection of paintings, furniture and books acquired by the Proby family since the early 17th-century, set in the tranquil and stately setting of a 15th-century house that is still a family home.

Open BHs; 30–31 Mar, 4, 5, 25, 26 May & 24, 25 Aug. Also Wed May–Aug & Sun Jul–Aug 2–5pm.

£1.70 (ch 85p).

🅰 🕃 🕂 ✖

ELVASTON
Derbyshire
Map **8** SK43

Elvaston Castle Country Park
Borrawash Rd
☎ Derby (0332) 71342 Park Manager, 73735 caravan/camp site warden

Attractive 200 acre country park landscaped in the early 19th century. Formal gardens, walled Old English Garden, parkland and woodland. Extensive topiary gardens. Exhibitions and displays. Events on the showground during the year. Caravan and Camp Site. *Working Estate Museum* recreates the lifestyle, work and craft skills associated with a country house estate at the turn of the century.

Park open daily 9–dusk. Estate museum open Etr–Oct Wed–Sat 1–5, Sun & BH 10–6. Details not confirmed for 1986.

Estate museum ✳ 50p (ch & pen 25p). Park free. Car park charge BH & wknds.

🅰 🕃 (in season) 🕂 ♿ (ground floor only in Museum) shop

ELY
Cambridgeshire
Map **5** TL58

The Stained Glass Museum located in North Triforium of Ely Cathedral
☎ Ely (0353) 5103 or Cambridge (0223) 60148

Museum founded to rescue and preserve fine stained glass from redundant churches and other buildings, dating from 14th century, which might otherwise have disappeared. Models show how stained-glass windows are designed and made. Also an exhibition of modern stained glass.

Open daily Mar–Oct Mon–Fri 10.30–4, Sat & BHs 11–4.30 & Sun 12–3.

80p (ch & students 40p) Party.

P (200 yds) ✖

EMBLETON
Northumberland
Map **12** NU22

Dunstanburgh Castle (1½m E)

Ruins of early 14th-century castle, facing the North Sea and built partly by John of Gaunt.

Open † see end of gazetteer.

✳ 50p (ch 16 & pen 25p).

(AM) (NT)

ENFIELD
Gt London (London plan 4 pages 174/175)

Forty Hall Forty Hill
London plan 4: **14** E5
☎ 01-363 4046

Built in 1629 for Sir Nicholas Raynton, Lord Mayor of London, the Mansion was modified in the early 18th century. Contemporary plaster ceilings and screen, 17th- and 18th-century furnishing

---

114

and paintings ceramics and glass. Also temporary exhibitions.

Open all year Tue–Fri 10–6 (5 pm Oct–Etr), Sat & Sun 10–6 (5 pm Oct–Etr).

Free.

 🅰 ⏄ 🕂 shop ✖

EPWORTH
Humberside
Map **8** SE70

Old Rectory
☎ (0427) 872268

Birthplace and former home of John and Charles Wesley, built in 1709 after a previous rectory had been destroyed by fire, and restored in 1957.

Open daily Mar–Oct, Mon–Sat 10–12 & 2–4 & Sun 2–4. Winter months by arrangements.

Donations usually given.

🅰 ⏄ (advance bookings only) & (ground floor & gardens only) shop ✖

ESHER
Surrey (London plan 4 pages 174/175)

Claremont London plan 4: **7** A1
Entrance by Claremont Lane A244
☎ (0372) 67841

Designed in 1772 by Henry Holland and Capability Brown for Clive of India to replace an earlier house. The façade has columned portico and there are fine fireplaces and plaster ceilings. Now a co-educational school run by Christian Scientists.

Open Feb–Nov, 1st wknd in month 2–5.

Admission fee payable.

🅰 shop ✖

Claremont Landscape Garden London plan 4: **8** A1
(on S edge of Esher, E of A307)

This, the earliest surviving example of an English landscape garden has recently been restored. It has a lake with an island pavilion, grotto, turf amphitheatre, viewpoint and avenue.

Open daily ex Xmas & New Year's day. Apr–Oct 9–7 or sunset; Nov–Mar 9–4.

70p.

(NT) (The house is not NT property)

ETON
Berkshire
Map **4** SU97

Dorney Court Dorney (off B3026 between Eton & Burnham)
☎ Burnham (06286) 4638

Enchanting brick and timber house, in tranquil setting; with tall Tudor chimneys and splendid great hall.

Open Etr wknd, then Sun & BH Mon–13 Oct. Also Mon & Tue Jun–Sep 2–5.30 (last admission 5 pm).

£2 (ch 10–16 £1).

🅰 ⏄ shop ✖ ⓥ

Enfield
—
Exeter

EUSTON
Suffolk
Map **5** TL87

Euston Hall
☎ Thetford (0842) 66366

An 18th-century house with a fine collection of 17th- and 18th-century paintings by Stubbs, Lely, Van Dyck and other masters. Pleasure grounds, gardens by John Evelyn, William Kent and Capability Brown. Also a 17th-century parish church in the Wren style.

Open 5 Jun–25 Sep on Thu only, 2.30–5.30.

£1.40 (ch 60p pen £1). Party 12+.

🅰 ⏄ 🕂 shop ✖ ⓥ

EVESHAM
Hereford and Worcester
Map **4** SP04

The Almonry Vine St
☎ (0386) 6944

A 14th-century stone and half-timbered building, associated with a former Benedictine abbey, and containing a museum of local history covering the culture and industry of the Vale of Evesham since prehistoric times. Tourist Information Centre.

Open Good Fri–Sep, Tue & Thu–Sun; 10–5 (Sun 2–5 only). Also open BH Mons.

40p (accompanied ch 16 free pen 25p).

P & (ground floor only) shop ✖

EWELL
Surrey
(London plan 4 pages 174/175)

Bourne Hall Cultural Centre Spring St
London plan 4: **2** C1
☎ 01-393 9573

18th-century house replaced by cultural centre, comprising museum, art centre, library, theatre hall and banqueting rooms. Collections embrace the human and natural history of the Epsom and Ewell area, and include costumes, dolls, toys and early photography. The Art Gallery has a continuous temporary exhibition programme. Other services include the identification of objects brought in by visitors.

Open all year Mon–Sat; Mon, Wed & Thu 10–5 (8pm Tue & Fri) & 9.30–8 on Sat.

Free.

🅰 ⏄ & ✖

EWLOE
Clwyd
Map **7** SJ26

Ewloe Castle
Remains of native Welsh castle in Ewloe woods, near where Henry II was defeated in 1157.

Accessible at all reasonable times.

Free.
(AM Cadw)

EXBURY
Hampshire
Map **4** SU40

Exbury Gardens Exbury Estate
☎ Fawley (0703) 891203

Woodland gardens extending to 200 acres. Contains the Rothschild collection of rhododendrons with azaleas and many tree specimens. Two acres of rock gardens.

Open daily 8 Mar–Etr 1–5.30 Etr–13 Jul 10–5.30.

£2 (ch & pen £1.50) Etr–Jul £1 (ch & pen 80p) Mar–Etr. Party.

🅰 ⏄ 🕂 & shop garden centre

EXETER
Devon
Map **3** SX99

The Devonshire Regiment Museum
Barrack Rd, Wyvern Barracks
☎ (0392) 218178

The exhibits cover the history of the Devonshire Regiment from its formation in 1685 to 1958 when the Regiment amalgamated with the Dorset Regiment. Exhibits include uniforms, weapons, medals, historical documents and military souvenirs collected by the Regiment over the years.

Open all year Mon–Fri 9–4.30. (Closed Sat, Sun & BHs).

Free. (Donations).

🅰 & (ground floor only) shop ✖

Guildhall High St
☎ (0392) 56724

Dates from 1330, partially rebuilt 1446, arches and façade added 1592–5, fine displays of oilpaintings, Guild Crests and civic silver and regalia.

Open all year Mon–Sat 10–5.15 (ex when used for Civic functions).

Free.

P (200 yds) & (ground floor only) ✖ coaches by arrangement.

Maritime Museum at Town Quay and Canal Basin; approach via Alphington Street and Haven Rd
☎ (0392) 58075

The largest collection of the worlds boats. Afloat, ashore and under cover, there are over 130 vessels most of which are on display. Features include the oldest working steam dredger 'Bertha', believed to have been built by Brunel, boats from the Far East, the fascinating Ellerman Collection of Portuguese craft and the Ocean Rowers Collection, which features →

boats which have been rowed across the Atlantic. There are many other exhibits besides. The museum buildings have featured in the BBC series 'The Onedin Line'.

Open daily, 10–6 summer, 10–5 winter. (Closed Xmas).

✳ £2 (ch £1, pen £1.60). Family tickets.

⚠ ⚿ (licensed) ⌙ ⅋ (ground floors only) shop

Royal Albert Memorial Museum
Queen St
☎ (0392) 56724

Founded in 1865, and extended several times. Large permanent displays of fine and applied art, natural history and ethnography and local industry. Of particular interest are collections of Devon paintings, Exeter silver, glass, lace, costume, local and foreign natural history. Programme of temporary exhibitions.

Open all year Tue–Sat 10–5.30.

Free.

P (200 yds) ⅋ (by arrangement ground floor only) ✘

St Nicholas' Priory Mint Ln, off Fore St
☎ (0392) 56724

Remains of 11th- to 16th-century Benedictine priory, with Norman undercroft. Tudor room, and 15th-century kitchen. Only complete monastic western range in England to have survived the Dissolution and be restored. Displays of pewter, furniture and wood carving.

Open all year Tue–Sat 10–1 & 2–5.15.

50p (ch 25p).

P (300 yds) ⅋ (ground floor & gardens only) ✘

Tuckers Hall Fore St
☎ (0392) 36244

Old Hall of the Weavers, Fullers and Shearman, occupied since 1471 by their incorporation which was granted Royal Charter in 1479–81. Wagon-roof and panelling of 1638.

Open Jun–Sep Tue, Thu & Fri 10.30–12.30; Oct–May Fri only 10.30–12.30.

Free.

P (100 yds) ✘

Underground Passages Princesshay
☎ (0392) 56724

Medieval aqueducts which once supplied water to the city.

Open all year Tue–Sat 2–4.30 (conditions permitting). Parties by arrangement.

✳ 50p (ch 25p).

P (100 yds) ✘

EXMOUTH
Devon
Map 3 SY08

A la Ronde Summer Ln (2m N on A376)
☎ (0395) 265514

Unique 16-sided house designed in 1795 by Jane and Mary Parminter. There are 20

Exeter — Falmouth

rooms, and the Shell Gallery in the 45-foot high octagonal centre is reached via two Gothic Grottos. Also featured is the feather frieze and dado decor. Situated in 12 acres of parkland with wide coastal views.

Open Etr–Oct Mon–Sat 10–6, Sun 2–7.

Guided tour ✳ £1.50 (ch 14 50p, pen £1). Party.

⚠ ⚿ ⌙ ⅋ (ex the Shell Gallery) shop ✘ Ⓥ

Country Life Museum Sandy Bay (1m SE)
☎ (0395) 274533

A museum for all the family. Large working museum with hundreds of exhibits. Thatched Devon cottage, Shire horses, ponies and many other friendly animals. Aviary.

Open May–Sep, daily from 10am.

£1.50 (ch 60p pen £1).

⚠ ⚿ ⅋ shop ✘

EYEMOUTH
Borders Berwickshire
Map 12 NT96

Eyemouth Museum Auld Kirk, Market Pl
☎ (0390) 50678

Opened in 1981 as a memorial to 129 local fishermen lost in the Great Fishing Disaster of 1881. The museum concentrates on the history of the area, and in particular, the town and also displays the 15-foot Eyemouth tapestry designed and worked for the centenary of the disaster.

Open Etr wknd–Oct, Mon–Sat 10–6; Sun 2–6.

70p (ch & pen 35p) (ch 5 free). Party 10 + .

P (25 yds) ⅋ (ground floor only) shop

EYNSFORD
Kent
Map 5 TQ56

Eynsford Castle

Remains of 12th-century castle including rectangular hall, walls and ditch.

Open † see end of gazetteer.

✳ 30p (ch 16 & pen 15p).

⚠ ⅋ (AM)

Lullingstone Castle (1m SW off A225)
☎ Farningham (0322) 862114

Mainly 18th-century house with fine 15th-century gate tower, the first large scale building to be built of brick throughout with cut brick for detail. Other notable features include; The Great Hall, State Dining Room, Library, Grand Staircase, State

Drawing Room, State Bedroom, Ante Room, and Church and grounds.

House open Apr–Oct, Sat, Sun & BH 2–6; Wed, Thu & Fri by arrangement. House & gardens, £2 (ch £1, pen £1.50).

⚠ ⚿ ⅋ (ground floor & gardens only) shop ✘ Ⓥ

Lullingstone Roman Villa (1½m W off A225)

Remains of Roman villa, with a fine tessellated pavement. Now completely roofed with additional exhibits in lighted gallery.

Open † see end of gazetteer.

✳ Summer £1 (ch 16 & pen 50p). Reductions in winter.

⚠ (charged) ⅋ (ground floor only) (AM) Ⓥ

FALKIRK
Central Stirlingshire
Map 11 NS87

Falkirk Museum
☎ (0324) 24911 ex 2472

District history exhibition with displays tracing the development of the area from earliest times to the present.

Open Mon–Sat 10.30–12.30 & 1.30–5.

Free.

P (200 yds) ⅋ (ground floor only) shop ✘

Rough Castle

One of the most remarkable forts on the Antonine Wall built by the Roman army in the 140's AD. The site covers one acre with double ditches and defensive pits.

Accessible at any reasonable time.

Free.

⚠ (AM)

FALKLAND
Fife Fife
Map 11 NO20

Falkland Palace and Garden
☎ (0337) 57397

Historic former hunting palace of the Stuart Kings and Queens, situated below the Lomond Hills. The mid 16th-century buildings include a notable courtyard façade. Chapel Royal and apartments restored. Royal tennis court of 1539, the oldest in Britain. Visitor Centre.

Palace & Garden open 28 Mar–Sep Mon–Sat 10–6 & Sun 2–6. Oct, Sat 10–6, Sun 2–6. (Last visitors to Palace 5.15pm).

Palace & gardens £1.40 (ch 16 70p). Garden only 80p (ch 16 40p). Party (NTS)

FALMOUTH
Cornwall
Map 2 SW83

Pendennis Castle

One of the coastal forts erected c1540 by Henry VIII, with Elizabethan and later additions. Exhibition of coastal defence of the Tudor period.

116

Open † see end of gazetteer.

✱ 60p (ch & pen 30p).

⛬ (AM)

Penjerrick Gardens (3m SW of Falmouth, off B3291 near Budock)
☏ (0326) 250659

Beautiful sub-tropical gardens, including display of flowering shrubs.

Open Mar–Sep, Wed & Sun 1.30–4.30.

30p (50p Apr & May) in box in garden.

P (50yds) ✗

FARLEIGH HUNGERFORD
Somerset
Map **3** ST85

Farleigh Castle

Ruined 14th-century castle with chapel containing monuments to the Hungerfords.

Open † see end of gazetteer.

✱ 50p (ch 16 & pen 25p).

⛬ (AM)

FARNBOROUGH
Warwickshire
Map **4** SP44

Hall

17th- and 18th-century house. Fine terrace walk with temples, wide views across Warwickshire towards Edge Hill.

Open Apr–Sep, Wed & Sat, May Day BH Sun & Mon 2–6.

Terrace walk Thu, Fri & Sun only 2–6.

£1.20. Terrace walk only 50p.

(NT)

FARNDON
Cheshire
Map **7** SJ45

Stretton Mill
☏ Tilston (08298) 276

A water-powered corn mill with two wheels dating from 16th to 19th century, recently restored by the County Museum Service. Exhibition in stables.

Open Etr Sat–Sep, Tue–Sun & BH Mons 2–6.

✱ 50p (ch 25p). Family ticket £1.25.

⛬ ⊼ shop

FARNHAM
Surrey
Map **4** SU84

Birdworld & Underwaterworld Bird park, gardens and aquarium. (3½m SW of town, on A325 beyond Wrecclesham).
☏ Bentley (0420) 22140

17 acres of garden and parkland containing all kinds of birds ranging from the tiny tanager to the great ostrich, and waterfowl. Sea Shore Walk. Aquarium housing tropical, freshwater and marine fish.

Open daily from 9.30 (Closed Xmas day).

£1.50 (ch 15 95p & pen £1.30 ex Sun & BHs). Parties 20+.

⛬ ☕ ⊼ ♿ shop ✗

Farnham Castle Keep

Ruined shell keep of castle originally erected 1129–71 by Bishop Henry de Blois.

Open see end of gazetteer. (Apr–Sep only).

✱ 30p (ch 16 & pen 15p).

⛬ (AM)

Farnham Museum 38 West St
☏ (0252) 715094

Geology, archaeology, local history and art housed in Willmer House, a fine example of Georgian brickwork.

Open Tue–Sat 11–5 & BH Mons 2–5. Also open by prior arrangement only Wed evenings, May–Aug. Closed 25 & 26 Dec.

Free.

P (100 yds) ♿ (ground floor only) shop ✗

FARWAY
Devon
Map **3** SY19

Farway Countryside Park (1½m S on unclass rd AA signposted on B3174)
☏ (040487) 224 or 367

A collection of rare breeds and present-day British farm animals can be seen in a beautiful farm setting with magnificent views over the Coly Valley. 189 acres of natural countryside. Pony, donkey cart rides and trekking available. Nature Trails.

Good Fri–Sep daily (ex Sat) 10–6 (last admission 5pm).

✱ £1.30 (ch 2 free ch 80p). Party.

⛬ ☕ (licensed) ⊼ shop

FAVERSHAM
Kent
Map **5** TR06

Fleur de Lis Heritage Centre
Preston St
☏ (0795) 534542

History and architecture of a thousand years vividly illustrated by award-winning displays, audio-visual programme and actual bygones in former 16th-century coaching inn. Official Tourist Information Centre.

Open Etr–Sep Mon–Wed, Fri & Sat 9.30–4.30. Oct–Etr 10–1 & 2–4.

50p (ch, students & pen 25p). Party 10+.

P (100 yds) shop

FELBRIGG
Norfolk
Map **9** TG23

Felbrigg Hall

One of the finest 17th-century houses in Norfolk with 18th-century furniture and pictures. Park with fine trees, woodland and lakeside walks.

Open (principal rooms & gardens) 29 Mar–26 Oct, Mon, Wed, Thu, Sat, Sun & BH 1.30–5.30. (Closed Good Fri).

£1.70 (ch 85p). Party 15+.

☕ (from noon) ✗ (NT)

FETTERCAIRN
Grampian *Kincardineshire*
Map **15** NO67

Fasque
☏ (05614) 201

Home of the Gladstone family since 1829. Four times Prime Minister, William Gladstone, lived at Fasque from 1830–1851. Also illustrated is the life and work of the many servants who contributed to the running of the household. Collection of agricultural and other local machinery. Extensive parkland with red deer and Soay sheep.

Open May–Sep Mon–Thu, Sat & Sun 1.30–5.30 (last entry 5).

£1.40 (ch 70p). Parties 25+.

⛬ shop ✗

FILBY
Norfolk
Map **9** TG41

Thrigby Hall Wildlife Gardens (on unclass road off A1064)
☏ Fleggburgh (049377) 477

Selection of Asian mammals, birds and reptiles displayed in the landscaped gardens of the Hall. Features include 250-year-old summer house, tropical house, bird house, ornamental waterfowl lake, yew walk. Also there is a slide theatre.

Open daily 10–5.

£1.50 (ch 80p pen £1).

⛬ ☕ Apr–Sep ⊼ ♿ shop ✗ (ex guide dogs)

FILKINS
Oxfordshire
Map **4** SP20

Swinford Museum (4m NE of Lechlade on A361)
☏ (036786) 365 (Apply to Mr Foster)

Old domestic articles, including cooking utensils, agricultural and rural craft tools.

Open Apr–Oct, Fri, Sat & Sun 9–6 by appointment.

Free (Donations).

⛬ ♿ ✗ ⛟

FINCHINGFIELD
Essex
Map **5** TL63

Spains Hall (1m NW on unclass road.)
☏ Great Dunmow (0371) 810266 (Sir J Ruggles-Brise) →

Flower and kitchen gardens, each with a greenhouse, and in the flower garden there is a large 17th-century Cedar of Lebanon. House contains many fine examples of 18th- and 19th-century furniture and works of art.

Garden open May–Jul, Suns & BH 2–5, House open by appointment.

House £1.50 (ch 75p) Gardens 75p (ch 40p).

⚠ ♿ (ground floor & gardens only) ✘

FINSTOWN
Orkney
Map **16** HY31

Maes Howe Chambered Cairn

Britain's finest megalithic tomb, of Neolithic date (c1800 BC). Masonry in a remarkable state of preservation, showing Viking carvings and runes.

Open, see end of gazetteer.

✱ £1 (ch & pen 50p).

(AM)

Stenness Standing Stones (3m SW off A965)

Remains of a stone circle, second millennium BC. Nearby is the Ring of Brogar (c2000 BC) consisting of a splendid circle of upright stones with a surrounding ditch.

Open at any reasonable time.

Free.

(AM)

FINTRY
Central Stirlingshire
Map **11** NS68

Culcreuch Castle
☎ (036086) 228

The castle itself dates from between 1320 and 1460, with later additions and is believed to be the oldest inhabited Clan Castle in central Scotland. It has been the home of the Barons of Culcreuch since 1699.

Open Daily throughout the year 10.30–dusk. Castle Tours available each hour on

---

Finchingfield — Folkestone

the hour as demand requires. Piper in attendance at Sun lunchtime Etr–Sep.

Castle Tours £1. Estate & gardens 60p (ch free).

⚠ 🍽 (licensed) ⌁ ♿ (ground floor & gardens) ✘ ⓥ

FIRLE
East Sussex
Map **5** TQ40

Firle Place
☎ Glynde (079159) 335

A mainly Georgian house, with Tudor core. South Downs home of the Gage family for over 500 years. It contains a connoisseur's collection of European and English Old Masters, English and Sèvres porcelain and fine furniture.

Open Jun–Sep, Sun, Wed & Thu; also Etr, Spring & May BH 2.15–5.

£2 (ch 90p) Party 25 +. Connoisseurs Day £2.50.

P 🍽 (licensed) shop ✘

FISHBOURNE
West Sussex
Map **4** SU80

Roman Palace Salthill Rd
☎ Chichester (0243) 785859 (Sussex Archaeological Society)

Occupied 1st to 4th centuries and the largest Roman Palace in Britain, with numerous mosaic pavements.

Open Mar & Apr, daily 10–5; May–Sep 10–6, Oct 10–5, Nov 10–4, Dec–Feb Sun only 10–4.

Admission fee payable. Party.

⚠ 🍽 ♿ shop ✘

FLIMWELL
Sussex
Map **5** TQ73

Bedgebury National Pinetum
(1½m N off A21)
☎ Goudhurst (0580) 211392

Established by the Forestry Commission in 1925 and contains 160 acres of trees, including the most comprehensive collection of conifers in Europe.

Open all year, daily 10–8 or dusk.

60p (school ch 30p).

⚠ 🍽 (wknds, Apr–Sep & BH's) shop

FLINT
Clwyd
Map **7** SJ27

Flint Castle

Ruined late 13th-century castle, erected by Edward I, with circular detached keep originally surrounded by moat.

Accessible at all reasonable times.

Free.

⚠ (AM Cadw)

FLIXTON
Suffolk
Map **5** TM38

Norfolk & Suffolk Aviation Museum
☎ Brook (0508) 50614

A collection of aircraft and aviation spanning the years from the Wright Brothers to present day. There are sixteen aircraft on static display outside a large specially converted barn containing the smaller items relating to the history of flight.

Open Etr Sunday–Oct Sun & BH 10–5; Jun–Aug Sun & Tue–Thu 7pm–9pm also Jul & Aug Wed & Thu 12–5.

Free.

⚠ ♿ (Assistance required) shop ✘ (in museum)

FOLKESTONE
Kent
Map **5** TR23

Museum & Art Gallery Grace Hill
☎ (0303) 57583

Local history, archaeology and natural science. Temporary art exhibitions.

FIRLE PLACE

**Nr. Lewes on A27
Eastbourne Road
Glynde (079159) 335**

In parkland setting under South Downs, beautiful home of the Viscount Gage. Connoisseurs collection of European and English Old Masters, Sèvres and English porcelain and fine French and English furniture. Historic American connections.

See gazetteer for opening times and admission prices.

Open all year, Mon, Tue, Thu & Fri 9–5.30, Wed 9–1 & Sat 9–5. (Closed BH).

Free.

P (100 yds) ✻

FORD
Northumberland
Map **12** NT93

The Lady Waterford Hall
☎ Crookham (089082) 224

Once the village school, it is now famous for the 19th-century murals painted by Louisa, Marchioness of Waterford, using children and their parents from the village and estate as models to portray Biblical scenes.

Open daily 9.30–6.

50p (ch 16 10p, pen 25p).

🅰 ♿

Heatherslaw Mill
☎ Crookham (089082) 338

A splendid example of a 19th-century water-driven double corn mill. One wheel restored to full working order. Flour milling on occasions. Permanent exhibition of millwright's tools. Stone-ground flour and other cereal products on sale.

Open Apr–Oct, daily 11–6.

Admission fee payable.

🅰 🍽 shop

FORDWICH
Kent
Map **5** TR15

Old Town Hall
☎ Canterbury (0227) 710358

Timber-framed building overlooking River Stour, thought to be the smallest and oldest Town Hall in England. Old Town jail also open.

Open Etr wk, then late May–Sep, Mon–Sat 11–4, Sun 2–4.

25p (ch 10p).

P (adjacent) ✻

FOREST
Guernsey *Channel Islands*
Map **16**

German Occupation Museum
☎ Guernsey (0481) 38205

Contains the largest exhibition of authentic Occupation relics to be found in the Channel Islands, including a tableau of an 'Occupation Kitchen', 'bunker rooms' and a new section of transport. Special tours arranged to explore the underground fortifications.

Open daily Jan–Apr 2–4.30; May–Oct 10.30–5; Nov 2–4.30.

80p (ch 14 40p pen & students 60p).

🅰 🍽 ♿ (ground floor only) shop ✻

Guernsey Zoo La Villiaze
☎ Guernsey (0481) 39176

With emphasis on smaller mammals and birds, the zoo is run by a Charitable Trust,

---

Folkestone

Freshwater

and is the Headquarters of Zoological Trust of Guernsey. It is concerned with conservation and education.

Open daily 10–6 (last admissions 5pm) (summer), 10–4 (winter). (Closed Xmas day).

✳ £1 (ch 60p) Party.

🅰 🍽 (licensed) Apr–Sep ♿ ✻

FORRES
Grampian *Moray*
Map **14** NJ05

Falconer Museum Tolbooth St
☎ (0309) 73701

Displays of local history, wildlife, geology, ethnography and archaeological finds from Culbin.

Open All year (ex PH); Oct–Apr, Mon–Fri 10–4.30; May–Sep, Mon–Sat 9.30–5.30 (6.30 Jul & Aug), also Sun Jul & Aug 2–6.30.

Free.

P (20 yds) ♿ (ground floor only) shop ✻

Suenos' Stone

A notable 20ft-high Dark Age monument with a sculptured cross on one side and groups of warriors on the reverse.

Accessible at all times.

Free.

(AM)

FORT AUGUSTUS
Highland *Inverness-shire*
Map **14** NH30

Great Glen Exhibition Canal Side
☎ (0320) 6341

History of the Great Glen from Pict to modern Scot. The Clans, battles and general history. Exhibits include, rare antiques and weapons. Mock smithy. Forestry exhibition and information on the canal and railway.

Open Etr–Nov 9–5.

Free.

P 🍴 ♿ shop ⓥ

FORT GEORGE
Highland *Inverness-shire*
Map **14** NH75

Fort George

One of the most outstanding 18th-century artillery fortifications in Europe. Built 1748–69; visited by Dr Johnson and Boswell in 1773.

Open Apr–Sep, Mon–Sat 9.30–7, Sun 2–7. Oct–Mar 9.30–4, Sun 2–4.

✳ 50p (ch & pen 25p).

P (AM)

Alae Queen's Own Highlanders Museum
☎ Inverness (0463) 224380

Housed in Fort George which was built 1748–1769. Exhibits include regimental uniforms, medals and pictures.

Open Apr–Sep, Mon–Fri 10–6.30, Sun 2–6.30; Oct–Mar Mon–Fri 10–4 (Closed Good Fri–Etr Mon, Xmas, New Year & BH).

Free.

P (500yds) ♿ (ground floor only) shop ✻

FORT WILLIAM
Highland *Inverness-shire*
Map **14** NN17

Inverlochy Castle

A well-preserved example of a 13th-century and later stronghold, noted for the famous battle fought nearby in 1645, when Montrose defeated the Campbells.

Under repair and interior not accessible. Can be viewed from outside.

Free.

(AM)

West Highland Museum Cameron Sq
☎ (0397) 2169

A museum of local and particularly Jacobite interest, including an exhibition about the '45 rising with the well-known 'secret portrait' of Prince Charles Edward Stuart.

Open Jun & Sep Mon–Sat 9.30–5.30; Jul & Aug 9.30–9pm; Oct–May 10–1 & 2–5.

✳ 30p (ch 15p).

P (600 yds)

FOWEY
Cornwall
Map **2** SX15

St Catherine's Castle

Ruined stronghold errected in 16th century by Henry VIII to defend coast and restored in 1855.

Open all year, daily, any reasonable time.

Free.

(AM)

FRAMLINGHAM
Suffolk
Map **5** TM26

Framlingham Castle

Built by Roger Bigod between 1177 and 1215. Fine curtain walls, thirteen towers, array of Tudor chimneys, and almshouses built within wall by Pembroke College, Cambridge in 1639.

Open † see end of gazetteer.

✳ 50p (ch 16p & pen 25p).

🅰 ♿ (ground floor & grounds only) (AM)

FRESHWATER
Isle of Wight
Map **4** SZ38

Museum of Clocks Alum Bay (2¼m SW)
☎ (0983) 754193 →

Standing in two acres of land in an area of outstanding natural beauty, surrounded by National Trust Land. The museum contains over 200 exhibits with clocks from all parts of the world dating from 1590, some rare and unusual.

Open Good Fri–Sep, Mon–Fri & Sun 10–5.

60p (ch 50p).

▲ ♿ shop ✗

FRITTON
Norfolk
Map **5** TG40

Fritton Lake Country Park
☎ (049379) 208

Walled garden. Shrubs, herbaceous borders, and paths through wood to lake noted for fishing. Fishing in season, fishing and rowing boats for hire. Adventure playground and also a windsurfing school, as well as basket-making facilities and an information centre. There is also a first-aid hut and nappy-changing facilities for infants.

Gardens & Grounds open Apr–15 Jun 11–6; 16 Jun–Sep 9am–7pm.

Admission fee payable.

▲ ☕ ⊓ ♿ shop ✗

FROGHALL
Staffordshire
Map **7** SK04

Froghall Wharf Passenger Service
Canal Basin, Foxt Rd ($\frac{1}{4}$m N A52)
☎ Ipstones (053871) 486

A canal trip along the Caldon Canal passing through the Churnet Valley, one of the most attractive sections of canal in the country. The cruise is aboard 'Birdswood', the only horse drawn boat on the Canal, providing peace and tranquility in a setting almost unchanged for 100 years. Also located at the wharf is the Eating House and Craft Centre.

Public Service provided Etr–Sep, Thu & Sun at 2pm and also every 1st and 3rd Sat in Summer months there are evening meal trips. Telephone for further details and reservations, including private charter. Eating House & Craft Centre open Spring Bank Hol–Sep Tue–Sun 11–6 & Oct–Spring Bank Hol Thu–Sun 11–5.

Trip £2.75 (ch £1.75). Evening trip including meal £7.25 (ch £6.25).

▲ ☕ (licensed) ♿ shop ✗

GAINSBOROUGH
Lincolnshire
Map **8** SK88

Old Hall Parnell St
☎ (0427) 2669

15th-century manor house with Tudor additions. Complete medieval Kitchen. Displays on Richard III and Life in medieval Lincolnshire.

Open Mon–Sat 10–5 & Sun (Etr–Oct only) 2–5. (Closed Xmas & New Years day).

✱ 50p (ch & pen 20p). Party.

☕ (Tues, pm.) shop ✗

GAIRLOCH
Highland *Ross-shire*
Map **14** NG87

Gairloch Heritage Museum Achtercairn
☎ Badachro (044583) 243

A converted farmstead now houses the museum which relates the way of life in the typical West Highland parish of Gairloch from the earliest times to the 20th century. Replica croft house room.

Open Etr–Sep, Mon–Sat 10–6.

30p (ch 15 10p).

▲ ☕ (licensed) shop

GAWSWORTH
Cheshire
Map **7** SJ86

Gawsworth Hall
☎ North Rode (02603) 456

Tudor black and white manor house associated with Mary Fitton, possibly the 'Dark Lady' of Shakespeare's sonnets, with rare tilting ground, pictures, armour and furniture. Open Air Theatre, Shakespeare last 2 weeks in Jun. Opera 2nd week in Jul.

Open 25 Mar–Oct daily 2–6 & 26 Dec–2 Jan 2–5 (Closed 21 & 22 Jun). Details not confirmed for 1986.

£1.80 (ch 90p) Party.

▲ ☕ ⊓ ♿ (garden only) shop

GERMAN UNDERGROUND HOSPITAL
Jersey *Channel Islands*
Map **16**

☎ Jersey (0534) 63442

Tunnelled out solid rock by slave labour and civilian population during the German Occupation of 1940–1945. It was only ever half completed but over a period of $2\frac{1}{2}$ years 43,900 tons of rock were removed and 6,020 m^3 of concrete used to line the wards and corridors. Lighting and special effects recreate working conditions and short video films tell the story of Jersey during the invasion, occupation and liberation. Photographs of war personalities, events, newspaper articles and German leaflets are displayed. The exhibition and museum includes an excellent collection of authentic German firearms etc and a Liberation Sculpture carved by local school children.

Open 9 Mar–9 Nov, daily 9.30–5.30, last entry 4.45pm; winter season Thu 12–5 & Sun only 2–5. (Closed 6 Jan–1 Feb & 24, 25 Dec).

✱ £2 (ch £1)

▲ ♿ shop ✗

GIGHA, ISLE OF
Strathclyde *Argyll*
Map **10**
See **Ardminish**

GILLING EAST
North Yorkshire
Map **8** SE67

Gilling Castle
☎ Ampleforth (04393) 238

14th-, 16th, and 18th-century house, now preparatory school for Ampleforth College, with Elizabethan great chamber noted for panelling, painted glass and ceilings (rest of house not open to public). Fine gardens.

Great chamber and hall, open weekdays 10–12 & 2–4; garden only Jul–Sep, Mon–Fri. (Closed Xmas & New Years day).

Great chamber free. Gardens 50p.

▲ ✗

GLAMIS
Tayside *Angus*
Map **15** NO34

Angus Folk Museum Kirkwynd Cottages

Row of restored 19th-century cottages, now housing the Angus Folk Collection of agricultural and domestic equipment and cottage furniture.

Open 28–31 Mar & May–Sep, daily 12–5 (last admission 4.30pm).

80p (ch 16 40p).

NTS

Glamis Castle
☎ (030784) 242

The ancestral seat of the Earls of Strathmore and Kinghorne, family home of Her Majesty Queen Elizabeth The Queen Mother and birthplace in 1930 of HRH The Princess Margaret. Mainly late 17th-century but with an older tower. The drawing room ceiling of 1621 and the painted panels in the chapel are notable. Legendary setting of Shakespeare's play 'Macbeth'.

Open Etr then May–Sep Mon–Fri & Sun 1–5.

✱ £1.80 (ch 90p pen £1.40). Grounds only 60p (ch Free pen 40p).

▲ ☕ ⊓ ♿ (gardens only) shop & garden centre

GLAN CONWY
Gwynedd
Map **6** SH87

Felin Isaf Mill (Located just south on A470)
☎ (049268) 646

17th-century working water mill recently restored, in full working order. Located within its own secluded gardens. Specialising in school group visitors.

Open all year daily 10–dusk.

60p (ch 30p).

   ♿ ⚲ ♿ 🚻 ♿ (ground floor & garden only)

shop ✖

GLANDFORD
Norfolk

Map **9** TG04

Shell Museum
☎ Cley (0263) 740081

Small museum with Dutch gables built 1915 to house a collection of seashells and curios from all corners of the world, collected by the late Sir Alfred Jodrell of Bayfield Hall.

Open Mon–Thu 10–12.30 & 2–4.30, Fri & Sat 2–4.30.

15p (ch 10p).

♿ ⚲ shop

GLASGOW
Strathclyde *Lanarkshire*

Map **11** NS56

Bellahouston Park Ibrox
☎ 041–427 4224 Park. 041–427 0558 Sports Centre

171 acres of parkland only 3 miles from the city centre. Site of the Empire Exhibition of 1938. Sunken garden, walled garden, and rock garden. Multi-purpose Sports Centre situated at west end of park, with adjacent all-weather Athletic Centre. Horse show.

Open daily end Apr–Aug 8–10, Sep–Apr 8–5 (times approximate).

Free. ♿ ⚲ (sports centre) ♿ 🏳

Botanic Garden (off Great Western Rd)
☎ 041–334 2422

Established in 1817, it contains an outstanding collection of plants. The Kibble Palace is a unique glasshouse with, among others, a famous collection of tree ferns. The main glasshouse contains numerous tropical and exotic plants. The 40 acres of gardens include systematic and herb gardens, and a chronological border.

The Kibble Palace open 10–4.45 (4.15 in winter). The main glasshouse open Mon–Sat 1–4.45 (4.15 in winter) Sun 12–4.45 (4.15 in winter). Gardens open daily 7–dusk.

Glan Conwy
—
Glasgow

Free.

♿ ♿ (garden only) 🏳

The Burrell Collection Pollok Country Park
☎ 041–649 7151

The Burrell Collection was opened to the public by HM the Queen on 21 October 1983 in an award-winning gallery, which makes the most of its superb natural setting. The Collection was formed by Sir William and Lady Burrell and comprises more than 8000 items. These include Chinese ceramics, bronzes and jades, Near Eastern rugs and carpets, Turkish pottery and artefacts from the ancient civilisations of Iraq, Egypt, Greece and Italy. European medieval art is represented by metalwork, sculpture, illuminated manuscripts, ivories and two of the most important museum collections in the world of stained glass and tapestries. The paintings range from the 15th to the early 20th centuries and include works by Memling, Bellini, Cranach, Rembrandt, Courbet, Millet, Boudin, Degas, Manet and Cezanne. There are also important collections of British silver and needlework.

Open Mon–Sat 10–5, Sun 2–5. (Closed 25 Dec & 1 Jan).

Free.

♿ ⚲ ♿ shop ✖ (ex guide dogs)

Cathedral Castle St
The most complete medieval Cathedral surviving on the Scottish mainland, dating mainly to the 13th and 14th-centuries.

Open see end of gazetteer.

Free.

(AM)

Crookston Castle
Probably 15th-century, with an earlier defensive ditch. Visited by Mary Queen of Scots and Darnley in 1565.

Open, see end of gazetteer (closed Wed pm & Friday in winter).

✴ 50p (ch & pen 25p).

(AM)

Glasgow Art Gallery & Museum
Kelvingrove Park
☎ 041–357 3929

The finest civic art collection in Great Britain. All schools and periods of European painting with emphasis on Dutch 17th-century, French 19th-century and Scottish art from 17th-century to the present day. Collections of pottery, porcelain, silver, sculpture, arms and armour, also archaeology, ethnography and natural history.

Open Mon–Sat 10–5, Sun 2–5 (Closed Xmas day & New Years day).

Free.

♿ ⚲ ♿ shop ✖ (ex guide dogs)

Greenbank Garden Clarkston (Off B767 on southern outskirts of the city)
☎ 041–639 3281

A small garden at which has been established a Gardening Advice Centre, particularly suitable for the owners of small gardens. Classes, demonstrations etc.

Garden open all year daily 9.30–sunset. Garden advice Thu 2–5 (at garden or by phone).

65p (ch 16 30p).

♿ (NTS)

Haggs Castle 100 St Andrews Drive
☎ 041–427 2725

Built in 1585, the castle houses a museum created for children. The theme is exploration of time – particularly the last 400 years since the castle was built. Activities in the adjacent workshop allow young visitors to become practically involved in the past. Easter, Summer and Autumn activity programmes, also Mary Queen of Scots Exhibition throughout 1986.

Open Mon–Sat 10–5 Sun 2–5 (Closed Xmas day & New Years day).

Free. Guided tours only if booked in advance. →

Glasgow Museums & Art Galleries

Art Gallery & Museum
Kelvingrove
Glasgow G3 8AG
Tel: 041-357 3929

The Burrell Collection
2060 Pollokshaws Road
Glasgow G43 1AT
Tel: 041-649 7151

The People's Palace
Glasgow Green
Glasgow G40 1AT
Tel: 041-554 0223

Pollok House
2060 Pollokshaws Road
Glasgow G43 1AT
Tel: 041-632 0274

Museum of Transport
25 Albert Drive
Glasgow G41-2PE
Tel: 041-423 8000

Haggs Castle
100 St Andrews Drive
Glasgow G41 4RB
Tel: 041-427 2725

Provand's Lordship
Castle Street
Glasgow G4 0RB
Tel: 041-552 8819

Rutherglen Museum
Rutherglen
Glasgow G73 1DQ
Tel: 041-647 0837

Open all year except Christmas Day and New Year's Day   Mon-Sat: 10am-5pm Sun: 2-5pm Admission Free

P &♿ (ground floor & garden only) shop ✺ (ex guide dogs)

Hunterian Art Gallery The University of Glasgow
☎ 041–339 8855 ext. 547

A major collection of works by James McNeill Whistler and Charles Rennie Mackintosh including reconstructed interiors from Mackintosh's Glasgow home. Also on display is a group of Dutch, Flemish, Italian and British 17th- and 18th-century paintings, bequeathed by the Gallery's founder, Dr William Hunter. There is a growing collection of 19th- and early 20th-century Scottish paintings, contemporary British art and sculpture and a holding of old-master to modern prints. Winner of the 1983 Sotheby Award for the best U.K. Gallery. Sculpture Courtyard. Changing programme of print exhibitions.

Main gallery open Mon–Fri 10–12.30 & 1.30–5; Sat 9.30–1. Mackintosh House Mon–Fri 10–12.30 & 1.30–5; Sat 9.30–1. Other areas Mon–Fri 10–5, Sat 9.30–1. (please telephone for details of public holiday closures).

50p (The Mackintosh House on weekday afternoons & Sat mornings). All other areas Free.

P (200 yds) &♿ (not the Mackintosh House) shop ✺

Hunterian Museum The University of Glasgow
☎ 041-339 8855 ext 4221

The museum is named after the 18th-century physician, Dr William Hunter, who bequeathed his own collections to the University. The geological, archaeological, ethnographical, numismatic and historical collections are exhibited in the main building of the University. Scottish Museum of the Year 1983 and 1984. Temporary exhibition programme.

Open Mon–Fri 10–5, Sat 9.30–1. (Please telephone for details of PH closures).

Free.

P (meters 100 yds) ♿ &♿ (ground floor. Lift by prior arrangement) shop ✺

Glasgow

Linn Park Cathcart (southern outskirts of Glasgow)
☎ 041-637 1147

Comprises more than 200 acres of pine, deciduous woodland and riverside walks. Britain's first public park nature trail (1965) features many varieties of flowers, trees, and insects. A children's zoo and a collection of British ponies and Highland cattle. There is also a ruined 14th-century castle.

Open daily 7–dusk.

Free.

P ♿ ⌂ ♿ &

People's Palace Museum Glasgow Green
☎ 041-554 0223

Contains a fascinating visual record of the history and life of the City. Exhibits include Medieval Glasgow, interesting relics of Mary, Queen of Scots, the Battle of Langside, the Tobacco Lords of the 18th century, and the history of the music hall. Fine examples of Glasgow craftsmanship, particularly pottery, and special displays illustrating social and domestic life, including women's suffrage, temperance and the two world wars. A wide range of pictures and noteworthy people and places. Winter gardens with tropical plants.

Open Mon–Sat 10–5, Sun 2–5. (Closed Xmas day & New Years day).

Free.

A ♿ & (ground floor only) shop ✺ (ex guide dogs)

Pollok Country Park
☎ 041-632 9299

Formerly a private estate, there are 361 acres of land containing an extensive collection of flowering shrubs and trees in a natural setting. There is a herd of 50 Highland cattle, a display rose garden, nature trails, and jogging track.

Demonstrations held fortnightly. Sat mornings.

Park always open. Demonstration and display garden open daily Mon–Thu 8–4, Fri 8–3. Weekends 8–6.30 (Etr–Sep) 8–4 (Oct–Etr).

Free.

A ⌂ & 🏛

Also **Pollok House**
☎ 041-632 0274

Situated within the grounds, a neo-Palladian building (1752) with Edwardian additions, containing the famous Stirling Maxwell Collection of Spanish paintings, furniture etc.

Open Mon–Sat 10–5, Sun 2–5. (Closed Xmas day & New Years day).

Free.

A ♿ & shop garden centre ✺ (ex guide dogs)

Provan Hall Auchinlea Rd
☎ 041-771 6372

Well restored 15th-century house considered most perfect example of a simple pre-Reformation house remaining in Scotland, set in Auchinlea Park. In the adjacent grounds are formal and informal gardens including garden for the blind.

For information on opening hours please telephone the above no.

Free.

A & 🏛

Provand's Lordship 3 Castle St
☎ 041-552 8819

Built in 1471 as a manse serving the Cathedral and St Nicholas Hospital, this is the oldest house in Glasgow. Mary Queen of Scots is reputed to have stayed in the house, which now has period displays from 1500 onwards and a fine collection of 17th century Scottish furniture. Latterly a confectioner's shop, the machines which made the sweets can also be seen.

Open all year; Mon–Sat 10–5 & Sun 2–5. (Closed Xmas day & New Years day).

Free.

P (100 yds) shop ✺ (ex guide dogs)

HUNTERIAN ART GALLERY
University of Glasgow
Outstanding collections of work by J.M. Whistler and the Scottish architect and designer, C.R. Mackintosh, including *The Mackintosh House* — reconstructed interiors from the architect's Glasgow home. Also Old Masters, British 18th Century portraits, 19th and 20th century Scottish painting. Major Print Collection. Sculpture Courtyard. Temporary Exhibition Programme. **Mon-Fri 9.30-5 Sat 9.30-1 (The Mackintosh House closed weekdays 12.30-1.30). 041-339 8855/5431**

Drawing Room, The Mackintosh House

Ness Hall Park Crookston
☎ 041–882 3554

Beautifully kept gardens with artificial ponds, featuring a variety of aquatic plants and stocked with fish. Extensive heather and rock gardens and woodland nature trails.

Open Apr–Sep daily 1–8; Oct–Mar daily 1–4.

Free.

⚠ � ✿

Rouken Glen Park Thornliebank

Fine park with lovely walks through the glen. Waterfall at head of the glen is a noted beauty spot. Large walled garden. Boating on picturesque loch.

Open daily dawn–dusk.

Free.

⚠ 𝒟 🚻 ⅙

Tenement House 145 Buccleuch St, Garnethill
(N of Charing Cross)

Representing a picture of the city's social history, this first floor Victorian tenement flat was built in 1892 and consists of two rooms, kitchen and bathroom, containing original box beds, closed kitchen range, sink, coal box, furniture etc.

Open 28 Mar–Oct daily 2–5; Nov–Mar Sat & Sun 2–4.

✳ 90p (ch 45p). Party (not exceeding 12 persons).

(NTS)

Museum of Transport 25 Albert Drive, near Eglinton Toll
☎ 041–423 8000

A life-size presentation of land transport, showing the development of the bicycle, horse-drawn vehicles, tramcars, Scottish motor cars from vintage to present day and railway locomotives, also the Clyde Room and subway Gallery with a reconstruction of a Glasgow underground railway station.

Mon–Sat 10–5, Sun 2–5. (Closed Xmas day & New Years day).

Free.

P 𝒟 ⅙ shop ✖ (ex guide dogs)

Glasgow — Glencoe

Victoria Park Whiteinch.
☎ 041–959 1146

This park has the best known fossilized tree stumps of the prehistoric Coal Age period, discovered in 1887, and housed in the Fossil Grove building. The park has extensive carpet bedding depicting centennial events.

Fossil Grove Building open Mon–Fri 8–4, Sat & Sun pm only. Park open daily 7am–dusk.

⚠ 🚻 ⅙

GLASTONBURY
Somerset
Map **3** ST43

Glastonbury Abbey
☎ (0458) 32267

Well-preserved 12th- and 13th-century ruins, with St Joseph's Chapel, Abbot's kitchen, and flowering thorn tree nearby, on site of first Christian church in British Isles. West of England Pilgrimage last Sat in June. Abbey Museum open in the ancient gatehouse with a model of the Abbey as it was in 1539.

Open daily, Jun, Jul, & Aug 9–7.30; Dec 9.30–4.30, Jan & Nov 9.30–5, Feb 9.30–5.30, Mar, Apr & Oct 9.30–6, May & Sep 9.30–7.

80p (ch 16 40p, ch 5 free) Party.

P 🚻 ⅙ (ground floor & gardens only) shop

Somerset Rural Life Museum
☎ (0458) 32903

Abbey Barn and Abbey Farmhouse. Late 14th-century barn of Glastonbury Abbey contains relics of farming in bygone days, cider making, peat cutting, withy cutting etc. The adjoining farmhouse displays life of a 19th-century Somerset labourer, and a typical farmhouse kitchen.

Open Mon–Fri 10–5, Sat & Sun 2–6.30 (2.30–5pm Nov–Etr). (Closed Good Fri & Xmas Day). To be confirmed.

✳ 50p (ch & pen 20p).

⚠ 𝒟 (Etr–Sep) 🚻 ⅙ (ground floor only) shop ✖

Tribunal

15th-century Court House of Abbey officials containing finds from late prehistoric Lake Village.

Open see end of gazetteer.

✳ 50p (ch 16 & pen 25p).

⚠ (AM)

GLEMHAM HALL
Suffolk
Map **5** TM36
(4½m S of Saxmundham off A12)
☎ Wickham Market 746219

17th-century house, in 350 acres of grounds, with panelled rooms, pictures and Queen Anne furniture.

Open Etr Mon–28 Sep Wed, Sun, BH 2.30–5.30.

£1.20 (ch 14 & pen 60p). Garden only – half price.

⚠ 𝒟 ⅙ (ground floor & garden only) ✖ Ⓥ

GLENCOE
Highland Argyll
Map **14** NN15

Glencoe & North Lorn Folk Museum

Housed in two heather-thatched cottages, one of cruck construction, in main street of Glencoe. Macdonald relics, local domestic and agricultural exhibits, and Jacobite relics, costumes and embroidery, and children's section.

Open mid May–Sep, Mon–Sat 10–5.30.

35p (ch 15p).

P (100 yds) ⅙ (ex one building) shop

Glencoe Visitor Centre
☎ Ballachulish (08552) 307

Situated at the northern end of Glen Coe, which offers over 14,000 acres of some of the finest climbing and walking country in the Highlands, the Visitor Centre is close to the site of the 1692 massacre. Ranger Naturalist service available.

Open 28 Mar–31 May & Sep–26 Oct daily 10–5.30 Jun–Aug daily 9–6.30.→

Glastonbury Abbey

The Abbey Gatehouse, Glastonbury

First Christian Sanctuary in the British Isles. Most important archaeological remains. in the West Country.
Holy Thorn, Unique Abbots' Kitchen, New Museum in Medieval Gatehouse contains exquisite model of the Abbey as it stood in 1539, and remains of the original Wattle and Daub Church which legend suggest was, in AD61, founded by Joseph of Arimathea.
Burial Place of King Arthur.
Picnic area.
Adults 80p, Children (under 16) 40p, (under 5 free).
Parties — Adults 70p, Students 60p, Organised School Parties 15p.
Recorded Guide Hire charge 50p per hiring.
Details from Custodian, Abbey Gatehouse, Glastonbury.

30p (ch 15p).
(NTS)

GLENFINNAN
Highland *Inverness-shire*
Map **14** NM98

Monument
☎ Kinlocheil (039783) 250

The monument stands in a superb setting of mountains at the head of Loch Shiel and was erected in 1815 to commemorate the Highlanders who followed Prince Charles Edward Stuart in 1745. Plaques give a dedication in English, Gaelic and Latin. Visitor Centre.

Open 28 Mar–Jun & Sep–26 Oct, daily 10–5.30. Jul–Aug daily 9–6.30.

55p (ch 25p).

△ (NTS)

GLENGOULANDIE DEER PARK
Tayside *Perthshire*
Map **14** NN75

(8m NW of Aberfeldy on B846)

☎ Kenmore (08873) 509

A fine herd of red deer, Highland Cattle, endangered species and other birds and animals live in the park in surroundings as like their natural environment as possible. Pets must not be allowed out of cars.

Open Etr–Oct, daily 9 am until 1 hr before sunset.

35p cars £2.

△ ⊓ shop

GLENLIVET
Grampian *Banffshire*
Map **15** NJ12

The Glenlivet Distillery Reception Centre. Off B9008 10m N of Tomintoul
☎ Glenlivet (08073) 427

The reception centre contains an exhibition of ancient artefacts used in malting, peat cutting and distilling. Distillery tour. Free whisky sample.

Open Etr–Oct, Mon–Sat 10–4.

Free.

△ ♿ (ground floor only) shop 🐕

GLENLUCE
Dumfries and Galloway *Wigtownshire*
Map **10** NX15

Glenluce Abbey (2m NW of the village.)

A Cistercian house founded in 1192. The ruins occupy a site of great beauty and are themselves of much architectural interest and distinction.

Open, see end of gazetteer (only open at weekends in winter).

✱ 50p (ch & pen 25p).

△ ♿ (AM)

GLOUCESTER
Gloucestershire
Map **3** SO81

City Museum & Art Gallery Brunswick Rd
☎ (0452) 24131

The Marling bequest of 18th-century walnut furniture, barometers and domestic silver. Paintings by Richard Wilson, Gainsborough, Turner etc, supplemented by art exhibitions throughout the year. Local archaeology including Roman mosaics and sculptures; natural history including a freshwater aquarium.

Open Mon–Sat 10–5 (Closed BH).

Free.

P (50 yds) ♿ (ground floor only) shop 🐕

City East Gate Eastgate St
☎ (0452) 24131

Roman and Medieval gate-towers and moat in an underground exhibition chamber. Adjacent to Bastion tower in Kings Walk.

Open May–Sep, Wed & Fri 2–5, Sat 10–12 & 2–5. (Bastion tower 26 Jul–Aug).

Free.

P shop 🐕

Folk Museum 99–103 Westgate St
☎ (0452) 26467

A group of half-timbered houses, Tudor and Jacobean, furnished to illustrate local history, domestic life and rural crafts. Civil War armour, Victorian toys, Severn fishing tackle, wooden ploughs etc. Reconstructed Double Gloucester dairy and wheelwright's shop. Pin factory with 18th-century forge.

Open Mon–Sat 10–5 (Closed BH).

Free.

P (100 yds) ♿ (ground floor only) shop 🐕

Regimental Museum The Gloucestershire Regiment, Custom House, 31 Commercial Rd
☎ (0452) 22682

Two hundred and ninety years of loyal service to the Crown, illustrated by uniforms, pictures, old weapons, models, personal relics and medals.

Open Mon–Fri 10–5, BH 10–5, some wknds 10–5.

50p (ch & pen 30p).

P (500 yds) shop 🐕

Robert Opie Collection – The Pack-age revisited The Albert Warehouse, Gloucester Dock
☎ (0452) 32309

A nostalgic journey back through the memories of your childhood brought vividly to life by the Robert Opie collection. See again the tins, cartons, packs, display cards, posters, hoardings, boxes and bottles which since Victorian times have crowded the shelves of Britain's corner shops. Continuous screening of vintage TV commercials and quiz sheets for children.

Open Tue–Sun & Bank Hols, 10–6. (Closed Xmas).

£1.25 (pen & students £1 ch 75p). Family tickets £3.75. Party 10+.

△ 🍷 (licensed) ♿ shop 🐕

GLYN CEIRIOG
Clwyd
Map **7** SJ23

Chwarel Wynne Mine & Museum
Wynne Quarry (on B5400)
☎ (069172) 343

A slate mine, museum and education centre, with nature trail set in a beautiful 12-acre site. Visitors may watch a video film of the history of the slate industry and take part in a half hour tour of the underground workings with detailed commentary by an experienced guide. Many museum exhibits.

Open Etr–Sep daily 10–5. Parties welcome at other times by prior appointment.

£1.25 (ch 85p).

🅰 ⬛ ⼗ shop Ⓥ

GLYNDE
East Sussex
Map **5** TQ40

Glynde Place
☎ (079159) 248

Elizabethan manor, substantially altered in the mid 18th century. Connoisseur's day last Wednesday of every month.

Open Jun–Sep Wed & Thu 2.15–5.30.

£1.80 (ch 90p) Party 20 + .

🅰 ⬛ ⼕ (ground floor only) ✗

GODALMING
Surrey
Map **4** SU94

Godalming Museum Old Town Hall, High St
☎ (04868) 4104

Dates from 1814. On site of earlier building, and now museum of local history.

Open Tue, Fri & Sat 3–5. Extended hours during summer please ring for details. Other times by appointment.

Free.

P (200 yds) shop

GODMANCHESTER
Cambridgeshire
Map **4** TL27

Island Hall Post Street
☎ Huntingdon (0480) 59676

A mid 18th century Mansion of architectural importance very much a

Glyn Ceiriog
Golspie

family home with fine panelled rooms. In a tranquil river-side setting, with an ornamental Island forming part of the gardens.

Open 7–29 Jun Sun only, then 2 Jul–21 Sep Wed & Sun 2.30–5.30. Parties at any time of the year by arrangement.

£1 (ch 40p).

P (30 yds) ⼕ ⼕ (ground floor & gardens only) ✗

GODOLPHIN CROSS
Cornwall
Map **2** SW63

Godolphin House (Situated between Townshend and Godolphin Cross on unclass road)
☎ Penzance (0736) 762409

Partly early Tudor house, former home of Earls of Godolphin, with notable granite colonnades added in 1635. Painting of the 'Godolphin Arabian' by John Wooton.

Open May & Jun Thu 2–5; Jul & Sep, Tue & Thu 2–5; Aug, Tue 2–5, Thu 10–1 & 2–5. Open BHs (ex Good Fri). Parties by arrangement at anytime throughout year including Sundays.

£1 (ch 50p).

🅰 ✗

GODSHILL
Isle of Wight
Map **4** SZ58

Natural History Centre High St
☎ (0983) 840333

Large display of British and tropical butterflies and birds set in a picturesque 17th-century squire's cottage, as well as a display of tropical shells and corals, precious and semi-precious stones. Replicas of the Crown Jewels in a Tower of London setting, Holograms & Tropical Aquarium.

Open Mar–1 Nov daily from 10am. 80p (ch & pen 50p). Party 20 + .

P (100 yds) 🅰 shop

Old Smithy Tourist Centre
☎ (0983) 840242

Former blacksmith's forge with a garden shaped like the island, and having aviaries of exotic birds and a herb garden. Gifts and crafts on sale also herbs & pot pourri.

Open end Mar-early Nov, daily including evenings in high season.

50p (ch 25p pen 30p).

🅰 🅰 shop

GOGAR
Lothian Midlothian
Map **11** NT17

Suntrap Gogarbank (1m S off A8 Edinburgh to Glasgow road
☎ 031–339 7283

3-acre garden containing a Gardening Advice Centre, with lecture hall, glasshouses, demonstrations etc, adapted to help owners of small gardens. Full details from Principal, Oatridge Agricultural College, Broxburn, West Lothian.

Garden open all year, daily 9.30–dusk. Advice Centre all year Mon–Fri 9.30–1 & 2–4.30 (also open on Sat & Sun Apr–Sep 2.30–5).

50p (ch accompanying adult free).

🅰 🅰 (parts of ground floor & garden only)

GOLSPIE
Highland Sutherland
Map **14** NH89

Dunrobin Castle (1m NE)
☎ (04083) 3177

The ancient seat of the Earls and Dukes of Sutherland. Much of the interior is open to the public and contains a wide variety of furniture, paintings and exhibits. Magnificent garden.

Open 1 Jun–15 Sep, Mon–Sat 10.30–5.30, Sun 1–5.30 (last admission 5pm).→

15th — 17th Century House

𝒢odolphin ℋouse

Former seat of the Earls of Godolphin.

Open May & June. Thursdays 2-5pm.
July and Sept, Tuesdays and Thursdays 2-5pm.
August Tuesdays 2-5pm, Thursdays 10am-1pm, 2-5pm.
Bank Holiday Mondays.
Adults £1, Children 50p.
Parties taken throughout the year by special arrangement.

Tel: Penzance 762409

125

£1.90 (ch 95p pen £1.30) Family Ticket £5. Party.

⚠ ⓛ ✗ (in house)

GOMERSAL
West Yorkshire
Map **8** SE22
Off M62 (junc 26)

Red House Oxford Rd
☎ Cleckheaton (0274) 872165

Built in 1660 of red brick, which because of its rarity at that time gave rise to its name. Associations with the Brontës, particularly Charlotte, who often spent weekends here with her schoolfriend Mary Taylor. She immortalised it in her novel 'Shirley' where it is described under the name of 'Briarmains'.

Open all year, Mon–Sat 10–5, Sun 1–5.

Free.

⚠ ⓖ (ground floor only) shop ✗

GOODRICH
Hereford and Worcester
Map **3** SO51

Goodrich Castle

12th- to 14th-century castle, originally founded in 11th century, and slighted after Civil War.

Open see † end of gazetteer.

✳ 60p (ch 16 & pen 30p).

⚠ ⓖ (grounds only) (AM)

GOODWOOD
West Sussex
Map **4** SU80

Goodwood House
☎ Chichester (0243) 774107

Homes of the Dukes of Richmond. Superb collections of paintings, furniture, porcelain, tapestries and family mementos.

Open May–mid Oct, Sun & Mon 2–5. Also Tue–Thu in Aug.

Admission fee payable.

⚠ ⓖ ✗ ⓥ

Golspie
—
Grasmere

GORDON
Borders Berwickshire
Map **12** NT64

Mellerstain House
(3m S on unclass road)
☎ (057381) 225

Adam house with fine plaster ceilings, period furniture and pictures. Terraced gardens and lake, Craft Festival 22–25 Aug.

Open Etr, then May–Sep Mon–Fri & Sun 12.30–5 (last admission 4.30pm).

£1.80 (ch 80p, pen £1.30). Party 20+.

⚠ ⓛ ⓖ (ground floor & gardens only) shop ✗ (in house) ⓥ

GOREY
Jersey Channel Islands
Map **16**

Mont Orgueil Castle
☎ Jersey (0534) 53292

Situated on a rocky headland, on a site of fortification dating back to the Iron Age. The castle, one of the best preserved examples in Europe of the medieval concentric castle, dates from the 12th to 13th centuries. A series of tableaux with commentary tells the history of the building.

Open Mar–Oct daily 9.30–6.

Admission fee payable.

P ⓛ shop

GOSPORT
Hampshire
Map **4** SZ69

Royal Navy Submarine Museum and HMS Alliance Haslar Pontoon
☎ (0705) 529217

The museum shows history and development up to the present nuclear age with models, trophies, medals, pictures and the actual midget

submarines. Built for World War II, the submarine Alliance has been fully restored to her seagoing condition. An audio-visual presentation is given before visitors go on board. Also on display is HM submarine No. 1 (known as Holland 1).

Open daily Apr–Oct 10–4.30, Nov–Mar 10–3.30.

£1.80 (ch & pen 90p).

⚠ ⓛ (licensed) ♨ shop ✗ ⓥ

GOUDHURST
Kent
Map **5** TQ73

Finchcocks (1½m SW on unclass rd off A262)
☎ (0580) 211702

Fine early Georgian house set in beautiful garden and parkland, containing a magnificent collection of historical keyboard instruments, restored to full playing condition. Musical tours on all Open days and private visits. Also concerts, courses, childrens events, fairs etc.

Open 30 Mar–28 Sep, Suns & BH Mon 2–6; Aug Wed–Sun 2–6. Private groups on other days by appointment from Apr–Oct.

£2.50 (ch £1.50) Party.

⚠ ⓛ ♨ ⓖ (ground floor only) shop ✗

GRASMERE
Cumbria
Map **11** NY30

Dove Cottage & The Grasmere & Wordsworth Museum
☎ (09665) 544

Dove Cottage was Wordsworth's home for his most creative years. It is preserved in the original condition as recorded in the journals of his sister Dorothy. The award winning museum presents a unique display of manuscripts, paintings and personnalia. There are special exhibitions throughout the year.

Open Apr–Sep Mon–Sat 9.30–5.30, Sun 11–5.30. Mar, Oct 8 & 9 Dec–5 Jan Mon–Sat 10–4.30, Sun 11–4.30.

✳ £2 (ch £1). Museum & exhibition only £1.25 (ch 60p). Family ticket. Party 15+.

▲ ♿ (ground floor only in Dove Cottage) shop 🐕

GRASSINGTON
North Yorkshire
Map **7** SE06

National Park Centre Colvend, Hebden Rd
☎ (0756) 752748

Visitor centre featuring interpretative display on Walking in Wharfedale. Audio-visual programme, maps, guides and local information.

Open Apr–Oct daily from mid morning to late afternoon.

Free.

▲ π ♿

GRAYS
Essex
Map **5** TQ67

Thurrock Museum Orsett Rd
☎ Grays Thurrock (0375) 33325

Local history, agriculture, trade and industrial collections. Also Palaeolithic to Saxon archaeology of borough.

Open all year, Mon–Fri 10–8 & Sat 10–5. (Closed BH).

Free.

P (50 yds) ♿ 🐕

GREAT
Placenames incorporating the word 'Great' such as Great Ayton and Great Yarmouth, will be found under the actual placenames, i.e. Ayton, Yarmouth.

GREAT CUMBRAE ISLAND
Strathclyde *Bute*
Map **10**

See Millport

GREENOCK
Strathclyde *Renfrewshire*
Map **10** NS27

McLean Museum & Art Gallery 9 Union St
☎ (0475) 23741

The museum displays exhibits relating to local history, ethnography, natural history, geology and shipping, including river paddle steamers and cargo vessels. Also relics of James Watt. The Inverclyde Art Exhibition and Greenock Art Club Exhibition are held here annually.

Open Mon–Sat 10–12 & 1–5.

Free.

P (100 yds) shop 🐕

GRÈVE DE LECQ
Jersey *Channel Islands*
Map **16**

British Army Barracks
☎ Jersey (0534) 82238

The barracks have recently been completely renovated and they now contain various displays of militaria and a selection of old Jersey horse-drawn vehicles together with the equipment used by a Jersey wheel-wright.

Open Apr–Sep, Tue–Fri 2–5.

25p (ch & pen 10p). NT members free.

▲ shop

GRIMES GRAVES
Norfolk
Map **5** TL88

(3m NE of Brandon)

Neolithic flint mines worked from underground galleries. Roughly worked flints were once exported for finishing elsewhere.

Open † see end of gazetteer.

* 60p (ch & pen 30p). A torch is useful.

▲ (AM)

GRIMSBY
Humberside
Map **8** TA20

Welholme Galleries Welholme Rd
☎ (0472) 59161 ext 401

Collection of Napoleonic and 19th-century ship models, marine paintings and fine china from Doughty Bequest. Folk-life collections and photographs of Lincolnshire life from collection of the late W.E.R. Hallgarth.

Open all year Tue–Sat 10–5. (Closed Xmas day & BHs).

Free.

▲ ♿ shop 🐕 (ex guide dogs)

GRIMSTHORPE
Lincolnshire
Map **8** TF02

Grimsthorpe Castle
☎ Edenham (077832) 205

Quadrangular Tudor house based on medieval tower in one corner and with Baroque North Front. Other alterations during the 18th and 19th centuries. Fine collection of portraits, other pictures and furniture. Formal gardens and Parkland.

Open 28 Jul–8 Sep daily 2–6.

Admission fee payable.

▲ ☕ ♿ (ground floor & gardens only) 🐕

GRIZEDALE
Cumbria
Map **7** SD39

Visitor & Wild Life Centre
☎ Satterthwaite (022984) 373

Operated by Forestry Commission in Grizedale Forest, there are dioramas illustrating deer and other wild life, history, industrial archaeology, geology, ecology and forest management. Also there is a forest information shop and Conservation tree nursery. There is a mile-long Milwood Forest nature trail and other walks nearby including the 9-mile Silurian Way, as well as wayfaring, woodland sculptures and observation hides.

Open Mar–Oct daily 10–5, Nov–Feb daily 11–4.

15p (ch 10p).

▲ π ♿ (ground floor & grounds) shop, garden centre

Also ***Theatre in the Forest***
☎ Satterthwaite (022984) 291

Features events covering classical, folk, natural history, jazz, drama and dance.

Open Tue–Sat 11–4.

GROSMONT
Gwent
Map **3** SO42

Grosmont Castle

Ruined Marcher stronghold, rebuilt in 13th century by Hubert de Burgh, on hill above Monnow Valley. One of three 'tri-lateral' castles of Gwent.

Open at all reasonable times.

Free.

(AM Cadw)

GUERNSEY
Channel Islands
Map **16**

See Câtel, Forest, St Andrew and St Peter Port

GUILDFORD
Surrey
Map **4** SU94

Guildford Castle Castle St
☎ (0483) 505050

Early 12th-century rectangular, three-storeyed keep affording fine views. The castle ditch has been transformed into a flower garden, seen at its best throughout the summer. Brass rubbing display. Open air theatre during summer.

Grounds open daily 8.30–dusk (Closed Xmas day); Keep open Apr–Sep 10.30–6.

* Keep 30p (ch 15p). Grounds free.

P (100 yds) ♿ (gardens only) shop

Guildford House Gallery 155 High St
☎ (0483) 503406 (ext. 3531)

Built in 1660, timber-framed building containing richly carved elm and oak staircase and finely decorated plaster ceilings. Monthly temporary art exhibitions including paintings, sculpture and craftwork.

Open Mon–Sat 10.30–4.50 (Closed a few days prior to each exhibition). For details of exhibitions please apply for leaflet.

Free.

P ♿ (ground floor only) shop 🐕

Guildford Musuem Castle Arch, Quarry St
☎ (0483) 503497 →

Local history, archaeology and needlework.
Open Mon–Sat 11–5 (Closed on certain PH).
Free.
P (200 yds) & (ground floor only) shop ✗

Loseley House (2½m SW)
☎ (0483) 571881
Elizabethan house with fine panelling, furniture, ceilings, carved chalk chimney-piece and tapestries. Farm tours.
Open end May–Sep Wed–Sat 2–5. Also Spring & Aug BH Mon. Farm tour 2.30–4.
£1.60 (ch 90p pen £1.40 on Fri only). Farm tour £1 Party 20+.
A ⚲ ⚏ & (ground floor & gardens only) Farm shop ✗ (ex car park on lead)

GUILSBOROUGH
Northamptonshire
Map **4** SP67

Guilsborough Grange Wildlife Park
West Haddon Rd (6m from junc 18 on M1)
☎ Northampton (0604) 740278
More than 400 animals and birds of 70 varieties set in beautiful natural surroundings in the grounds of a 19th-century country house. There are 'birds of prey' displays as well as a children's playground and pets corner.
Open daily 10–7 or dusk.
Jan–Feb £1.50 (ch & pen 75p) Mar–Oct £2 (ch & pen £1). Nov–Dec £1.50 (ch & pen 75p).
A ⚲ ⚏ & shop

GUISBOROUGH
Cleveland
Map **8** NZ61

Gisborough Priory
Fine remains of east end of church of the 14th century. The priory, founded in first half of the 12th century housed Augustinian canons.
Open see end of gazetteer
✱ 30p (ch 16 & pen 15p).
A & (AM)

GUITING POWER
Gloucestershire
Map **4** SP02

Cotswold Farm Park (3½m NE on unclass road)
☎ (04515) 307
An exhibition of the development of British livestock breeding on a typical Cotswold farm. Rare farm animals, local handicrafts on sale.
Open May–Sep daily 10.30–6.
£1.50 (ch & pen 75p). Party.
A ⚲ ⚏ & shop ✗ (in exhibition)

GWEEK
Cornwall
Map **2** SW72

Guildford
—
Halifax

Seal Sanctuary
☎ Mawgan (032622) 361
Hospital and five pools for the care of sick and injured seals. There is also a nature trail and aquarium.
Open daily 9.30–6.
✱ £1.50 (ch 75p pen £1.20).
A & shop
See advertisement under Helston

HADDINGTON
Lothian East Lothian
Map **12** NT57

Jane Welsh Carlyle Museum Lodge St
☎ (062082) 3738
Former home of Jane Baillie Welsh who later married Thomas Carlyle, both who were very much influential thinkers of the last century. The drawing-room, the small exhibition room, the garden room, and the Regency gardens are open to visitors.
Open Apr–Sep Wed–Sat 2–5.
✱ 50p (accompanied ch free, pen 30p).
P (100 yds) & (gardens only) ✗

HADDON HALL
Derbyshire
Map **8** SK26

Haddon Hall (2m SE Bakewell)
☎ Bakewell (062981) 2855
12th- to 15th-century house with notable chapel and hall and terraced rose gardens. Most probably the finest example of a medieval home. Various events and exhibitions planned.
Open Apr, May, Jun & Sep Tue–Sun; Jul & Aug Tue–Sat & BH's; 11–6.
£2.20 (ch 16 £1.10). Party 30+.
A ⚲ (licensed) shop ✗

HADLEIGH
Essex
Map **5** TQ88

Hadleigh Castle
Founded in 1231 by Hubert de Burgh and rebuilt by Edward III in the 14th century, walls are of Kentish rag and castle retains two of its original towers.
Accessible any reasonable time.
Free.
(AM)

HAILES
Gloucestershire
Map **4** SP02

Hailes Abbey
Remains of Cistercian house founded by Earl of Cornwall in 1246. Roof bosses, tiles and other relics in Museum.

Open † see end of gazetteer.
✱ 60p (ch 16 & pen 30p).
A (AM) (NT)

HAILSHAM
East Sussex
Map **5** TQ50

Michelham Priory 2½m W
☎ (0323) 844224 (Sussex Archaeological Society)
Augustinian Priory, founded in 1229 on earliest moated site. 14th-century gatehouse and 16th-century Tudor house. 17th-century furniture, stained glass, tapestries and Sussex ironwork. Six acres of garden including physic garden. Garden Art & Science exhibition, working watermill. Art exhibition in Tudor Great Barn. Sussex crafts shop.
Open 25 Mar–Oct, daily 11–5.30.
£1.50 (ch 6–16 70p) disabled & schools 50p. Party.
A ⚲ (licensed) ⚏ & (garden only)

HALIFAX
West Yorkshire
Map **7** SE02

Bankfield Museum & Art Gallery
Boothtown Rd, Akroyd Park
☎ (0422) 54823 & 52334
Built by Edward Akroyd in the 1860s, this Renaissance-style building, set in the centre of parkland on a hill overlooking the town, contains one of the finest and most representative collections of costume and textiles from all periods and all parts of the world. There are new galleries of costume and toys. There are also displays of local natural history, and the museum of the Duke of Wellington's Regiment with a display which re-opens mid summer 1986. The Museum mounts regular temporary exhibitions, both from its collection, and also travelling art exhibitions.
Open all year Mon–Sat 10–5 & Sun 2.30–5. (Closed Xmas & New Year's day).
Free.
A & (ground floor & park only) shop ✗

Calderdale Industrial Museum Square Rd
☎ (0422) 59031
On display are over 100 machines representing Calderdale's industrial heritage during the past 150 years. In addition to local textile machinery there are machines that work leather, make cork linings, draw wire and wrap toffees. There are street scenes of Halifax in the 1850's, reconstructions of a grocer's, pawnbroker's, pub and basement dwelling house – all with authentic sounds and smells.
Open Tue–Sat 10–5. Sun 2–5. (Closed Mon ex BH).
40p (ch, pen & unemployed 20p).
P (100 yds) & shop ✗

Piece Hall
☎ (0422) 68725

128

Unique and outstanding 18th-century cloth hall, restored and converted; museum, exhibition galleries; antique, craft and souvenir shops.

Open daily 10–5 (Closed Xmas & New Year's day). Individual facilities vary.

Free.

P (200 yds) 🖵 ♿ (ground floor only) shop

Shibden Hall Folk Museum of West Yorkshire Godley Ln
☎ (0422) 52246

Early 15th-century half-timbered house overlooking 90 acres of parkland. The rooms are set out to reflect the different periods the house has been lived in. The vast 17th-century barn contains a fine collection of horse drawn vehicles. Craft workshops surround a cobbled courtyard. Craft weekends 22 & 23 Mar, 5 & 6 Jul, 23 & 24 Aug & 22 & 23 Nov.

Open Apr–Sep Mon–Sat 10–6, Sun 2–5; Oct, Nov & Mar Mon–Sat 10–5, Sun 2–5; Feb Sun only 2–5. (Closed Dec & Jan).

50p (ch & pen 20p). May–Aug 60p (ch & pen 30p). Party.

⚠ 🖵 ♨ ♿ (ground floor & gardens only) shop ✖

HALLAND
East Sussex
Map **5** TQ51

Bentley Wildfowl & Motor Museum
☎ (082584) 573

Hundreds of wildfowl from all over the world – Black Swans – Ne-Ne Geese – Mandarin Ducks – Flamingoes, Cranes and Peacocks. Fascinating Veteran, Edwardian and Vintage vehicles from the golden age of motoring. Bentley House with its splendid antique furniture and fine wildfowl paintings.

Open Apr, May, Jun & Sep, Mon–Sat 11–4.30, Jul–Aug daily & BH 10–5, Oct–Mar (museum & grounds only) wknds 11–4, (Closed Dec) (Dates to be confirmed for 1986).

✳ £1.80 (ch 90p, pen £1.30). Family ticket (2 adults + up to 4 children) £4.75. Party 11 +.

⚠ 🖵 ♨ ♿ shop ✖ Ⓥ

Halifax
—
Hampton Court

HAM
Gt London (London plan 4 pages 174/175)

Ham House (annexe of Victoria & Albert Museum) London plan 4: **24** B2

An outstanding Stuart house, built in 1610, redecorated and furnished in the 1670s by the Duke and Duchess of Lauderdale; much of this furniture still in its original rooms today.

Open Tue–Sun & BH Mons. 11–5. (Closed Good Fri, 5 May & 24–26 Dec & 1 Jan). £1.60 (ch & pen 80p). Children under 12 must be accompanied by an adult. Admission arrangements may be subject to change.

Grounds Free.

✖ (NT) and Victoria & Albert Museum

HAMILTON
Strathclyde Lanarks
Map **11** NS75

Hamilton District Museum 129 Muir St
☎ (0698) 283981

Local history museum in a 17th-century coaching inn with original stable and 18th-century Assembly Room with musicians' gallery. Displays include prehistory, art, costume, natural history, agriculture and local industries of the past. Transport museum and reconstructed Victorian kitchen.

Open Mon–Sat 10–5.

Free.

⚠ ♿ (ground floor only) shop ✖

HAMMERWOOD
East Sussex
Map **5** TQ43

Hammerwood Park
☎ Woldingham (088385) 2366 or Cowden (034286) 594

This Georgian house was the first main work of the architect Latrobe, and was

built in 1792. Restoration, begun in 1982, has been partly completed, and the restoration techniques are explained by the guides. It contains collections illustrating social history.

Open Etr Mon–Sep, Wed, Sat & BH Mon 2–5.30.

£1.50.

⚠ 🖵 ♨ ♿ (ground floor only) shop

HAMPTON COURT
Gt London (London plan 4 pages 174/175)

Hampton Court Palace
London plan 4: **22** B2

Built by Cardinal Wolsey in the early 16th century; the Palace has notable gatehouse, clock court and great hall. Large additions by Sir Christopher Wren, include Fountain Court, c. 1689. Fine state apartments and banqueting rooms; the orangery houses Mantegna Cartoons as well as a vine. Kitchen and maze of special interest. Fine gardens and park near River Thames.

State apartments open Apr–Sep, Mon–Sat 9.30–6, Sun 11–6; Oct–Mar, Mon–Sat 9.30–5, Sun 2–5; (Closed Good Fri, 24–26 Dec & Jan 1).

Admission fee payable.

⚠ (30p) (Dept. of Environment)

Royal Mews Exhibition Palace Barracks
☎ 01–943 3838

Housed in the 'Horse Guards' section of the Palace Barracks, which is believed to be the earliest surviving purpose-built barracks in the country, work having begun in 1689, the collection includes a wide variety of Royal transport. Exhibits include a rare French char-a-banc once used by Queen Victoria for picnic and shooting parties, also displayed is her state sledge. Of particular interest to children are the model cars used by various members of the Royal Family when children. The original State Land Rover is also on exhibit.

Open daily Spring & Summer 10.30–5; wknds only Autumn & Winter.

✳ 30p (ch, pen & students 15p).

P

HAMILTON DISTRICT MUSEUM
Step into the past at Hamilton District Museum, a restored coaching inn, now the oldest building in the town. Re-live the coaching era in our restored stable and fascinating transport section. Stroll through the elegant 18th century Assembly Room with original plasterwork and musicians' gallery, and then savour the atmosphere of our reconstructed Victorian kitchen.

129 MUIR STREET, HAMILTON.
Telephone Hamilton 283981

HANBURY
Hereford and Worcester
Map **3** SO96

Hanbury Hall

Pedimented, red brick, Queen Anne period house, dating from 1701; noted for hall and staircase painted by Sir James Thornhill. Good plaster decoration in Long Room, contemporary orangery and Watney collection of porcelain.

Open Etr Sat–Mon 2–5; Apr & Oct Sat & Sun 2–5; May–Sep, Wed–Sun & BH Mon 2–6. Evening visits for parties by prior arrangment (3rd Wed each month only).
£1.50.

ℒ shop (NT)

HANDCROSS
West Sussex
Map **4** TQ22

Nymans Garden

Thirty acres of gardens featuring flowering shrubs and roses.

Open 29 Mar–Oct, incl BH Mon, 11–7 (or sunset). Last admission 1 hr before closing. (Closed Mon & Fri).
£1.30.

✖ (NT)

HARDKNOTT CASTLE ROMAN FORT
Cumbria
Map **7** NY20

On Hardknott Pass above Eskdale, 375ft square fort with three double gateways enclosing walled and ramparted area of almost three acres. Situated above western end of steep and narrow pass (maximum gradient 1 in 3), fort was occupied in mid 2nd century.

Accessible any reasonable time.

Free.

(AM)

HARDWICK HALL
Derbyshire
Map **8** SK46

(2m S M1 Junc 29)

☎ Chesterfield (0246) 850430

Elizabethan mansion built in 1597 by Robert Smythson for famous Bess of Hardwick (Dowager Countess of Shrewsbury). Remarkable for vast area of windows, fine tapestries, needlework and Cavendish portraits. High Great Chamber and walled courtyard gardens.

House & garden open 29 Mar–Oct, Wed, Thu, Sat, Sun & BH Mon 1–5.30 or sunset. (Closed Good Fri). Park open all year daily.

House & garden £2.50 (ch £1.20). Garden only £1.20 (ch 60p).

△ ℒ (Apr–Oct) (licensed) ⊞ ㋐ (gardens only) shop Country park 40p parking ✖ (in house) (NT) (NGS)

HAREWOOD
West Yorkshire
Map **8** SE34

Hanbury
—
Hartlepool

Harewood House & Bird Garden
☎ (0532) 886225

Home of the Earl and Countess of Harewood, the house was designed in 1759 by John Carr of York and Robert Adam, with 19th-century alterations by Sir Charles Barry. It contains splendid Chippendale furniture, English and Italian paintings and Chinese and Sèvres porcelain. The grounds landscaped by Capability Brown, offer lakeside and woodland walks and displays of shrubs and flowers. The bird garden and tropical paradise garden contain many exotic species such as flamingoes, macaws, snowy owls and penguins. There is an adventure playground.

Open Apr–Oct daily from 10am, House from 11am. Feb, Mar & Nov Sun only.

✱ £3 (ch £1.20) Party. 24hr recorded information service.

△ ℒ (licensed) ⊞ ㋐ shop ⓥ

HARLECH
Gwynedd
Map **6** SH35

Harlech Castle

Built 1283–90 by Edward I and captured by Owain Glyndwr in 1404. Rectangular fortress on concentric plan with massive gatehouse. Wide views of Snowdonia and Lleyn peninsula across Tremadoc Bay.

Open † see end of gazetteer.

✱ 90p (ch 16 & pen 45p).

△ shop (AM Cadw)

HARLOW
Essex
Map **5** TL41

Harlow Museum Passmores House, Third Avenue
☎ (0279) 446422

The exhibits cover various aspects of local history from Roman to modern and also natural history and geology. Housed in an early Georgian building, set in gardens; part of the medieval moat from the earlier house can be seen.

Open daily, Tue & Thu 10–9, Wed & Fri–Mon 10–5. (Closed Xmas).

Free.

△ ㋐ (ground floor & gardens only) shop ✖

Mark Hall Cycle Museum & Gardens
Muskham Rd Off First Av
☎ (0279) 39680

History of the bicycle 1819–1980s, with fifty machines on display from an 1819 hobby horse to a 1982 plastic machine. 3 walled period gardens, Tudor Herb garden and cottage garden.

Open daily 10–5 (dusk in winter). (Closed Xmas).

Free.

△ ㋐ shop ✖

HARRAY
Orkney
Map **16** HY31

Corrigall Farm Museum
☎ (085677) 411

Restored Orkney farmstead dating from mid 19th century with grain-drying kiln, furnishings and implements of the period.

Open Apr–Sep, Mon–Sat 10.30–1 & 2–5. Sun 2–7.

Free.

△ ㋐ shop ✖

HARROGATE
North Yorkshire
Map **8** SE35

Harlow Car Gardens Crag Lane, Otley Rd
☎ (0423) 65418

60 acres of ornamental and woodland gardens, and the Northern Trial Grounds.

Open all year daily 8–7.30 or sunset.

£1.50 (accompanied ch free, pen £1). Party 20 +.

△ ℒ ⊞ ㋐ shop & garden centre ✖ (ex guide dogs)

HARTLAND
Devon
Map **2** SS22

Hartland Quay Museum

Displays four centuries of shipwreck in parishes of Hartland, Welcombe, Clovelly (Devon) and Morwenstow (Cornwall); geology, natural history, coastal history and trade.

Open Etr wk, then Whit–Sep daily 11–5.

Admission fee payable.

△ ✖

HARTLEBURY
Hereford and Worcester
Map **7** SO87

Hereford & Worcester County Museum
Hartlebury Castle
☎ (0299) 250416

Country crafts and industries, horse-drawn vehicles, gipsy caravans, period furnishings, costumes, toys and dolls, forge and wheelwright's shop.

Open Mar–Oct Mon–Fri 2–5, Sun 2–6, BH 11–5 (Closed Good Fri).

40p (ch & pen 20p). Family ticket (2 adults & 3 ch max) £1.

△ ℒ ⊞ ㋐ (ground floor & gardens only) shop ✖

HARTLEPOOL
Cleveland
Map **8** NZ53

Gray Art Gallery & Museum Clarence Rd
☎ (0429) 66522 (ext 259)

Permanent collection of pictures. Museum collections feature local history, archaeology, engineering, Indian idols, porcelain, British birds; working blacksmith's shop in museum grounds. Monthly temporary exhibitions.

Open Mon–Sat 10–5.30, Sun 3–5 (Closed Good Fri, Xmas & New Year's day).

Free.

⚠ ♿ (ground floor & gardens only) shop 🐕

Maritime Museum Northgate
☎ (0429) 72814

Collections feature the maritime history of the town and its shipbuilding industry. Also reconstructed fisherman's cottage, a ship's bridge and an early lighthouse lantern.

Open Mon–Sat 10–5 (Closed Good Fri, Xmas & New Year's day).

Free.

⚠ shop 🐕

HARTLEY WINTNEY
Hampshire
Map **4** SU75

West Green House Garden
(1½m W on unclass road)

Charming early 18th-century house with delightful walled garden.

Open Apr–Sep. Garden Wed, Thu & Sun 2–6; House Wed 2–6 by appointment only. Apply: Lord McAlpine of West Green, 40 Bernard St, London WC1N 1LG (last admission 5.30).

Garden 80p House & garden £1.20.

🐕 (NT)

HARVINGTON
Hereford and Worcester
Map **7** SO87

Harvington Hall
☎ Chaddesley Corbett (056283) 267

Moated Elizabethan manor house with secret hiding places.

Open Etr–Sep Tue–Sat 11.30–1 & 2–6, Sun 2–6, Oct–Nov & Feb–Etr, Tue–Sat 2–6 or dusk if earlier. Open BH Mons but closed following Fri (Closed Good Fri). Other times by appointment. Last admission ½ hr before closing time.

£1.25 (ch 65p).

⚠ ☕ ♿ (grounds only) shop 🐕

HARWICH
Essex
Map **5** TM23

The Redoubt
☎ (0255) 503429

180 ft-diameter circular fort surrounded by dry moat, built 1808 to defend port against Napoleonic invasion. Walls are 8ft thick, and 18 rooms were provided to contain stores, ammunition, and quarters for 300 men. Now being restored by Harwich Society and contains three small museums.

Open Etr–Oct Sun 10–12 & 2–5.

✱ 25p. Coach parties by arrangement.

P ☕ shop 🐕

HASCOMBE
Surrey
Map **4** SU94

Winkworth Arboretum (1m NW on B2130)

A hillside of nearly 100 acres planted with shrubs and rare trees; also bluebells and two lakes. Best displays in May and end of Oct.

Open daily.

80p (£1 May & Oct–mid Nov).

(NT).

HASTINGS
East Sussex
Map **5** TQ80

Fishermen's Museum Rock a Nore Rd
☎ (0424) 424787

Former fishermen's church, now museum of local interest, including the last of Hastings luggers built for sail.

Open Spring BH–Sep Mon–Thu, Sat & Sun 10.30–12 & 2.30–6.

Free.

P (100 yds) ♿ 🐕

Hastings Castle Castle Hill
☎ (0424) 424242

Remains of Norman castle on cliffs. Excavations were made 1825 and 1968, and old dungeons were discovered 1894.

Open 26 Mar–28 Sep 10.15–4.45.

✱ 55p (ch 30p).

P (100 yds) ♿ (gardens only) shop

Hastings Embroidery
Town Hall, Queen's Rd
☎ (0424) 424242

A 74-metre-long embroidery by the Royal School of Needlework showing great events in British history from 1066 to modern times. Panels are part embroidery and part appliqué, using threads, cords, metals, lace, jewels and appropriate cloths from a variety of sources. Also on display is a scale model of the Battle of Hastings and exhibition of dolls in period costume.

Open Jun–Sep, Mon–Fri 10–5, Sat 10–1 & 2–5; Oct–May, Mon–Fri 11.30–3.30. Last admission ½ hour before closing (Closed BH Oct–May).

65p (ch 16 & pcn 30p) Party 20+.

P (500 yds) ♿ shop 🐕

See advertisement on page 132

Hastings Museum & Art Gallery
Cambridge Rd
☎ (0424) 435952

Collections of natural history of Hastings, archaeology and history of Hastings and neighbouring areas. Sussex ironwork and pottery. Fine and applied art. Durbar Hall (Indian Palace). Extensive collection of pictures, and a special Exhibition Gallery.

Open Mon–Sat 10–1 & 2–5, Sun & BH 3–5 (Closed Good Fri & Xmas).

Free.

⚠ (limited) ♿ (ground floor only) 🐕

Museum of Local History Old Town Hall, High St
☎ (0424) 425855
Archaeology and history of Hastings, especially fishing industry and the Cinque Ports.
Open Etr–Oct Mon–Sat 10–1 & 2–5; Nov–Mar Sun only 3–5 (Closed Good Fri).
✱ 15p (ch 10p) School parties by arrangement.
P & (ground floor only) ✻

St Clement's Caves
☎ (0424) 424242
Cut into the slopes of West Hill, extending over 4 acres, and associated with smugglers.
Open daily 26 Mar–28 Sep 10.15–5.15. Sat & Sun in Winter, 10.15–12.15 & 2.15–4.15.
✱ 70p (ch 35p).
P (300 yds) shop ✻

HATFIELD
Hertfordshire
Map **4** TL20

Hatfield House
☎ (07072) 62823
The historic home of the Marquess of Salisbury, a magnificent Jacobean house built 1607–11 by Robert Cecil, standing in a great park and gardens. Special exhibition of Fashion through the Ages plus the National Collection of Model

Hastings — Haughmond Abbey

Soldiers, open one hour before house.
Open 25 Mar–12 Oct, Weekdays 12–5, Sun 2–5.30. (Closed Mon except B.H. 11–5. Closed Good Fri).
Admission fee payable.
⚠ ♫ licensed (in Old Palace Yard) ⊶ &
shop, garden centre ✻

The Old Palace Hatfield House
☎ (07072) 62055 or 62030
Standing within the gardens is the surviving wing of the Royal Palace in which Queen Elizabeth I spent much of her childhood.
Elizabethan banquets held throughout the year. Tue, Thu, Fri, and Sat evenings, other evenings & luncheons for privately booked parties.
⚠ & (ground floor only)

HATHERN
Leicestershire
Map **8** SK42

Whatton House Gardens Long Whatton
(4½m NW of Loughborough on A6 between Hathern & Kegworth)
☎ Loughborough (0509) 842268

The 25-acre gardens display flowering shrubs and have water, rose and Chinese gardens. A dog cemetery and Dutch garden, also a Bogy Hole, a curious garden ornament built 1885.
Open Etr–Sep, Sun & BH Mon 2–6.
Admission fee payable.
⚠ ♫ & garden centre

HAUGHLEY
Suffolk
Map **5** TM06

Haughley Park
☎ Elmswell (0359) 40205
Newly restored house, dating from 1620, built on E-plan with crow-stepped gables and octagonal chimneys. Fine gardens.
Open May–Sep, Tue 3–6.
✱ £1 (ch 16 50p).
⚠ & (ground floor only) ✻ ♿

HAUGHMOND ABBEY
Shropshire
Map **7** SJ51
(3m NE of Shrewsbury off B5062)
Extensive remains of a house of Augustinian canons founded about 1135. Chapter House has fine Norman doorway and the abbot's lodging is exceptionally well preserved.
Open see end of gazetteer

'They've managed to get you and the Sarge, but I don't think it's very much like me.'

H^{the}astings Embroidery

... starts where the Bayeux Tapestry left off. Made by the Royal School of Needlework, the Embroidery is 74 metres long and features 81 great events in British history from The Battle of Hastings to modern times.
NEW: Tape Tour available this year.

✳ 50p (ch 16 & pen 25p).
&. &. (AM)

HAVANT
Hampshire
Map **4** SU70

Havant Museum East St
☎ (0705) 451155

The museum shares this late 19th-century building with a flourishing arts Centre. Local history displays can be seen in two rooms off the main exhibition gallery. A display of firearms and their history, formed by C.G. Vokes, is on the first floor of the museum.

Open Tue–Sat 10–5.

Free.

&. &. (ground floor only) shop

HAVEN STREET
Isle of Wight
Map **4** SZ58

Isle of Wight Steam Railway The Railway Station
☎ Wootton Bridge (0983) 882204

Locomotives in operation include former LSWR tank engine Calbourne (1891) and LBSCR/Freshwater Yarmouth & Newport Railway, Freshwater (1876), which operate in their Southern Railway liveries. Rolling stock in use includes 60–70 year old LBSCR/SECR carriages, plus vintage goods wagons. Steam trains operate through 1¾ miles of unspoilt countryside. There is also the Steam Extravaganza– late summer BH weekends.

Trains run Etr Sun & Mon; Sun & BH May–Sep; Jul & Aug Thu, and then daily week prior to late summer BH. First train 10.45am, last train 4.45pm.

✳ 70p Platform ticket. Travel 3rd class rtn £1.50 (ch 75p) 1st class rtn £2 (ch £1). Party 10 +. Postal applications to: R. Newman, Passenger Agent, Railway Station, Haven Street, Nr Ryde IOW PO33 4DS.

&. ⚏ ⏚ &. (with assistance) shop

HAVERFORDWEST
Dyfed
Map **2** SM91

Haverfordwest Castle, Museum, Art Gallery & Record Office
☎ (0437) 3708

Ruined 12th-century stronghold, slighted after Civil War, converted in 18th and 19th century, used as a jail until 1820, when new county jail was built, later became police HQ and recently converted to museum (including military items associated with the Pembroke Yeomanry) and art gallery.

Museum open Tue–Sat 10–5.30 Summer, 11–4 winter. (Closed Good Fri, 25 & 26 Dec & 1 Jan). Record Office open Mon– Thu 9–4.45, Fri 9–4.15. Parties book in advance. Castle ruins open daily during daylight, at visitors' own risk.

✳ Museum 50p (ch & pen 25p).

Haughmond Abbey
—
Haxted

&. ⏚ &. (ground floor & gardens only)
shop ✖ (ex in grounds)

HAVERTHWAITE
Cumbria
Map **7** SD38

Lakeside & Haverthwaite Railway
☎ Newby Bridge (0448) 31594

Preserved here are two 2–6–4 class 4 Fairburn tank engines and nine other locomotives, together with diesel locomotives, passenger and freight rolling stock.

Trains operational Good Fri–Etr Tue then May–Sep daily, also Apr & Oct Sun only. Site open daily (ex 24 Dec–3 Jan & some Saturdays).

£1.75 return (ch 85p), £1.05 single (ch 70p). Party, Family tickets for rail/Sealink cruisers on Windermere.

&. at Haverthwaite Station ⚏ at Haverthwaite Station &. shop garden centre

HAWES
North Yorkshire
Map **7** SD89

National Park Centre Station Yard
☎ (09697) 450

Interpretative display relating to farming in the Yorkshire Dales. Audio-visual programme, maps, guides and local information available.

Open Apr–Oct daily mid morning–late afternoon.

Free.

&. &.

Upper Dales Folk Museum Station Yard
☎ (09697) 494

Collection of folk life, trades and occupations of the Upper Dales including sheep and hay farming, peat cutting, hand knitting and cheese making.

Open Apr–Sep, Mon–Sat 11–5, Sun 2–5; during Oct the museum will be open Tue, Sat & Sun only.

✳ 40p (ch & pen 20p). Family ticket £1.

&. shop ✖

HAWICK
Borders *Roxburghshire*
Map **12** NT51

Museum & Art Gallery Wilton Lodge Park
☎ (0450) 73457

Situated in the centre of Wilton Lodge Park, one of the finest natural parks in Scotland, the museum contains exhibits of natural history, local history, hosiery trade, archaeology, geology, coins and

medals. The Art Gallery has exhibitions throughout the year.

Open Apr–Sep, Mon–Sat 10–12 & 1–5 & Sun 2–5; Oct–Mar, Mon–Fri 1–4, Sun 2–4.

✳ 45p (ch 16 pen & unemployed 25p). Party 20 +.

P (400 yds) ⚏ (in park) ⏚ (Park) &. (ground floor only) ✖

HAWKINGE
Kent
Map **5** TR24

Kent Battle of Britain Museum
☎ (030389) 2779

Largest and most comprehensive collection of remains of British and German aircraft that fought in the Battle of Britain. The display is housed in the actual buildings of the famous former Battle of Britain RAF station. The new Dowding Memorial Hangar, due to open Easter 1986, will contain the full size replicas of the Hurricane, Spitfire and Me 109 used in the Battle of Britain films.

Open Etr–Sep, Sun & BH 11–5.30; Jul & Aug Mon–Sat 1–5.

✳ 80p (ch 14 40p).

&. ⚏ (Sun only) &. shop ✖

HAWORTH
West Yorkshire
Map **7** SE03

Brontë Parsonage Museum
☎ (0535) 42323

The parsonage was the home of the three gifted 19th-century novelists Charlotte, Emily and Anne. Contains Brontë relics.

Open Apr–Sep daily 11–5.30; Oct–Mar daily 11–4.30. (Closed 1–21 Feb & 24–26 Dec).

✳ 50p (ch & pen 25p).

P (20 yds) &. (ground floor only) shop ✖

Keighley & Worth Valley Railway & Museum Keighley, Haworth and Oxenhope
☎ (0535) 43629 24-hour Talking timetable, or enquires 45214

32 steam engines, 7 diesels. Trains from Keighley (connections with BR) to Oxenhope via Haworth.

Weekend service, but daily Jul, Aug & Spring BH week.

Admission fee payable.

&. ⚏ (at station when service operates) ⏚ shop

HAXTED
Surrey
Map **5** TQ44

Watermill Museum
☎ Edenbridge (0732) 862914

Late 16th-century mill on 14th-century foundations, weather-boarded, with a mansard roof and adjoining the mill house on Eden Water. Museum contains mill machinery, two working waterwheels, and a picture gallery.→

Apr–Jun, Sat, Sun & BHs; Jul–Sep daily 2–6.

£1.50 (ch 75p).

 ⚠ 🍽 shop

HAYLE
Cornwall
Map **2** SW53

Paradise Park
☎ (0736) 753365

A collection of colourful and exotic birds, including some rare and endangered species. Among these are the St Vincent Parrot, thick-billed Parrot from Mexico, Hyacinthine Macaw, Great African Wattled Crane and Toco Toucans. There is also Paradise Farm, a collection of rare breeds of domestic animals. Miniature railway. Paradise Brewery, pub and amusement centre.

Open daily 10–dusk. (Last admissions Oct–Mar 4pm, Apr & Sep 5pm, May–Aug 6pm).

£2.40 (ch 14 £1.20).

⚠ 🍽 (licensed) 🚻 ᴚ shop ✖ (in Bird Garden)

HAYWARDS HEATH
West Sussex
Map **4** TQ32

Borde Hill Garden (1½m N on Balcombe Rd)
☎ (0444) 450326

A large garden with woods and parkland, rare trees and shrubs. Renowned for its rhododendrons, azaleas, camellias and magnolias.

Open Mar & Oct, Sat & Sun 10–6; Apr–Sep Tue–Thu, Sat, Sun & BH's 10–6.

£1.50 (ch 50p) Party 20 + . Season tickets £10 double £6 single.

⚠ 🍽 (licensed) 🚻 ᴚ plant sales

HEACHAM
Norfolk
Map **9** TF63

Norfolk Lavender Caley Mill (on A149)
☎ (0485) 70384

Largest growers and distillers of lavender in Britain. Harvest during Jul to mid Aug. Herb and Rose garden.

Open Oct–May Mon–Fri only 9–4; Jun–Sep daily 9.30–6. Parties should be booked in advance. Individual tours (times vary).

60p (ch 13 free). Grounds free.

⚠ 🍽 ᴚ shop & herb shop ⓥ

HEBDEN BRIDGE
West Yorkshire
Map **7** SD92

Automobilia Billy Ln, Old Town, Wadsworth
☎ (0422) 844775

A restored three-story former textile warehouse contains a collection of Austin

---

Haxted
—
Helston

Sevens, Morris cars, motorcycles and various items of motoring interest.

Open BHs & Apr–Oct, Tue–Sun, noon–6; Nov–Mar, Sat & Sun, noon–6. Parties by arrangement. Guided tours on request.

65p (ch 14 & pen 45p). Party 10 + .

⚠ 🍽 ᴚ (basement and ground floor only) shop ✖ (ex guide dogs) ⓥ

HECKINGTON
Lincolnshire
Map **8** TF14

Windmill Station Rd
☎ Sleaford (0529) 60765

The only surviving eight-sail windmill, built in 1830 with five sails. Destroyed by a storm in 1890 and rebuilt in 1892 using materials from Boston's eight-sail mill.

Open Sat, Sun & BH's 2–4.30 & during week by appointment. Parties by arrangement.

30p (ch 15p) (working) 20p (ch 10p) (static).

✖

Also **Craft/Heritage Centre**

Craft workshops, wide variety of working craftsmen including silversmith, spinning & weaving, fabric painting, fine leatherwork, woodwork and silk flowers. Heritage displays and sale of exhibition work of Lincolnshire craftsmen.

Open Mon–Sat 10.30–5, Sun 2–5 & BH Mon's (Closed Xmas).

Free.

⚠ 🍽 ᴚ (ground floor only) shop ✖ (in windmill)

HEDINGHAM
See entry under Castle Hedingham, page 80

HELENSBURGH
Strathclyde Dumbartonshire
Map **10** NS28

The Hill House Upper Colquhoun St
☎ (0436) 3900

Overlooking the estuary of the River Clyde this house is considered to be the finest example of the domestic architecture of Charles Rennie Mackintosh.

Open daily 1–5 (Closed Xmas & New Year).

£1 (ch 50p).

NTS

HELMINGHAM
Suffolk
Map **5** TM15

Helmingham Hall Gardens
☎ (047339) 363

Moated house with two drawbridges which are raised every night. Moated gardens in ancient deer park, Highland cattle, large herd of over 500 red and Fallow deer, and safari rides. Fresh vegetables and flowers from garden on sale in addition to East Anglian crafts from stable shop.

Gardens open every Sun 4 May–28 Sep, 2–6.

£1.20 (ch 70p pen 90p) Party.

⚠ 🍽 🚻 ᴚ (gardens only) shop garden centre

HELMSHORE
Lancashire
Map **7** SD72

Helmshore Textile Museums Higher Mill, Holcombe Rd
☎ Rossendale (0706) 226459

These two mill museums show many aspects of the history of Lancashire's textile industry. The Museum of the Lancashire Textile Industry is housed in a former 19th century textile mill. It includes an exhibition display gallery; also a full set of condenser cotton preparation and spinning machines. Higher Mill Museum is an 18th century fulling mill complete with a large (18 foot diameter) rimgeared waterwheel, Fulling stocks and other woollen finishing machinery. The spinning mules, waterwheel and other machines are demonstrated regularly.

Open Mar–Jun, Sep & Oct Mon–Fri (also Sat Apr–Jun & Sun Sep & Oct) 2–5; Jul & Aug Mon–Fri 10–1 & 2–5, Sat & Sun 2–5. Also BH wknds Nov–Feb, open for pre-booked parties only. Dates not confirmed for 1986.

✳ 70p (ch, pen & students 30p). Family £1.70.

⚠ 🍽 🚻 ᴚ (ground floor, spinning room & gardens only) shop ✖ (ex guide dogs)

HELMSLEY
North Yorkshire
Map **8** SE68

Helmsley Castle

Ruined 12th- and 13th-century stronghold with domestic buildings added in 14th century.

Open, † see end of gazetteer.

50p (ch 16 & pen 25p).

⚠ (AM)

HELSTON
Cornwall
Map **2** SW62

Cornwall Aero Park & Flambards Victorian Village
☎ (03265) 4549 or 3404 due to change to (0326) 574549 or (0326) 573404

Award-winning all-weather family leisure park with large exhibition hall set in beautiful landscaped gardens, Flambards Victorian Village, an authentic life-size Victorian village with shops, carriages and fashions. 'Britain in the Blitz' How did we survive? This recreation of a life-size street offers a stunning 'Blitz' experience. The Aero Park consists: historic aircraft, motor vehicles, Battle of Britain War Gallery, helicopters, Concorde Flight Deck and SR2 Simulator. Also special exhibitions and children's amusements.

Open daily, Etr–Oct 10–5.

£2.80 (ch £1.40 pen £2). Party 15+.

🛆 ⬛ 🐾 ♿ (ground floor & gardens only) shop & garden centre ✖ Ⓥ

Helston Folk Museum Old Butter Market
☎ (03265) 61672

Folk museum covering local history and articles from The Lizard Peninsula. Various summer exhibitions.

Open Mon, Tue, Thu–Sat 10.30–12.30 & 2–4.30, Wed 10.30–noon. Touring schools and visiting groups welcome.

Free.

P (400 yds) ♿ shop ✖

HENFIELD West Sussex
Map **4** TQ21

Woods Mill Shoreham Rd (1m S Henfield on A2037 at junction with Horn Ln)
☎ (0273) 492630

Wildlife and countryside exhibition and nature trails set in natural surroundings. The wildlife and countryside exhibition is housed in an 18th century water mill and includes live animals, audio-visual programmes and an accurate model of an oak tree. In the 15 acres of grounds there is a superb trail around woodland, meadow, marsh, streams and a lake. There is a dipping pond where children →

may net and identify specimens (nets are provided).

Open Good Fri–28 Sep Tue–Thu & Sat 2–6; Sun & BH's 11–6.

Weekdays £1 (ch 50p). Wknds & BH £1.20 (ch 60p). Party.

⚠ shop ✗

HENLEY-IN-ARDEN
Warwickshire
Map **4** SP16

Guildhall High St
☎ (05642) 2309

Gabled, timber framed building of 1448, restored in 1915, with outside staircase leading from Dutch-style garden to hall with fine roof timbering.

Open any reasonable time on application to *Custodian, Guild Cottage.*

Free (donations).

P (300 yds) ✗

HENLEY-ON-THAMES
Oxfordshire
Map **4** SU78

Greys Court (3m W.)
☎ Rotherfield Greys (04917) 529

A gabled Elizabethan house with fine chimney-pieces and plasterwork. Medieval fortified courtyard with three towers and a keep remain from the former 13th-century house and there is a 200ft-deep well with 19ft-wide wooden donkey wheel. A new feature is the 'Archibishops' Maze.

Open 29 Mar–Sep, garden Mon–Sat, house Mon, Wed & Fri, 2–6.

Garden £1.30. House & Garden £1.80.
☑ (Wed & Sat) (NT)

HEREFORD
Hereford and Worcester
Map **3** SO54

Churchill Gardens Museum & Brian Hatton Art Gallery 3 Venn's Lane
☎ (0432) 268121 ext 207

Branch museum located in Regency house with fine grounds. Victorian nursery, butler's pantry and parlour, costumes, furniture and water colours.

Henfield
—
Herne Common

New Room of Straw, 18th and early 19th-century rooms and costume display corridor. Also the Hatton Gallery primarily devoted to works by the local artist Brian Hatton.

Open all year Tue–Sat and (Sun in summer only) 2–5. (Closed Mon ex BH's).

30p (ch & pen 15p).
⚠ shop ✗

Hereford Museum & Art Gallery Broad St
☎ (0432) 268121 ext 207

Roman tessellated pavements, natural history, bee keeping display with observation hive, English watercolours, local geology and county's archaeology, also folk life and folklore material. Exhibitions at City Art Gallery change every month.

Open Tue, Wed & Fri 10–6, Thu 10–5, Sat 10–5. (Summer); Sat 10–4. (Winter).

Free.
& shop ✗

Museum of Cider Pomona Place, Grimmer Rd
☎ (0432) 54207

The museum shows cider making through the ages with the huge French beam press, reconstructed farm cider house, working cooper, champagne cellars and working cider-brandy distillery.

Open Apr, May & Oct, daily (ex Tue) 10–5.30; Jun–Sep daily 10–5.30.

90p (ch & pen 60p). Party.
⚠ shop Ⓥ

The Old House High Town
☎ (0432) 268121 ext 207

A fine specimen of Jacobean domestic architecture (c. 1621). Furnished in 17th-century style on three floors including a Kitchen, Hall, and bedrooms with four-poster beds.

Open Tue–Fri 10–1 & 2–5.30 (Sat in summer 10–1 & 2–5.30, 10–1 in winter) Mon 10–1. Also open BH Mons.

30p (ch & pen 15p). Free on Mon.
Shop ✗

St John & Coningsby Museum 110 Widemarsh St
☎ (0432) 272837 mornings

Early 13th-century hall arranged with armour and other subjects connected with the Order and Chapel of knights of St John, with almshouses added in 1614 by Sir Thomas Coningsby of Hampton Court. Unique Friars' Preaching Cross in adjoining public gardens.

Open Etr–Sep daily (ex Mon & Fri) 2–5.

25p (ch 10p). Party.
⚠ ₮ (ground floor & garden only)
shop ✗

HERMITAGE
Borders Roxburghshire
Map **12** NY59

Hermitage Castle

An old Douglas stronghold, mainly 14th-century, and well restored.

Open, see end of gazetteer.

✱ 50p (ch & pen 25p).
⚠ (AM)

HERNE COMMON
Kent
Map **5** TR16

"Brambles" Wildlife Park & Butterfly World Wealdon Forest Park
☎ Canterbury (0227) 712379

A beautiful woodland area of some 20 acres of the remaining piece of the old Weald of Kent and is situated on the A291 halfway between Herne Bay and Canterbury. Features are the Woodland Park with its nature trails which pass enclosures of mainly British animals, the Forest Playground, the Childrens Farm, with miniature buildings where young and baby domestic farm animals mingle with the visitors, and Butterfly World, a large covered garden, where you can see free-flying British and tropical butterflies, feeding and pairing among their natural

---

DINMORE MANOR
MANOR HOUSE, CLOISTERS, MUSIC ROOM AND GARDENS

Open throughout the year. Splendid views as far as the Malverns.

The Chapel is one of only three in England, dedicated to the Knights Hospitallers of St. John of Jerusalem.

Beautiful flowers in bloom throughout the season, with a magnificent panorama over the gardens from the walkway on top of the cloisters.

Situated to the west of the A49, south of Dinmore Hill, which is midway between Hereford and Leominster.

See gazetteer entry for further details.

food plants. There are also plentiful woodland birds to be seen in the park which has become a small haven for a tremendous variety. New for 1985, Tudor Herb Garden.

Open Etr–Oct, daily 10–5.

£2 (ch & pen £1). Party.

🅰 ⬛ 🜛 shop & garden centre ✠ Ⓥ

HERSTMONCEUX
East Sussex
Map **5** TQ61

Royal Greenwich Observatory (Herstmonceux Castle) Entry off Wartling Rd
☎ (0323) 833171 ext 3320

Public exhibition, grounds and Telescopes can be visited. Castle also opens occasionally.

Open Etr–Sep, daily from 10.30–5.30. Last admission 4.30.

✱ £1.50 (ch & pen £1). Party 20 + .

🅰 ⬛ 🜛 ♿ (ground floor only) shop

Sussex Farm Heritage Centre Tilley La, Windmill Hill
☎ (0323) 832182

The Heritage Centre is the home of some of the finest award winning Shire horses in the South-East. They can be admired at close quarters along with an impressive collection of rare and historic agricultural machinery and horse drawn farm

---

Horno Common
Highdown

equipment. This ranges from a complex threshing machine to the simple brewery dray. The farm machinery is in regular use and there is a collection of livestock, including several rare breeds. Demonstrations, wagon rides and working classes are planned for 1986.

Open all year, 10–5 (or dusk).

£1.50 (pen £1 ch 50p).

🅰 ⬛ 🜛 ♿ shop

HERTFORD
Hertfordshire
Map **4** TL31

Hertford Castle & Gardens
☎ (0992) 552885

The original castle was built by the Normans; the walls and motte preserve the plan of that structure. The Edward IV gatehouse still remains, with wings added in the 18th and 20th centuries. The grounds are open to the public and band . concerts are held on the open days.

Open 1st Sun in each month May–Sep 2.30–4.30.

Free
P (50 yds) ♿ (ground floor only) ✠

HEVER
Kent
Map **5** TQ44

Hever Castle and Gardens (3m SE Edenbridge off B2026)
☎ Edenbridge (0732) 865224

Enchanting 13th century double-moated Castle, childhood home of Queen Anne Boleyn. Spectacular Italian Gardens and picturesque lake. Open air Theatre season. Group accommodation and Banqueting facilities all year in the 'Tudor Village'.

Open 28 Mar–2 Nov (Closed 11 Jun) Gardens 11–6, last entry 5pm. Castle open from noon.

Castle & Gardens £3 (ch £1.50) Gardens only £1.75 (ch 90p) Special Private pre-booked guided tours available all year.

🅰 ⬛ (licensed) ♿ (ground floor & gardens only) shop & garden centre ✠ (in Castle)

HIGHDOWN
West Sussex
Map **4** TQ00

Highdown (N off A259 halfway between Worthing & Littlehampton).
☎ Worthing (0903) 501054 →

Gardens laid out in chalk pit on Highdown Hill, with rock plants, flowering shrubs and daffodils, as well as excellent views. Gardeners Sunday, 1st Sun in May.

Open all year Mon–Fri 10–4.30; wknds & BH's Apr–Sep 10–8.

Free.

 🅰 🗓 🎪 ♿ 🏮

HIGH WYCOMBE
Buckinghamshire
Map 4 SU89

Wycombe Chair Museum Castle Hill House, Priory Av
☎ (0494) 23879

Fine house set in gardens and museum of chairs, old tools, and chair-making apparatus.

Open Tue–Sat 10–1 & 2–5 (Closed Sun, Mon & BH's).

Free.

P (adjacent) ♿ (ground floor only) shop ✖

HIMLEY
Staffordshire
Map 7 SO89

Himley Hall (6m S of Wolverhampton off A449, 4m N of Stourbridge off A449)
☎ Dudley (0384) 55433 ext 5425

Extensive parkland with 9 hole golf course, model village, trout and coarse fishing (extra charge). Hall **not** open to the public.

Grounds open daily 8am–8pm or ½hr before dusk.

Free.

 🅰 🗓 🎪 ♿

HITCHIN
Hertfordshire
Map 4 TL12

Hitchin Museum & Art Gallery Paynes Park
☎ (0462) 34476

Contains local and natural history collections, costume and Victoriana. Regimental Museum of the Hertfordshire Yeomanry. Special temporary exhibitions changed monthly. Good collection of

---

Highdown
—
Holdenby

watercolours, especially those by local Quaker artist Samuel Lucas Snr 1805–1870.

Open Mon–Sat 10–5 (Closed BH).

Free.

🅰 ♿ (ground floor only) shop ✖

HOAR CROSS
Staffordshire
Map 7 SK12

Hoar Cross Hall (off A515 & B5234 near Newborough & Abbots Bromley)
☎ (028375) 224

Elizabethan-style Victorian mansion, designed by Henry Clutton, interior fittings by G. F. Bodley. Fine oak panelling, richly moulded ceilings, William Morris wallpaper, furniture, fine collection of Victorian costumes, furnishings and paintings. Also there is a private chapel, and twenty acres of woodland and gardens at present under restoration, and a magnificent Church of Holy Angels adjacent to grounds. Mediaeval Banquets held Sep–May.

Open Spring BH–early Sep, Sun. Please telephone for weekday opening arrangements. (Throughout the year for school parties and educational visits by appointment.)

£1.40 (ch 60p).

🅰 🗓 ♿ shop ✖ (in house) Ⓥ

HODNET
Shropshire
Map 7 SJ62

Hodnet Hall Gardens (6m SW Market Drayton, 12m NE Shrewsbury)
☎ (063084) 202

Re-designed Elizabethan-style Victorian house (not open to public), with 60 acre landscaped garden. Collection of big-game trophies in 17th-century tearooms. Plants are usually for sale.

Open daily from 28 Mar–28 Sep, weekdays 2–5, gardens until 6.30. Sun, BH Mon & Tue following, 12–6.
✻ £1.20 (ch 60p). Party 25+.
🅰 🗓 ♿ shop

HOGHTON
Lancashire
Map 7 SD62

Hoghton Tower (5m SE Preston on A675)
☎ (025485) 2986

16th-century fortified hilltop mansion with magnificent banqueting hall where, in 1617, the 'Loin of Beef' was knighted by James I. Also, the King's bedchamber, audience chamber, ballroom and other state rooms; the Tudor Well House with its horse-drawn pump and oaken windlass; the underground passages, with 'The Lancashire Witches' dungeons and the wine cellar. Walled gardens, lawns and grounds with views of sea, moors, hills of Lake District and Welsh mountains. Permanent dolls house and dolls collection.

Open Etr Sat, then every Sun to Oct 2–5; also Sats in Jul & Aug and BHs, 2–5.

£1.50 (ch 50p).

🅰 🗓 shop ✖ (ex grounds)

HOLDENBY
Northamptonshire
Map 4 SP66

Holdenby House Gardens
☎ Northampton (0604) 770786

During the reign of Elizabeth I this was the largest house in England and in the Civil War Charles I was imprisoned here for four months. Today only the remains of its fine gardens can be seen. Other features are an Elizabethan garden with fragrant and silver borders, museum, lakeside train rides, donkey rides and nature trail. Rare breeds of farm animals.

Open Apr–Sep, Sun & BH Mon 2–6, Jul & Aug also Thu 2–6.

✻ Gardens £1.20 (ch 60p pen £1). House & gardens open to parties of 20+ Tue–Thu (booking necessary).

🅰 🗓 ♿ shop & garden centre

HOLKER
Cumbria
Map **7** SD37

Holker Hall & Park
Nr Grange-over-Sands
☎ Flookburgh (044853) 328

House dates from the 16th century and contains interesting woodcarving, stonework and a fine collection of paintings and furniture, 122 acres of park with formal and woodland gardens. Deer park, Motor museum with over 100 cars and motorcycles featuring a full-size replica of Sir Malcolm Campbell's world-record-breaking car 'Bluebird'. Baby animal farm, children's adventure playground. Craft and Countryside museum. Hot-air ballooning some weekends weather permitting. Special events include horse-riding and driving trials, model aircraft rallies, Historic vehicle rallies.

Open Etr Sun–26 Oct. Sun–Fri 10.30–6 last admission 4.30. Hall closes 4.30.
fr £1.50 (discount for children). Party 20 +.
🅰 🍷 (licensed) ⛱ ♿ (ground floor & gardens only) shop ⓥ

HOLKHAM
Norfolk
Map **9** TF84

Holkham Hall (1½m W of Wells-next-the-Sea off A149) Entrance by Almshouses Gate in Holkham village
☎ Fakenham (0328) 710227

Palladian mansion, built 1734 by William Kent and home of Coke of Norfolk and the Earls of Leicester. Marble Hall and state apartments with Rubens, Van Dyck, Claude Poussin and Gainsborough paintings. Holkham Pottery, also Holkham bygones collection of agricultural and rural craft tools. Garden centre and large park.

Open Jun & Sep Mon, Thu & Sun 1.30–5; Jul & Aug Mon, Wed, Thu & Sun 1.30–5; Spring & Summer BH Mons 11.30–5.
Hall £1.30 (ch 5–15 50p pen £1). Bygones £1 (ch 5–15 50p pen 75p). Party 20 +.
🅰 🍷 ♿ (ground floor & gardens) shop garden centre ✖ (in buildings)

Holker
—
Honiton

HOLLINGBOURNE
Kent
Map **5** TQ85

Eyhorne Manor SW of village
☎ (062780) 514

15th-century half timbered house with 17th-century additions. Laundry museum and also herb garden.

Open 1st wknd in May–Jul, Sat & Sun 2–6; Aug Tue–Thu Sat & Sun 2–6 & BH in this period.
£1.10 (ch 60p).
🅰 🍷 ✖

HOLT
Wiltshire
Map **3** ST86

The Courts
Gardens only with lily pond and arboretum.
Open Apr–Oct, Mon–Fri 2–6.
£1.
🅰 (NT) ⓥ

HOLWAY
Clwyd
Map **7** SJ17

Grange Cavern Military Museum
Grange Ln
☎ Holywell (0352) 713455

2¼ acre Cavern, 60 to 100 ft below the surface, quarried for its limestone in the early 19th century. Houses over seventy military vehicles and one of the largest collections of militaria and specialist military items in Great Britain. Falklands exhibition. The temperature in the Caverns is about 50 °F.

Open Etr–Oct daily 9.30–6. Feb & Mar wknds only 10–5. Last admission 1 hr before closing.
Admission fee payable.
🅰 🍷 licensed ⛱ ♿ shop ✖

Lindisfarne Castle
☎ Berwick (0289) 89244

A 16th-century castle, restored in 1903 by Sir Edwin Lutyens with garden designed originally by Gertrude Jekyll.

Open Good Fri–6 Apr daily. 7 Apr–end Apr, Wed Sat & Sun 11–5. May–Sep, Sat–Thu 11–5. Oct, Sat & Sun 11–5. Island not accessible two hours before and four hours after high tide, other times by previous arrangement with Caretaker.
£2.20 Jun–Aug. Other times £1.70. Party.
🅰 (NT)

Lindisfarne Priory
☎ Berwick (0289) 89200 ·

The cradle of English Christianity in the north, situated on Holy Island which is accessible at low tide across a causeway. Tide tables are posted at ends of causeway or telephone Custodian on above number.

Open †, see end of gazetteer.
50p (ch 16 & pen 25p).
🅰 (AM)

HONITON
Devon
Map **3** ST10

Allhallows Museum High St (next to church)
☎ Farway (040487) 307

Superb display of Honiton lace with craft demonstrations Jun–Aug. Also exhibits of local historical interest.

Open Etr Sat & Mon then mid May–Oct Mon–Sat 10–5.
40p (ch 10p).
P (400 yds) ♿ (ground floor only) shop ✖

Honiton Pottery 30–34 High St
☎ (0404) 2106

Visitors can tour the pottery at leisure and see the several stages of the craft during normal working hours.

Pottery open Mon–Thu 9–12 & 2–4.30. Fri 4pm. Shop Mon–Sat 9–5.30. →

Free.

⚪ ♻ (small coffee shop) shop

HORNSEA
Humberside
Map **8** TA24

Hornsea Museum (The North
Holderness Museum of Village Life) 11
Newbegin
☎ (04012) 3443

*Housed in a former farmhouse with its
associated out-buildings, the collection
reflects the village life and local history of
North Holderness. It accurately depicts
the dairy, kitchen, parlour and bedroom of
a typical farmhouse over a century ago.
The tools of local craftsmen – the
Coopers, Cartwrights, Wheelwrights and
Blacksmiths, and the hand farm
implements of the period are also
displayed in their settings. There is also a
photograph exhibition room, a local
industry display and features on the lives
of local personalities.*

Open Etr–19 Jul & 11 Sep–Oct daily 2–5;
20 Jul–10 Sep, Mon–Sat 11–5. Sun 2–5.

45p (ch 25p pen 35p).

P (50 yds) shop

Hornsea Pottery Rolston Rd
☎ (04012) 2161

*Factory tours, seconds shop, gift shop,
fashion shop. 'World of Wings' Birds of
Prey Conservation Centre. Butterfly World
Adventure Playground, picnic area and
coffee shop. 'Minidale' model village
(open early May–Sep) and 28 acres of
landscaped gardens with lake. Special
events for most Sundays & Bank Holidays
from Easter onwards.*

Open daily from 10am. (Closed Xmas wk).

Nominal charge for entry into attractions &
certain amenities.

⚪ (free) ⚷ & shop

HORRINGER
Suffolk
Map **5** TL75

Ickworth (2½m SW of Bury St Edmunds)
*An elliptical rotunda (1794–1830) with
18th-century and Regency French
furniture, silver and pictures. The formal
garden is noted for its fine trees.*

Open Etr, Apr & Oct wknds only. May–
Sep Tue, Wed, Fri, Sat, Sun & BH Mons
1.30–5.30. Closed 6 Jun. Park open daily.

Wknd & BH £1.50 (ch 75p) plus 50p
access. Midweek £1.20 (ch 60p) plus 50p
access. Party 15+ .

♻ & ✕ (in house or garden ex guide
dogs) (NT)

HORSEY
Norfolk
Map **9** TG42

Drainage Windmill
*Erected in 1912 on the foundations of an
earlier mill and restored after being struck
by lightning.*

Accessible 20 Apr–Sep 11–5 (Balcony
closed May & Jun).

50p.

(NT)

HORSHAM
West Sussex
Map **4** TQ13

Horsham Museum 9 The Causeway
☎ (0403) 54959

*16th-century timbered house with walled
garden planted with herbs and English
cottage garden flowers. Displays include
costume and accessories, toys, early
cycles, domestic life, Sussex rural crafts,
local history, archaeology and geology.
Regular temporary exhibitions throughout
the year.*

Open Tue–Fri, 1–5. Sat 10–5.

Free.

P (at rear) & (ground floor & garden only)
shop ✕

HOUGHTON
Norfolk
Map **9** TF72

Houghton Hall (1½m off A148 between
Kings Lynn & Fakenham)
☎ East Rudham (048522) 569

*One of the finest examples of Palladian
architecture in England, designed by
Colen Campbell and Thomas Ripley. Built
in the 18th century for Sir Robert Walpole,
state rooms have interior decorations and
furniture by William Kent and contain
paintings and china. Stables with heavy
horses and Shetland ponies, harness
room and coach house. Model soldier
collection. Beautiful parkland.*

Open Etr Sun–last Sun Sep. Thu, Sun &
BH's 12–5.30. House not open before 1.30
on Suns.

£2 (ch 50p under 5 free, pen £1.50). Party
20+ .

⚪ ⚷ & shop Ⓜ

HOUSESTEADS
Northumberland
Map **12** NY76

Roman Wall (Housesteads Museum)
Nr Bardon Mill

*Roman fort of 'Vircovicium' with mile-
castles and 3-mile stretch of wall.
Museum has finds excavated in area.*

Open † see end of gazetteer.

✱ 80p (ch & pen 40p). Reductions in
winter.

⚪ (AM) & (NT)

HOVE
East Sussex
Map **4** TQ20

British Engineerium off Nevill Rd
☎ Brighton (0273) 559583

*Restored Victorian water pumping station
including the original working beam
engine of 1876 and French Corliss
horizontal engine which gained first prize
at the Paris International Exhibition of
1889. Plus traction engines, fire engines
etc. The exhibition hall contains many
hundreds of full size and model engines
including marine steam engines, hot air
and internal combustion engines, early
electric motors and hand and domestic
tools. Exhibitions throughout the year.*

Open daily 10–5 (Closed wk prior to
Xmas). In steam Sundays & BH.

£1.80 (ch, students & pen £1).

P ⚷ & (ground floor only) shop ✕ Ⓜ

HOWICK
Northumberland
Map **12** NU21

Howick Hall Gardens & Grounds
Entrance by East Lodge
☎ Longhoughton (066577) 285

*Late 18th-century mansion with fine
gardens and grounds.*

Gardens & grounds only open Apr–Sep,
daily 2–7.

50p (ch & pen 30p).

⚪

HUDDERSFIELD
West Yorkshire
Map **7** SE11

Art Gallery Princess Alexandra Walk
☎ (0484) 513808 ext 216

*Contains a permanent collection of British
oil paintings, watercolours, drawings,
sculpture from mid 19th century onwards.
Temporary loan exhibition throughout the
year. Scherer gallery of Bamforth
photographs, lantern slides and
postcards.*

Open Mon–Fri 10–6, Sat 10–4 (Closed
Sun).

Free.

⚪ & ✕

Tolson Memorial Museum
Ravensknowle Park
☎ (0484) 30591 & 41455

*Geology, natural history, archaeology, folk
life, toys, development of cloth industry
and collection of horse-drawn vehicles.*

Open Mon–Sat 10–5; Sun 1–5 (Closed
Xmas).

Free.

⚪ & (ground floor & garden only) shop ✕

HUGHENDEN
Buckinghamshire
Map **4** SU89

Hughenden Manor (1½m N of High
Wycombe)
☎ High Wycombe (0494) 32580

Disraeli's old home, remodelled by him in

1862, with furniture and books. Within a 169 acre estate.

Open 31 Mar–Oct. House & Garden Wed–Sat 2–6; Sun & BH Mon 12–6; Mar, Sat & Sun only 2–6. (Closed Good Fri).

£1.70 (£1.30 Thu & Fri).

(NT)

HULL
Humberside
Map **8** TA02

Ferens Art Gallery Queen Victoria Sq
☎ (0482) 222737

Contains a collection of works by European Old Masters; 19th-century marine paintings from Humberside; 20th-century English art and a regular programme of visiting exhibitions.

Open Mon–Sat 10–5, Sun 1.30–4.30 (Closed Good Fri, 25 & 26 Dec).

Free.

P (200 yds) ⚟ (ex Sun) shop ✕

Maister House 160 High St

Georgian house (1743), with stone and wrought iron staircase and balustrade, some ornate stucco work and finely carved doors. Staircase and entrance hall only, shown all year.

Open Mon–Fri 10–4 (Closed BH).

50p (incl. guide book).

(NT)

Town Docks Museum Queen Victoria Sq
☎ (0482) 222737

Displays include 'Whales and Whaling', 'Fishing and Trawling', 'Hull and the Humber', 'Ships and Shipping', plus Victorian Court Room.

Open Mon–Sat 10–5, Sun 1.30–4.30 (Closed Good Fri, 25 & 26 Dec).

Free.

P (200 yds) ⚟ (ex Sun) ৬ (ground floor only) shop ✕

Transport & Archaeological Museum
36 High St
☎ (0482) 222737

Development of road transport through the ages. Archaeology of Humberside and Roman mosaics including the Horkstow Pavement.

Open Mon–Sat 10–5, Sun 1.30–4.30 (Closed Good Fri, 25 & 26 Dec).

Free.

P (at Wilberforce House) shop ✕

Wilberforce House 23–25 High St
☎ (0482) 222737

Early 17th-century mansion, where William Wilberforce was born, with Jacobean and Georgian rooms and slavery displays. Secluded garden.

Open Mon–Sat 10–5, Sun 1.30–4.30 (Closed Good Fri, 25 & 26 Dec).

Free.

⚠ ⌁ ৬ (ground floor only) shop ✕

Hughenden
—
Ilfracombe

HUNTERSTON
Strathclyde *Ayrshire*
Map **10** NS15

Hunterston Power Station
☎ West Kilbride (0294) 823668

Nuclear Power Station of advanced gas-cooled reactor (AGR) type. Guided parties of about 12 are taken on tours of the premises and also see audio-visual presentation on nuclear power generation.

Open May–Sep Mon–Sat at 10, 11.30, 2 & 3.30; Sun 2 & 3.30 (by telephone appointment only).

Free (ch 11 accepted if accompanied by an adult).

⚠ ✕

HUNTINGDON
Cambridgeshire
Map **4** TL27

Cromwell Museum
Grammar School Walk
☎ (0480) 52861

Restored Norman building, once a school where Oliver Cromwell and Samuel Pepys were taught, now Museum of Cromwellian relics.

Open Apr–Oct, Tue–Fri 11–1 & 2–5, Sat & Sun 11–1 & 2–4; Nov–Mar, Tue–Fri 2–5, Sat 11–1 & 2–4, Sun 2–4. (Closed BHs ex Good Fri).

Free.

P (500 yds) shop ✕

Hinchingbrooke House (½m W on A141)
☎ (0480) 51121

Tudor and later mansion, incorporating medieval Nunnery. Former home of the Cromwells and Earl of Sandwich now restored and used as a school.

Open Apr–Aug, Sun & BH Mons 2–5.

75p (ch & pen 50p) Party 20 + .

⚠ ⚟ ৬ (ground floor only) shop

HUNTLY
Grampian *Aberdeenshire*
Map **15** NJ53

Huntly Castle

Formerly Peel of Strathbogie, and dates largely from 1602. It has elaborate heraldic embellishments.

Open see end of gazetteer.

✳ 50p (ch & pen 25p).

⚠ (AM)

Huntly Museum The Square
☎ Peterhead (0779) 77778

Local history and changing special exhibitions every year. Governed by North East of Scotland Library Committee.

Open all year, Tue–Sat 10–12 & 2–4.

Free.

P (10 yds-limited) shop ✕ (ex guide dogs)

HURST CASTLE
Hampshire
Map **4** SZ38

Hurst Castle
On peninsula 4m S of Lymington.

Erected 1544 by Henry VIII, occupied during the Civil War by Cromwell's forces and refortified in mid 19th-century. Accessible by foot or by boat from Keyhaven. (Weather permitting).

Open †, see end of gazetteer.

✳ 50p (ch 16 & pen 25p).

Nearest car park on beach 1½m.
⚟ (Apr–Sep) (AM)

HURSTPIERPOINT
West Sussex
Map **4** TQ21

Danby
☎ (0273) 833000

Elizabethan E-shaped house dating from 1593. Early in the 18th century the south front was re-faced.

Open May–Sep, Wed & Thur 2–5. (Last admission 4.30).

50p (ch 25p).
⚠ ✕

HYTHE
Kent
Map **5** TR13

Romney, Hythe & Dymchurch Railway.
For details see gazetteer entry under **New Romney**.

IGHTHAM
Kent
Map **5** TQ55

Ightham Mote (2½m S off A227)
☎ Plaxtol (0732) 810378

Late medieval moated manor house extensively remodelled in the early 16th century. Features include the Great Hall Old Chapel and Crypt circa 1340. Tudor Chapel with painted ceiling.

Open 28 Mar–Oct. Mon, Wed, Fri & Sun 11–5. Pre-booked parties Thur only. Open Good Fri & BH Mon.

£1.60 (ch 16 £1) Parties by arrangement.

⚠ ৬ (ground floor & gardens only). (NT).

ILFRACOMBE
Devon
Map **4** SS54

Chambercombe Manor (1m E off A399)
☎ (0271) 62624

One of England's oldest houses circa 1066. This attractive Norman Manor has Elizabethan additions, a haunted room, Priest Hole, Private Chapel (1086), ancient wishing well, waterfowl pond and herb garden. →

141

Open Good Fri–Sep Mon–Fri 10.30–12.30
& 2–4.30. Sun 2–4.30. (Closed Sat).
£1.50 (ch 75p).
⚠ ⤺ ♿ (gardens only) shop ✸ ⓥ

Hele Mill (1m E)
☎ (0271) 63162
*This mill dates back to 1525. It has been
restored to full working order and is
producing wholemeal flour. There is an
18ft overshot water wheel and inside
there are many interesting items of mill
machinery.*
Open Etr–Oct Mon–Fri 10–5, also Sun
2–5.
✳ 60p (ch 30p).
⚠ shop ✸

Ilfracombe Museum Runnymede
Gardens, Wilder Rd
☎ (0271) 63541
*History, Victoriana, archaeology, geology,
photographs. Costume, china & natural
history.*
Open Etr–Oct daily, 10–5.30; Nov–Etr
10–1.
40p (ch 10p & pen 20p).
⚠ ♿ shop ✸

Watermouth Castle (3m NE off A399)
☎ (0271) 63879
*One of North Devon's finest castles now
offers entertainment for the family
including mechanical music
demonstrations, handcarts of yesteryear
in the great hall, rural bygones, animated
scenes in the dungeon.*
Open Etr–Spring BH, Sun–Thu 2.30;
Spring BH–Sep Mon–Fri fr 11 (Jul & Aug fr
10) Sun fr 2. Oct Sun–Thu fri 2.30. Last
admission 4pm. (Opening times under
review).
✳ £2 (ch 13 £1.50) Party.
⚠ ⤺ ⤲ ♿ (ground floor & garden only)
shop ✸

ILKLEY
West Yorkshire
Map **7** SE14

Manor House Museum
Castle Yard, Church St.
☎ (0943) 600066

Ilfracombe

Inveraray

*Elizabethan manor house, built on site of
Roman fort, showing exposed Roman wall
and collections of Roman material.
Exhibitions by regional contemporary
artists and craftsmen.*
Open Apr–Sep Tue–Sun 10–6; Oct–Mar
10–5. Also open BH Mons. (Closed Good
Fri & Xmas.)
Free.
P (100 yds) ♿ shop ✸

INGLISTON
Lothian *Midlothian*
Map **11** NT17

Scottish Agricultural Museum
Royal Highland Showground
☎ 031–333 2674
*Displays of original farming tools,
equipment and models showing how the
land was worked and those living in rural
Scotland.*
Open May–Sep, Mon–Fri 10–4, Sun 12–5.
Party.
Free.
P (200 yds) shop ✸ (ex guide dogs)

INSTOW
Devon
Map **2** SS43

Tapeley Park
☎ (0271) 860528
*Home of the Christie family of
Glyndebourne, the house contains fine
furniture, porcelain and 18th-century
Italian plasterwork ceilings. Beautiful
Italian garden, woodland walk to memorial
lily pond and walled kitchen garden.
Superb views overlooking the Taw and
Torridge Estuary to the open sea.*
Open Etr–Oct Tue–Sun & BH Mon, 10–6.
During winter, gardens only in daylight
hours. Conducted tours of the house
when numbers permit.

✳ Gardens only £1 (ch 50p). Tour of
House plus gardens £2 (ch £1).
⚠ ⤺ ♿ (ground floor & gardens only)
shop & garden centre ⓥ

INVERARAY
Strathclyde *Argyll*
Map **10** NN00

Argyll Wildlife Park Dalchenna
☎ (0499) 2264 & 2098
*Scotland's newest wildlife park featuring
100 species of swan, geese and duck –
some extremely rare. Also a collection of
rare owls. Several species of mammal;
deer, wildcat, badger etc. can also be
seen. Included is an illustrated nature
walk through coniferous forest.*
Open daily 9–6.30 (or dusk).
£1.75 (pen £1.40 ch 90p).
⚠ ⤺ ⤲ shop & garden centre

Inveraray Bell Tower
☎ Kilchrenan (08663) 314 or Inveraray
(0499) 2433
*The 126ft tower was planned in 1914, and
the ring of ten bells was hung in the great
bell tower chamber in 1931. From the roof
of the tower is an excellent view .
Exhibition of vestments and campanology
and there will be a 'ring-in' daily during
Inveraray Week at the end of July
beginning of Aug. Telephone for details of
events.*
Open May–Sep Mon–Sat 10–1 & 2–5, Sun
3–6.
50p (ch & pen 25p).
P (100 yds) ♿ (ground floor & gardens
only) shop

Inveraray Castle
☎ (0499) 2203
*A fine mansion of the late 18th century,
the ancestral home of the Dukes of Argyll.
The great armoury hall, staterooms,
tapestries and furniture are of note. There
is a combined operations museum within
castle grounds. Castle gardens open on
selected weekends.*
Open last Sat Mar–2nd Sun Oct daily.
(Closed Fri ex Jul & Aug) 10–1 & 2–6. Apr–
Jun & Sep–Oct, Sun 1–6. Jul & Aug daily

Inveraray Castle

A fine mansion of the late 18th century,
the ancestral home of the Dukes of Argyll.
Castle gardens open on selected weekends.

*For opening times and admission prices
see gazetteer entry.*

10–6, Sun 1–6. Last admissions 10.00 &
5.30. Woodland Walks all year
£2 (ch 16 £1, pen £1.50). Family ticket
£5.50. Party 20+.

⚠ ⚖ (licensed) ⴹ ♿ (ground floor only)
shop ✠ Ⓥ

INVERESK
Lothian *Midlothian*
Map **11** NT37

Inveresk Lodge Garden
*Garden featuring numerous varieties of
plants for small gardens.*

Gardens only shown Mon, Wed & Fri 10–
4.30, and on Sun 2–5 (when house is
occupied).

✽ 40p (ch accompanied by adult 20p).
(NTS)

INVERURIE
Grampian *Aberdeenshire*
Map **15** NJ72

Inverurie Museum Town House, The
Square
☎ Peterhead (0779) 77778
*Thematic displays changing at four- or six-
monthly intervals. Permanent local history
and archaeology exhibition. Established in
1884, this museum is now governed by
the North East Scotland Library Service
Committee.*

Open all year Mon–Fri 2–5, Sat 10–12.

| Inveraray |
| — |
| Ironbridge |

Free.

P (50 yds) shop ✠ (ex guide dogs)

IPSDEN
Oxfordshire
Map **4** SU68

Wellplace Bird Farm
☎ Checkendon (0491) 680092 or 680473
*Over 100 varieties of birds; pet lambs,
goats, monkeys, chipmunks, donkeys,
otters, ponies, racoons etc.*

Open Apr–Sep daily, 10–5.30. (6pm Sun)
✽ 75p (ch 30p).

⚠ ⚖ ⴹ ♿ shop garden centre ✠

IPSWICH
Suffolk
Map **5** TM14

Christchurch Mansion Soane St (South
side of Christchurch Park)
☎ (0473) 53246
*16th-century town house with period
furnished rooms, up to 19th century. Art
gallery attached with Suffolk artists
collection and temporary exhibitions.*

Open all year (ex Xmas, Good Fri & some
BH). Mon–Sat 10–5, Sun 2.30–4.30 (dusk
in winter).
Free.

Guided tours by written request to
Director of Recreation & Amenities, Civic
Centre, Civic Drive, Ipswich.

⚠ ♿ (ground floor & gardens only) shop
✠

The Museum High St
☎ (0473) 213761
*Local geology. Prehistoric to medieval
archaeology in eastern counties, and
natural history collection. Asia, Africa,
America and Pacific gallery with
commentary plus a Roman gallery.
Temporary exhibition programme.*

Open all year (ex Sun, Xmas, Good Fri &
some BH) Mon–Sat 10–5.
Free.

P (400 yds) ♿ (ground floor only) shop ✠

IRONBRIDGE
Shropshire
Map **7** SJ60

Ironbridge Gorge Museum
☎ (095245) 3522
*A unique series of industrial monuments,
among them the first iron bridge in the
world. The Ironbridge Gorge Museum
covers an area of some six square miles in* →

143

the Severn Gorge. **Blist Hill Open Air Museum.** *42-acre woodland site, with reconstructed Victorian village showing how people lived and worked in the 1890's: gas lit streets shops, offices, restored canal and Hay Inclined Plane.*

Coalbrookdale Museum and Furnace Site. *The blast furnace where Abraham Darby perfected the technique of smelting iron ore using coke as a fuel. Associated with the furnace is a museum of iron- and steel-making.* **Coalport China Museum.** *Original buildings, workshop and social history displays about the Coalport China Company active here from the late 18th-century to 1926.* **Severn Warehouse** *Visitor Centre, Exhibits, displays and slide shows introducing the Ironbridge Gorge.*

Open Apr–Oct, daily 10–6; Nov–Mar, daily 10–5. (Closed Xmas day).

Admission varies from individual site fee to passport or zone tickets covering all or some areas only.

⚠ ⚟ (at Blist Hill Museum) ⟐ shop ✻ (ex Blist Hill) Ⓥ

IRVINE
Strathclyde *Ayrshire*
Map **10** NS34

Eglinton Castle & Gardens
Irvine Rd, Kilwinning
☎ (0294) 74166 ext 373

Late 18th-century castle, built for 13th Earl of Eglinton. Castle ruin set in a 12-acre garden. Site of the famous Eglinton Tournament of 1839.

Open all year during daylight hours.

Free.

⚠ 🚻 ⟐ (gardens only)

ISLE OF ARRAN
Strathclyde *Bute*
Map **10**
see **Brodick**

ISLE OF BARRA
Western Isles *Inverness-shire*
Map **13**
see **Castlebay**

Ironbridge
—
Isleworth

ISLE OF BUTE
Strathclyde *Bute*
Map **10**
see **Rothesay**

ISLE OF GIGHA
Strathclyde *Argyll*
Map **10**
see **Ardminish**

ISLE OF LEWIS
Western Isles *Ross & Cromarty*
Map **13**
see **Arnol, Callanish** and **Carloway**

ISLE OF MAN
Map **6**
see **Ballaugh, Castletown, Cregneish, Douglas, Laxey, Peel, Ramsey** and **Snaefell Mountain**

ISLE OF MULL
Strathclyde *Argyll*
Map **10 & 13**
see **Craignure** and **Dervaig**

ISLE OF SKYE
Highland *Inverness-shire*
Map **13**
see **Armadale, Colbost, Dunvegan,** and **Kilmuir**

ISLE OF WIGHT
Map **4**

Places of interest are indicated on location map 4. Full details will be found under individual place names within the gazetteer.

ISLEWORTH
Gt London (London Plan 4 pages 174/175).

Syon House London plan 4: **52** B3
Approach via Park Rd off Twickenham Rd.
☎ 01-560 0881
(during opening hours only)

Founded in 1415 as a monastery and remodelled in the 18th century with splendid interiors by Robert Adam, in particular the superbly coloured ante-room and the gallery library. Fine portraits and furniture. Exterior refaced c 1825. 'Northumberland' lion on east front. Notable garden layout by Capability Brown (see below). House overlooks River Thames. British Craft Show in Sep.

Open 1 Apr–29 Sep, Sun–Thu. (Closed Fri & Sat) 12–5. Last tickets 4.15. Open Suns only during Oct 12–5. Details not confirmed for 1986.

✻ House only 85p (ch 17 & pen 50p) Party 25 + . Combined ticket for house & gardens £1.50 (ch 17 & pen 70p).

P (150 yds) ⚟ ⟐ (gardens only) shop & garden centre ✻

Syon Park London plan 4: **53** B3
Follow A315 off A310 to Busch corner, and enter via Park Rd, Isleworth entrance.
☎ 01-560 0881

In grounds of Syon House (see above) 55 acres of gardens on bank of River Thames opposite Kew Gardens, only 9 miles from Central London. Laid out in mid 16th-century, it is said to be the first place in which trees were planted purely for ornament, and it owes much of its present beauty to Capability Brown. The Great Conservatory, built 1820 by Fowler, was the first large glass and metal construction of its kind in the world, and was the inspiration for the Crystal Palace at the Great Exhibition of 1851. It now houses a magnificent display of house plants. The 6-acre rose garden has thousands of roses. Syon Park has one of the largest garden centres in England. Also the site of the British Motor Industry Heritage Trust and London Butterfly House. Children's play area.

Open 18 Mar–28 Oct daily 10–6; 29 Oct–17 Mar 10–dusk. (Closed Xmas). Conservatory closed during Winter months. Details not confirmed for 1986.

✻ 80p (ch 17 & pen 50p) Combined ticket for house & park £1.50 (ch 17 & pen 70p). Rose Garden 10p.

⚠ ⚟ (licensed) ⟐ (gardens only) shop garden centre ✻

Heritage Motor Museum (Syon Park)
☎ 01-560 1378
Also on display in the park is a collection of more than 90 vehicles covering the history of much of the British motor industry. Special displays during summer.
Open daily 10–5.30 (4pm Nov–Mar).
(Closed Xmas).
£1.60 (ch & pen 90p) Family ticket £3.75
P (150 yds) ⬚ (within 100 yds) ♿ shop ✹
ⓥ

JARROW
Tyne and Wear
Map **12** NZ36

St Paul's Church & Monastery, Bede Monastery Museum & Jarrow Hall
Church Bank
☎ 091–489 2106
Standing in a conservation area on the south bank of the River Tyne, St Paul's Church (AD685) is famous as the home of the Venerable Bede. During his lifetime the monastery of St Paul was celebrated as a centre of learning and culture. The chancel of the present building is the church in which he worshipped and has a window with Saxon stained glass. Excavation on the south side of the church has revealed plan of the monastery in which he lived. Important archeological finds from the excavations of St Paul's Monastery are housed in the

---

Isleworth
—
Jedburgh

Bede Monastery Museum in Jarrow Hall, where the story of this great monastery is told with the assistance of an audio-visual programme. The Hall, circa 1785, has an exhibition on the recent past of Jarrow, a craft shop and changing exhibitions.

Open Apr–Oct Tue–Sat & BH Mons 10–5.30, Sun 2.30–5.30; Nov–Mar Tue–Sat 11–4.30, Sun 2.30–5.30. Church open as above but incl. Mon.
✳ 45p (ch, unemployed & pen 20p, students 30p).
⬚ ⬚ ♿ (ground floor only) shop

JEDBURGH
Borders Roxburghshire
Map **12** NT62

Jedburgh Abbey
One of the four famous border monasteries founded by David I. The remains of the church are mostly Norman or Transitional. There is a small museum with many carved fragments and some important monuments.

Open, see end of gazetteer. (Closed Thu afternoon & Fri in winter).

50p (ch & pen 25p)
▵ (AM)

Castle Jail Castlegate
☎ (0835) 63254
This is the former county prison, dating from 1820–3, on the site of the medieval castle, demolished in 1409. There were three blocks, used for different categories of prisoners. Possibly the last surviving example of its kind. A small museum is also open to visitors.
Open Etr–mid Sep Mon–Sat 10–12 & 1–5, Sun 2–5.
✳ 40p (ch 16 & pen 20p). Party 20+.
P (street 100 yds) ✹

Mary Queen of Scots House
Queen St
☎ (0835) 63331
A historic and picturesque house built in the 16th century where Mary Stuart was reputed to have stayed in 1566. Now a museum with exhibits relating to the Queen and to the earlier story of Jedburgh and district.
Open Etr–Oct, Mon–Sat 10–12 & 1–5, Sun 1–5 (& 10–12 Jun–Oct only).
✳ 50p (ch 16, unemployed, students & pen 35p). Party 20+.
P (50 yds) shop ✹

VISIT

Syon Park

Brentford Middlesex Telephone 01-560 0882
GARDENS OPEN ALL YEAR
LONDON BUTTERFLY HOUSE
BRITISH HERITAGE MOTOR MUSEUM
SYON HOUSE OPEN EASTER-END OF SEPTEMBER NOON-5pm

Also shop at England's most comprehensive horticultural Garden Centre

JERSEY
Channel Islands
Map **16**

see **German Military Underground Hospital, Gorey, Grève de Lecq, La Hôugie Bie, St Helier, St Mary's, St Ouen, St Peter, St Saviour,** and **Trinity**

JODRELL BANK
(Nuffield Radio Astronomy Laboratories)
Cheshire
Map **7** SJ77
(3m NE of Holmes Chapel off A535)
☎ Lower Withington (0477) 71339

Mark 1A (250ft) radio telescope is one of the largest fully steerable radio telescopes in the world. Display material and working models on view. Also planetarium and aboretum.

Open 11 Mar–Oct daily 10.30–5.30; Nov–10 Mar weekends only 2–5. (Closed Xmas & New Year).

Jodrell Bank visitor centre ✻ £2 (school ch £1, ch 5 free, pen £1). Includes Planetarium, Gardens & Aboretum (Infants not admitted to the Planetarium).

🅰 ⬛ (licensed) 🚻 ♿ shop ✻ (in buildings)

KEDLESTON HALL
Derbyshire
Map **8** SK33

(4m NW of Derby)
☎ Derby (0332) 842191

Adam mansion, standing in 500-acre park with lakes. Home of the Curzon family since 1100. Magnificent marble hall, state rooms and collection of fine pictures; 12th-century church; Indian museum. Canadian geese colony in park.

Open Etr Sun, Mon & Tue, then every Sun fr 27 Apr–31 Aug; also BH Mons & Tue ex 6 May.

Park, gardens & church 12–6; Hall 1–5.30. Open for Parties Mon–Thu by prior arrangement with the curator.

Hall, museum, park, gardens & church ✻ £2.20 (ch 6–14 £1.10); park gardens and church £1.10.

🅰 ⬛ shop ✻ Ⓥ

Jersey
—
Kelso

KEIGHLEY
West Yorkshire
Map **7** SE04

Cliffe Castle Museum
Spring Gdns Ln, (NW of town on A629)
☎ (0535) 64184

Mansion of circa 1878 given by Sir Bracewell Smith. Contains collections of natural and local history, dolls, ceramics, geological gallery, craft workshops, and interesting exhibitions programme. Play area and aviary in adjacent park. Also rooms with French furniture from Victoria and Albert Museum.

Open Apr–Sep Tue—Sun 10–6; Oct–Mar Tue–Sun 10–5. Also open BH Mons. (Closed Good Fri & Xmas.)

Free.

🅰 ⬛ shop ✻

East Riddlesden Hall Bradford Rd
☎ (0535) 607075

Typical Yorkshire manor house dating from 17th century with contemporary plasterwork and oak panelling. In the grounds is a small secluded garden and one of the largest medieval tithe barns in the North of England.

Open Apr, May, Sep & Oct, Wed–Sun & BH Mon 2–6; Jun–Aug 11–6. Last admission 5.30.

✻ £1.20 (ch 60p). Party 15 + .

🅰 ⬛ shop ♿ (ground floor only) ✻ (NT)

KELLIE CASTLE & GARDENS
Fife
Map **12** NO50

(2m N of St Monans off B9171)
☎ Arncroach (03338) 271

A mainly 16th- and 17th-century building, fine example of the domestic architecture of the Scottish lowlands. Notable plasterwork and panelling painted with

---

'romantic' landscapes. Audio-visual shows.

Castle open 28 Mar–Apr & Oct, Sat & Sun 2–6. May–Sep daily 2–6. Garden and grounds all year, daily 10–sunset.

Castle and gardens £1.40 (ch 70p); gardens only 60p (ch accompanied by an adult 30p). Party 20 + .

(NTS)

KELLING
Norfolk
Map **9** TG04

Kelling Park Aviaries Weybourne Rd
☎ Holt (026371) 2235

Situated in 4 acres of beautiful gardens is this fine collection of European and tropical birds, including ornamental pheasants, cockatoos, macaws and flamingoes. Water garden, children's playground, and planned for 1986 a working pottery. Also the North Norfolk Steam Railway will be running frequent trains into the grounds.

Open daily 10–dusk.

✻ £1 (ch & pen 50p).

🅰 ⬛ (licensed) shop ✻ (in aviaries)

KELMARSH
Northamptonshire
Map **4** SP77

Kelmarsh Hall (on A508)
☎ Maidwell (060128) 276

Set in lovely grounds, this Palladian house was built between 1728 and 1732 by James Gibbs who was also architect for the Church of St Martin-in-the-Fields. Interesting features inside the house include elegant pieces of Regency furniture. Minton china, ornate stucco plasterwork and many paintings.

Open Etr–Sep, Sun & BH, 2.15–5.30.
£1 (ch 50p).

🅰 ⬛ shop & garden centre

KELSO
Borders Roxburghshire
Map **12** NT73

Floors Castle
☎ (0573) 23333

Home of Duke and Duchess of Roxburghe. Built in 1721 by William Adam with later additions by W H Playfair. Contains superb French and English furniture, tapestries and paintings. Magnificent walled garden. Children's playground.

Castle open 27 Apr–30 Sep Sun–Thu. Also open Fri during Jul & Aug 11–5.30 (last admission to Castle 4.45pm). Walled garden & garden centre daily 9.30–5. (On Fri's throughout the rest of the season & during Apr & Oct the castle will be open to coach parties by appointment only.)
£1.80 (ch 8 & over £1.20, pen £1.60). Grounds £1.20. Party 25 + .
P (100 yds) ⚏ (licensed) ⌂ ⅋ (ground floor & garden only) shop & garden centre

Kelso Abbey

Little but the abbey church remains, and that only in imposing fragments which are almost wholly of Norman and Transitional work.

Open, see end of gazetteer.

Free.

⅋ (AM)

KEMERTON
Hereford & Worcester
Map **3** SO93

The Priory
☎ Overbury (038689) 258

The main feature of this four-acre garden is the long herbaceous borders planned in colour groups. There is also a stream and sunken garden with raised beds for alpine plants in the early summer. Many interesting and unusual plants, shrubs and trees. There is a small nursery where a good selection of plants of rarer varieties are available.

Open May–Sep each Thu, also following Suns, 25 May, 22 Jun, 13 Jul, 3 & 24 Aug & 7 Sep. 2–7 pm.

50p (ch 20p)
⅋ ⅋ garden centre

KEMNAY
Grampian *Aberdeenshire*
Map **15** NJ71

Kelso
—
Kenilworth

Castle Fraser (2½m S off B993)
☎ Sauchen (03303) 463

This castle is considered to be the most spectacular of the castles of Mar. The massive Z-plan castle, with splendid architectural embellishments was begun about 1575 and incorporates an earlier castle. It was completed in 1636. 'An exhibition tells the story of 'The Castles of Mar'.

Open May–Sep, daily 2–6 (last admission 5.15). Gardens & grounds open all year 9.30–sunset.

Castle £1.40 (ch 70p). Party. Grounds by donation.

⅋ (NTS)

KENDAL
Cumbria
Map **7** SD59

Abbot Hall Art Gallery Kirkland
☎ (0539) 22464

Fine house designed by Carr of York in 1759. Ground floor rooms restored to period decor. Romney and Gardner paintings, Gillow furniture and objets d'art. Modern galleries displaying contemporary and period, fine and decorative arts. Varied programme of temporary exhibitions including paintings, sculpture and crafts. Craft workshop.

Open Mon–Fri 10.30–5.30, Sat & Sun 2–5. (Closed Good Fri & 2 weeks Xmas/New Year.)
✱ 70p (ch, pen & students 40p). Art gallery and museum £1 (ch pen 50p).
⅋ shop ✖

Abbot Hall Museum of Lakeland Life & Industry Kirkland
☎ (0539) 22464

Housed in Abbot Hall's Stable Block. Recaptures the working and social life of this unique area, its people & places. Various changing exhibitions. Victorian

---

Cumbrian street scene 'Queensgate' and newly opened farming display.

Open Mon–Fri 10.30–5, Sat & Sun 2–5. (Closed Good Fri & 2 weeks Xmas/New Year.)
✱ 70p (ch, pen & students 40p). Art gallery and museum £1 (ch & pen 50p).
⅋ ⅋ (ground floor only) shop ✖

Kendal Museum Station Rd
☎ (0539) 21374

Museum of natural history and archaeology. Gallery of local archaeology/ history and of Lakeland natural history featuring dioramas and new World Wildlife Gallery.

Open Mon–Fri 10.30–5 & Sat 2–5. (Closed Sun, Good Fri & Xmas–New Year).
40p (ch 5–16 20p, pen & students 25p).
⅋ ⅋ shop ✖

KENILWORTH
Warwickshire
Map **4** SP27

Kenilworth Castle

The Keep dates from 1155–70, with later great hall by John of Gaunt. Further additions, including gatehouse, now known as Lord Leicester's Buildings, built by the Dudleys during the 16th century.

Open, see end of gazetteer.
✱ 80p (ch & pen 40p).
⅋ (AM)

Stoneleigh Abbey
☎ (0926) 52116 or 57766

Originally a Cistercian Abbey, one of the great attractions of the house is the interlocking of periods. Stoneleigh Abbey has been described as the grandest, most dramatic Georgian mansion of Warwickshire. Amongst the first stately homes to open to visitors the Abbey was severely damaged by fire in 1960 but reopened in 1984 after extensive restoration. Three wings are now open, plus the private quarters, when booked in advance. Children's adventure playground, animal farm, model railway (Suns & BH only), woodland walks. →

FLOORS CASTLE
Kelso, Roxburghshire, Scotland Scotland's largest inhabited Castle
LOCATION OF THE FILM 'GREYSTOKE' (Ancestral home of Tarzan)
Home of the Duke and Duchess of Roxburghe. Situated in the beautiful and historic border country and overlooking the River Tweed, the town of Kelso and the ruins of Roxburgh Castle.
Open 27th April to 30th September, Sunday to Thursday inclusive, except during the months of July and August when it will be open Sunday to Friday inclusive, 11.00a.m. to 5.30p.m. (last admission to Castle 4.45p.m.)

Party rates on request from:
Roxburghe Estate Offices
Kelso, Roxburghshire
Tel. 0573 23333

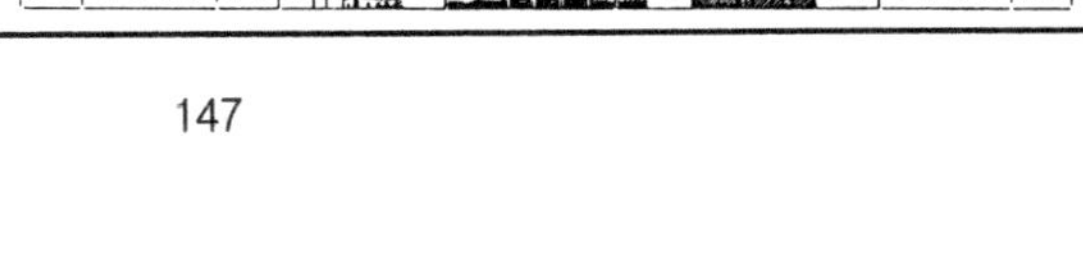

Open Etr Sun–Sep, Sun, Mon & Thu; 1–
5.30. (Closed 24 & 25 Aug). Last
admission 4.30pm. Gardens open 11.30–
5.30.

£2.20 (ch £1.10 & pen £1.10 wkdays only).
Grounds only £1.10 (ch 55p & pen 55p
wkdays only). Garden season tickets £6
(ch £3).

⚠ ⚓ (licensed) ⟊ ♿ shop ✘ (ex guide
dogs) Ⓥ

KESWICK
Cumbria
Map 11 NY22

Keswick Park Museum & Art Gallery
☎ (0596) 73263

*Outstanding among the exhibits are many
manuscripts and various relics of Hugh
Walpole and Robert Southley, two
manuscripts of Wordsworth, a geological
collection, and a fine scale model (1834)
of the Lake District. Good park
surrounding museum.*

Open Apr–Oct, Mon–Sat 10–12.30 &
2–5.30.

✱ 50p (ch & pen 25p). Party.
P ♿ shop ✘

Lingholm
(Turn off A66 for Portinscale & continue for
1m on the road to Grange.)
☎ (0596) 72003

*Formal and woodland gardens with a
large collection of rhododendrons,
azaleas and other interesting shrubs.*

Open Apr–Oct, daily 10–5.

✱ £1.25 (ch accompanied free).
⚠ ⚓ ⟊ ✘ Ⓥ

Mirehouse (4m NW on A591)
☎ (0596) 72287 (for catering) 74317

*Manor house dating from the 17th century
with beautiful rooms and original furniture.
Portraits and manuscripts of Francis
Bacon, Tennyson and Carlyle. Victorian
nursery. The walk through the grounds
and along the lake shore passes the place
where Tennyson wrote much of 'Morte
d'Arthur'. A converted 19th-century forest
sawmill houses the tea room. Two
adventure playgrounds, one for the under
11's and the other for older children.*

House open Apr–Oct, Wed, Sun & BH
Mon 2–5. Grounds, daily 10.30–5.30.
House & grounds £1.30 (ch & students
65p). Grounds 50p (ch 35p). Party.
⚠ (½m) ⚓ (daily 10.30–5.30) ⟊ ♿
(ground floor & gardens only) ✘ (House &
tearoom)

KETTERING
Northamptonshire
Map 4 SP87

Alfred East Art Gallery Sheep St
☎ (0536) 85211

*Approximately twelve exhibitions visit the
gallery each year, each lasting for about
three weeks.*

Kenilworth
–
Kilchurn

Open Mon–Wed, Fri & Sat 2–5.
Free.
P (300 yds) ♿ ✘

KEW
Gt London (London plan 4 pages 174/
175).

Kew Gardens (Royal Botanic Gardens)
London Plan 4: 28 B3
☎ 01-940 1171 ext 4118

*Extending to 300 acres, with over 50,000
different types of plants and flowers.
Museums and glasshouses with orchids,
ferns, cacti and many rare specimens.
Exotic Pagoda was work of Sir William
Chambers in 1761. (See also below).*

Gardens open from 10 to between 4 &
8pm (depending on season); museums &
glasshouses from 10am, some buildings
close lunchtime. (Closed Xmas day & New
Years day.)

✱ 25p (ch 10 free).
⚠ ⚓ ♿ shop ✘ (ex guide dogs)

Kew Palace London Plan 4: 29 B3

*Dutch-gabled 17th- to 18th-century house
with souvenirs of George III. Queen
Charlotte died here in 1818. Stands in the
Royal Botanical Gardens at Kew. (See
above).*

Open Apr–Sep daily 11–5.30.
Admission fee payable.
⚠ (Dept. of Environment)

and **Queen Charlotte's Cottage**

*Built in 1772 for the Queen, wife of George
III. The interior remains as it was in the
18th century when royalty were in
residence. (See also above).*

Open Apr–Sep 11–5.30 Sat, Sun & BH.
Admission fee payable.
(Dept. of Environment)

KIDDERMINSTER
Hereford & Worcester
Map 7 SO87

Hartlebury Castle State Rooms
Hartlebury (5m S Kidderminster)
☎ Hartlebury (0299) 250410

*Historic seat of the Bishops of Worcester
since 850. Fortified in 13th century, the
present red sandstone castle was rebuilt
after being sacked in the Civil War and
was Gothicised in 18th century. State
Rooms included the Mediaeval Great Hall,
and the 18th century Hurd Library and
Saloon.*

Open Etr–7 Sep 1st Sun in month plus BH
Mon also Wed (Etr–Aug) 2–5
50p (ch 25p). Party 30 + Guided tour by
advanced booking only.
⚠ ⚓ ♿ (ground floor only) shop ✘

Severn Valley Railway
*For details see gazetteer entry under
Bridgnorth.*

KIDWELLY
Dyfed
Map 2 SN40

Kidwelly Castle

*12th-century fortress with additions of
following two centuries and circular ovens
of great size. Chapel dating from c 1400.*

Open † see end of gazetteer.
✱ 70p (ch 35p).
⚠ shop (AM Cadw)

Kidwelly Industrial Museum
☎ (0554) 891078

*A fascinating museum located on the
banks of the Gwendraeth Fach River in
the remains of the Kidwelly Tinplate
Works, where tinplate was hand-made.
Original machinery and buildings are
displayed together with an exhibition
about the history of the area. Other
features include a winding engine and pit-
head gear along with a coal mining
exhibition, steam crane and two
locomotives.*

Open Etr–Sep daily 10–5 but Sat & Sun
2–5. Last admission 4.15pm. Other times
by arrangement.

✱ 75p (ch 5–15, students, unemployed &
pen 30p). Party.
⚠ ⚓ ⟊ ♿ shop ✘

KILBARCHAN
Strathclyde *Renfrewshire*
Map 10 NS46

Weaver's Cottage
☎ (05057) 5234

*An early 18th-century weaver's house,
containing looms, weaving equipment
and domestic utensils.*

Open Apr–May, Sep–Oct, Tue, Thu, Sat &
Sun 2–5, Jun–Aug, daily 2–5.
✱ 60p (ch 30p)
(NTS)

KILCHRENAN
Strathclyde *Argyll*
Map 10 NN02

Ardanaiseig
(3m NE at end of unclass rd)
☎ (08663) 333

*The gardens have azaleas,
rhododendrons, rare shrubs and trees.
Magnificent views across Loch Awe.*

Open Etr–Oct daily 8.30–dusk.
£1 (ch free)
⚠ Garden Centre ✘ 🚗

KILCHURN
Strathclyde *Argyll*
Map 10 NN12

Kilchurn Castle (2m W of Dalmelly)

148

Picturesque Campbell stronghold on Loch Awe, dating from mid-15th century; contains earliest surviving purpose-built barracks in Scotland erected in 1693.

Open daily 9–7.

(AM)

KILDRUMMY
Grampian *Aberdeenshire*
Map **15** NJ41

Kildrummy Castle

A splendid, ruined, 13th-century fortress with an imposing gatehouse and notable 15th- and 16th-century additions.

Open, see end of gazetteer.

✱ 50p (ch & pen 25p)

⚠ (AM)

Kildrummy Castle Garden Trust
(Alford–Strathdon road A97 off A944).
☎ (03365) 264, 277 & 337

Two of the Trustees are the Professors of Forestry and Botany, University of Aberdeen. At foot of the medieval castle lies the water garden running under a copy of the 14th-century Brig O'Balgownie. Facing south is the shrub bank. The ancient quarry from which the ruins were built, contains a variety of alpines and shrubs from overseas. Plants for sale.

Open Apr–Oct daily 9–5.

50p (ch 15 10p). Car park 10p.

⚠ ⌇ ᵬ (gardens only)

KILLERTON HOUSE & GARDEN
Devon
Map **3** SS99

(5m NE of Exeter on B3185 off B3181)
☎ Exeter (0392) 881345

18th-century house containing the Paulise de Bush collection of costume, shown in a series of room settings furnished in different periods ranging from the second half of the 18th century to the present day. 15 acres of gardens with rare trees and shrubs. The estate covers more than 6,000 acres.

Open 28 Mar–Oct, 11–6. Last admission 5.30. Garden open all year during daylight.

Kilchurn
—
Kilmun

✱ House & gardens £2.30 (ch 5–17 £1.15) garden only £1.50. Party.

⚠ ⌂ (licensed) ᵬ shop (NT) (NGS)

KILLIECRANKIE
Tayside *Perthshire*
Map **14** NN96

Pass of Killiecrankie Visitors Centre
☎ Pitlochry (0796) 3233

Situated close to the site of the battle (1689) where the Jacobite army, led by 'Bonnie Dundee', routed King William's troops. Wooded gorge walk. Ranger/naturalist service. The Visitors' Centre has exhibitions.

Open 28 Mar–June & Sep–24 Oct, daily 10–6, Jul & Aug, daily 9.30–6.

✱ 10p (ch free).

⚠ (NTS)

KILMARNOCK
Strathclyde *Ayrshire*
Map **10** NS43

Dean Castle Dean Rd
☎ (0563) 26401

Fortified tower built 1350 with lower keep, Great Hall and Upper Hall in perfect condition. Exhibitions of the Howard de Walden collection of European arms, armour and tapestries, early keyboard and other musical instruments. Palace has Banqueting Hall, kitchen and tower in equally good condition. Restoration shows Dean Castle as it was in 14th and 15th century, 200 acres of Country Park with nature trail. Concerts of period music and other historical performances.

Open 12 May–22 Sep Mon–Fri 2–5, Sat & Sun 12–5. Last entry 4.30. Details not confirmed for 1986. Organised parties throughout the year by arrangement.

✱ 50p (ch 16 & pen free).

P (200 yds) ⌂ ⌇ ᵬ (limited areas of

---

ground floor & gardens only) shop
🛆 (in castle)

Dick Institute Elmbank Ave
☎ (0563) 26401

Exhibits of geology (including fossils), small arms, shells, ethnography, numismatics, and archaeological specimens. Also art gallery (paintings and etchings), and library containing Ayrshire and Burns printed books.

Open May–Sep Mon, Tue, Thu & Fri 10–8, Wed & Sat 10–5; Oct–Apr Mon–Sat 10–5. Free.

⚠ ᵬ (ground floor only) 🛆

KILMARTIN
Strathclyde *Argyll*
Map **10** NR89

Dunadd Fort (3m S, A816)

A prehistoric hillfort incorporating walled enclosures. It was once the capital of the ancient Scots kingdom of Dalriada.

Accessible at all reasonable times.

Free.

(AM)

KILMUIR
Isle of Skye, Highland *Inverness-shire*
Map **13** NG24

Skye Cottage Museum
☎ Duntulm (047052) 279

The museum consists of four thatched cottages portraying the croft house of 100 years ago. It shows a fine collection of implements, tools, etc, used by the men and women of the Highlands and a very interesting collection of old letters, papers and pictures is on display.

Open mid May–Sep, Mon–Sat 9–6.

50p (ch 20p).

⚠ ᵬ shop

KILMUN
Strathclyde *Argyll*
Map **10** NS18

Kilmun Arboretum & Forest Plots
☎ (036984) 666

A large collection of conifer and broadleaved tree species planted in plots →

and specimen groups. Established by the Forestry Commission in 1930, and now extending to 100 acres on a hillside overlooking the Holy Loch. (Entrance and car park at Forestry Commission District Office, Kilmun, from which an illustrated guide book is available.)

Open all year during daylight hours.

Free.

🅐

KILSYTH
Strathclyde *Stirlingshire*
Map **11** NS77

Colzium House & Estate
☎ (0236) 823281

Partly a museum, with attractive walled garden, ice house and old castle associated with Montrose's victory over the Covenanters in 1645.

House open Etr wknd–Sep wknd, Mon–Fri 9–5, Sun 10–6. (Closed when booked for private functions). Grounds open at all times. Museum open Wed 2–8.

Free.

🅐 ⛾ ♨ ₺ (ground floor & gardens only)

KILVERSTONE
Norfolk
Map **5** TL98

Kilverstone Wildlife Park
☎ Thetford (0842) 5369 or 66606

50-acre wildlife and miniature horse stud, specialising in South American animals and birds, including 7 species of South American cats, also 18 species of monkeys, grissons, maned wolves, tapirs, parrots, penguins, and miniature donkeys. Pets corner, patting area, English walled garden, deer park, riverside walk, and adventure playground. Also, a miniature railway.

Open daily 10–6.30 (dusk in winter).

✳ £1.45 (ch 4–14 95p pen £1.40).

🅐 ⛾ (Late Mar–Oct, licensed) ₺ shop & garden centre ✗

KIMMERIDGE
Dorset
Map **3** SY97

Kilmun
—
King's Lynn

Smedmore (¾m SE)
☎ Corfe Castle (0929) 480717

Jacobean, Queen Anne and Georgian House. Antique dolls, marquetry furniture and walled gardens. Interesting plants and shrubs.

Open Jun–Aug Wed 2.15–5.30 (last admission 5pm). Also Sun before Aug BH & first two Weds in Sep.

✳ £1.20 (ch 60p). Garden only 60p (ch free).

🅐 ₺ Ⓥ

KINCRAIG
Highland *Inverness-shire*
Map **14** NH80

Highland Wildlife Park
☎ (05404) 270

Native animals of Scotland past and present, including wolves, bears, reindeer, wildcat and European Bison.

Open Apr–Oct daily 10–6. Details not confirmed for 1986.

✳ £5.50 per car.

🅐 ⛾ ♨ ₺ (ground floor & gardens) shop ✗

KINGSBRIDGE
Devon
Map **3** SX74

Cookworthy Museum of Rural Life
The Old Grammar School, Fore St
☎ (0548) 3235.

Local museum illustrating life in South Devon, commemorating William Cookworthy, Quaker 'father' of English china-clay industry, born in Kingsbridge. This old former grammar school, utilises original schoolrooms of 1670, with Victorian kitchen and scullery, costume room and comprehensive local history collection. Farm gallery illustrates farming history of the area. Walled garden.

Open Apr–Sep Mon–Sat 10–5; Oct Mon–Fri 10.30–4. Details not confirmed for 1986.

✳ 60p (ch & pen 30p). Family Ticket £1.80.

P (100 yds) ₺ (ground floor & garden only) shop ✗

Kingsbridge Miniature Railway
The Quay
☎ Bickington (062682) 361

A 7¼ inch gauge passenger carrying miniature railway, ⅓m trip.

Open Etr, then mid May–mid Sep daily 11–5.

50p.

P ✗

KINGSDON
Somerset
Map **3** ST52

Lytes Cary Manor

Home of Lyte family for 500 years, preserving 14th-century chapel and 15th-century great hall.

Open Apr–Oct Wed & Sat 2–6, last admission 5.30.

£1.50.

🅐 (NT)

KING'S LYNN
Norfolk
Map **9** TF62

Lynn Museum Market St
☎ (0553) 775001

Exhibits on local archaeology, geology and natural history. Medieval Pilgrims' badges of special interest. Temporary exhibitions throughout year.

Open Mon–Sat 10–5. (Closed Good Fri, Xmas & New Year).

20p 24 May–Sep; winter 15p (ch 5p students & UB40s 10p).

P (100 yds) ₺ shop ✗

Museum of Social History 27 King St
☎ (0553) 775004

Costume, ceramics, glass, toys and domestic material.

Open Tue–Sat 10–5. (Closed Good Fri, Xmas & New Year).

20p 24 May–Sep; winter 10p (ch 5p students & UB40s 24 May–Sep 10p: winter 5p).

P (100 yds) & (ground floor only) shop ✻

St George's Guildhall Kings St

The largest surviving medieval guildhall in England, now used as a theatre.

When not in use as a theatre or cinema open Mon–Fri 10–1 & 2–5. Sat 10–12.30. (Closed 1 Jan, Good Fri, 25 & 26 Dec).

Free.

(NT)

KINGSWEAR
Devon
Map 3 SX85

Coleton Fischacre Garden Coleton (1¾m E on unlcass roads)
☎ (080425) 617

An 18 acre garden set in a stream fed valley and created by Lady Dorothy D'Oyly Carte between 1925 and 1940. Planted with a wide variety of uncommon trees and rare and exotic shrubs.

Open 28 Mar–Oct, Wed, Fri & Sun 11–6. £1.20. Party.

⚠ garden centre (NT)

KINGSWINFORD
West Midlands
Map 7 SO88

Broadfield House Glass Museum
Barnett Ln,
☎ (0384) 273011

Displays of glass from the Roman period to the present day but concentrating on the coloured, cut and engraved glass produced in nearby Stourbridge in the last century. Slide and video displays, museum shop. Glass making studios.

Open Tue–Fri & Sun 2–5, Sat 10–1 & 2–5. BHs 2–5.

75p (ch, students & pen 40p). Party 15+.

⚠ & (ground floor only) shop ✻

KINGTON
Herefordshire
Map 3 SO25

Hergest Croft Gardens (½m W off A44)
☎ (0544) 230160

Large gardens with trees, shrubs, flowers and herbaceous borders, and an old-fashioned kitchen garden. Also has a woodland valley filled with rhododendrons some 30 feet tall.

Open 27 Apr–14 Sep daily; also open Suns only in Oct. 1.30–6.30.

£1.20 (ch 60p). Party 20+.

⚠ ⚖ (Suns & BH in May & Jun) & shop & garden centre

KINGUSSIE
Highland *Inverness-shire*
Map 14 NH70

King's Lynn
Kirkcaldy

Highland Folk Museum Duke St
☎ (05402) 307

Contains an interesting display of Highland crafts and furnishings; a farming museum; reconstructed Hebridean mill and primitive 'black house', and a turf walled house from the Central Highland, set in 6 acres of garden. Various special events.

Open Apr–Oct, Mon–Sat 10–6, Sun 2–6; Nov–Mar, Mon–Fri 10–3.

£1 (ch & pen 50p).

⚠ ⊞ shop ⓥ

Ruthven Barracks (½m SE of Kingussie)

The best preserved of the four infantry barracks built by the Hanovarian Government in the Highlands following the Jacobite uprising of 1715.

Open any reasonable time.

Admission Free.

(AM)

KINROSS
Tayside *Kinross-shire*
Map 11 NO10

Kinross House Gardens
☎ (0577) 63467

Dates from 1685 to 1692, from designs by Sir William Bruce.

Gardens only open May–Sep, daily 2–7.

£1 (ch 40p).

⚠ & ✻

Loch Leven Castle Castle Island

Built in the 14th century this castle is most notable for the escape of Mary Queen of Scots in 1568, after a year's imprisonment. The castle is five storeys in height, with round towers guarding the outer wall.

Open Apr–Sep 9.30–7 (Sun 2–7).

Free. ✻ Ferry charge 50p (ch & pen 25p).

(AM)

KIRBY MISPERTON
North Yorkshire
Map 8 SE77

Flamingo Land Zoo & Holiday Village
Kirby Misperton Hall
☎ (065386) 300 (Holiday Village) & 287 (Zoo)

A late 18th-century house and 300-acre zoo and family funpark. Over 1,000 animals and over 30 other attractions included in admission charge. Many undercover attractions and large lake.

Open Apr–Sep, daily 10–5.30 or 6.30 according to season.

✻ £0 (ch & pen 4 Free). (Includes all rides, slides & shows).

⚠ ⚖ (licensed) ⊞ & shop ⓥ.

KIRBY MUXLOE
Leicestershire
Map 4 SK50

Kirby Muxloe Castle (off B5380)

A ruined, moated 15th-century fortified manor house, built of brick.

Open, see end of gazetteer.

✻ 50p (ch 16 & pen 25p).

(AM)

KIRKBEAN
Dumfries and Galloway *Dumfriesshire*
Map 11 NX95

Arbigland Gardens
(1m SE, adjacent to Paul Jones cottage)
☎ (038788) 213

The gardens and dower house of this mansion have been evolving through three centuries. Paul Jones, the US Admiral worked here with his father who was the gardener in the 1740s. Woodland, water and formal gardens.

Gardens open May–Sep, Tue, Thu & Sun 2–6. House open 24 May–1 Jun & 23–31 Aug.

Gardens £1 (ch 50p). House £1 (ch 50p). Parties by prior arrangement.

⚠ ⚖ & shop ⓥ

KIRKCALDY
Fife
Map 11 NT29

Art Gallery & Museum War Memorial Grounds (next to Kirkcaldy Station)
☎ (0592) 260732

A unique collection of fine Scottish paintings, new historical displays and a full programme of changing art, craft and local history exhibitions. Temporary exhibitions throughout the year.

Open Mon–Sat 11–5, Sun 2–5. (Closed local Hols).

Free.

⚠ ⊞ shop ✻

John McDouall Stuart Museum
Rectory Lane, Dysart
☎ (0592) 260732

Set in the National Trust restored 18th-century house which was the birthplace of John McDouall Stuart (1815–1866) the first explorer to cross Australia. The award winning displays describe his journeys and the Australian wilderness.

Open Jun–Aug daily 2–5.

Free.

⚠ shop ✻

Ravenscraig Castle

A prominent ruined structure, founded in 1460, and perhaps the first castle designed for defence with firearms.

Open, see end of gazetteer.→

✻ 50p (ch & pen 25p).
(AM)

KIRKCUDBRIGHT
Dumfries and Galloway
Kirkcudbrightshire
Map **11** NX65

Maclellan's Castle
*A notable ruined mansion dating from
1582.*
Open, see end of gazetteer. Closed Mon–
Fri in winter.

✻ 50p (ch & pen 25p)
🏛 (AM)

Stewartry Museum St Mary Street
☎ (0557) 30797
*A museum displaying objects connected
with Galloway, including firearms,
domestic and agricultural implements,
and a good natural history section.*
Open Etr–Jun & Sep–Oct 11–1 & 2–4,
Jul & Aug 11–5.
50p (ch 14 25p).
🏛 ⅙ (ground floor only)

KIRKHAM
North Yorkshire
Map **8** SE76

Kirkham Priory
*Beautifully situated by River Derwent,
with particularly fine sculptured 13th-
century gatehouse.*
Open †, see end of gazetteer.

✻ 30p (ch 16 & pen 15p).
🏛 ⅙ (AM)

KIRKHILL
Highland *Inverness-shire*
Map **14** NH54

Moniack Castle (Highland Winery)
☎ Drumchardine (046383) 283
*Once a fortress of the Lovat chiefs and
their kin, it is today the centre of an
enterprise unique in Scotland – that of
commercial wine making. The winery
produces a wide range of wines including
"country wines" such as Elder Flower and
Silver Birch, red and white wines and
mead. An additional feature is the Wine
Bar/Bistro. 7 miles from Inverness on the
A862 Beauly rd.*
Open Mon–Sat 10–5.
Free.
🏛 ⚓ (licensed) ⅂⊢ shop.

KIRKOSWALD
Strathclyde *Ayrshire*
Map **10** NS20

Souter Johnnie's Cottage
☎ (06556) 603 or 274
*A thatched 18th-century cottage, former
home of the village cobbler, John
Davidson, the original Souter Johnnie of
Burns' poem 'Tam O'Shanter'. Life-size
figures of the Souter and his friends in the
garden.*

Kirkcaldy
Knockando

Open 28 Mar–Sep, daily 12–5.
Also by appointment.

✻ 60p (ch accompanied by adults 30p).
(NTS)

KIRKWALL
Orkney
Map **16** HY41

Bishop's Palace
*A ruined palace dating originally from the
12th century. Round tower built by Bishop
Reid with addition of c. 1600 by Patrick
Stewart, Earl of Orkney.*
Open, see end of gazetteer. (Closed Fri
afternoon & Sat in winter). Apply to
custodian of Earl Patrick's Palace.

✻ 50p (ch 25p)
(AM)

Earl Patrick's Palace
*Built c. 1607 by Patrick Stewart, Earl of
Orkney, and considered one of the finest
Renaissance buildings in Scotland.
Although roofless, much still remains
including the notable oriel windows.*
Open, see end of gazetteer, ex Oct–Mar,
Mon–Thu 9.30–dusk, Sun 2–dusk, Fri
morning only.

✻ 50p (ch 25p).
P (AM)

Tankerness House Broad St
☎ (0856) 3191
*Dating from the 16th century, this is one
of the finest vernacular town houses in
Scotland. It is now a museum of Orkney
history with archaeological collections.*
Open Mon–Sat 10.30–12.30 & 1.30–5
(May–Sep Sun 2–5).
Free.
P (20 yds) ⅙ (ground floor only) shop ✻

KIRRIEMUIR
Tayside *Angus*
Map **15** NO35

Barrie's Birthplace 9 Brechin Rd
☎ (0575) 72646
*A small house containing personal
mementoes of Sir James Barrie who was
born here in 1860. Includes a Peter Pan
display.*
Open 28–31 Mar & May–Sep Mon–Sat
11–5.30, Sun 2–5.30.

✻ 60p (ch accompanied by adult 30p).
(NTS)

KNARESBOROUGH
North Yorkshire
Map **8** SE35

Knaresborough Castle
☎ Harrogate (0423) 503340

*Remains of 14th-century stronghold high
above the River Nidd, including the keep,
two baileys, and gatehouses. Also* **Old
Courthouse Museum** *open in castle
grounds.*
Open Etr, 3–5 May then 24 May–30 Sep
daily; 10–5. Guided tours on request.
Parties of schoolchildren apply to the
Curator, Harrogate Museum & Art Gallery
Service, Dept. of Technical Services,
Knapping Mount, Harrogate.
Tel. no. as above.
Castle 30p (ch 15p), Castle & Courthouse
50p (ch 25p) Disabled free.
🏛 ⅙ (ground floor only) shop ✻

KNEBWORTH
Hertfordshire
Map **4** TL22

Knebworth House & Country Park
Direct access from A1(M) at Stevenage
(South) roundabout
☎ Stevenage (0438) 812661
*Knebworth House, family home of the
Lyttons since 1490, was transformed 150
years ago by the spectacular high gothic
decoration of Victorian novelist and
statesman Edward Bulwer Lytton and
internally has a magnificent State Drawing
Room in the gothic style and a superb
Jacobean Banqueting Hall. Lord Lytton's
vice-royalty and the great Delhi Durbar of
1877 are commemorated in a fascinating
British Raj exhibition. Formal gardens
were simplified by Lutyens and include a
Jekyll herb garden. The 250 acres of
parkland contain a new adventure
playground with Fort Knebworth, nature
trail and deer park and is the setting for
'special events'.*
Open Apr–May, Sun. BH & school
holidays then daily (ex Mon) 24 May–14
Sep & 21–28 Sep. House & gardens 12–5,
Park 11–5.30.

✻ £2.50 (ch & pen £2); Park only £1.50.
Party.
🏛 ⚓ (licensed) ⅂⊢ ⅙ (ground floor &
gardens) shop ⓥ.

KNIGHTSHAYES COURT
Devon
Map **3** SS91
(2m NE of Tiverton)
☎ Tiverton (0884) 254665
*Interesting 19th-century house with rich
Victorian interior set in large woodland
gardens. Flowering shrubs, azaleas,
rhododendrons and unique topiary.*
Open daily 28 Mar–Oct. Garden from
11am; House 1.30–6 (last admission
5.30pm).
House & Garden £2.30 (ch £1.15).
Garden only £1.50 (ch 75p). Party 15+.
🏛 ⚓ (licensed) shop & garden centre ✻
(NT) (NGS)

KNOCKANDO
Grampian *Moray*
Map **15** NJ14

152

Tamdhu Distillery
☎ Carron (03406) 221

Visitors are able to see the complete
process of whisky being made.

Open Etr–Sep, Mon–Fri 10–4.

Free.

⚠ & (ground floor only) shop

KNUTSFORD
Cheshire
Map **7** SJ77

Tatton Park (3½m from M6, Junction 19,
or M56 Junction 7; entrance by Rostherne
Lodge on Ashley Road; 1½m NE of
Junction A5034 with A50)
☎ Knutsford (0565) 54822

Late 18th-century mansion by Samuel and
Lewis Wyatt. Tenants' Hall museum
contains State Coach, veteran cars,
hunting trophies, and curiosities. 50 acres
of ornamental gardens; 15th-century Old
Hall; 1930s farm; 1,000 acres of parkland,
including lake one mile long. Historical
and woodland trails.

Park & gardens daily (ex Xmas day). 18
May–Aug; House 1–5 (Sun & BH 12–5);
Gardens 11–5.30 (Sun & BH 10.30–6). Old
Hall (Jul & Aug 12–5). Farm 11–4. Etr–17
May & Sep–Oct; House 1–4 (5pm Sun &
BH); Garden 11.30–5 (10.30–5 Sun & BH);
Old Hall open 12–4 (5 Sun & BH), Farm
12–4. Winter, Park 11–dusk; Garden 1–4
(Sun & BH 12–4). House & Old Hall (Nov &
Mar Sun only) 1–4.

House £1.10 Garden 80p (60p in winter);
Old Hall 85p; Farm 80p; Reductions for ch
& pen; Park £1 per car. An additional
charge may be made at time of special
events.

⚠ 🎭 ✹ (in house) shop & garden centre
(NT)

LACOCK
Wiltshire
Map **3** ST96 Village is NT property

Lacock Abbey

13th-century cloisters, house dating from
1540 and later, octagonal Tudor tower,
half timbered gables in courtyard and
18th-century 'Gothic' hall by Sanderson
Miller. Fox Talbot conducted
photographic experiments here in 1835

Knockando
—
Lamport

and a museum of his work is now open at
the entrance gate.

House & grounds 29 Mar–Oct Wed–Mon;
Nov–Mar closed except to historical and
other societies by written arrangement.
£1.80 (ch 90p).

⚠ Shop & information room ✹ (NT)

LA HOUGUE BIE
Jersey Channel Islands
Map **16**

Jersey Museum
☎ Jersey (0534) 53823

Prehistoric burial mound containing
Neolithic tomb, surmounted by medieval
chapels. Underground shelter containing
German Occupation Museum. Agricultural
museum, railway exhibition in original
guard's van of Jersey Eastern Railway.
Archaeology and geology.

Open Mar–Oct Tue–Sun 10–5 (other times
by appointment).

80p (ch & pen 40p).

⚠ 🎭 ♿ & (ground floor & gardens only)
shop ✹

LAMBERHURST
Kent
Map **5** TQ63

Bayham Abbey (2m W in East Sussex)

In wooded River Teise valley on Kent
border, ruins dating back to 13th century
and including parts of church, cloistered
buildings and gatehouse. Preservation
work still in progress and museum to be
opened with other facilities for visitors.

Open, see end of gazetteer. Apr–Sep only.

✶ 50p (ch 16 & pen 25p).

⚠ & (AM)

Owl House Gardens
(1m NE off A21)
☎ 01-235 1432

13 acres of romantic walks, spring
flowers, azaleas, roses, rhododendrons,

---

rare flowering shrubs and ornamental fruit
trees surround the Marchioness of
Duffrein & Ava's 16th-century 'Owlers' or
smugglers' haunt, the Owl House. Wide
expansive lawns lead to woodlands of
oak, birch and informal sunken water
gardens.

Open daily & BH weekends 11–6.

£1 (ch 50p).

⚠ ♿ & (gardens only) shop

Scotney Castle Garden (1m SE)
☎ (0892) 890651

14th-century and later moated castle in a
picturesque landscaped garden.

Open 29 Mar–16 Nov, Wed–Fri 11–6; Sat
& Sun 2–6. (Closed Good Fri). Old Castle
open May–25 Aug same times.

£1.80 (ch 90p).

⚠ shop (NT)

LAMPHEY
Dyfed
Map **2** SN00

Lamphey Palace

Ruined 13th-century palace of the
Archbishops of St Davids. Later portion
added by Bishop Gower.

Open, see end of gazetteer.

✶ 50p (ch 16 & pen 25p).

⚠ shop (AM Cadw)

LAMPORT
Northamptonshire
Map **4** SP77

Lamport Hall
(8m N of Northampton on A508)
☎ Maidwell (060128) 272

The house, most of which dates from the
17th and 18th century, is set in an
attractive park, the garden contains one
of the earliest Alpine rock gardens in
England. Home of the Isham family for
over 400 years, the Hall is now owned by
Lamport Hall Trust. The south-west front
is the work of John Webb, pupil and son-
in-law of Inigo Jones. The music hall
contains Webb's stone chimney piece
and 18th-century plasterwork by John
Woolston. There is a fine collection of
family portraits and some of the Stuarts
together with other 17th-century →

KNEBWORTH

HOUSE, GARDENS & PARK

Family home of the Lyttons since 1490.
this magnificent Stately Home, with its
beautiful LUTYENS GARDENS including
the Jekyll Herb Garden, presents a mirror
of English history over the past five
centuries. Lord Lytton's term as Viceroy
of India is depicted in a unique exhibition
of the BRITISH RAJ.
Within the 250-acre Park the new
ADVENTURE PLAYGROUND is a great
favourite with the younger generation. An
exciting addition in 1985 was the
construction of FORT KNEBWORTH.
with an impressive array of modern
activity equipment within its imposing
stockades. Other popular features

include the ASTROGLIDE, narrow gauge
steam railway and museum, licensed
cafeteria in 16th century tithe barn, and
gift shop.
Many special events are also held in the
Park.

Open Sundays, Bank Holidays,
School holidays April — May
Daily 26th May — 16th September except Mondays,
plus 23rd & 30th September
Party bookings welcomed April —
September (except Mondays)
Park 11 a.m. – 5.30 p.m. **House &**
Gardens 12 noon – 5.00 p.m.
For details please telephone Stevenage
(0438) 812661
Own direct access from A1(M) at
Stevenage South (A602)

paintings, including work by Van Dyck, Guido Reni, Mierevelt, Maratti, Lely, etc and a collection of china and furniture.

Open Etr–Sep Sun & BH Mon 2.15–5.15; Jul & Aug Thu 2.15–5.15. Study centre for school visits, contact Education Officer on Maidwell (060128) 508.

£1.50 (ch 16 75p, pen £1.20). Party 30 + (by appointment).

⚠ ⚖ ⌲ shop ✸ ⓥ

LANCASTER
Lancashire
Map **7** SD46

Shire Hall Castle Pde
☎ (0524) 64998

The great Shire Hall, of Gothic-revival design, adjoins the castle and has a unique display of the shields of Monarchs, Constables and High Sheriffs from 1129 AD. The Crown Court, with its barbarous branding iron, has the questionable distinction of having handed out the greatest number of death sentences of any court. Hadrian's Tower and the 'Drop Room' adjoining 'Hanging Corner' contain grim relics of the brutalities of early prison life. All tours are guided.

Open Etr–Sep, daily 10.30 (1st tour)–4 (last tour). Court requirements always take priority – it is advisable to telephone before visiting except in August.

✻ 60p (ch 30p). Part tour when Court in session 40p (ch 20p) (ch 5 free).

⚠ (limited) shop ✸

City Museum Market Sq
☎ (0524) 64637

Georgian building with archaeology and history collections and Museum of the King's Own Royal Lancaster Regiment.

Open Apr–Oct daily 11–5, Nov–Mar daily 2–5. (Closed Xmas & New Year).

Free.

P (200 yds) ⓖ (ground floor only) shop ✸

See also **15 Castle Hill** An early 19th-century furnished cottage.

Open Apr–Sep, Mon. Tue, Thu & Sat 2–4.45.

20p (includes 1 child free).

Hornsea Pottery Wyresdale Rd
☎ (0524) 68444

Set in 42 acres of landscaped parkland including 19-acre Rare Breeds Survival Unit, children's farmyard, factory tours, café and picnic area. Special events most Sundays and Bank Holidays from Easter onwards. Also new attractions with individual admission prices.

Open Nov–Mar 10–4; Apr–Oct 10–5 & Jul & Aug 10–6. Provisional dates.

✻ Factory Tour, Children's Farmyard & 'Rare Breeds' Tour, 60p each tour (ch, pen & disabled 40p).

⚠ (free) ⚖ (licensed) ⌲ ⓖ shop

Lamport
—
Largs

Judges' Lodgings, Gillow & Town House Museum & Museum of Childhood Church St
☎ (0524) 32808

This fine 17th-century town house contains two distinct museums. The Gillow & Town House Museum displays the history and products of the famous Lancaster cabinet-making firm of Gillows; together with period room settings containing furniture by Gillows and other local cabinet-makers, including a parlour c. 1750, dining room and servants' hall c. 1820 and bedroom c. 1850. The Museum of Childhood has a display of dolls from the famous Barry Elder Doll Collection, showing the variety and types of dolls produced over the past three ' centuries, toys, games and childhood material. Victorian schoolroom, Edwardian day and night nurseries.

Open Apr & Oct, Mon–Fri 2–5, May & Jun, Mon–Fri 2–5, Jul–Sep, Mon–Fri 10.30–1 & 2–5, Sat 2–5, BH wknds (ex Xmas).

✻ 40p (ch 20p). Party.

P (100 yds) ⚖ (Jun–Sep 2–4.30) shop ✸

Maritime Museum St George's Quay
☎ (0524) 64637

Former Custom House displaying the maritime trade of Lancaster, the Lancaster Canal and the Fishing Industry of Morecambe Bay.

Open daily, 11–5 Apr–Oct, 2–5 Nov–Mar.

Free.

P ⓖ shop

LAND'S END
Cornwall
Map **2** SW32
☎ Sennen (073687) 501

The most Westerly tip of the English mainland, Land's End offers an intriguing insight into life thousands of years old. The 200 acre site provides fascinating aspects of Celtic culture in its wild landscape. The origins of Land's End, its natural history, and man's relationship with the area can also be explored in a series of detailed exhibitions.

Site open all year; exhibitions open 23 Mar–2 Nov daily 9.30–5.30.

£1.50 (ch free). Free access to Headland.

⚠ (charged) ⚖ (licensed) ⌲ ⓖ (ground floor only) shop

LANGBANK
Strathclyde Renfrewshire
Map **10** NS37

Finlaystone Country Estate (1m W)
☎ (047554) 285

Gardens, garden centre and woodland walks, and jogging trail.

Woodland & gardens, open all year daily 60p (ch 40p). House with doll and Victorian collections open Apr–Aug, Suns only 2.30–4.30, 80p (ch 40p).

⚠ ⚖ (Apr–Sep, Sat & Sun 2–5) ⌲ ⓖ (ground floor) garden centre

LANGHOLM
Dumfries & Galloway Dumfriesshire
Map **11** NY38

Craigcleuch Scottish Explorers' Museum (2m NW Langholm on B709)
☎ (0541) 80137

Baronial mansion house with collection of artifacts in wood, jade, ivory, coral and hundreds of rare tribal sculptures and Prehistoric stone pipes carved as animals and birds. Also Oriental paintings and children's dolls. Panoramic views overlooking the 'Gates of Eden' woodland walks.

Open May–29 Sep daily 10–5.30. Other times by appointment.

£1 (ch 50p).

⚠ ⓖ (ground floor only) shop ✸ ⓥ

LANHYDROCK
Cornwall
Map **2** SX06

Lanhydrock

Restored 17th-century mansion in richly wooded setting, with fine gatehouse and picture gallery with plaster ceiling and 17th- to 20th-century family portraits. The Victorian servants' quarters are particularly interesting.

Open Apr–Oct, daily 11–6 last admission 5.30. Winter gardens Nov–Mar during daylight hours.

£2.60 Gardens only £1.50.

⚖ (NT)

LANREATH
Cornwall
Map **2** SX15

Lanreath Mill & Farm Museum
Churchtown
☎ (0503) 20321 or 20349

This museum of rural heritage has a large collection of vintage exhibits from farmhouse, dairy and yard. Also mill workings retrieved from a derelict mill house.

Open Etr–Oct, daily 11–1 & 2–5 (Jun–Sep 10–6)

£1 (ch 50p).

⚠ ⚖ ⌲ ⓖ shop

LARGS
Strathclyde Ayrshire
Map **10** NS25

Kelburn Country Centre
(2m S off A78)
☎ Fairlie (047556) 685 or 554

The historic estate of the Earls of Glasgow, on the Firth of Clyde. Beautiful gardens and spectacular scenery. It offers *nature trails, gardens with rare trees, exotic and unusual shrubs from all over the world. Also Kelburn Glen, parts of which have been cultivated and the rest left in its wild state with waterfalls and pools. 18th-century farm buildings set round a village square have been turned into shops.* Adventure course and pony trekking available.

Open Etr–mid Oct, daily 10–6.

£1.50 (ch & pen £1). Party.

⚠ Ⓛ (licensed) ⼗ shop garden centre Ⓥ

Skelmorlie Aisle

A splendid example of a Renaissance monument, erected by Sir Robert Montgomery of Skelmorlie in 1636, stands in an aisle, formerly the north transept of the old church of Largs, and is the only portion now preserved.

Open Apr–Sep (see end of gazetteer). Admission on application to keykeeper in winter.

50p (ch & pen 25p).

(AM)

LASSWADE
Lothian *Midlothian*
Map **11** NT26

Edinburgh Butterfly Farm Melville Nurseries
☎ 031-663 4932

Delicate, richly coloured free flying

Largs
Launceston

butterflies from all over the world can be seen amidst exotic plants, trees and flowers. Also to be seen are unusual and dangerous insects including scorpions and tarantulas. The tropical pools are filled with giant waterlillies and a variety of colourful fish all surrounded by lush jungle vegetation.

Open 24 Mar–Oct, daily 10–5.30.

£1.75 (ch 95p pen £1.25)

⚠ Ⓛ ⼗ ⚹ garden centre & shop

LAUDER
Borders *Berwickshire*
Map **12** NT54

Thirlestane Castle
☎ (05782) 254

One of Scotland's finest buildings, with magnificent ceilings. Owned by the Maitland family since the 12th century. Attractive parkland and riverside setting. Home of the Border Country Life Museum, with static and working displays.

Open 11 May–30 Jun & Sep, Wed & Sun; 30 Jun–1 Sep daily (ex Fri). Castle & Museum 2–5; Grounds 12–6. £2 (ch & pen £1.50). Family £5. Party 30 +.

⚠ Ⓛ ⼏ ⚹ (ground floor & gardens only) shop

LAUGHARNE
Dyfed
Map **2** SN31

Dylan Thomas' Boat House
☎ (099421) 420

One-time waterside home of Wales' most famous 20th-century poet and in a superb location on the "Heron Priested Shore" of the Taf Estuary. The Boat House comprises a sitting room with original furniture plus many family photographs; an art gallery, audio and audio-visual presentation and interpretative panels on the life and works of Dylan Thomas.

Open Etr–Oct, daily 10–6. Groups out of season by arrangement with South Wales Tourist Council, Ty Croeso, Swansea. Tel. (0792) 465204.

80p (ch & pen 40p).

P Ⓛ Book & record shop

LAUNCESTON
Cornwall
Map **2** SX38

Launceston Castle

Formerly known as Dunheved and the one-time seat of William the Conqueror's brother, fine round keep forms part of the 12th- to 13th-century remains. →

Open †, see end of gazetteer.

✳ 50p (ch 16 & pen 25p).

♿ ᕲ (grounds only) (AM)

Launceston Steam Railway Newport
☎ (0566) 5665

*A 2 foot gauge railway offering a 2¼ mile
round trip behind a steam locomotive over
100 years old. Also a motor and motor
cycle museum with early machine tools
and items of mechanical and scientific
interest.*

Open Good Fri, Etr day & Spring BH then
Jun–Sep daily 11–5. Also Santa Specials
Dec Sat & Sun 2–5.

✳ £1.30 (ch & pen 70p. Family £3.50.
Party.

♿ ⚏ 🚻 ᕲ (ground floor only) shop ⓥ

Lawrence House
☎ (0566) 2833

*Mid Georgian house, part of which is now
a museum of local interest.*

Open Apr–Sep, Mon–Fri 10.30–12.30 &
2.30–4.30, other times by appointment.

50p (ch 20p).

(NT)

LAVENHAM
Suffolk
Map **5** TL94

Guildhall

*Picturesque, restored timber-framed
building, built in 1529, the former hall of
the Guild of Corpus Christi.*

Open 29 Mar–26 Oct daily 11 & 2–5.30.

£1 (ch 50p).

Shop ⚏ (Jun–Sep 2–5) 🐾 (ex guide
dogs) (NT)

Little Hall Market Pl
☎ (0787) 247179

*Headquarters of the Suffolk Preservation
Society, the 15th-century 'hall' house
contains the Gayer-Anderson collection of
antique furniture, pictures, ceramics,
books, sculptures etc.*

Open 29 Mar–19 Oct, Sat, Sun & BH
2.30–6. Parties by appointment.

60p (ch 30p).

♿ 🐾

The Priory Water St
☎ (0787) 247417

*Once the home of a rich wool merchant
this fine medieval timber-framed building
has been beautifully restored. On display
is a permanent exhibition of photographs
illustrating the restoration work plus
paintings, drawings and stained glass by
Ervin Bassanyi.*

Open 28 Mar–6 Apr then 3 May–Sep Mon–
Sat; Sun only in Aug & BHs 2–5.30.
Guided tours for groups by appointment.

£1 (ch 11–16 50p ch 11 free).

P (100 yds) 🐾 ⓥ

Launceston
—
Leeds

LAWERS
Tayside *Perthshire*
Map **11** NN64

Ben Lawers (Visitors Centre)
☎ Killin (05672) 397

*Situated on the slopes of Perthshire's
highest mountain (3,984ft) noted for
variety of Alpine flowers and species of
birds. There is a nature trail and Ranger/
Naturalist service. Audio-visual display in
Visitors Centre.*

Open 28 Mar–May & Sep, daily 11–4. Jun–
Aug, daily 10–5.

✳60p (ch 30p).

♿ (NTS)

LAXEY
Isle of Man
Map **6** SC48

Laxey Wheel
☎ Douglas (0624) 26262

*The Big Wheel 'Lady Isabella', 72½ft in
diameter, was constructed in order to
keep the lead mines free from water.*

Open Etr weekend–Sep. Details not
confirmed for 1986.

✳ 40p (ch & pen 25p).

♿ 🚻 shop

LAXFIELD
Suffolk
Map **5** TM27

Laxfield & District Museum The
Guildhall
☎ Ubbeston (098683) 357

*Housed in a 16th-century building, the
museum contains mainly 19th-century
items relating to village life. Displays
change from year to year but include
village shops, domestic interior, odd-job
man's workshop, costume, agricultural
implements, the archaeology of Laxfield
and photographs. Working beehive.*

Open late May–Sep, Wed, Sat, Sun & BH
2–5. Parties & school groups by prior
arrangement.

Free.

P shop 🐾

LAYER MARNEY
Essex
Map **5** TL91

Layer Marney Tower (off B1022)
☎ Colchester (0206) 330202

*Magnificent 16th-century brick and
terracotta tower, entrance gate-tower to
Lord Marney's mansion. West wing has
similar architectural detail; south side
incorporates two-storeyed long gallery.*

Gallery, tower and grounds open Apr–

Oct, Sun & Thu, also Tue during Jul & Aug
2–6. BH wknds (Sun & Mon) 11–6.

£1 (school children 30p, under school age
free).

♿ 🚻 ᕲ (ground floor only) shop ⓥ

LEA
Derbyshire
Map **8** SK35

Rhododendron Gardens
☎ Dethick (062984) 380

*Attractive woodland gardens of three-
and-a-half acres featuring rhododendrons,
azaleas and rock garden. Plant sales.*

Open 20 Mar–Jul, daily 10–7.

50p & £1 May–20 Jun (ch 25p).

P (10 yds) ⚏ shop & garden centre (NGS)

LEAMINGTON SPA
Warwickshire
Map **4** SP36

**Warwick District Council Art Gallery &
Museum** Avenue Rd
☎ (0926) 26559

*The art gallery specialises in British,
Dutch and Flemish paintings and water
colours of the 16th to 20th century. The
museum contains ceramics, Delft,
Satlglaze, Wedgwood, Whieldon,
Worcester, Derby Ware etc, and an 18th-
century glass collection. Temporary
Exhibitions.*

Open Mon–Sat 10–1pm & 2–5. Also Thu
evenings 6–8pm. (Closed Good Fri, 3
days Xmas & New Years day).

Free.

P ᕲ 🐾 (ex guide dogs)

LEEDS
Kent
Map **5** TQ85

Leeds Castle see **Maidstone**

LEEDS
West Yorkshire
Map **8** SE33

Leeds Industrial Museum
Armley Mills, Canal Rd
☎ (0532) 637861

*Built on an impressive island site, this
unique 1806 mill now displays the city's
industrial past. Exhibits include working
water wheels, locomotives, engines,
textile, clothing and printing machinery,
and a 1920's cinema. Armley Mill is also
accessible from the Leeds & Liverpool
canal and forms part of a history trail
along the Kirkstall Valley in Leeds.*

Open Apr–Sep, Tue–Sat 10–6, Sun 2–6
(last admission 5pm) Oct–Mar, Tue–Sat
10–5, Sun 2–5 (last admission 4pm).
(Closed Mon ex BHs).

55p (ch 16 & pen 20p).

P 🚻 ᕲ shop 🐾

Middleton Colliery Railway
Moor Rd, Hunslet
☎ (0532) 645424

First railway authorised by Act of Parliament in 1758, and first to succeed with steam locomotives in 1812. Number of industrial locomotives and examples of rolling stock are in use. Steam trains each weekend in season, from Tunstall Road roundabout (junct 45 on M1) to Middleton Park, which includes picnic area, fishing, nature trail, swings etc.

Open Etr–Sep, Sat & Sun 2–4.30; BH Sun & Mon 11–4.30. Train trips every ½hr. (Sat services are diesel hauled).

✽ 60p return (ch 40p)

⚠ ⚒ ⏟ ♿ (with assistance) shop

Temple Newsam House & Park (on south-east outskirts of city)
☎ (0532) 647321

Splendid Tudor and Jacobean house, standing in over 900 acres of parkland, landscaped by 'Capability' Brown. Georgian rooms and a collection of furniture, decorative arts and paintings. Lord Darnley was born here, and later the house was owned by Lord Halifax.

Open all year Tue–Sun & BH Mons 10.30–6.15 or dusk; Weds, May–Sep 10.30–8.30. (Closed 25 & 26 Dec).

✽ 55p (ch & pen 20p, students free).

⚠ ⏟ ♿ (ground floor only) shop ✘ (in House)

LEEK
Staffordshire
Map **7** SJ95

Brindley Mill & Museum Mill St (A523)
☎ (0538) 384195

Designed by James Brindley 1752, and used as a corn-mill until the late 1940s. Between 1970 and 1974 a preservation trust restored the derelict building and put the old machinery, which had remained intact, into working order. The museum is devoted to the life and work of the great canal builder and to the craft of milling. A delightful waterside garden is at the rear of the mill.

Open Etr–Oct Sat, Sun & BH Mon 2–5; Jul & Aug also Mon, Tue & Thu 2–5.

Admission fee payable.

P (50 yds) shop ✘

LEICESTER
Leicestershire
Map **4** SK50

Belgrave Hall Off Thurcaston Rd
☎ (0533) 666590

A fine early 18th-century house and gardens, now a museum with furnishings, stables with coaches and an agricultural collection.

Open all year Mon–Thu & Sat 10–5.30, Sun 2–5.30. (Closed Xmas).

Free.

P (in street) ♿ (ground floor & gardens only) shop ✘

Guildhall Guildhall Lane
☎ (0533) 554100

Leeds
—
Leighton Buzzard

Medieval Guildhall and later the Town Hall of Leicester. Great Hall, Mayor's Parlour, Library and police cells.

Open all year, Mon–Thu & Sat 10–5.30. Sun 2–5.30. (Closed Fri and 25 & 26 Dec).

Free.

P (100 yds) shop ✘

Jewry Wall Museum & Site
St Nicholas Circle
☎ (0533) 554100

Museum of archaeology from prehistoric times to 1500. Remains of Roman baths and Jewry Wall.

Open all year Mon–Thu & Sat 10–5.30. Sun 2–5.30. (Closed Fri and 25 & 26 Dec). (Jewry Wall open any reasonable time).

Free.

P (100 yds) ♿ shop ✘

John Doran Museum East Midland Gas, Leicester Service Centre, Aylestone Rd
☎ (0533) 549414 ext 2192

Housed in a historic building, a part of the Aylestone Road Gasworks, is a collection of all aspects of the history of the manufacture, distribution and utilisation of gas, with documentary material as well as old appliances and equipment.

Open Tue–Fri 12.30–4.30.

Free.

⚠

Leicestershire Museum & Art Gallery
New Walk
☎ (0533) 554100

Collections of 18th- to 20th-century English paintings and drawings, unique collection of 20th-century German Expressionist art, ceramics, silver, Egyptology. New geology and natural history environmental galleries in preparation. Extensive reference and study collections in Art and Natural Sciences with a very active educational programme.

Open Mon–Thu & Sat 10–5.30, Sun 2–5.30. (Closed Fri & Xmas).

Free

⚠ ♿ shop ✘

Leicester Museum of Technology
Abbey Pumping Station, Corporation Rd
☎ (0533) 661330

Knitting gallery, power gallery, transport items, steam shovel. Original beam engines 1891.

Open Mon–Thu & Sat, 10–5.30, Sun 2–5.30. (Closed Fri & Xmas).

Free.

⚠ ♿ (ex beam engines) shop ✘

Leicestershire Record Office
57 New Walk
☎ (0533) 554100

Extensive collection of official and private archives, both rural and urban, relating to the County of Leicestershire.

Open Mon–Thu 9.15–5, Fri 9.15–4.45, Sat 9.15–12.15. (Closed Sun & BH).

Free.

⚠ ♿ shop ✘ 🅿

Museum of Royal Leicestershire Regiment Oxford St
☎ (0533) 554100

Housed in Magazine Gateway the museum contains mementos, battle trophies and relics of the Leicestershire Regiment.

Open Mon–Thu & Sat 10–5.30, Sun 2–5.30. (Closed Fri & Xmas).

Free.

P shop ✘

Newarke Houses The Newarke
☎ (0533) 554100

Social history of the city from 1500 to present day. 19th-century street scene, 17th-century room, local clocks, musical instruments.

Open Mon–Thu & Sat 10–5.30, Sun 2–5.30. (Closed Fri & Xmas).

Free.

P ♿ shop ✘

University of Leicester Botanic Gardens Beaumont Hall, Stoughton Drive South, Oadby (3½m SE A6)
☎ (0533) 717725

The gardens occupy an area of about 16 acres and include botanical greenhouses, rose, rock, water and sunken gardens, trees, herbaceous borders and a heather garden. They comprise the grounds of four houses: Beaumont, Southmeade, Hastings and The knoll which are used as student residences.

Open Mon–Fri 10–4.30.

Free.

P (roadside) ♿ garden centre ✘

Wygston's House Museum of Costume Applegate
☎ (0533) 554100

Displays of English costume from 1769 to 1924. Reconstruction of draper's, milliner's and shoe shops of 1920s.

Open Mon–Thu & Sat 10–5.30, Sun 2–5.30. (Closed Fri & Xmas).

Free.

P (100 yds) ♿ (ground floor only) shop ✘

LEIGHTON BUZZARD
Bedfordshire
Map **4** SP92

Narrow Gauge Railway
Pages Park Station, Billington Rd
☎ (0525) 373888

Original light railway was built to carry sand in 1919, and after its redundancy in →

1967 the railway society took over its 3½ mile length. Now 2ft gauge passenger carrying line, volunteer operated, through varied scenery. 18 diesel, steam and petrol locomotives. Steam gala 22 Jun.

Operating dates Suns 16 Mar–9 Nov, Etr wknd; BH Mons & Weds 30 Jul & 6, 13 & 20 Aug. Trains run to Stonehenge Works. Return journey lasts 1 hr 10 mins.

Return ticket £1.90 (ch 5–15 & pen 95p ch 5 free).

⚠ ⚏ & shop ⓥ

LEIGHTON HALL
Lancashire
Map **7** SD47

(3m N of Carnforth off A6)
☎ Silverdale (0524) 701353

Neo-Gothic mansion with fine interior, including early Gillow furniture, Lillian Lunn model figures. Extensive grounds. Large collection of Birds of Prey. Regular flying displays each afternoon at 3.30, weather permitting.

Open May–Sep, 2–5 (last admission 4.30pm). (Closed Sat & Mon ex BH Mons).

House & grounds £1.50 (ch 15 90p). Party 25 +.

⚠ ⚏ & (ground floor) shop ✻ (ex park) ⓥ

LEISTON
Suffolk
Map **5** TM46

Leiston Abbey

Remains of this 14th-century abbey include choir and transepts of church, and ranges of cloisters. Georgian house built into the fabric.

Accessible any reasonable time.

Free.

⚠ & (AM)

LELANT
Cornwall
Map **3** SW53

Cornucopia-Caswell's Cornish Heritage
☎ Hayle (0736) 752676

Model village built to scale and portraying in miniature a selection of Cornwall's most interesting buildings. The delightfully landscaped grounds also include a museum, water gardens, art gallery and tin mining exhibition. Indoor model railway, Legend of King Arthur exhibition and new museum sections on smuggling and Cornish characters. Children's area.

Open Etr–Oct daily 10–5, high season 10am–10pm.

✻ £1.80 (ch 5–16 90p pen £1.30).

⚠ ⚏ & (ground floor only) shop ✻

LERWICK
Shetland
Map **16** HU44

Clickheinen (½m S of Lerwick)

Leighton Buzzard
—
Leyburn

A prehistoric settlement occupied for over 1,000 years. Remains include a partially demolished broch.

Open see end of gazetteer.

Free.

(AM)

Fort Charlotte (overlooking harbour)
Artillery fort begun in 1665 to protect Sound of Bressay in Anglo-Dutch War; completed in 1781 during American War of Independence.

Open see end of gazetteer.

Free.

(AM)

LETCHWORTH
Hertfordshire
Map **4** TL23

First Garden City Museum
296 Norton Way South
☎ (0462) 683149

Thatched house with extension, containing the original offices of the architects of the Garden City, Barry Parker and Raymond Unwin. Displays explain the concept and development of Letchworth as the First Garden City.

Open Mon–Fri 2–4.30, Sat 10–1 & 2–4. Closed BH. Other times by arrangement.

Free.

P (100 yds) & (ground floor & gardens) shop ✻

Museum & Art Gallery Broadway
☎ (0462) 685647

Museum contains displays of archaeological material of North Hertfordshire including important Iron Age and Roman finds from Baldock. Natural history gallery. Monthly art exhibitions.

Open Mon–Sat 10–5. (Closed BHs).

Free.

⚠ & (ground floor only) shop ✻

LEUCHARS
Fife
Map **12** NO42

Earlshall Castle
☎ (033483) 205

A 16th-century castle set amidst pleasant wooded parkland. A renowned feature of the Castle is its long gallery with painted ceiling depicting the arms of the principal families of Scotland and fabulous mythological beasts. In addition there are Jacobite relics, arms and armour, antique furniture, porcelain and paintings on display throughout the Castle. The gardens are famous for their topiary yews in the form of chessmen. Craft fair 1–4 Aug.

Open 29–31 Mar & 3 Apr–28 Sep Thu–Sun 2–6 (last admission 5.15pm).
£1.50 (ch 5–16 & pen £1). Party.
⚠ (300 yds) ⚏ ⊼ & (ground floor & gardens) shop ✻ ⓥ

LEVENS
Cumbria
Map **7** SD48

Levens Hall
☎ Sedgwick (0448) 60321

Elizabethan mansion added to 13th-century pele tower. Fine pictures and Charles II furniture. There is also a unique steam engine collection. The famous topiary garden, laid out in 1692, still adheres to the original plan.

House & gardens open Etr Sun–Sep, Sun–Thu 11–5. Steam collection 2–5.

House & garden ✻ £2.20, garden £1.30 (ch £1.10 house & garden 70p garden) Party.

⚠ ⚏ (licensed) ⊼ & (gardens only) shop & garden centre ✻ (ex carpark) ⓥ

LEWES
East Sussex
Map **5** TQ41

Castle & Barbican House Museum of Sussex Archaeology High St
☎ (0273) 474379
(Sussex Archaeological Society)

Norman castle with shell keep and 14th-century barbican.

Castle & Museum open all year Mon–Sat 10–5.30 & Sun 11–5.30 Apr–Oct (last entry 5pm).

Admission fee payable. Party.

P (50 yds) shop ⓥ

Museum of Local History Anne of Cleves House, Southover High St
☎ (0273) 474610
(Sussex Archaeological Society)

Attractive, timber-framed building, mainly 16th-century. It contains a museum of domestic equipment, a collection of Sussex ironwork and a history gallery.

Open mid Feb-mid Nov, Mon–Sat 10–5.30 (last admission 5pm). Also Sun afternoon Apr–Oct 2–5.30. (Last entry 5pm)

✻ 70p (ch 35p). Party.

P (50 yds) shop ✻ ⓥ

LEWIS, ISLE OF
Western Isles
Ross & Cromarty
Map **13** NB
See **Arnol, Callanish, and Carloway**

LEYBURN
North Yorkshire
Map **7** SE19

Constable Burton Hall Gardens
(3½m E on A684)
☎ Bedale (0677) 50428

Large informal garden, with extensive

borders, alpines, roses, walks amongst fine trees, small lake.

Open Apr–1 Aug daily 9–6.

✱ 50p (ch 10 & pen free).

⚠ ♿

LEYLAND
Lancashire
Map **7** SD52

British Commercial Vehicle Museum
King St
☎ (0772) 451011

Largest commercial vehicle museum in Europe, it aims to represent the whole of the British commercial vehicle industry. Forty restored vehicles on display ranging from the horse drawn era to present day.

Open Etr–28 Sep, Tue–Sun 10–5; Oct & Nov wknds 10–5; also BH.

£1 (ch & pen 50p). Party 15+.

⚠ ⛩ ♿ shop ✖

LICHFIELD
Staffordshire
Map **7** SK10

Hanch Hall
(3m NW on B5014 Handsacre)
☎ Armitage (0543) 490308

A small mansion exhibiting a combination of Tudor, Jacobean, Queen Anne and Georgian architecture. Inside there is a fine Jacobean staircase, ornate plaster ceiling and an observation tower. Contents on view in the 20 rooms include a rare Regency four-poster bed used by the poet Percy Bysshe Shelley and various collections including needlework, antique dolls, costumes, early parchments, waxworks and a postal display. Exhibits include items from the District Council Museum.

Open 30 Mar–28 Sep Sun, BH Mon & following Tue 2–6; also Tue, Wed, Thu & Sat 2–6 Jun–Sep.

£1.70 (ch 90p). Party 20+.

⚠ ☕ ♿ (ground floor & gardens only) shop ✖

Lichfield Heritage Exhibition & Treasury St Mary's Centre, Market Sq.
☎ (0543) 256611

Housed in the ancient Guild Church of St Mary's, the Heritage Exhibition and Treasury are situated on the newly constructed mezzanine floor. The Heritage Exhibition shows the history of the city through its people in a most imaginative and lively way, with an audio-visual presentation of the Civil War and the siege of Lichfield Cathedral. The Treasury now houses fine examples of the silversmith's craft.

Open daily 10–5. (Closed Xmas, New Year & Spring BH Mon).

70p (ch & pen 30p). (Joint ticket with Samuel Johnson Birthplace Museum 85p). School parties.

P (222 yds) ☕ ♿ shop ✖

Samuel Johnson Birthplace Museum
Breadmarket St
☎ (05432) 24972

Birthplace of the great lexicographer, Dr Samuel Johnson in 1709, now a Johnson Museum.

Open May–Sep & Aug BH, Mon–Sat 10–5, Sun 2.30–5; Oct–Apr, Mon–Sat 10–4. (Closed Good Fri, BH, Xmas & New Year).

Admission fee payable.

P (300yds) shop ✖

LILFORD PARK
Northamptonshire
Map **4** TL08

(on A605 between Oundle & Thrapston)
☎ Clopton (08015) 648 or 665

240-acre park with birds, children's farm, adventure playground, crafts/gift centre, garden centre. Special events include crafts market at Easter, and East of England Motor Show at Spring BH. Lilford Hall, a 17th-century Jacobean building, stands in the park, but is not open at present to the public except for some events.

Open daily Etr–Oct, 10–6 (or dusk).

Mon–Sat £1.20 (ch 16 60p, ch 3 free), Sun £1.40 (ch 16 70p, ch 3 free). Excluding some events.

⚠ ☕ ⛩ shop garden centre ✖ Ⓥ

LILLESHALL
Shropshire
Map **7** SJ71

Lilleshall Abbey
(1½m SW off A518 on unclass rd)

An abbey of Augustinian canons established shortly before the middle of the 12th century. Considerable remains of 12th- and 13th-century church with aisleless nave.

Open, see end of gazetteer. (Apr–Sep only).

✱ 30p (ch 16 & pen 15p).

⚠ (AM)

LIMPSFIELD
Surrey
Map **5** TQ45

DeTillens
☎ Oxted (08833) 3342

15th-century Wealden Hall House, with kingpost roof. Contains large collection of orders and decorations from all parts of the world.

Open May–Jun, Sat 2–5; Jul–Sep, Wed, Sat & BH 2–5. Parties at other times by arrangement.

£1.50 (ch 75p).

⚠ ♿ (gardens only)

LINCOLN
Lincolnshire
Map **8** SK97

Greyfriars City & County Museum
Broadgate
☎ (0522) 30401

Former friary, dating from 13th century, with fine barrel roof in upper room. Fine display of Lincolnshire archaeology and natural history.

Open Mon–Sat 10–5.30, Sun 2–5. (Closed Good Fri & Xmas).

✱ 25p (ch 18 10p). Additional charge for special exhibitions.

P ♿ (ground floor only) shop ✖

Lincoln Castle Castle Hill
☎ (0522) 25951

11th-century and later structure, founded by William the Conqueror and retaining Norman bailey and two motte mounds. Parapet walk on walls. Unique Victorian prison chapel. Medieval joust & Fayre in July.

Open Apr–Oct, Mon–Sat 10–6 (5 in Oct); Nov–Mar, Mon–Sat 10–4 (5 in Mar); Suns Apr–Oct 11–6 (5 in Oct).

40p (ch 14 & pen 20p). Party 20+.

P shop ✖

Museum of Lincolnshire Life
Lincolnshire Museums, Burton Rd
☎ (0522) 28448

This museum has been designed to give a picture of all aspects of the county's life over the last 200 years and features horse-drawn and passenger vehicles, farm implements, industrial machinery and domestic and commercial life. Also Royal Lincolnshire Regiment collection.

Open all year Mon–Sat 10–5.30; Sun 2–5.30.

40p (ch 18 20p) Special rates for some events.

⚠ ♿ (ground floor & gardens only) shop ✖

National Cycle Museum Brayford Wharf North, Brayford Pool
☎ (0522) 45091

Exhibition of cycles dating from 1818 to the present day showing the evolution of cycles and cycling, together with related artifacts and accessories.

Open Etr–Oct daily 10–5, Nov–Etr Fri–Sun 10–5. Times are provisional only.

✱ 30p (ch 15p). Party.

P (multi-storey) ♿ shop ✖

Usher Gallery Lindum Rd
☎ (0522) 27980

Collection of water-colours by Peter de Wint, miniatures, glass, ceramics and watches. Large display of coins and medals; Tennyson memorabilia. Temporary exhibitions.

Open Mon–Sat 10–5.30, Sun 2.30–5. (Closed Good Fri & 25–26 Dec).⟶

25p (ch & students 10p).
P (adjacent) & shop ✻

LINDSEY
Suffolk
Map **5** TL94

St James's Chapel Rose Green

Small thatched flint and stone chapel, built in the 13th century.

Open, see end of gazetteer.

Free.

& (AM)

LINLITHGOW
Lothian *West Lothian*
Map **11** NS97

Blackness Castle (4½m NE)

A 15th-century tower and later stronghold, formerly a Covenanters' prison. Massive 17th-century artillery emplacements.

Open, see end of gazetteer. (Closed Mon afternoon & Tue in winter).

✻ 50p (ch & pen 25p).

⚠ (AM)

House of Binns (4m E off A904)
☎ Philipstoun (050683) 4255

A magnificent 17th-century house with plaster ceilings. General Tam Dalyell raised the Royal Scots Greys here in 1681. Panoramic viewpoint in grounds.

Open 29–31 Mar & May–Sep, daily (ex Fri) 2–5 last admission 4.30. Parkland daily 10–sunset.

✻ £1.20 (ch 60p). Party. Members of the Royal Scots Dragoon Guards free when in uniform.

(NTS)

Linlithgow Palace

A fine, but ruined 15th- to 17th-century royal palace with notable chapel, great hall and quadrangle fountain. Mary Queen of Scots was born here.

Open, see end of gazetteer.

✻ £1 (ch & pen 50p).

⚠ (AM)

LINTON
Cambridgeshire
Map **5** TL54

Linton Zoological Gardens
Mortimer House, Hadstock Rd
☎ Cambridge (0223) 891308

Established in 1972 this zoo has concentrated on conservation and education, and includes big cats, bears, monkeys, wallabies, porcupines, llamas, parrots, macaws, birds of prey, snakes, spiders and insects etc. Baby animals can usually be seen. Animals and birds are housed in landscaped enclosures, covering 10 acres, as similar as possible to their natural habitats. Flower beds, shrubberies and exotic trees provide botanical interest. National Zoo month Jul 1986.

Open daily 10–7 or dusk (ex 25 Dec). Last

Lincoln
—
Liverpool

---

admission ¾ hour before closing time.

✻ £1.75 (ch 2–14 90p, pen £1.20). Party 20+.

⚠ ⚓ (Mar–Oct) ⚲ & shop ✻ (ex carpark)

LIPHOOK
Hampshire
Map **4** SU83

Bohunt Manor
☎ (0428) 722208

Medium-sized woodland gardens with lakeside walk, water garden, roses, herbaceous borders and collection of over 50 ornamental ducks, geese and cranes. Several unusual trees and shrubs include a handkerchief tree, Judas tree and one of the tallest tulip trees in the south. Property has been given to the World Wildlife Fund.

Open daily Mon–Fri 12–5; Sat & Sun by appointment only.

50p (ch 10p).

⚠ & ✻

Hollycombe House Steam Collection Railways & Woodland Gardens
(1½m SE on unclass Midhurst Rd)
☎ (0428) 723233

A collection of steam-driven equipment including a 2ft-gauge railway in woodland setting ascending to spectacular views of South Downs. Hollycombe tramway, running between the steam farm and the saw mill and a 7¼ inches miniature railway. Bioscope show with historic films and fairground organ. Engine room of Paddle Steamer 'Caledonia' (ex HMS Goatfell) in process of restoration. Demonstrations of threshing and steam rolling, traction engine rides and other items. Woodland gardens and walks. Festival of steam on May Day.

Open Etr–Sep, BH & Sun, also 17–31 Aug 12–6, rides 2–6.

£1.80 (ch & pen £1.20).

⚠ ⚓ ⚲ shop ✻ Ⓥ

LITTLE DEAN
Gloucestershire
Map **3** SO61

Littledean Hall
☎ Dean (0594) 24213

A historic manor house depicting the evolution of a manorial hall from the early Norman period. The north front stands on what is believed to be the remains of a Saxon hall, built over a ruined Roman building. Panelled interiors, museum and water gardens. Excavation, restoration and conservation of a major Roman temple, which was discovered in January

---

1984 is the largest structure of its type so far found in Britain. Museum under development.

Open Apr–Oct, daily 2–6. BH weekends & peak holiday period 11–6.

£1 (ch over 8 50p, pen 90p).

⚠ & (gardens only)

LITTLEHAMPTON
West Sussex
Map **4** TQ00

Littlehampton Museum 12A River Rd
☎ (0903) 715149

Six galleries of maritime paintings, early photographs of the town and river, historic maps, and local archaeology. Special exhibitions.

Open Apr–Sep Tue–Sat; Oct–Mar Thu–Sat 10.30–1 & 2–4.

Free.

P & (ground floor only) shop

LITTLE NESS
Shropshire
Map **7** SJ41

Adcote School
(7m NW Shrewsbury off A5)
☎ Baschurch (0939) 260202

'Country Life' described this as 'the most controlled, coherent and masterly of the big country houses designed by Norman Shaw'. Includes William Morris stained glass windows and de Morgan tiled fireplaces, also landscaped gardens.

Open 24 Apr–11 Jul (ex 24–28 May) & 12–30 Sep, daily 2–5. Other times by appointment.

Free. (Governors reserve the right to make a charge.)

⚠ ✻

LIVERPOOL
Merseyside
Map **7** SJ39

Bluecoat Chambers School Ln
☎ 051–709 5297

A fine Queen Anne building in Liverpool's city centre with cobbled quadrangle and garden courtyard. Built as a charity school in 1717, it now houses a gallery, concert hall, artists' studio and craft shop.

Open Mon–Sat 9–6. Bluecoat gallery Tue–Sat 10.30–5. (Closed Xmas, Etr & BH's).

Free.

P (200 yds) ⚓ & (ground floor & gardens only) shop

Croxteth Hall & Country Park
(5m NE of city centre)
☎ 051–228 5311

Former home of the Earls of Sefton set in beautiful 500-acre park. Hall with displays, furnished rooms and costume groups on the theme of an Edwardian house party. There is also a Victorian walled garden, a farmyard with rare breeds of animals and a miniature railway. Regular events and attractions held throughout the season

160

and an award winning educational service.

Open Good Fri–last Sun in Sep, daily 11–5. Hall also open Oct 11–5. Heritage Exhibition only, 11–4 Nov–Etr. Farm also open Oct 11–5, Nov–Etr 1–4 (Closed Xmas & New Year). NB these times have not been confirmed for 1986.

✳ Hall, Farm & Walled Garden £1.20 (ch & pen 60p). Country Park Free. In winter Heritage Exhibition only, 20p (ch & pen 10p).

⚠ ⏚ ✚ ᕗ (ground floor & gardens only) shop ✗ (ex country park) Ⓥ

Liverpool City Libraries
William Brown St
☎ 051-207 2147

One of the oldest and largest public libraries in the country, with over two million books. Temporary Exhibitions.

Open Mon–Fri 9–9 (Sat 9–5).

Guided tours by prior arrangement.

Free.

P ⏚ ᕗ ✗

Merseyside Maritime Museum
Pier Head
☎ 051-236 5567

A multi-acre museum in restored 19th-century docklands. Boat Hall, Pilotage Building, Piermaster's House, Cooperage, Albert Warehouse containing varied displays about the Port of Liverpool. Floating craft, quayside trail, outdoor exhibits of maritime crafts.

Open 28 Feb–Autumn, daily 10.30–5.30 (last admission 4.30pm). Winter opening, phone for details.

✳ 40p (ch, students & pen 20p). Party 20+.

⚠ (charged) ⏚ (licensed) ᕗ (ground floor only) shop

Sudley Art Gallery Mossley Hill Rd
☎ 051-724 3245

Contains the Emma Holt Bequest of fine 19th-century British paintings and sculpture.

Open Mon–Sat 10–5, Sun 2–5. (Closed Good Fri, 24–26 Dec & New Years day).

Free (Donation). ⚠ ✗

Walker Art Gallery William Brown St
☎ 051-227 5234 ext 2064

Outstanding general collection of European paintings, sculpture and drawings dating from 1300 to the present day, especially notable for Italian and Netherlandish paintings.

Open Mon–Sat 10–5 Sun 2–5. (Closed Good Fri, 24–26 Dec & New Years day).

Free (Donation).

P ⏚ shop ✗

LIVERPOOL UNIVERSITY BOTANIC GARDENS
Cheshire
Map **7** SJ37
(Off A540 near Ness-on-Wirral)
☎ 051-336 2135

This beautiful learning garden contains fine trees and shrubs, rock terrace, water gardens, herbaceous borders and rose collection. Visitor centre. Public lectures 2 Mar & 6 Apr. 'Azalea Day' 10 May; 'Azalea Walk' 24 May.

Open daily 9–sunset. (Closed Xmas day).

✳ £1.30 (ch 8–16 & pen 70p).

⚠ ⏚ ✚ ᕗ shop

LLANALLGO
Gwynedd
Map **6** SH48

Din Lligwy Ancient Village (1m NW off A5205)

Remains of 4th-century village, with two circular and seven rectangular buildings encircled by pentagonal stone wall.

Accessible at all reasonable times.

Free.

(AM Cadw)

LLANBEDR
Gwynedd
Map **6** SH52

Maes Artro Tourist Village
☎ (034123) 497 or 467

This complex of craft shops and entertainments is close to the beautiful Cambrian Coast and stands in 10 acres of grounds, woodland and gardens. The attractions include aquarium, model village, recreated old Welsh street and adventure playground. The craft shops display a large variety of products. Pets corner, animal house and TV film sets.

Open Etr–Mid Oct, daily 9–6.

✳ £1.25 (ch 95p).

⚠ ⏚ ✚ ᕗ shop

LLANBERIS
Gwynedd
Map **6** SH56

Dolbadarn Castle

Native Welsh stronghold with a three storeyed 13th-century round tower.

Accessible at all reasonable times.

Free.

⚠ (limited) (AM Cadw)

Lake Railway Llyn Padarn
☎ (0286) 870549

Narrow-gauge steam railway. Four-mile journey commencing from and returning to Gilfach Ddu, adjacent to the Welsh Slate Museum and the centre of the Padarn Country Park. Railway line was formerly used to carry slate from the Dinorwic Quarries to Port Dinorwic. The steam locomotives date from 1889–1948; coaches built specially for railway.

Trains run frequently every day (ex Sat) Etr–Sep 10.30–4.30 in peak season.

Fare £1.70 (ch 5–15 90p) Discount for family.

Party—apply to Commercial Manager.

⚠ ⏚ ✚ ᕗ (some parts inaccessible) shop

Snowdon Mountain Railway
☎ (0286) 870223

First opened in 1896, the only public rack and pinion railway in Britain (800mm gauge). Climbs 4⅔ miles to the summit of Snowdon, providing views of North Wales, →

NESS GARDENS
University of Liverpool Botanic Gardens
Ness, Neston, South Wirral L64 4AY

10 miles N.W. of Chester, off A540

Extensive garden with sweeping lawns and fine displays of specimen trees and shrubs. Rhododendron and Azalea borders. Rock, Heather, Rose and Water gardens. Visitor Centre with slide sequences and indoor exhibitions. Picnic area and Tea Room.

Admission charge: £1.30, Senior Citizens & Children (8-16) 70p.

For full details and party bookings contact:
The Director. Tel. 051-336-2135

Isle of Man and the Wicklow Mountains of Ireland on clear days.

Open week before Etr–early Oct daily from 9am (weather permitting). No weekend services early or late season.

✱ £8.50 return (ch £5.50) for 2½ hour trip.

⚠ ☕ (& licensed at summit) shop

The Welsh Slate Museum Gilfach Ddu (¼m off A4086)
☎ (0286) 870630

The museum, a branch of the National Museum of Wales, is located within the workshops of the former Dinorwic slate quarry which at one time employed over 3000 men. Much of the original plant and machinery can be seen, including a foundry and the famous 50ft water wheel, as well as machinery from other redundant Welsh quarries. Visitors can see a blacksmith at work, slate-splitting displays, and also a new gallery interpreting the significance of the Welsh slate industry.

Open Etr–May daily 9.30–5.30; Jun–Sep daily 9.30–6.30 (Closed Oct–Etr).

80p (ch & pen 40p).

⚠ ⛩ ♿ shop (AM Cadw)

LLANDRINDOD WELLS
Powys
Map **3** SO06

Llandrindod Wells Museum Temple St
☎ (0597) 4513

Archaeological exhibits, and objects excavated from Roman Camp at Castell Collen to north of town. Paterson doll collection is on show. Victorian Spa gallery with period costume and 19th-century chemist's equipment. Temporary exhibitions throughout the year.

Open Mon–Fri 10–12.30 & 2–5, Sat 10–12.30 also 2–5 Apr–Sep.

Free.

P (50 yds) ♿ (ground floor only) shop ✗

LLANDYSUL
Dyfed
Map **2** SN44

Maesllyn Woollen Mill Museum
☎ Rhydlewis (023975) 251

Preserving the atmosphere of a 19th-century woollen mill, where the changes from hand spinning and weaving to powered machinery are explained and demonstrated. Some machinery is driven from the restored water wheels. Photographic, audio and other displays. An interesting nature trail follows the course of the waterways.

Open Mon–Sat 10–6, Sun 2–6 (summer); Mon–Fri 10–5 (winter).

✱ 80p (ch 40p, pen 60p). Party.

⚠ ☕ (Etr–Oct) ⛩ ♿ (ground floor only) shop ✗ (in building)

LLANELLI
Dyfed
Map **2** SN50

Parc Howard Art Gallery & Museum
☎ (0554) 773538

Situated in a pleasant park, and containing a permanent collection of paintings. Llanelli pottery and museum exhibits. From Mar to Oct a programme of exhibitions of paintings, porcelain, sculpture etc is in operation.

Open daily 10–6.

Free.

P (50 yds) ♿ (grounds only) shop

LLANFAIR CAEREINION
Powys
Map **6** SJ10

Welshpool & Llanfair Light (Steam) Railway (2ft 6in gauge)
☎ (0938) 810441

Open between Welshpool & Llanfair Caereinon (8m) includes Austrian and Colonial locomotives.

Open Etr–5 Oct weekends; Spring BH; 17 Jun–10 Jul Tue, Wed & Thu; daily 12 Jul–Aug. Trains from Llanfair at 11, 1.45, and 4.15pm daily running period.

Return £3.70 (ch 3–15 £1.85) Single £2.40 (ch £1.20). Family ticket £8.

⚠ ☕ (at Llanfair Stn) ⛩ ♿ shop

LLANGOLLEN
Clwyd
Map **7** SJ24

Canal Museum & Passenger Boat Trip Centre The Wharf
☎ Chester (0244) 335180 or Llangollen (0978) 860702

The museum illustrates the fascinating story of Britain's great canal era by means of static and working models, photographs, murals, slides. Also horsedrawn passenger boat trips along the beautiful Vale of Llangollen can be enjoyed.

Open Etr then Whit–Sep daily 10.30–5.

Museum 50p (ch 30p). Party.

P ♿ (ground floor only). shop

Llangollen Station
☎ (0978) 860951

Situated alongside the River Dee. Great Western Railway Station restored, in town centre, with locomotives and rolling stock on display. Passenger trains run between Llangollen and Berwyn Station (approx. 3½ mile round trip). Special coach for disabled on steam hauled trains only.

Station open weekends, all year Steam hauled trains Etr Sun & every Sun & BH until mid Oct, diesel trains Jul–Aug Sat, 1–5.

Station Free; Return Fares £1.20 (ch 60p).

P (500 yds) ☕ ♿ (ground floor) shop

Plas Newydd Butler Hill
☎ (0978) 860234

Home from 1780–1831 of the 'Ladies of Llangollen', Lady Eleanor Butler and Sarah Ponsonby. The house contains carved panels, stained glass windows, leather cloth wall covering and original household and personal items together with, pictures, prints and letters.

Open May–Sep, Mon–Sat 10–7.30, Sun 11–4. Oct–Apr, weekdays by arrangement.

✱ 40p (ch & pen 25p).

⚠

Valle Crucis Abbey

Abbey founded in 1201 for Cistercian monks by Madog ap Grufydd, Prince of Powys. The remaining buildings date mainly from the 13th century.

Open † see end of gazetteer.

✱ 50p (ch 16 & pen 25p).

⚠ shop (AM Cadw)

LLANGYBI
Gwynedd
Map **6** SH44

St Cybi's Well

Rectangular structure, known also as Ffynnon Gybi, with dry-stone structure covering adjacent pool. Interior has wall niches and the corbelled beehive vaulting of Irish type is unique in Wales.

Accessible at all reasonable times.

Free.

(AM Cadw)

LLANIDLOES
Powys
Map **6** SN98

Old Market Hall
☎ Welshpool (0938) 4759

Half-timbered building, standing in open arches, with museum on upper floor.

Open Etr, then Spring BH–Sep daily 11–1 & 2–5.

Free.

P (200 yds) shop ✗

LLANRHIDIAN
West Glamorgan
Map **2** SS49

Weobley Castle

12th- to 14th-century fortified manor house above Gower marshland.

Open 15 Mar–15 Oct weekdays 10–7, Sun 1–7; 16 Oct–14 Mar weekdays 10–4, Sun 1–4.

✱ 40p (ch 16 & pen 20p).

⚠ (AM Cadw)

LLANRUG
Gwynedd
Map **6** SH56

Bryn Bras Castle & Grounds
(½m SE of A4086)
☎ Llanberis (0286) 870210

Early Victorian Romanesque castle.
Lovely grounds, including stream,
waterfalls, pools, hydrangeas,
rhododendrons, woodland and mountain
walks with panoramic views.

Open Spring BH–Sep, Mon–Fri & Sun 1–5;
Mid Jul–Aug 10.30–5.

✹ £1 (ch 15 50p).

⚠ ⚹ shop ✖ ⓥ

LLANRWST
Gwynedd
Map **6** SH86

Gwydyr Castle
☎ (0492) 640261

Historical royal residence, magnificently
furnished from the Tudor and Victorian
period. Beautiful grounds with more than
30 peacocks.

Open Jul–mid Sep daily 10–5pm; Etr–Jun
& mid Sep–Oct daily 10–5. Other times by
appointment.

✹ Castle & grounds £1.50 (ch 75p).

⚠ ⚹ ⅋ ♿ (ground floor & gardens only)
shop

Gwydyr Uchaf Chapel
Former private chapel of Gwydyr Castle
dating from 1673. Noted for rare Welsh
painted roof of the period.

Accessible at all reasonable times.

✹ 30p (ch 16 & pen 15p).

(AM Cadw)

LLANSTEPHAN
Dyfed
Map **2** SN31

Llanstephan Castle
Remains of 11th- to 13th-century
stronghold on west side of Towy estuary.

Accessible at all reasonable times.

Free.

(AM Cadw)

LLANTHONY
Gwent
Map **3** SO22

Llanthony Priory
Augustinian foundation c. 1108 most of
the present structure being 12th- or 13th-
century and including west towers, north
nave arcade and south transept. Former
Priest's House is now a hotel. The
Honddhu valley scenery in Black
Mountains is very picturesque but roads
are narrow especially northwards towards
lofty Gospel Pass leading to Hay-on-Wye.

Open at all reasonable times.

Free.

⚠ (AM Cadw)

LLANTILIO CROSSENNY
Gwent
Map **3** SO31

Llanrug
—
Lochmaben

Hen Gwrt
Rectangular enclosure of medieval house
which is still surrounded by moat.

Open any reasonable time.

Free.

(AM Cadw)

LLANTWIT MAJOR
South Glamorgan
Map **3** SS96

Town Hall
☎ (04465) 3707

Originally 12th-, and largely 17th-century
medieval courthouse and market, known
once as the 'Church loft'. Retains original
plan and comprises two storeys, Curfew
bell now in church.

Open all year Mon–Fri 9–4, by
appointment.

Free.

⚠ (adjacent) ✖

LLANUWCHLLYN
Gwynedd
Map **6** SH82

Bala Lake Railway
☎ (06784) 666

Narrow-gauge railway running 4½m from
Llanuwchllyn station, alongside Bala Lake
to Bala. Four ex-Dinorwic quarry steam
engines built between 1889 and 1903 also
diesel locomotives. Llanuwchllyn Station
buildings (1867) have been extended to
give better facilities and the latest corridor
coach has invalid facilities installed. The
railway also has one of the remaining four
original GWR signal boxes with 21-lever
double-twist frame installed in 1896. Also
a large selection of slate wagons and a
gunpowder van. There are also early and
later pattern Lancashire and Yorkshire
railway signals in use. Model engine gala
30 & 31 Aug 1986.

Open Etr–Sep daily 9–6, then wknds only
to mid Oct.

✹ £2 return (ch £1). Family ticket £5.

⚠ ⚹ ⅋ ♿ ⓥ

LLANYSTUMDWY
Gwynedd
Map **6** SH43

Lloyd George Memorial Museum
☎ Criccieth (076671) 2654

David Lloyd George, the famous Liberal
Prime Minister, was educated in the
village and died at the house of Ty
Newydd in 1945.

Open May–Sep Mon–Fri 10–5 also Sat &
Sun 2–4 in Jul & Aug. Details not
confirmed for 1986.

✹ 50p (ch & pen 25p). Family ticket £1.

P (50 yds) ♿ shop ✖

LLAWHADEN
Dyfed
Map **2** SN01

Llawhaden Castle
Ruined 13th-century fortified residence of
Bishop of St David's.

Open see end of gazetteer.

✹ 40p (ch 16 & pen 20p).

(AM Cadw)

LOCHAWE
Strathclyde *Argyll*
Map **10** NN12

Cruachan Power Station
(3m W off A85, near Pass of Brander)
☎ Taynuilt (08662) 673

This important power station of the North
of Scotland Hydro electric Board pumps
water from Loch Awe to a spectacular
high-level reservoir up on Ben Cruachan.

Open Etr–Oct 9–4.30.

£1 (ch 10–15 50p).

⚠ ⚹ ⅋ ♿ shop ✖

See advertisement under Edinburgh

LOCHCARRON
Highland *Ross and Cromarty*
Map **14** NG83

Strome Castle (3m SE)
A fragmentary ruin of a stronghold of the
Macdonalds of Glengarry, blown up by
Kenneth Mackenzie of Kintail in 1602.
There are wide views across the inner
Sound to Scalpay, Raasay and the
Coolins of Skye.

Accessible at all reasonable times.

Free.

(NTS)

LOCHGILPHEAD
Strathclyde *Argyll*
Map **10** NR88

Kilmory Castle Gardens
☎ (0546) 2127

Thirty acres of grounds immediately
surrounding the castle; although suffering
years of neglect until acquired by present
owners rare trees and shrubs have
miraculously survived. Begun in the 18th
century the gardens are now being
restored to their former magnificence.
Woodland walks and nature trails.

Open all year 9–dusk.

Free.

⚠ ⅋ ✖

LOCHMABEN
Dumfries and Galloway *Dumfriesshire*
Map **11** NY08

Rammerscales (3m S off B7020)
☎ (038781) 361

A Georgian manor house begun in 1760
containing a fine circular staircase,
elegant public rooms, and a long library at
the top of the house. There are Jacobite
relics and links with Flora Macdonald. →

Also a small collection of works by
modern artists.
Open 4–29 May Sun, Tue & Thu; 3 Aug–14
Sep alternate Sun & every Tue, Wed &
Thu, 2–5. Other times during the season
by appointment.

£1 (ch 14 50p).

⚠ ⏲

LOCHTY
Fife
Map **12** NO50

Lochty Private Railway
☎ Kirkcaldy (0592) 264587

Steam trains run from Lochty to
Knightsward, hauled by the restored War
Department Tank Locomotive No 16.

Regular services Sundays only 15 Jun–7
Sep, 2–4.45pm.

Return fare 80p (ch 14 50p). Party 10 + .

⚠ shop

Lochmaben
—
Lode

LOCHWINNOCH
Strathclyde Renfrewshire
Map **10** NS35

Lochwinnoch Community Museum
Main St
☎ (0505) 842615

A series of changing exhibitions reflecting
the historic background of local
agriculture, industry and village life.

Open Mon, Wed & Fri 10–1, 2–5 & 6–8;
Tue & Sat 10–1 & 2–5.

Free.

⚠ ♿ ✕

LODE
Cambridgeshire
Map **5** TL56

Anglesey Abbey
(6m NE of Cambridge on B1102)

Remodelled c.1600 the house
incorporates a 13th-century monastic
undercroft. The 100 acres of gardens
were laid out this century and include a
long avenue of trees and sculptures.
Visitors' centre display show how these
unique gardens were developed.

Abbey & gardens open 29 Mar–27 Apr
wknds only & BH Mon. 30 Apr–12 Oct
Wed–Sun 1.30–5.30. Gardens only open
29 Mar–29 Jun Wed–Sun. 30 Jun–12 Oct
daily.

£2 (ch £1), garden only £1 (ch 50p). Party
15 + .

✡ (from 12.30pm) ✕ (NT)

THE COMPLETE
ATLAS OF
BRITAIN

AA

Up-to-date road maps at a generous
scale of 4 miles to the inch, plus more
than 60 large-scale town plans, airport
plans, motorway maps with important
junctions highlighted, distance charts,
route-planning and local radio maps,
make this one of the AA's most popular
road atlases.

There is a comprehensive index of more than 25,000 place names, and a
special section of London plans, with a separate index of London street
names

London Gazetteer

E1 Stepney and east of the Tower of London

Historic Ship Collection St Katharines Dock, Plan 3: **10** C3

☎ 01–481 0043

Maritime Trust's Historic Ship Collection comprises a number of British sailing and steam-powered vessels of the 19th and early 20th century. Individual display in each ship.

Open daily 10–5. (Closed Xmas day, New Year's eve & New Year's day).

£1.80 (ch, students & pen 80p). Party.

P (200 yds) ⚤ 🏧 ♿ (pontoons only) shop ✶

E2 Bethnal Green

Bethnal Green Museum of Childhood Cambridge Heath Rd, Plan 4: **1** E4

☎ 01–980 2415

A branch of the Victoria and Albert Museum. Its chief exhibits are toys, dolls and dolls' houses; model soldiers, puppets, games, model theatres, wedding dresses, children's costume and Spitalfield silks.

Open Mon–Thu & Sat 10–6, Sun 2.30–6 (Closed Fri, Spring BH Mon, 24–26 Dec & New Years day).

LONDON Greater London, Plans 1–4 pages 168 to 177.

Places within the London postal area are listed in postal district order commencing East, North, South and West. Other places within the county of London or surrounding area are listed under their respective place names.

Their locations are indicated on each plan by a number followed by the grid reference e.g. A3.

Free.

♿ ♿ shop ✶ (ex guide dogs)

Geffrye Museum Kingsland Rd Plan 4: **15** E4

☎ 01–739 8368

A collection of furniture and woodwork from the Elizabethan period to 1939, including a reconstruction of John Evelyn's 'closet of curiosities', contained in the former almshouses built c.1713.

Open Tue–Sat 10–5, Sun 2–5 & BH Mons 10–5 (Closed Mon, Good Fri, 24–26 Dec & New Years day).

Free.

P (200 yds) ⚤ ♿ (ground floor only) shop ✶

E6 East Ham

Interpretative Centre, St Mary Magdalene Churchyard Nature Reserve Norman Rd, Plan 4: **50** F4

☎ 01–470 4525

Displays relating to natural history and history of churchyard nature reserve.

Open Tue–Thu & Sun 2–5.

Free.

♿ shop ✶

E14 Poplar

National Museum of Labour History Limehouse Town Hall, Commercial Rd, Plan 4: **38** E3

☎ 01–515 3229

The visual history from late 18th century to 1945 is portrayed in two sections, from autocracy to democracy, and the turn to socialism 1881 to 1945. The prime concern of this large and rare collection is to portray the development of democracy over the last 200 years. →

London plans overleaf: gazetteer con-tinues on page 178

PASSMORE EDWARDS MUSEUM
...theres more to us than meets the eye!

Romford Road, Stratford, London E15 4LZ   Tel: 01-519 4296

- **INTERPRETATIVE CENTRE & NATURE RESERVE**
  Norman Road, East Ham,
  London E6 4HN   Tel: 01-470 4525

- **NORTH WOOLWICH OLD STATION MUSEUM**
  Pier Road, North Woolwich,
  London E16 2JJ   Tel: 01-474 7244

NEWHAM
LEISURE SERVICES

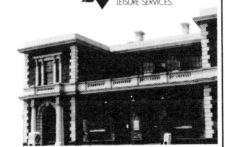

Key to London Plans

The locations of establishments listed below will be found on the London Plans on the following pages. Details of the establishments can be found under the London Postal District which follows the establishment name.

LONDON PLAN 1

		London Postal District	Grid reference
1	Chelsea Physic Garden	SW3	D1
2	Commonwealth Institute	W8	A4
3	Geological Museum	SW7	B3
4	Kensington Palace State Apartments & Court Dress Collection	W8	A4
5	Leighton House	W14	A4
6	Linley Sambourne House	W8	A4
7	Madame Tussaud's	NW1	D6
8	National Army Museum	SW3	D1
9	Natural History Museum	SW7	B3
10	London Planetarium	NW1	D6
11	Science Museum	SW7	B3
12	Victoria & Albert Museum	SW7	C3
13	Wallace Collection	W1	E6
14	Wellington Museum	W1	E4

LONDON PLAN 2

		London Postal District	Grid reference
1	Agnew's Galleries	W1	A4
2	Banqueting House	SW1	C3
3	British Craft Centre	WC2	C5
4	British Museum	WC1	C6
5	Cabinet War Rooms	SW1	C2
6	Courtauld Institute Galleries	WC1	B6
7	Dickens House	WC1	D6
8	Dr Johnson's House	EC4	E5
9	Guinness World of Records	W1	B4
10	Houses of Parliament	SW1	C2
11	Imperial Collection	SW1	C2
12	Imperial War Museum	SE1	E2
13	Lancaster House	SW1	A3
14	London Diamond Centre	W1	A5
15	London Transport Museum	WC2	C4
16	Mall Galleries	SW1	B3
17	Marlborough House	SW1	B3
18	Middle Temple Hall	EC4	E4
19	Tradescant Trust Museum	SE1	D6
20	Museum of Mankind	W1	A4
21	National Gallery	WC2	C4
22	National Portrait Gallery	WC2	C4
23	Pollock's Toy Museum	W1	B6
24	Public Records Office Museum	WC2	E5
25	Queens Gallery	SW1	A2
26	Royal Academy of Arts	W1	A4
27	Royal Mews	SW1	A2
28	The Sir John Soane Museum	WC2	D5
29	Tate Gallery	SW1	C3

LONDON PLAN 3

		London Postal District	Grid reference
1	Cuming Museum	SE17	A1
2	Guildhall	EC2	B4
3	HMS Belfast	SE1	C2
4	Lloyds of London	EC3	C4
5	London Dungeon	SE1	C2
6	Monument	EC3	B3
7	Museum of London	EC2	A4
8	Museum of the Order of St John	EC1	A5
9	National Postal Museum	EC1	A4
10	Historic Ship Collection	E1	C3
11	Stock Exchange	EC2	B4
12	Telecom Technology Showcase	EC4	A3
13	Tower of London	EC3	C3
14	Wesley's House & Museum	EC1	B5

LONDON PLAN 4

Some of the establishments listed below are not included in the London section of the gazetteer although they appear on this map. The centre column therefore indicates the position of entries within the alphabetical gazetteer or the London section of the guide.

		Gazetteer placename or London Postal District where applicable	Grid reference
1	Bethnal Green Museum	E2	E4
2	Bourne Hall Cultural Centre	Ewell	C1
3	Carlyle's House	SW3	D3
4	Chessington Zoo	Chessington	B1
5	Chiswick House	W4	C3
6	Church Farm House Museum	NW4	C5
7	Claremont	Esher	A1
8	Claremont Landscape Gardens	Esher	A1
9	Cricket Memorial Gallery	NW8	D4
10	Cutty Sark Clipper Ship	SE10	E3
11	Dulwich Picture Gallery	SE21	E2
12	Eltham Palace	SE9	F2
13	Fenton House	NW3	C4
14	Forty Hall	Enfield	E5
15	Geffyre Museum	E2	E4
16	Gipsy Moth IV	SE10	E3
18	Grange Museum	NW10	C4
19	Gunnersbury Park Museum	W3	B3
20	Hall Place	Bexley	F2
21	Ham House	Ham	B2
22	Hampton Court Palace	Hampton Court	B2
23	Hogarth's House	W4	C3
24	Horniman Museum	SE23	E2
25	Keats House	NW3	D4
26	Kenwood Iveagh Bequest	NW3	D4
27	Kew Bridge Pumping Station	Brentford	B3
28	Kew Gardens	Kew	B3
29	Kew Palace	Kew	B3
30	Lawn Tennis Museum	SW19	C2
31	Livesey Museum	SE15	E3
32	London Toy & Model Museum	W2	C3
33	London Zoo	NW1	D4
34	Marble Hill House	Twickenham	B2
35	Museum of Artillery in the Rotunda	SE18	F3
36	Musical Museum	Brentford	B3
37	National Maritime Museum	SE10	E3
38	National Museum of Labour History	E14	E3
39	North Woolwich Old Station Museum	E16	F3
40	Old Royal Observatory	SE10	E3
41	Orleans House Gallery	Twickenham	B2
42	Osterley House	Osterley	B3
43	Passmore Edwards Museum	E15	F4
44	Priory Museum	Orpington	F1
45	Queen Elizabeth Hunting Lodge	Chingford	F5
46	Rangers House	SE3	E3
47	Royal Air Force Museum	NW9	C5
48	Royal Mews Exhibition	Hampton	B2
49	Royal Naval College	SE10	E3
50	Interpretative Centre St Mary Magdalene Churchyard Nature Reserve	E6	F4
51	South London Art Gallery	SE5	E3
52	Syon House	Isleworth	B3
53	Syon Park	Isleworth	B3
53A	Thames Barrier Centre	SE18	F3
54	Tower Bridge Walkway	SE1	E3
55	Vestry House Museum	E17	E5
56	Wembley Stadium	Wembley	B4
58	William Morris Gallery	E17	E5
59	Windmill Museum	SW19	C2
60	Winter Gardens	SE9	F2

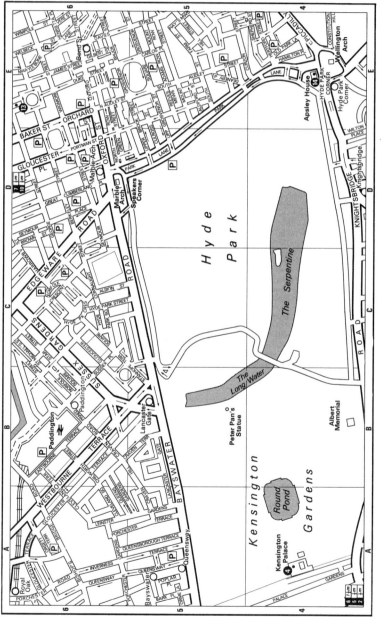

See key to London Plans–pages 166–7

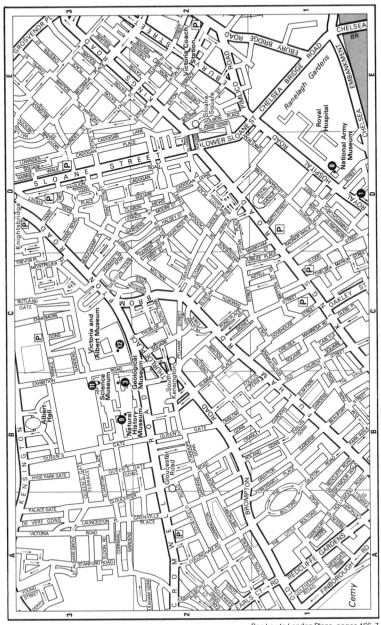

See key to London Plans–pages 166–7

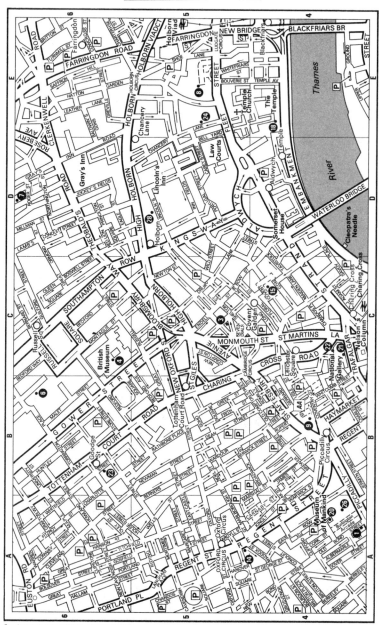

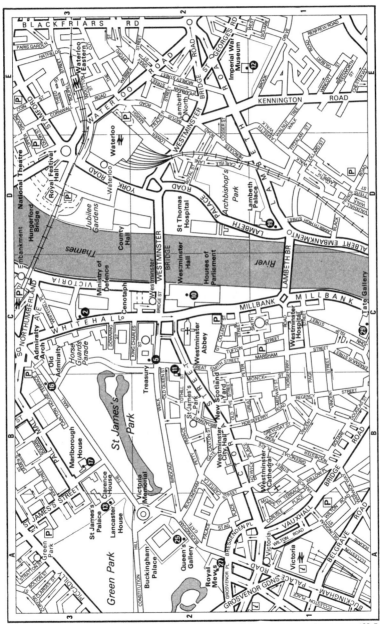

See key to London Plans–pages 166–7

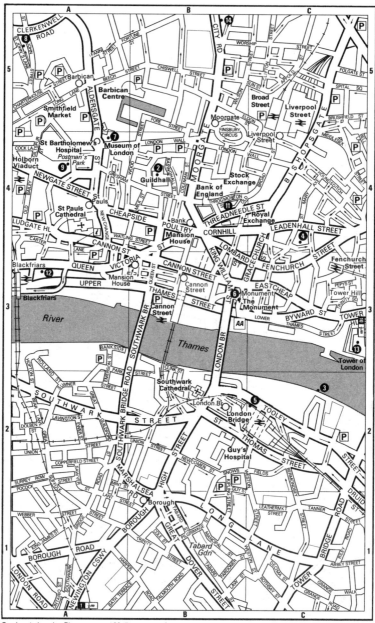

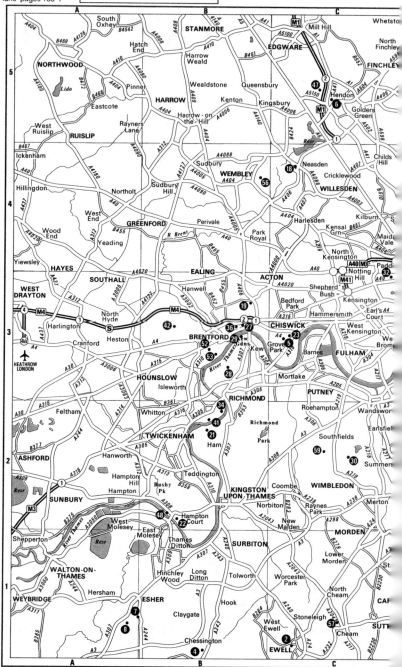

London Postal Districts and ways in and out of London

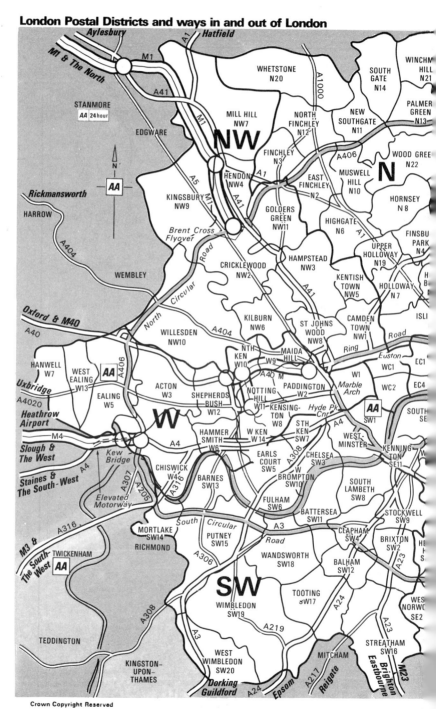

Crown Copyright Reserved

176

London Postal Area Boundary
London Postal District Boundaries
Main Roads into and out of London
Signposted North and South Circular
Roads & Ring Road
Other Main Roads

Service Centre **AA**

Scale of Miles

0   1   2   3   4

London Gazetteer cont.

Open Tue–Sat 9.30–5, Sun 2.30–5.30.
Free.
P (in street) shop 🦮

E15 Stratford

Passmore Edwards Museum
Romford Rd, Plan 4: **43** F4
☎ 01-519 4296
Greater London and Essex archaeology,
biology, geology and history.
Open Mon–Wed & Fri 10–6, Thu 10–6, Sat
10–1 & 2–5, Sun & BH's 2–5.
Free.
🅿 ♿ (ground floor only) shop 🦮
See advertisement on page 165

E16 North Woolwich

North Woolwich Station Musuem Pier
Rd, Plan 4: **39** F3
☎ 01-474 7244
Imposing restored station building with
three galleries of photographs, models, an
original turntable pit and restored booking
hall. Each Sunday a locomotive is
steamed.
Open Mon–Sat 10–5; Sun & BH 2–5.
Free.
P (250 yds) ♿ shop

E17 Walthamstow

Vestry House Museum of Local History
Vestry Rd, near Hoe St, Plan 4: **55** E5
☎ 01-527 5544 ext 4391
A small museum located in a former 18th-
century workhouse standing in the
conservation area 'Walthamstow Village'.
Historical items of local interest from the
Stone Age onwards include a
reconstructed Victorian parlour. The
Bremer Car, probably the first British
internal combustion engine car, can be
seen. Local archives are available for
consultation by appointment.
Open Mon–Fri 10–5.30, Sat 10–5 (Closed
BH).
Free.
P (20 yds) ♿ (ground floor only) shop 🦮

William Morris Gallery Water House
Lloyd Park, Forest Rd, Plan 4: **58** E5
☎ 01-527 5544 ext 4390
William Morris lived in this house, known
as 'Water House' from 1848–56. There are
exhibits of his fabrics, wallpapers and
furniture. Also ceramics by William de
Morgan, furniture by Gimson and Barnsley
and work by Mackmurdo and the Century
Guild. Pre-Raphaelite pictures, sculpture
by Rodin.
Open Tue–Sat 10–1 & 2–5, and 1st Sun in
each month 10–12 & 2–5 (Closed Mon &
PH's).
Free.
🅿 ♿ (ground floor & gardens) shop 🦮

London E14
—
London EC3

EC1 Clerkenwell & Farringdon

National Postal Museum King Edward
Building, King Edward St, Plan 3: **9** A4
☎ 01-606 3769 & 01-432 3851
Contains probably the finest and most
comprehensive collection of postage
stamps in the world. Included are: the RM
Phillips collection of 19th-century Great
Britain (with special emphasis on the One
Penny Black and its creation); the Post
Office Collection; a world-wide collection
including practically every stamp issued
since 1878; and the philatelic
correspondence archives of Thomas de la
Rue and Co who furnished stamps to over
150 countries between 1855 and 1965.
Within these collections are thousands of
original drawings and unique proof sheets
of every British stamp since 1840. Special
exhibitions, and visits for up to 40 people
may be arranged, with a guide and film
show.
Open Mon–Thu (ex. BH) 10–4.30, Fri 10–4.
Free.
🅿 ♿ (ground floor only) shop 🦮

Museum of the Order of St John St
John's Gate, St John's Ln, Plan 3: **8** A5
☎ 01-253 6644 ext 35
16th century Gatehouse, former entrance
to the medieval Priory of the Order of St
John of Jerusalem. Now headquarters of
the Modern Order, whose charitable
foundations include St John Ambulance
and the Ophthalmic Hospital in
Jerusalem. Norman Crypt and 15th
century Grand Priory Church. A collection
of paintings, silver, furniture and historical
medical instruments, certificates,
textbooks and memorabilia of notable
early St John personalities and pioneers.
Special features are St John's role in the
development of medical transport and its
service in the Boer and two World Wars.
Open Tue & Fri 10–6, Sat 10–4. (Closed
Etr, Xmas wk and BH's). Guided tours 11
& 2.30.
Donations.
🅿 ♿ (ground floor only) shop 🦮

Wesley's House & Museum 47 City Rd,
Plan 3: **14** B5
☎ 01-253 2262
The house in which John Wesley lived and
died is now a museum, containing a large
collection of his personal possessions,
etc. Also **Wesley's Chapel** built 1778,
completely restored 1978. A new Musuem
of Methodism has been added.
Museum open Mon–Sat 10–4 and by
arrangement. Chapel open daily. Main
service 11am Sun followed by lunch &
tour of chapel and museum.
£1.50 (includes both museums).

P (street) ♿ (ground floor only) shop 🦮
(ex guide dogs) Ⓥ

EC2 City of London; Bank of England,
Liverpool Street Station

Guildhall Plan 3: **2** B4
☎ 01-606 3030
Rebuilt in 1411 but only the walls of the
great hall, porch and crypt survive from
the medieval building. It was severely
damaged in the Great Fire and the Blitz.
Restoration work, completed in 1954 was
carried out to designs by Sir Giles Scott.
Here the Court of Common Council, which
administers the city, meets and
entertains. The **Guildhall Library**
contains an unrivalled collection of books,
manuscripts, and illustrations on all
aspects of London. The **Guildhall Clock
Museum** with 700 exhibits illustrates 500
years of time keeping.
Guildhall open Mon–Sat 10–5, May–Sep,
BH & Sun 2–5 also; Guildhall Library open
Mon–Fri 9.30–5 (closed BH); Guildhall
Clock Museum open Mon–Fri 9.30–5
(closed BH).
Free.
♿ (ground floor only) 🦮

Museum of London London Wall Plan 3:
7 A4
☎ 01-600 3699 ext 240
The museum was formed by
amalgamating the former London
Museum and the Guildhall Museum. The
present purpose-built premises were
opened in 1976 and the museum is
devoted entirely to London and its people.
Everything on show contributes to the
story of London during the past 2,000
years. Included are treasures from the
City, a barber's shop from Islington,
sculptures from the Temple of Mithras, a
1930 Ford, Selfridge's lift, a medieval
hen's egg, a Roman bikini and the Great
Fire experience.
Open Tue–Sat 10–6, Sun 2–6 (Closed BH
& Xmas). Parties by arrangement.
Free.
P (200 yds) 🍽 (licensed) ♿ shop 🦮

Stock Exchange Plan 3: **11** B4
☎ 01-588 2355
The centre of industrial finance, where
stocks and shares in individual companies
are bought and sold. The trading floor
may be viewed from the gallery and
guides are present to describe the scene.
A colour film may be seen by prior
arrangement.
Open Mon–Fri 9.45–3.15 last guided tour
2.30. (Closed PH's). Parties must book in
advance.
Free.
🅿 ♿ shop 🦮

EC3 City of London; Monument, Tower
of London

178

Lloyds of London Lime St, Plan 3: **4** C4
☎ 01-623 7100

The world's leading insurance market move into a new headquarters building of advance design in May 1986. It incorporates a purpose built exhibition encompassing Lloyds 300 years in the City as well as a visitors viewing area.

Open to public from early Jun.

Open Mon–Fri, 10–4.

&. &. (by appointment) shop ✹

The Monument Monument St, Plan 3: **6** B3
☎ 01-626 2717

Erected by Wren and Hooke 1671–77 to commemorate the Great Fire of 1666, which is reputed to have started in nearby Pudding Lane. It stands 202ft high and from the railed-in summit, a climb of 311 steps, there is an extensive view.

Open Apr–Sep, Mon–Fri 9–6, Sat & Sun 2–6, Oct–Mar Mon–Sat 9–2 & 3–4. Details not confirmed for 1986.

✷ 50p (ch 25p).

P (Tower Hill Car Park) ✹

Tower of London Plan 3: **13** C3
☎ 01-709 0765

Begun by William the Conqueror in the 11th century in the south-east angle of the wall of Roman Londinium. The Keep or White Tower, which was built soon after the conquest, now contains the **Royal Armouries**. These consist of the national collection of arms and armour based on the great arsenal of Henry VIII. Four of Henry VIII's personal armours may be seen. There are also displays of tournament and sporting arms, arms and armour from the Middle Ages to the 17th century and oriental armour. Also the **Jewel House** where the crown jewels are displayed. Also the **Royal Fusiliers Museum**, containing uniforms, including those worn by George V as colonel-in-chief, regimental silver and china, four dioramas of famous battles, and campaign medals, among them 10 Victoria Crosses, including the prototype approved by Queen Victoria.

Open Mar–Oct, Mon–Sat 9.30–5, Sun 2–5; Nov–Feb, Mon–Sat 9.30–4. (Closed 1 Jan, Good Fri & 24–26 Dec. Jewel House closed Feb).

Admission fee payable.

P (½m) shop (Dept. of Environment)

EC4 City of London; Blackfriars, Cannon Street and Fleet Street

Dr Johnson's House 17 Gough Sq, Plan 2: **8** E5
☎ 01-353 3745

Gough Square was built circa 1700 and the timber used in the construction of the building is American white and yellow pine. Dr Johnson lived here (1749–1759) and here he compiled his famous English dictionary (a first edition is on display) and wrote The Rambler and The Idler. The

---

house was opened as a museum in 1914 and contains a fine collection of prints as well as letters and other relics.

Open May–Sep daily 11–5.30; Oct–Apr 11–5. (Closed Sun, BH, Xmas Eve & Good Fri).

✷ £1 (ch, students & pen 50p).

&. shop ✹

Middle Temple Hall The Temple Plan 2: **18** E4
☎ 01-353 4355

A fine example of Tudor architecture built during the reign of Queen Elizabeth I and completed about 1570. Hall features double hammer beam roof. Also stained glass showing shields of past readers. The most treasured possession is the 29ft-long high table, made from a single oak tree of Windsor Forest. Another table was made from timbers of the Golden Hind in which Sir Francis Drake, a member of the Middle Temple, sailed around the world. Portraits of George I, Elizabeth I, Anne, Charles I, Charles II, James, Duke of York and William III line the walls behind the high table.

Open Mon–Sat 10–12 & 3–4.30 (Closed BH).

Free.

&. ✹ ♿

Telecom Technology Showcase
135 Queen Victoria St, Plan 3: **12** A3
☎ 01-248 7444

Two display floors featuring the past, present and future of Britain's telecommunications. There are many working exhibits charting 200 years of progress from the earliest telegraphs, to satellites and optical fibres.

Open Mon–Fri 10–5. (Closed BH).

Free.

P &. shop ✹ (ex guide dogs)

N17 Tottenham

Bruce Castle Museum Lordship Ln, Plan 4: **5** E5
☎ 01-808 8772

An E-shaped part Elizabethan, part Jacobean and Georgian building, with an adjacent circular 16th-century tower, which stands in a small park. The museum contains sections on local history, postal history and the Middlesex Regiment, also known as the 'diehards'.

Open prior to Etr 1986 Tue–Fri 10–5; Sat 10–12.30 & 1.30–5 (Closed Sun, Mon & BH). From Etr 1986 daily 1–5 (Closed Good Fri, Xmas & New Years day).

Free.

&. shop ✹

Euston and King's Cross Stations

London Planetarium Marylebone Rd, Plan 1: **10** D6
☎ 01-486 1121 (Laserium 01-486 2242)

Here the night skies are projected in all their beauty onto the inside of the dome from the two-ton Zeiss instrument, to an accompanying commentary. An exhibition called 'The Astronomers' includes wax figures such as Einstein and Galileo in three-dimensional representations of their discoveries. Laser light concerts most evenings.

Open all year daily (ex 25 Dec) star shows 11–4.30.

Admission fee payable. Party 10+.

P (500 yds) ⬆ shop ✹

London Zoo (Regents Park) Plan 4: **33** D4
☎ 01-722 3333

One of the most comprehensive collections of animals in the world with over 8000 animals on view. Among the many world firsts that the zoo can claim are a reptile house opened in 1849, an aquarium in 1853 and an insect house in 1889. In recent years many new pavilions have been built including a giant walk-through aviary designed by Lord Snowdon. New Lion Terraces. The London and Whipsnade Zoos are supported by the most professionally complete veterinary and research services to maintain high animal management standards.

Open Mon–Sat 9–6 (Mar–Oct), 10–dusk in winter, Suns & BH close at 7 or dusk whichever is earlier (Closed Xmas day).

✷ £3.20 (ch 16 £1.60 ch under 5 free students £2.50 & pen £1.25).

Party 20+.

P (outer circle of Park after 11 and in car park 500 yds from main gate after 10) ⬆ (licensed) ♿ &. (ground floor & gardens only) shop ✹

Madame Tussaud's Marylebone Rd, Plan 1: **7** D6
☎ 01-935 6861

Founded in Paris, Madame Tussaud's Wax Exhibition settled in London in 1835. Exhibits include new versions of the tableaux and Chamber of Horrors, historical figures, HRH the Princess of Wales, kings, queens, sportsmen and other famous figures.

Open all year 10–5.30 (Closed Xmas day).

Admission fee payable. Party 10+.

P (500 yds) ⬆ &. shop ✹

NW3 Hampstead and Swiss Cottage

Fenton House Hampstead Grove, Plan 4: **13** C4
☎ 01-435 3471 →

A William and Mary house, built c.1693, set in walled garden. Collections include notable Oriental, Continental and English china, needlework, furniture and the Benton Fletcher Collection of early keyboard instruments. Some concerts in summer.

Open Mar, Sat & Sun 2pm–6pm; 31 Mar–Oct, Sat–Wed 11–6 (last admission 5). £1.70 (£1.30 Mon & Tue ex BH's).

(NT)

Keats House Keats Grove, Plan 4: **25** D4
☎ 01-435 2062

Regency house, former home of the poet Keats. Ode to the Nightingale was written in the garden. Manuscripts and relics.

Open all year Mon–Sat 10–1 & 2–6, Sun & BH 2–5. (Closed Good Fri, Etr Sat, May Day, 25–26 Dec & 1 Jan).

Free. Guided tours by appointment.

P (200 yds) & (ground floor only) shop ✖

Kenwood, Iveagh Bequest Hampstead Ln, Plan 4: **26** D4
☎ 01-348 1286

Mansion re-modelled c.1765 by Robert Adam, with fine grounds, bequeathed to the nation in 1927 by Lord Iveagh. Notable library, furniture, and works of art including paintings by Rembrandt, Hals, Vermeer, Reynolds and Gainsborough. Collections of 18th-century shoebuckles and jewellery. Summer exhibition. Concerts.

Open daily; Apr–Sep 10–7; Feb, Mar & Oct 10–5; Nov–Jan 10–4.

Free. (charges for special exhibitions).

P (limited) ⚏ & (ground floor & garden only) shop ✖

NW4 Hendon

Church Farm House Museum
Greyhound Hill, Plan 4: **6** C5
☎ 01-203 0130

Old gabled house, dating from 1660s, now museum of local interest. Period furnished kitchen and dining room. Changing exhibitions.

Open all year (ex Good Fri, 25 & 26 Dec, 1 Jan) Mon–Sat 10–1 & 2–5.30 (Tue 10–1 only), Sun 2–5.30.

Free.

⚠ & (garden only) shop ✖

NW8 St Johns Wood

Cricket Memorial Gallery Lord's Ground, Plan 4: **9** D4
☎ 01-289 1611

Founded about 1865, with collections of cricket bygones and 18th-century paintings of cricket. Collection of pictures and other exhibits, a library of cricket literature, enriched by the notable book collections of A L Ford and Sir Julien Cahn.

Open on match days Mon–Sat 10.30–5, other times by appointment.

London NW3
London SE1

50p (ch & pen 25p). Library open free of charge to students by appointment with the Curator.

P & (ground floor & grounds only) shop ✖

NW9 Colindale

Royal Air Force Museum Plan 4: **47** C5
Entrance via M1, A41 (Aerodrome Rd, off Watford Way) or A5 (Colindale Av, off Edgware Rd).
☎ 01-205 2266 ext 38

The museum, on the former Hendon airfield, covers all aspects of the history of the RAF and its predecessors. Over 40 aircraft are on display from the Bleriot XI to the 'Lightning'. Twelve galleries depict over 100 years of military aviation history. The Battle of Britain Museum has been built on a site adjacent to the main Museum. It contains British, German and Italian aircraft which were engaged in the great air battle of 1940. Also in the same complex is the vast new Bomber Command Museum which contains a striking display of famous bomber aircraft including the Lancaster, Wellington and Vulcan.

Open all year Mon–Sat 10–6, Sun 2–6. (Closed Good Fri, May Day, 24–26 Dec & 1 Jan).

RAF Museum free. Battle of Britain Museum £1 (ch & pen 50p). Bomber Command Museum £1 (ch & pen 50p). Party 20+.

⚠ ⚏ (licensed) ⛟ & shop ✖

NW10 Harlesden, Willesden

Grange Museum Neasden Ln (centre of roundabout), Plan 4: **18** C4
☎ 01-452 8311

Dating from around 1700, the building originally formed part of the outbuildings of a large farm and was later converted into a Gothic cottage. Permanent collections tell the story of the area that is now the London Borough of Brent. Changing temporary exhibitions, local history library, display on the British Empire Exhibition for which Wembley Stadium was built. Two period rooms of late 19th century and early 20th century, and reconstructed draper's shop.

Open all year (ex BH) Mon–Fri 12–5 (8pm Wed), Sat 10–5.

Free. Parties by advanced booking only.

⚠ & (ground floor & gardens only) shop ✖

SE1 Southwark

HMS Belfast Symons Wharf, Vine Lane, Tooley St, Plan 3: **3** C2
☎ 01-407 6434

This 11,000 ton cruiser, which is now part of the Imperial War Museum, is permanently moored in the Pool of London as a floating naval museum.

Open daily 20 Mar–Oct 11–5.50 last admission 5.20; Nov–19 Mar 11–4.30 last admission 4. (Closed Good Fri, May Day, 24–26 Dec & 1 Jan).

£2 (ch 5–16 & pen £1) Party.

⚠ ⚏ (summer only) shop ✖

Imperial War Museum Lambeth Rd, Plan 2: **12** E2
☎ 01-735 8922

Founded 1917 and established 1920 by Act of Parliament, this museum illustrates and records all aspects of the two World Wars and other military operations involving Britain and the Commonwealth since 1914. Extensive renovation and redevelopment will entail gallery closures from 1986 and a major interim exhibition on the two world wars is being mounted while the work is in progress. Various reference departments, open by appointment only.

Open all year, daily Mon–Sat 10–5.50, Sun 2–5.50. (Closed Good Fri, May Day, 24–26 Dec & 1 Jan).

Free.

P (meters) & shop ✖ (ex guide dogs)

The **London Dungeon** 28/34 Tooley St, Plan 3: **5** C2
☎ 01-403 0606

The world's only medieval horror museum. Vast dark vaults house strange and horrifying scenes of man's inhumanity to man in Britain's dark past. Awarded the British Tourist Authority award for Outstanding Tourist Enterprise. Viewing takes approx 1 hour.

Open all year, Apr–Sep 10–5.30, Oct–Mar 10–4.30. (Closed Xmas).

£3.50 (ch 14 & pen £2) Jun–Aug £3.80 (ch £2.20) Party 10+.

P (300 yds) ⚏ & shop ✖ ⓥ

Tower Bridge Walkway Plan 4: **54** E3
☎ 01-407 0922

The glass-covered walkway, 142ft above the Thames gives visitors panoramic views over London. Exhibitions illustrating the history and workings of the bridge are in both Towers. The original engine rooms may be seen on the South side of the bridge.

Open Apr–Oct 10–6.30; Nov–Mar 10–4.45 (last tickets sold 45 minutes before closing time). (Closed Good Fri, May Day, Xmas, New Years day).

£2 (ch 5 & pen £1, ch 5 free). Party.

P (100 yds) & shop ✖

Tradescant Trust Museum of Garden History St Mary-at-Lambeth, Lambeth Palace Rd, Plan 2: **19** D6
Enquiries to: The Tradescant Trust, 74 Coleherne Court, London SW5 0EF
☎ 01-373 4030

Historic building and newly made period knot garden containing 17th-century plants. Nearby stand the tombs of the John Tradescants (father & son) and Captain Bligh of the 'Bounty'. Temporary exhibitions.

Open Mon–Fri, 11–3; Sun 10.30–5. (Closed from 2nd Sun in Dec to 1st Sun in Mar).

Free.

P (50–150 yds) ⚏ ⚹ (ground floor & gardens only) shop

SE3 Blackheath

Rangers House Chesterfield Walk, Plan 4: **46** E3
☎ 01-853 0035

Suffolk collection of Jacobean and Stuart portraits housed in 18th-century villa, former home of Philip Stanhope, 4th Earl of Chesterfield. Collection contains a set of portraits by William Larkin, among the finest to survive from the Jacobean period and a small collection of Old Masters. Three first floor rooms house the Dolmetsch collection of musical instruments, on loan from the Horniman Museum. Also chamber concerts and poetry readings. Educational programme, holiday projects & workshop.

Open all year daily 10–5 (4pm Nov–Feb). (Closed Good Fri & 24–25 Dec).

Free.

P (limited) ⚹ (ground floor only) shop ✹

SE5 Camberwell

South London Art Gallery Peckham Rd, Plan 4: **51** E3
☎ 01-703 6120

Presents ten exhibitions a year. Exhibits include Victorian paintings and drawings; a small collection of contemporary British art; 20th-century original prints. A collection of topographical paintings and drawings of local subjects.

Open only when exhibitions are in progress, Tue–Sat 10–6, Sun 3–6 (Closed Mon).

London SE1
—
London SE10

Free.

P (nearby) shop ✹

SE9 Eltham

Eltham Palace Plan 4: **12** F2
☎ 01-859 2112 (ext 255). Advisable to contact Admin Officer before visit.

Noted for great hall with 15th-century hammer-beam roof. An old bridge spans the moat.

Open Nov–Mar, Thu & Sun 10.30–4; Apr–Oct, Thu & Sun 10.30–6. Opening arrangements subject to possible alteration.

Free.

(AM)

Winter Gardens Avery Hill Park, Plan 4: **60** F2
☎ 01-850 3217

Approximately 750 species of tropical and temperate plants in cold, temperate and tropical houses, a collection second only to the Royal Botanical Gardens at Kew. Nursery production unit open spring BH weekend. Tennis and putting available.

Open all year Mon–Fri 1–4; Sat, Sun & BH 11–4 (6pm summer). (Closed 1st Mon each month & 25 Dec).

Free.

△ ⚹

SE10 Greenwich

Cutty Sark Clipper Ship Greenwich Pier, Plan 4: **10** E3
☎ 01-858 3445

The Cutty Sark is a famous Tea and Wool Clipper built in 1869 and preserved in dry dock since 1957.

Open daily 10.30–5, Sun 2.30–5, 6pm in summer. (Closed 24–26 Dec & 1 Jan).

Admission fee payable.

P (600 yds) ⚹ (Tweendeck only) shop✹

Gipsy Moth IV Greenwich Pier, King Williams Walk, Plan 4: **16** E3
☎ 01-858 3445

The yacht in which Sir Francis Chichester sailed single-handed round the world in 1966–67, starting the fashion for 'Round the World' sailing races.

Open daily Apr–Oct 10.30–6.

Admission fee payable.

P (600 yds) ✹ ⌨

National Maritime Museum Romney Rd, Plan 4: **37** E3
☎ 01-858 4422 (Information Desk ext 221)

Fine collections illustrating man's relationship to the sea.

Open all year, daily Mon–Fri 10–5 (6pm summer), Sat 10–5.30 (6 in summer), Sun 2–5.30, 5 in winter. (Closed Good Fri, May Day, 24–26 Dec & 1 Jan).

✳ £1, combined ticket with observatory £1.50 (ch, students, unemployed, pen & disabled 50p, combined ticket 75p). Family ticket £4. Party 10+. Spaceworks Exhibition until Dec 86.

P (5 mins) ⚏ (licensed) ⚹ (ground floor only) shop ✹ (ex guide dogs)

Old Royal Observatory Plan 4: **40** E3
☎ 01-858 1167

In Greenwich Park, which was laid out in plans by Le Nôtre, famous French gardener of time of Louis XIV, the Observatory is part of National Maritime Museum. Exhibits of astronomical, horological and navigational interest. Actual work of observatory now carried out at Herstmonceux Castle.

Open all year daily Mon–Fri 10–5 (6pm summer), Sat 10–5.30 (6 in summer), Sun 2–5.30, 5 in winter. (Closed Good Fri, May Day, 24–26 Dec & 1 Jan).

✳ £1, combined ticket with museum £1.50 (ch, students, unemployed, pen & disabled 50p, combined ticket 75p). Family ticket £4. Party 10+. Planetarium gives public shows during school holidays, Tue, Thu, Fri 2.30 & 3.30; special programmes on Sat in summer →

(information from Schools Liaison Officer 01-858 4422).

P (opposite) & (ground floor only) shop ✖ (ex guide dogs)

Royal Naval College Plan 4: **49** E3
☎ 01-858 2154

Group of buildings designed by Webb (late 17th-century) and Wren (early 18th-century), with additions by Hawksmoor, Vanbrugh and Ripley. Formerly Naval Hospital, becoming College in 1873. Chapel rebuilt in 18th century, and Painted Hall ceiling by Sir James Thornhill.

Open all year (Painted Hall & Chapel only) daily (ex Thu) 2.30–5 (last admission 4.45pm). (Closed Xmas day).

Free.

P (500 yds) shop ✖

SE15 Peckham

Livesey Museum 682 Old Kent Rd, Plan 4: **31** E3
☎ 01-639 5604

Museum displays one major exhibition every year, dealing mainly with Southwark's past and present, including permanent exhibition of Southwark Street furniture in the courtyard.

Open when exhibition in progress, Mon–Sat 10–5.

Free.

P (200 yds) ⇶ & (ground floor only) shop ✖

SE17 Walworth

Cuming Museum 155/157 Walworth Rd, Plan 3: **1** A1
☎ 01-703 3324 ext 32

Contains Roman and medieval finds from the suburb of Southwark, south of London Bridge. Examples from the local 'Delft' pottery industry, items associated with Dickens and Michael Faraday (born locally in 1791), the equipment of a family dairy firm which served the neighbourhood for over 150 years. Also a collection relating to London superstitions.

Open all year Mon–Fri 10–5.30 (7pm Thu), Sat 10–5.

Free.

P (100 yds) shop ✖

SE18 Woolwich

Museum of Artillery in the Rotunda Repository Rd, Plan 4: **35** F3
☎ 01-856 5533 ext 385

Circular structure designed by John Nash, which stood at one time in St James's Park. It contains a very interesting collection of artillery.

Open all year, Apr–Oct, Mon–Fri 12–5, Sat & Sun 1–5; Nov–Mar, Mon–Fri 12–4, Sat & Sun 1–4 (Closed Good Fri, 24–26 Dec & 1 Jan).

Free.

⚠ ⇶ & (ground floor only) shop

London SE10
London SW1

Thames Barrier Centre Unity Way, Plan 4: **53A** F3
☎ 01-854 1373

Justifiably described as the 'Eighth Wonder of the World', the ⅓ mile span barrier built to save London from disastrous flooding is the World's largest movable flood barrier representing an extraordinary feat of British engineering. The nearby exhibition building has displays and an audio-visual programme explaining the flood threat and the construction of the £480 million project. Barrier gates raised for testing monthly.

Open daily 10.30–5 (6pm Apr–Sep). (Closed Xmas & New Year's Day).

Free.

⚠ ᗹ (licensed) ⇶ & (ex riverside) shop ✖ (ex guide dogs)

SE21 Dulwich

Dulwich Picture Gallery College Rd, Plan 4: **11** E2
☎ 01-693 5254

First public art gallery in England housed in building designed in 1814 by Sir John Soane. Notable collection of Old Masters, including works by Gainsborough, Poussin, Raphael, Rembrandt, Rubens and Watteau.

Open all year Tue–Sat 10–1 & 2–5, Sun 2–5 (Closed Mon).

60p (pen & students 30p ch 16 free).

P (street) & shop ✖

SE23 Forest Hill

Horniman Museum London Rd, Plan 4: **24** E2
☎ 01-699 2339

Ethnographical and large natural history collections including vivaria. Exhibition of musical instruments from all parts of the world. Extensive library and lectures and concerts in spring and autumn. Special exhibitions. Education Centre programmes.

Open all year Mon–Sat 10.30–6, Sun 2–6 (Closed 24–26 Dec).

Free.

P (100 yds) ᗹ shop ✖ (ex guide dogs)

SW1 Westminster St James's Park, Victoria Station, Knightsbridge, Lower Regent St

Banqueting House Palace of Whitehall, Plan 2: **2** C3
☎ 01-212 4785

Built in 1619, to a design by Inigo Jones, for James I. It is in severe classical style, and the interior is enriched by Rubens' paintings. During the 17th century London court life was centred here and many

---

historic events took place here, including the execution of Charles I in 1649, the restoration of Charles II, and the offer of the throne to Prince William of Orange and Princess Mary.

Open Tue–Sat 10–5, Sun 2–5. (Closed Good Fri & 24–26 Dec). May also be closed at short notice for government functions.

Admission fee payable.

& (Dept. of Environment)

Cabinet War Rooms Clive Steps, King Charles St, Plan 2: **5** C2
☎ 01-930 6961

The rooms comprise the most important surviving part of the underground emergency accommodation provided to protect Winston Churchill, his War Cabinet and Chiefs of Staff of Britain's armed forces against air attacks in the Second World War. Amongst the nineteen rooms are the Cabinet Room, the Transatlantic Telephone Room, the Map Room (where information about operations on all fronts was collected) and the Prime Minister's Room. The more important rooms have been left preserved intact since the War, others have been carefully restored to their wartime appearance.

Open Tue–Sun also Etr Mon, Spring BH & Summer BH 10–5.50 (last admission 5.15pm). (Closed Good Fri, May Day BH, Xmas Eve–Boxing Day & New Year's Day).

£2.50 (ch, students, unemployed & pen £1.25).

⚠ & shop ✖ (ex guide dogs)

Houses of Parliament Plan 2: **10** C2
☎ 01–219 3090 & 3100

A mid 19th-century building in Gothic style based on a design by Sir Charles Barry with additional detail by Augustus Pugin, the original building having been destroyed by fire in 1834. Two chambers are set either side of a central hall and corridor, the House of Lords to the south and the House of Commons to the north. The clock tower, 320ft high contains Big Ben, the bell weighing 13¾ tons and the Victoria tower stands 340ft high. The House of Commons suffered bomb damage in 1941 and a new chamber was constructed to the design of Sir Giles Gilbert Scott and opened in 1950.

To gain admission to the Strangers' Galleries join the queue at St Stephens entrance from approx. 4.30pm Mon–Thu, approx 9.30am Fri (House of Commons). From approx 2.30pm Tue, Wed & some Mons, 3pm Thu & 11am Fri (House of Lords) **or** by arrangement with MP (House of Commons) or Peer (House of Lords).

Free although guides require payment if employed.

P (100 yds) & (by arrangement) bookstall ✖ (ex guide dogs) ⚐

also **Westminster Hall**
☎ 01–219 3090

Built 1097–99 by William Rufus, it is the oldest remaining part of Westminster. The glory of the hall is the cantilever or hammerbeam roof, the earliest and largest roof of its kind in existence, built between 1394 and 1401.

Tours by arrangement with an MP only Mon–Thu am (Closed Sat & BH).

Free although guides require payment if employed.

P (100 yds) ♿ (by arrangement) 🐕 (ex guide dogs) 🚌

Imperial Collection (Crown Jewels of the World), Central Hall, Plan 2: **11** C2
☎ 01-222 0770

Includes over 150 reproductions of crowns, tiaras, orbs, sceptres, swords, garters, jewellery etc., together with reproductions of the most famous diamonds in the world. Many pieces on show are the only copies, as the originals were lost or destroyed in wars or revolutions. Among replicas from 15 countries can be seen the Crown of Charlemagne of the Holy Roman Empire; the Vatican Crown; Crowns and jewellery from Bavaria, Austria, Hungary, Prussia and Germany.

Open Jan–Sep, Mon–Sat 10–6. Oct–Dec, Mon–Sat 11–5. (Closed Good Fri & Xmas day).

£2 (ch £1).

P (meters) shop Ⓥ

Lancaster House Stable Yard, Plan 2: **13** A3

Built in the 19th century by the 'Grand Old Duke of York' and originally called 'York House'. It is now used as a centre for government hospitality.

Open Etr–mid Dec (ex during government functions), Sat, Sun & BH 2–6.

Admission fee payable.

⛺ (Dept of Environment)

Mall Galleries The Mall, Plan 2: **16** B3
☎ 01-930 6845

The exhibition galleries of the Federation of British Artists, where thirteen Art Societies administered by this organisation hold their annual exhibitions.

Open all year, daily 10–5.

£1 depending on exhibition (ch & pen half price). Gallery friends free.

P (metered) ♿ Ⓥ

Queens Gallery (Buckingham Palace, Buckingham Palace Rd, Plan 2: **25** A2
☎ 01-930 3007 ext 430 or 01-930 4832 ext 321

Items from the Royal Collection are housed in a building originally designed as a conservatory by John Nash in 1831, and later converted by Blore into a chapel in 1843. After suffering severe bomb damage in 1940, the building was eventually reconstructed in 1962, partly as the Private Chapel of Buckingham Palace and partly as an art gallery.

Exhibits display various aspects of the Royal Collection.

Open all year, Tue–Sat & BH Mon 11–5, Sun 2–5 (ex for short periods between exhibitions).

Admission fee payable.

⛺ ♿ (ground floor only) shop 🐕 (ex guide dogs)

Royal Mews Buckingham Palace Plan 2: **27** A2
☎ 01-930 4832 ext 634

Designed by John Nash and completed in 1825. The Royal Mews contains the state coaches, including the Gold State Coach made in 1762, with panels painted by the Florentine artist Cipriani. It has been used for every coronation since. The collection also includes the Irish State Coach, together with private driving carriages and royal sleighs. In the stables are kept the Windsor Greys and Cleveland Bay carriage horses.

Open Wed & Thu 2–4 (ex Royal Ascot week) and at other times when published.

✱ 30p (ch & pen 15p).

P (ground floor only) shop 🐕 (ex guide dogs)

Tate Gallery Millbank, Plan 2: **29** C1
☎ 01-821 1313 & Recorded Information 01-821 7128

Opened in 1897 the gallery houses the national collections of British painting of all periods, modern foreign painting and modern sculpture. There is also a large collection of contemporary prints. Hogarth, Blake, Turner, Constable and the Pre-Raphaelites are particularly well-represented in the British Collection and the Modern Collection traces the development of art from Impressionism through postwar European and American art including Abstract Impressionism and Pop, to the present day.

Open all year (ex Good Fri, May Day, 24–26 Dec & 1 Jan) 10–5.50, Sun 2–5.50.

Free (ex for special exhibitions). Free lectures, films and guided tours most days.

P (metered) 🍷 (licensed) 12–3 (closed Sun) 🍷 (coffee shop) 10.30–5.30, Sun 2–5.15 ♿ shop 🐕 (ex guide dogs)

SW3 Chelsea

Carlyle's House Cheyne Row Plan 4: **3** D3
☎ 01-352 7087

Built in 1708, it is a fine example of an 18th-century town house. Here Thomas Carlyle and his wife Jane lived from 1834 to 1865 and entertained among others Dickens, Thackeray, Browning and Tennyson. Many of Carlyle's letters, personal possessions and furniture are preserved, including an early piano on which Chopin played and the desk where Carlyle wrote his books.

Open 29 Mar–Oct, Wed–Sun & BH Mons 11–5.

£1.30. No parties over 20 persons.

⛺ (ex meter) (NT)

Chelsea Physic Garden 66 Royal Hospital Rd, Plan 1: **1** D6
☎ 01-352 5646

The second oldest botanic garden in England, about 50 years younger than the one at Oxford. It was set up in 1673 to grow plants for recognition and study for medicinal and general scientific use.

Open 13 Apr–19 Oct, Wed, Sun & BH, 2–5. Additional opening during Chelsea Flower Show week.

£1.50 (ch & students £1).

P ♿ shop

National Army Museum Royal Hospital Rd, Plan 1: **8** D1
☎ 01-730 0717

Contains a permanent chronological display of the history of the British, Indian and Colonial forces from 1485. Among the exhibits are uniforms, weapons, prints, photographs, manuscripts, letters, glass, china, silver and relics of British commanders and mementos of Britain's soldiers. There is a special display of the orders and decorations of the Duke of Windsor and also those of five great field marshals—Lord Roberts, Gough, Kitchener and Wolseley and Sir George White VC. The picture gallery includes portraits by Beechy, Romney and Lawrence, battle scenes and pictures of Indian regiments. The reading room is open Tue–Sat 10–4.30 to holders of readers' tickets, obtainable by written application to the Director.

Open all year 10–5.30, Sun 2–5.30. (Closed Good Fri, 5 May, 24–26 Dec & 1 Jan).

Free. Lectures etc for school parties.

P (metered) ♿ shop 🐕

SW7 South Kensington

Geological Museum Exhibition Rd Plan 1: **3** B3
☎ 01-589 3444

Established at present premises in 1935, The Geological Museum now forms part of the British Museum (Natural History). Its exhibits include a piece of the Moon and the largest exhibition on basic earth science in the world—The Story of the Earth. This is split into four main sections: the Earth in Space, which includes an exhibit showing that an observer 150 million light years away, looking through an immensely powerful telescope, would see dinosaurs roaming around in a Jurassic landscape; The Earth's Interior and Crust; Geological processes; and Geological Time. There is also a famous collection of fine gem-stones, showing →

them in their parent rock, in natural crystal form and in their final cut state. The regional geology of Great Britain, and ore deposits of the world are also displayed. Permanent exhibitions, British Fossils and Britain Before Man, and an exciting new exhibition Treasures of the Earth.

Open all year Mon–Sat 10–6, Sun 2.30–6. (Closed Good Fri, May Day, 24–26 Dec & 1 Jan).

Free.

P (metered) & (ex mezzanine floor) shop ✗

Natural History Museum Cromwell Rd
Plan 1: **9** B3
☎ 01-589 6323

In the Hall of Human Biology visitors can learn more about the way their bodies work, while 'British Natural History' shows over 2000 of our native plants and animals. A new exhibition 'Whales and their Relatives' explores the life of sea mammals. Other Permanent exhibitions include 'Man's Place in Evolution', 'Origin of Species', 'Dinosaurs and their living Relatives', and 'Introducing Ecology'. In other parts of the Museum there are many traditional displays of living and fossil plants and animals, minerals, rocks and meteorites from the national collections. Exhibits of special interest include a life-size model of a blue whale, the Cranbourne meteorite, a specimen of a coelacanth (a fish known as a living fossil) and the British bird pavilion where visitors can hear recordings of many different bird songs. As the museum is currently reorganising its public displays, some of the galleries may be temporarily closed. There are public films and lectures on Tue, Thu and Sat. Leaflet available on request.

Open daily Mon–Sat 10–6, Sun 2.30–6. (Closed Good Fri, May Day, 24–26 Dec & 1 Jan).

Free.

P (meters) ⬭ & (ex British Natural History Exhibition) shop ✗

Science Museum Exhibition Road
Plan 1: **11** B3
☎ 01-589 3456 ext 632

London SW7
—
London W1

Extensive collections, including aero-engines; agriculture, astronomy; atomic and nuclear physics; rail; road; sea and air transport; civil, electrical, marine and mechanical engineering; telecommunications, domestic appliances, 'Gas Industry' gallery, etc. Two galleries with items from the Wellcome Collection of the History of Medicine, galleries on Printing, Paper making and Lighting. Also a children's gallery with many working demonstrations. Exhibition on space technology opens mid Jul 1986. New gallery on Plastics.

Open all year, 10–6, Sun 2.30–6. (Closed Good Fri, May Day, 24–26 Dec & 1 Jan).

Free.

P (meters) ⬭ & shop ✗

Victoria and Albert Museum
Cromwell Rd, Plan 1: **12** C3
☎ 01-589 6371 ext 372. Recorded Information Service 01-581 4894

Queen Victoria laid the foundation stone for the present building in 1899 and the building designed by Sir Aston Webb was opened in 1909 by Edward VII. In it were placed the art treasures from the South Kensington Museum, which had been built under the direction of Prince Albert from money derived from the Great Exhibition of 1851. It now contains one of the world's outstanding collections of fine and applied arts. Special exhibitions include Constable paintings, the Raphael Cartoons and the Great Bed of Ware.

Open all year 10–5.50, Sun 2.30–5.50. (Closed Good Fri, May Day, 24–26 Dec & 1 Jan).

Donations—suggested £2 (Ch 12, Students & pen 50p).

P (Exhibition Rd & Cromwell Rd metered) ⬭ (licensed) & shop ✗

SW19 Wimbledon
Wimbledon Lawn Tennis Museum
Church Rd, Plan 4: **30** C2
☎ 01-946 6131

Museum, within the grounds of The All England Tennis Club, is the only one of its kind in the world and shows something of the games which preceded and helped in the conception of lawn tennis. Traces the development of the game over the last century. Also includes Library, the archives of which comprise collections, postcards, autographs and other ephemera. Audo visual theatre.

Open all year Tue–Sat 11–5, Sun 2–5. (Closed Mon & BHs).

£1.50 (ch & pen 75p).

⚠ shop ✗

Wimbledon Windmill Museum Windmill Rd
Plan 4: **59** C2
☎ 01-788 7655

This windmill built in 1817, houses the museum which displays the history of windmilling in pictures, models and the machinery and tools of the trade.

Open Etr–Oct, Sat, Sun & Bhs.

25 (ch 10p).

⚠ shop

W1 West End Piccadilly Circus, St Marylebone and Mayfair

Agnew's Galleries 43 Old Bond St, Plan 2: **1** A4
☎ 01-629 6176

London galleries established in 1860 as expansion of the Vittore Zanetti art business which originated in Manchester. Thomas Agnew, who entered the business in 1817, later became a partner. In 1932 a limited company, Thomas Agnew and Sons, was formed. Annual exhibitions include a water-colour exhibition devoted to English water-colours and drawings of the 18th and 19th centuries in Jan & Feb, and a selling exhibition of Old Master paintings from the 14th to 19th centuries. There are also exhibitions of French and English drawings from c1800 to the present day,

THE WIMBLEDON LAWN TENNIS MUSEUM
ALL ENGLAND CLUB, CHURCH ROAD, WIMBLEDON, SW19 5AE.
The new and enlarged Museum opened in June 1985. Fashion, trophies, replicas and memorabilia are on display representing the history of lawn tennis. An audio visual theatre shows films of great matches and the opportunity is now given to observe the famous Centre Court from the Museum. The Museum shop offers a wide range of attractive souvenirs.
Open Tuesday — Saturday 11am — 5pm
  Sunday 2pm — 5pm
Closed Mondays, Public & Bank Holidays and on the Friday, Saturday, and Sunday prior to the Championship. During the Championship. Admission to the Museum is restricted to those attending the tournament. Admission. Adults £1.50 Children & O.A.P.'s 75p.
Limited facilities are available for disabled visitors who are most welcome.

work by English painters of this century, and loan exhibitions in aid of charity. Many works pass through Agnew's on their way to famous art galleries and museums.

Open all year Mon–Fri, 9.30–5.30, 6.30pm Thu, during major exhibitions. (Closed BH).

Free, ex for some loan exhibitions.

P (Arlington St & Savile Row) & 🚪

Apsley House (see **Wellington Museum** entry).

London Diamond Centre 10 Hanover St, Plan 2: **14** A5
☎ 01-629 5511

A unique exhibition on diamonds where visitors can see diamond cutters and polishers practising their craft, a goldsmith creating jewellery exclusively for the London Diamond Centre and many other interesting aspects about the craft and industry. A feature is a walk-in diamond mine and a video on diamond mining. Another part of the exhibition displays a collection of replicas of some of the world's most historic diamonds, shapes in which diamonds can be cut, diamonds that glow under ultra-violet light and many other interesting aspects of the craft and industry.

Open Mon–Sat 9.30–5.30 (Oct–Apr Sat 9.30–1.30). Other times by arrangement.

£3.25 (ch £2.95) (includes a free memento in the form of a brilliant cut stone [not a diamond] in a presentation case, which value far exceeds the admission fee.

P shop ✖

Guinness World of Records
The Trocadero, Piccadilly Circus Plan 2: **9** B4
☎ 01-439 7331

The museum has been designated to bring to life many of the records within the famous Guinness Book of Records. It has six theme areas, corresponding with the sections of the book; the Human World, the Animal World, Our Planet Earth, Structures and Machines, the Sports World, the World of Entertainment and British Innovation and Achievement.

Open daily from 10am (last admission 10pm). (Closed Xmas day).

✳ £2.50 (ch 5–15 £1.50, pen £1.75). Party 10+.
P & shop ✖

Museum of Mankind
6 Burlington Gdns, Plan 2: **20** A4
☎ 01-437 2224 ext 43

Houses the exhibitions, library and offices of the ethnography department of the British Museum. Its collections embrace the art and material culture of tribal, village and other pre-industrial societies, from most areas of the world excluding Western Europe. Also archaeological collections from the Americas and Africa. A few important pieces are on permanent exhibition, but the museum's policy is to mount a number of temporary exhibitions

London W1
London W4

usually lasting for at least a year. A separate store in Shoreditch contains the reserve collection which can be made available for serious study by arrangement. Film shows and educational services also available.

Open all year Mon–Sat 10–5, Sun 2.30–6. (Closed Good Fri, May Day, 24–27 Dec & 1 Jan).

Free.

P (100 yds) shop ✖ (ex guide dogs)

Pollock's Toy Museum 1 Scala St, Plan 2: **23** B6
☎ 01-636 3452

The museum occupies two little houses joined together: the rooms are small and connected by narrow winding staircases. The collection is wide-ranging and covers items from all over the world. It includes a 19th-century toy theatre workshop, toy theatre with performances and slide shows, dolls, optical and mechanical toys, young girl's nursery, folk toys, English tin toys and teddy bears.

Open Mon–Sat 10–5. (Closed Good Fri, Etr Mon, Spring BH Mon, Summer BH Mon & Xmas).

Admission fee payable.

P (metered) & (ground floor only) shop ✖

Royal Academy of Arts (Burlington House, Piccadilly, Plan 2: **26** A4
☎ 01-734 9052

Founded in 1768 by George III. The summer exhibition, from May to Aug, shows works by living artists, and loan exhibitions of international importance are held throughout the year. Treasures of the academy include the Michelangelo Tondo.

Open daily 10–6 (incl Sun).

£1.50–£3 (ch, students, pen & group visitors reduced price).

🍴 ⚓ (licensed) & shop ✖

Wallace Collection Hertford House, Manchester Sq, Plan 1: **13** E6
☎ 01-935 0687

An outstanding collection of works of art bequeathed to the nation by Lady Wallace in 1897, displayed in the house of its founders. Includes pictures by Titian, Rubens, Gainsborough and Delacroix together with an unrivalled representation of 18th-century French art including paintings, especially of Watteau, Boucher and Fragonard, sculpture, furniture, goldsmiths' work and Sèvres porcelain. Also valuable collections of majolica, European and oriental arms and armour.

Open all year Mon–Sat 10–5, Sun 2–5. (Closed Good Fri, May Day, 24–26 Dec & 1 Jan).

Free.
P (meters) & shop ✖

Wellington Museum Apsley House, 149 Piccadilly, Plan 1: **14** E4
☎ 01-499 5676

Apsley House was designed by Robert Adam, built 1771–8 and extended by Benjamin Wyatt in 1828–1830, under the direction of the Duke of Wellington who purchased it in 1817. It was presented to the nation by the 7th Duke of Wellington in 1947, and opened to the public in 1952. Exhibits include famous paintings, silver, porcelain, orders and decorations and personal relics of the first duke (1769–1852); also Canova's great marble figure of Napoleon Bonaparte. An amusing collection of political caricatures on display.

Open all year 10–6, Sun 2.30–6. (Closed Mon, Fri, May Day, 24–26 Dec & 1 Jan).

80p (ch students & pen 40p).

P (meters) & ✖

W2 Bayswater, Paddington

London Toy & Model Museum October House, 21–23 Craven Hill, Plan 4: **32** C3
☎ 01-262 9450/7905

Victorian building housing one of the finest collections of commercially made toys and models with an emphasis on trains, cars and boats. Pleasant garden. Extensive garden railway.

Open Tue–Sat 10–5.30, Sun 11–5. (Closed PH ex BH Mons).

£1.80 (ch 15 & pen 60p students £1.20). Party.

P (meters) 🍴 & (ground floor & gardens only) shop ✖ Ⓥ

See advertisement on page 186

W3 Acton

Gunnersbury Park Museum Popes Ln, Plan 4: **19** B3
☎ 01-992 1612

Early 19th-century former Rothschild mansion, in fine park, now museum of local interest for the London Borough of Ealing and Hounslow showing archaeological discoveries, transport items, costume and topographical and social material. Rothschild coaches on display. Rothschild Victorian kitchens open to public on certain summer weekends. Crafts demonstrations and exhibitions.

Open Mar–Oct Mon–Fri 1–5, Sat, Sun & BH 2–6; Nov–Feb, Mon–Fri 1–4, Sat, Sun & BH 2–4. (Closed Good Fri & 24–26 Dec).

Free.
🍴 & (ground floor only) shop ✖

W4 Chiswick

Chiswick House Plan 4: **5** C3
Domed mansion, considered to be the finest example of Palladian architecture of Great Britain. Built 1725–30 with interior →

185

decoration by William Kent. It has now been well restored.

Open mid Mar–mid Oct, daily 9.30–6.30, mid Oct–mid Mar, Sun & Wed–Sat 9.30–4.

✻ 60p (ch & pen 30p).

⚠ ⚲ (AM)

Hogarth's House Hogarth Ln, Great West Rd, Plan 4: **23** C3
☎ 01-994 6757

17th-century house where Hogarth lived for 15 years, with engravings, drawings and other relics.

Open all year 11–6 (4pm Oct–Mar), Sun 2–6, 4pm Oct–Mar. (Closed Tue, Good Fri, 1st 2 wks Sep, last 3 wks Dec & 1 Jan).

Free.

P (50 yds)

W8 Kensington

Commonwealth Institute (Kensington High St, Plan 1: **2** A4
☎ 01-603 4535

Contains over 40 exhibitions depicting life in the countries of the Commonwealth. Also library, art gallery, and Arts Centre.

Open Mon–Sat 10–5.30, Sun 2–5. (Closed Good Fri, May Day, 24–26 Dec & 1 Jan).

Free in daytime, evening admission fee payable.

⚠ ⚲ (licensed) ⚹ shop ✖ (ex guide dogs)

London W4
—
London W14

Kensington Palace State Apartments & Court Dress Collection
Plan 1: **4** A4
☎ 01-937 9561

The Palace was acquired by King William III in 1689 and remodelled and enlarged by Sir Christopher Wren and is today still a Royal residence. Queen Victoria was born and brought up here. Contained within the state apartments are pictures and furniture from the royal collection. The redecorated Victorian rooms and the room devoted to the Great Exhibition can be seen. Also on view is a colourful new museum, the **Court Dress Collection.** Its exhibits provide a glimpse into a bygone age when 'society' was still exclusive, with displays of costumes worn at court from 1750 to the present day.

Open Mon–Sat 9–5, Sun 1–5. Last admission 4.30 pm. (Closed Good Fri, 24–26 Dec & 1 Jan).

Combined ticket £2 (ch & pen £1) Party 10+.

P (Bayswater Rd) ⚹ (ground floor only) shop ✖ (Dept. of Environment)

Linley Sambourne House
18 Stafford Ter, Plan 1: **6** A4
☎ 01-994 1019 (The Victorian Society)

The home of Linley Sambourne (1845–1910), chief political cartoonist at Punch. The magnificent artistic interior has survived almost unchanged. The fixtures and fittings have been preserved, together with many of Sambourne's own pictures.

Open Wed 10–4, Sun 2–5. Mar–Oct. £1.50. Parties at other times by arrangement.

P shop ✖ ⓥ

W14 West Kensington

Leighton House 12 Holland Park Rd, Plan 1: **5** A4
☎ 01-602 3316

Leighton House is a uniquely opulent and exotic example of High Victorian taste. Built for the President of the Royal Academy, Frederic, Lord Leighton, by George Aitchison, the main body of the house was completed in 1866. The fabulous Arab Hall, with its rare middle-eastern tiles, fountain and gilded decoration, is a 19th-century Arabian Nights' creation finished in 1879. Fine Victorian paintings by Lord Leighton and his contemporaries hang in the rooms, and there are three galleries for exhibitions of modern and historic art. The

quiet garden is ornamented with Lord Leighton's sculpture.

Open all year daily 10–5 (6pm during temporary exhibitions). Garden open Apr–Sep 11–5. (Closed Sun & BH).

Free.

P (street & ½ mile) ⌗ & (ground floor only) ✗

WC1 Bloomsbury, Holborn

British Museum Great Russell St
Plan 2: **4** C6
☎ 01-636 1555

Founded in 1753, one of the great museums, showing the works of man from all over the world from prehistoric to comparatively modern times. The galleries are the responsibility of the following departments: Egyptian; Greek and Roman; Western Asiatic; Prehistoric and Romano-British; Medieval and Later; Coins and Medals; Oriental; Prints and drawings. Each year, special exhibitions focus more detailed attention on certain aspects of the collections. Programmes on request. Gallery talks (Mon–Sat) Lectures (Tue–Sat) and Films (Tue–Fri). Children's trail at all times.

Open all year, daily 10–5, Sun 2.30–6. (Closed Good Fri, May Day, 24–26 Dec & 1 Jan).

Free.

London W14
—
London WC2

P ⊉ (licensed) & shop ✗ (ex guide dogs)

Courtauld Institute Galleries Woburn Sq, Plan 2: **6** B6
☎ 01-387 0370 & 01-580 1015

The galleries of London University contain the most important collection of Impressionist paintings in Britain, including work by Monet, Renoir, Degas, Cézanne, Van Gogh, Gauguin and Toulouse-Lautrec. Also Princes Gate Collection of Old Master paintings and drawings, including works by Bernardo Daddi, the Master of Flemalle, Pieter Bruegel, Michelangelo and Rubens.

Open all year Mon–Sat 10–5, Sun 2–5. (Closed Etr, Xmas & most BH).

✳ £1 (ch, pen & students 50p).

P (meters in Gordon Sq) ✗

Dickens House 48 Doughty St
Plan 2: **7** D6
☎ 01-405 2127

Dickens lived here during his twenties and here completed Pickwick Papers and wrote Oliver Twist and Nicholas Nickleby. Pages of the original manuscripts of his

---

early books and others are on view together with valuable first editions in the original paper parts of his works, his special marriage licence; his family Bible which contains a personal record of his sons and daughters and many other personal relics. Entrance includes the Suzannet Rooms.

Open daily 10–5, last admission 4.30 pm. (Closed Sun, BH, Good Fri & Xmas wk).

£1 (ch 16 50p, pen & students 75p). Families £2.

P & (ground floor only) shop ✗ ⓥ

WC2 Covent Garden, Leicester Square, Strand and Kingsway

British Crafts Centre
43 Earlham St, Plan 2: **3** C5
☎ 01-836 6993

Programme of special exhibitions and retail display including wallhangings, furniture, studio ceramics, pottery, wood, jewellery etc. Books and magazines for craft and design.

Open all year Mon–Fri 10–5.30, Sat 11–5. (Closed Sun, Mon & BH).

Free.

P (500 yds) & (ground floor only) ✗

London Transport Museum The Piazza, Covent Garden, Plan 2: **15** C4
☎ 01-379 6344

Housed in the former Flower Market in →

THE DICKENS HOUSE MUSEUM & LIBRARY
48 DOUGHTY STREET, LONDON, WC1N 2LF.

Whilst living at 48 Doughty Street, Dickens finished *Pickwick Papers* and wrote *Oliver Twist* and *Nicholas Nichleby*. Here may be seen the study in which this young man, in his early twenties, wrote these books and created such immortal characters as Fagin, Bill Sykes, the Artful Dodger, the Squeers and Crummles families and wrote the famous Fanny Squeers letter. Pages of the original manuscripts of his early books and others are on view, together with valuable first editions in the original paper parts of most of his works. Here also is a collection of several hundreds of his letters; his special marriage licence; his family Bible with his personal record of his sons and daughters, two of whom were born in this house; the reading desk he used on all his Reading Tours and many personal relics. It was here, too, that Dickens entertained, in the dining room and drawing room, many of the literary and artistic celebrities of his time and where his lifelong friendship with his biographer, John Forster started. Entrance to the House includes the Suzannet Rooms containing the unique Suzannet collection.
Open to the public on weekdays 10-5. Closed Sns & Bank Hols.
Adults £1, Students 75p, Children 50p, Families £2. Groups by arrangement. Tel. 01-405 2127.

London Transport Museum in Covent Garden
MAKE IT YOUR NEXT STOP

Come and 'drive' a modern bus, a tram and an Underground train.

See the horse buses, motor buses, trams, trolleybuses, steam and electric Underground trains.

See gazetteer entry for admission details.

Covent Garden. The museum tells the story of the development of London's transport from its earliest beginnings right up to the present day. Vehicles include steam locomotives, trams, buses, trolleybuses, railway coaches and horse buses, there are also extensive displays using working and static models, posters, and audio-visual material. One can 'drive' a modern bus, a tram and a tube train. A reference library is available by appointment. Film shows and other activities at weekends. 'Underground women' 9 Dec 85–6 May 86 and 'Metroland' 22 May–27 Nov.

Open daily 10–6, last admission 5.15pm. (Closed Xmas).

✱ £2.20 (ch 16 students, unemployed & pen £1). Disabled free. Family ticket £5. Party 20 + .

P (metered—free at wknds after 1.30pm Sats) ⚲ (daily) ᶜ shop ✖ (ex guide dogs)

National Gallery Trafalgar Sq
Plan 2: **21** C4
☎ 01–839 3321 & recorded information: 01-839 3526

Founded by vote of Parliament in 1824, but was first opened in the present building in 1838. The gallery houses the national collection of masterpieces of European painting from the 13th to 19th century. Collection includes van Eyck's Arnolfini Marriage, Velazquez's The Toilet of Venus, Leonardo da Vinci's cartoon: The Virgin and the Child with SS Anne and John the Baptist, Rembrandt's Belshazzar's Feast, Titian's Bacchus and Ariadne, and many more. Lunchtime lectures and guided tours daily; quizzes and worksheets available for children. Constantly changing programme of exhibitions, usually highlighting certain aspects of the collection.

Open daily Mon–Sat 10–6, Sun 2–6. (Closed Good Fri, May Day, 24–26 Dec & 1 Jan).

Free.

P (50 yds in Whitfield St) ⚲ (licensed) ᶜ shop ✖

London WC2
Longleat House

National Portrait Gallery 2 St Martin's Pl, Plan 2: **22** C4
☎ 01-930 1552

Contains national collection of portraits of the famous and infamous in British history, including paintings, sculpture, miniatures, engravings, photographs, and cartoons. Special exhibitions several times a year.

Open all year 10–5, Sat 10–6 & Sun 2–6. (Closed Good Fri, May Day, 24–26 Dec & 1 Jan).

Free (ex special exhibitions).

P (100 yds in Orange St) shop ✖

Public Record Office Museum Chancery Ln, Plan 2: **24** E5
☎ 01-405 0741

The Public Record Office contains records of central government dating from the Norman Conquest to the present day. The museum is at present closed but will re-open Apr 86 with a 900th anniversary exhibition for Domesday Book.

Open Mon–Sat 10–6. Parties at other times by arrangement.

£2.50 (reductions for ch, pen & unemployed) Party.

P (metered at Lincoln's Inn Fields) ᶜ shop ✖ ⇎

The Sir John Soane's Museum 13 Lincoln's Inn Fields, Plan 2: **28** D5
☎ 01-405 2107

The house of Sir John Soane (1753–1837), the architect, built in 1812 and containing his collections of antiquities, sculpture, paintings, drawings, and books, including the Sarcophagus of Seti I (1292 BC), The Rake's Progress and the Election series of paintings by William Hogarth. Architectural Drawings Collection open by appointment.

Open all year (ex BH) Tue–Sat 10–5.

Free.
⚠ ᶜ (ground floor only) ✖

Gazetteer

continued
LONDON COLNEY
Hertfordshire
Map **4** TL20

Mosquito Aircraft Museum Salisbury Hall
☎ Bowmansgreen (0727) 22051 (5m S of St Albans on A6)

Eighteen De Havilland aircraft including three Mosquitos, Vampire, Venom and Horsa aircraft.

Open Etr–Oct, Sun 10.30–5.30 also Jul–Sep, Thu 2–5.30.

75p (ch 25p).
⚠ ᶜ shop

LONG CRENDON
Buckinghamshire
Map **4** SP60

Courthouse (2m N of Thame)
Partly half-timbered 14th-century building, probably at one time a wool store.

Upper-storey open 29 Mar–Sep, Wed 2–6. Sat, Sun & BH Mons 11–6.

60p.
(NT)

LONGLEAT HOUSE
Wiltshire
Map **3** ST84

Entrance on Warminster – Frome Rd A362
☎ Maiden Bradley (09853) 551

Built for Sir John Thynne in 1580 and decorated in the Italian Renaissance style during the 19th century, with fine libraries, state rooms, ceilings, pictures and furniture. Safari Park, summer only, with hundreds of wild animals. Outstanding views from Heaven's Gate and Sheerwater Lake. Gardens designed by Russell Page. Victorian kitchens, Maze, BBC 'Dr Who' exhibition, and Dolls Houses.

House open Etr–Oct daily 10–6, Nov–Etr daily 10–4. (Closed 25 Dec.) Safari Park closed in winter.

House £2 (ch £1 pen £1.50). Discount ticket for all attractions £6 (Ch £4, pen £5). Safari Park prices not confirmed for 1986.

🅰 ⟐ (licensed) ⊞ ᕕ (ground floor & gardens only) shop & garden centre

LONG MELFORD
Suffolk
Map 5 TL84

Kentwell Hall
☎ Sudbury (0787) 310207

A mellow redbrick Tudor manor surrounded by a broad moat. Externally little altered with E-plan and inner courtyard intact. The efforts being made to save this delightful house and the fact it is once again a thriving family home give Kentwell its unique flavour. Additional attractions include a brick paved mosaic maze, rare breed farm animals, farm implements, bygones and craft tools. Exhibition of Tudor style costumes.

Open 2–6; Etr Fri–Tue; 2 Apr–19 Jun Wed, Thu & Sun; Closed 22 Jun–13 Jul for Historical recreation of Tudor domestic life (special rates apply); 16 Jul–30 Sep Wed–Sun. Also BH Sat, Sun & Mon 12–6.

£2 (ch 5–16 £1 pen £1.40 Thu only). Parties 20+ pre-booked.

🅰 ⟐ ᕕ (ground floor & gardens only) shop ✹

Melford Hall
A turreted brick Tudor mansion, little changed since 1578 with the original panelled banqueting hall, an 18th-century drawing-room, a Regency library and a Victorian bedroom. Fine furniture and Chinese porcelain and a special Beatrix Potter display.

Open 29 Mar–28 Sep, Wed, Thu, Sun & BH Mon 2–6.

£1.50 (ch 70p). Party 15+.

✹ (NT)

LONG WITTENHAM
Oxfordshire
Map 4 SU59

Pendon Museum
(3m N of Didcot, 1m SW of Clifton Hampden at W end of village)
☎ Clifton Hampden (086730) 7365 (for open times only).

Detailed and historically accurate model railway and village scenes, showing the English countryside as it was in the 1930s.

Open Sat & Sun afternoons & Summer BH 11–6 (Closed Xmas).

✳ £1 (ch 15 & pen 60p ch 4 free).

🅰 (limited) ⟐ shop ✹ (ex guide dogs)

Longleat House
—
Lowestoft

LOOE
Cornwall
Map 2 SX25

The Monkey Sanctuary
Murrayton (3m ENE off B3253)
☎ (05036) 2532

Seen in a wooded sanctuary is this rare Amazon Woolly monkey species, which is also bred here. Talks are given morning and afternoon, with indoor meetings in rainy weather. Visitors advised to bring children under 4 on dry days only. Monkeys actually meet the visitors.

Open from Sunday before Etr for 2 weeks, then 1st Sunday in May–Sep daily 10.30–6.

£2 (ch £1 pen £1.30).

🅰 ⟐ ᕕ ✹ (car park only)

LOTHERTON HALL
West Yorkshire
Map 8 SE43
(10m E of Leeds, off B1217, near Aberford)
☎ Leeds (0532) 813259.
(Enquiries for Bird Garden 645535)
The Edwardian home of the Gascoigne family, now a country house museum, with furniture, pictures, silver and ceramics from Gascoigne collection and works of art from Leeds collections. There is a gallery of Oriental art and a display of British fashion, contemporary crafts and special exhibitions. An audio-visual presentation is available in the house. Edwardian garden, bird garden, and deer park.

Open May–Sep, Tue–Sun 10.30–6.15 or dusk; Thu until 8.30. Also open BH Mon.

55p (ch & pen 20p, students with union card free).

🅰 ⟐ (licensed) ⊞ ᕕ (ground floor only) shop ✹ (park only)

LOUGHBOROUGH
Leicestershire
Map 8 SK51

Great Central Railway Great Central Rd
☎ (0509) 230726 or 216433

Operational private steam railway running over five miles from Loughborough Central to Rothley, all trains calling at Quorn and Woodhouse. Museum and locomotive depot at Loughborough Central. Buffet car on trains, restaurant as advertised. Leisurerail Centre. Etr Sat–Mon 'Road/Rail '86' and Sep 6 & 7 'Road/Rail Diesel '86'.

Open Sat, Sun & BH Mon & Tue, also Wed May–Sep. (Closed Good Fri & 25 Dec).

£2 (ch & pen £1). Family ticket 2 adults & 3 ch £5.50.

🅰 at Quorn ⟐ (Loughborough Central and Rothley) ᕕ shop ⓥ

LOWER BEEDING
West Sussex
Map 4 TQ22

Leonardslee Gardens
(at S junction of A279 & A281)
☎ (040376) 212

World renowned spring garden with magnificent rhododendrons and azaleas in a lake-filled valley with delightful views and reflections.

Open 19 Apr–15 Jun 10–6; 21 Jun–28 Sep wknds only 2–6 & Oct wknds only 10–5.

May £2.20 (ch £1), other times £1.50 (ch £1). Party.

🅰 ⟐ ᕕ (garden only) shop & garden centre ✹

See advertisement on page 190

LOWESTOFT
Suffolk
Map 5 TM59

East Anglia Transport Museum
Chapel Rd, Carlton Colville
☎ Norwich (0603) 625402
Situated on a 3-acre site containing a range of historic cars, commercial vehicles, trams, buses and trolleybuses, in addition to various items of transport interest. A tram service operates during opening hours, also a narrow-gauge railway.

Open Etr, wknds & BH May–Sep, Sat 2–4, Sun & BH 11–5, Aug Mon–Fri 2–4.

£1 (ch 5–14 50p, pen 70p) Includes tram ride. Party.

🅰 ⟐ ᕕ (ground floor only) shop

Maritime Museum
Sparrows Nest Park, Whapload Rd
☎ (0502) 61963
The museum houses models of fishing and commercial ships, old and new, a lifeboat display and art gallery. Also shipwrights' tools and fishing gear etc.

Open May–Sep, daily 10–5. Other times by arrangement.

25p (ch 15, students & pen 15p).

P (50yds) ᕕ (ground floor only) shop

Royal Naval Patrol Service Association (Naval Museum) Sparrows Nest Gdns
☎ (0502) 86250
The museum includes collections of hundreds of photographs from World War II, models of minesweepers and naval ships, war relics, war medals, naval uniforms and the 'Victoria Cross' room.

Open Etr BH & May–Oct, daily 10–12 & 2–4.30. Coach parties by appointment. Free.

🅰 ⟐ (licensed) ᕕ (ground floor only) shop

189

LOWTHER
Cumbria
Map **12** NY52

Lowther Park
(5m S of Penrith off A6)
☎ Hackthorpe (09312) 523

Deer, rare breeds of cattle and sheep can be viewed in a wild and natural setting. Leisure park for all the family. Adventure playground.

Open Etr–mid Sep, daily 10–5.

✳ £2 (pen £1.50).

⚠ ⴲ ⴺ shop ✖

LUCTON
Hereford and Worcester
Map **3** SO46

Mortimer's Cross Water Mill

18th-century undershot-type watermill which was working until 1940.

Open Apr–Sep, Thu only 12–5.

✳ 30p (ch & pen 15p).
(AM)

LUDGERSHALL
Wiltshire
Map **4** SU25

Ludgershall Castle (7m NW of Andover on A342)

Norman motte and bailey castle retaining

Lowther
—
Luton

---

large earthworks and flint walling of later royal castle.

Open all reasonable times.

Free.

ⴺ (part of site only). (AM)

LUDLOW
Shropshire
Map **7** SO57

Ludlow Castle
☎ (0584) 3947

Ruined castle, one of England's most important ancient monuments. The present structure dates from the 11th to 16th century including tower, great hall and chamber.

Open May–Sep daily 10–6.30; Oct–Nov & Feb–Apr 10.30–4. (Closed Dec & Jan).

60p (ch 16 30p).

P (50 yds) ⴺ (ground floor only) ✖

Ludlow Museum Butter Cross
☎ (0584) 3857

New displays tell the story of the foundation of a planned Norman town and its subsequent importance as the capital

---

of the Marches of Wales; a Georgian residential centre and a Victorian market town.

Open 24 Mar–27 Sep Mon–Sat 10.30–1 & 2–5. Also Sun 10.30–1 & 2–5 Jun–Aug only.

35p (ch & pen free).

P (200 yds) shop ✖

LUTON
Bedfordshire
Map **4** TL02

Luton Hoo Entrance at Park St gates
☎ (0582) 22955

Magnificent Wernher Collection of art treasures including tapestries and pictures; also Russian Fabergé jewellery, in a country mansion designed originally by Robert Adam.

Open 22 Mar–12 Oct, Mon, Wed, Thu, Sat & Good Fri 11–5.45; Sun 2–5.45 (gardens 6pm).

Houses and gardens £2 (ch £1). Gardens only £1 (ch 50p).

⚠ ⵊ (licensed) ⴲ ⴺ shop ✖ (NGS)

Museum and Art Gallery Wardown Park
☎ (0582) 36941

Collections illustrate natural history, culture, and industries of Luton and Bedfordshire with particular reference to

---

Leonardslee Gardens
Lower Beeding, Nr. Horsham, Sussex
Telephone: 040 376 212

Rhododendrons and Azaleas flowering in spring in a beautiful lake-filled valley, with fabulous views and reflections.

OPEN: Spring 19 April — 15 June Every day 10am - 6pm
Summer 21 June — 28 Sept Weekends only 2pm - 6pm
Autumn October weekends 10am - 5pm

ADMISSION CHARGES:
May — Adults £2.20: Children £1: Coach parties £1.80
All other times: Adults £1.50: Children £1: Coach Parties £1.20. Coach parties welcome by prior arrangement.

FREE PARKING   NO DOGS PLEASE   CAFETERIA
*Leonardslee Gardens are situated at juction of A279 & A281
4½ miles south-east of Horsham.*

straw hat and pillow lace trade. 'Luton Life' gallery includes a reconstructed 'street' display.

Open Mon–Sat 10.30–5, Sun 1.30–6 (1.30–5 in winter). (Closed Sun Dec–Jan, Xmas & New Years day).

Free.

▲ ♿ (ground floor only) shop ✕ ,

LYDDINGTON
Leicestershire
Map **4** SP89

Bede House

Former home of Bishops of Lincoln, converted into hospital, or bede house, by Lord Burghley in 1602.

Open, see end of gazetteer. (Apr–Sep only).

✱ 50p (ch 16 & pen 25p).

(AM)

LYDFORD
Devon
Map **2** SX58.

Lydford Castle Midway between Okehampton & Tavistock off A386

Remains of mid 12th-century stone keep, altered a century later. The lower floor was once a prison and the upper floor became Stannary Court to administer local tin mines.

Open all reasonable times.

Free.

▲ (AM)

Lydford Gorge (8m N of Tavistock on unclass rd)
☎ (082282) 320

Scooped into succession of potholes by River Lyd, the gorge emerges into steep, oak-wooded valley. 90ft high White Lady Waterfall.

Open 28 Mar–Oct, daily 10.30–6.

£1.20. Party.

shop (NT)

LYDIARD PARK
Wiltshire
Map **4** SU18
(1m N of M4 (junc 16) on unclass rd)
☎ Swindon (0793) 770401

Fine Georgian mansion set in pleasant park, together with the adjoining parish church of St Mary, which contains memorials to the St John family.

Open Weekdays 10–1 & 2–5.30. Sun 2–5.30. (Closed Good Fri & Xmas).

Free.

▲ ☕ Ħ ♿ shop ✕

LYDNEY
Gloucestershire
Map **3** SO60

Dean Forest Railway
(1m N at New Mills on B4234)
☎ Dean (0594) 43423

A number of locomotives, coaches, wagons and railway equipment on show at Norchard just outside Lydney. Also guided tours available by arrangement. Preservation Rally 19 Oct '86. Santa Specials Dec 7, 14 & 21 '86.

Open daily for static display. Steam days BH Sun & Mon. 16 Mar, 20 Apr & 18 May, every Sun Jun–Sep & every Wed in Aug.

£1.20 (ch & pen 70p). Party 20+. Prices include unlimited train rides (steam days only).

▲ ☕ ♿ shop

LYME REGIS
Dorset
Map **3** SY39

Lyme Regis Museum Bridge St
☎ (02974) 3370

Small museum preserving old fire engine of 1706, prints, documents, old lace exhibition, an extensive collection of geological specimens and local history exhibits. Also on display is a remarkable recent collection of fossils from the Blue Lias rock, including several ichthyosaurs.

Open Apr–Oct, Mon–Sat 10.30–1, 2.30–5, Suns 2.30–5.

✱ 30p (ch & students 10p).

P (100 yds) shop ✕

LYMPNE
Kent
Map **5** TR13

Lympne Castle
☎ Hythe (0303) 67571

Restored Norman to 15th-century structure, modernised in 1905, once owned by Archdeacons of Canterbury. Gardens have extensive views over Romney Marsh and across Channel to French coast.

Open Jun–Sep & BH daily 10.30–6. Other times by arrangement.

✱ 75p (ch 20p).

▲ Ħ shop

Port Lympne Zoo Park, Mansion and Gardens
☎ Hythe (0303) 64646

Many different animals including, Indian elephants, wolves, rhinos, African leopards, Siberian and Indian tigers, monkeys and chimpanzees. Also there are safari trailer rides through animal paddocks (visitors are advised to check this in advance). The mansion was built by architect Sir Herbert Baker. Many of the original internal features have survived, the most notable being the recently-restored 'Rex Whistler Tent Room', Moroccan patio, and hexagonal library where the Treaty of Paris was signed after the First World War. There is also the long hall with concentric patterned marble, mosaic floor, and 15 acres of spectacular gardens.

Open daily 10–5 (Closed Xmas day).

✱ £3 (ch & pen £2). Party.

▲ ☕ Ħ ♿ (ground floor only) shop ✕

See advertisement on page 192

LYNTON
Devon
Map **3** SS74

Lyn and Exmoor Museum St Vincent's Cottage

History of life of Exmoor housed in →

THE WERNHER COLLECTION, LUTON HOO
LUTON, BEDFORDSHIRE LU1 3TQ
HOUSE AND GARDENS OPEN
March 22nd - October 12th 1986.
Mon.Wed.Thurs.Sat and Good Friday 11am-5.45pm.
Admission £2.00 Gardens £1.00.
Children Half Price.
Reduced Party Rates by Prior Arrangements
Licensed Restaurant
AN EXHIBITION TRACING THE WERNHER FAMILY INVOLVEMENT WITH LUTON HOO, THEIR CONNECTIONS WITH HORSE RACING AND THE HISTORY OF THE HOUSE.
Further details from the administrator
Tel. Luton (0582) 22955.

restored 17th-century building. One of the oldest in resort with unique slab roof. Exhibition of old Exmoor arts, crafts and implements and reconstruction of an Exmoor kitchen. Scale models of old Lynton/Barnstaple railway and lifeboat.

Open Apr–Sep, Mon–Fri 10–12.30 & 2–5, Sun 2–5. (Closed Sat). Details not confirmed for 1986.

✳ 30p (ch 14 10p).

P (100 yds) ✖

LYVEDEN NEW BIELD
Northamptonshire
Map **4** SP98

(4m SW Oundle)
☎ Benefield (083 25) 358

Shell of unfinished two storeyed Greek Cross house, designed c. 1600 by Sir Thomas Tresham to symbolise the Passion.

Open daily. Party by arrangement with the Custodian.

60p (ch 30p).

P (½m) 🚗 (NT)

MACCLESFIELD
Cheshire
Map **7** SJ79

Hare Hill (4m NW off B5087)
Walled garden with pergola, rhododendrons and azaleas; parkland.

Lynton — Machynlleth

Open Apr–end Oct Wed, Thu, Sun & BH Mons 2–5.30. Parties by written appointment with the Head Gardener.

80p Dogs on leads only.

(NT)

Macclesfield Museum and Art Gallery
West Park, Prestbury Rd
☎ (0625) 24067

Contains a notable collection of Egyptian antiquities, oil paintings, and sketches including work by CF Tunnicliffe ARA and Landseer, and drawings and prints of a topographical nature. Also a small silk exhibition and a stuffed Giant Panda.

Open Etr Sat–Sep, Tue–Sun 2–4.30; Oct–Sat before Etr, Sat & Sun & BH 2–4.30.

Free.

🅿 ✖

Paradise Mill Working Silk Museum
Old Park Ln
☎ (0625) 618228

A typical Victorian silk mill, the Jacquard handlooms in their original setting are being restored to demonstrate the skills of a dying craft. Supporting exhibitions give

---

an impression of working conditions in the 1930's.

Open Tue–Sun 2–5, also BH Mon. (Closed Good Fri, Xmas & New Years day).

80p (ch & pen 40p). Family ticket £2 Parties by arrangement.

P (100 yds). 🅿 ♿ (by arrangement) shop ✖ (ex guide dogs)

MACHYNLLETH
Powys
Map **6** SH70

Centre for Alternative Technology
☎ (0654) 2400

An old slate quarry overlooking Snowdonia National Park, a working demonstration independent of mains services, showing the possibilities of living with only a small share of the earth's dwindling resources, and creating a minimum of pollution and waste. Research, low energy studies, monitoring of equipment, housing and horticulture. Demonstrations of windpower, solar energy and vegetable growing. Residential courses available throughout the year.

Open daily 10–5 or dusk (Closed Xmas).

£1.75 (ch 70p, under 5 free, pen, students & unemployed £1).

🅿 ♿ 🚻 ♿ shop & garden centre ✖ Ⓥ

MADRON
Cornwall
Map **2** SW43

Trengwainton Garden
(2m W of Penzance, on B3312)

Gardens displaying a magnificent collection of shrubs, including magnolias and rhododendrons. Walled garden containing tender and sub-tropical plants not grown elsewhere in England.

Open Mar–Oct, Wed–Sat also BH 11–6.

£1.30.

(NT)

MAESGWM
Gwynedd
Map **6** SH72

Maesgwm Visitor Centre
☎ Ganllwyd (034140) 666

Located just off A470, 8 miles north of Dolgellau in the heart of Coed y Brenin. The centre depicts the forest environment life and work of this great forest and also the story of the local gold mines. Completely refurbished in 1985. Guide leaflets available for the nearby trail, numerous picnic places and 50 miles of waymarked walks.

Open Etr–Sep, daily 10–5.

A parking fee will be levied for 1986.

 ♿ ⛲ ♿

MAIDENHEAD
Berkshire
Map **4** SU88

The Courage Shire Horse Centre
Cherry Garden Lane, Maidenhead Thicket (off A4, ½m W of A4/A423/A423M jct)
☎ Littlewick Green (062882) 3917

Set in attractive Berkshire countryside. Up to twelve Shire horses, each weighing around a ton, can be seen in the timber-built stables. Comprehensive display room giving history of the Shire horse and showing prizes won by the horses. Farrier's shop, pets corner, and playground.

Open Mar–Oct, Tue–Sun & BH 11–5 (last admission 4pm).

Madron
―
Malham

✳ £1.50 (ch 4–15 & pen 75p). Party 20 + .
♿ ⛲ ⛲ ♿ shop ⓥ

Henry Reitlinger Bequest Oldfield, Guards Club Rd
☎ (0628) 21818

Collection of pottery, sculpture, paintings, drawings, ceramics, and glass.

Open Apr–Sep, Tue & Thu 10–12.30 & 2.15–4.30, first Sun in each month 2.30–4.30. Other times by prior arrangement in writing.

Free.

♿ (limited) ♿ (ground floor only) ♨

MAIDSTONE
Kent
Map **5** TQ75

Museum and Art Gallery Chillington Manor, St Faith's Street
☎ (0622) 54497

Rebuilt in 1562, with medieval wing brought from East Farleigh. Now museum and art gallery, containing Japanese room, Anglo-Saxon jewellery, glass and volume II of the Lambeth Byelaw circa 1170. Exhibitions by local and national artists. Includes Museum of Royal West Kent Regiment.

Open all year Mon–Sat 10–5.30. (Closed BH.) During rebuilding some galleries may be closed.

Free.

P (20 yds) ♨

Leeds Castle (5m E on B2163 off A20)
☎ (0622) 65400

Described by Lord Conway as 'the loveliest castle in the world' it was named after Led, Chief Minister of Ethelbert IV, King of Kent, in AD 857. Built on two islands in the middle of a lake, and set in 500 acres of landscaped parkland the castle was originally a Norman stronghold until converted into a royal palace by

---

Henry VIII. Beautifully furnished and restored, it was a royal residence for over three centuries. Museum of Medieval Dog Collars. Culpeper Flower Garden, greenhouses, vineyard, water and woodland gardens, duckery and aviary. Various special events including annual open air Concert and open air ballet, "Kentish Evenings" every Sat all year.

Open 28 Mar–Oct daily 11–5, Nov–Mar Sat & Sun 12–4.

Castle & grounds £3.65 (ch £2.65, students & pen £3.15); Grounds £2.65 (ch £1.65, students & pen £2.15) Party.

♿ ⛲ (licensed) ⛲ ♿ (ground floor & gardens only) shop garden centre ♨

Stoneacre Otham (3m SE)

A small half-timbered, mainly late 15th-century manor house with great hall, crown post roof and garden.

Open Apr–Sep, Wed & Sat 2–6 (last admission 5). Guided tours.

£1.10.

(NT)

Tyrwhitt Drake Museum of Carriages
The Archbishop's Stables, Mill St
☎ (0622) 54497

Late medieval stables containing interesting museum of horse-drawn carriages and vehicles. Near Archbishop's Palace.

Open weekdays 10–1 & 2–5; Apr–Sep only Sun 2–5, BH 11–5.

✳ 60p (ch 30p).

P ♿ (ground floor only) ♨

MALHAM
North Yorkshire
Map **7** SD86

Yorkshire Dales National Park Centre
☎ Airton (07293) 363

Visitor Centre with interpretative display and audio-visual theatre for group use. Maps, walks, guides and local information available.

Open Apr–Oct, daily mid morning to late afternoon.

Free.

♿ ♿

193

MALTON
North Yorkshire
Map **8** SE77

Castle Howard (6m SW)
☎ Coneysthorpe (065384) 333

Magnificent 18th-century house designed by Vanbrugh for Charles Howard, 3rd Earl of Carlisle; still occupied by Howard family. The house contains famous collection of porcelain, paintings and furniture and is surrounded by extensive grounds, with lakes and fountain, Hawksmoor's great Mausoleum and Vanbrugh's restored Temple of the Four Winds. Costume galleries in the 18th-century stable court house Britain's largest private collection of 18th to 20th-century costume.

Open 25 Mar–Oct. Grounds & plant centre 10. House, Costume Galleries & cafeteria 11–5, last admission 4.30.

Admission charges not quoted.

▲ ☕ (licensed) ♿ shop ✖

Malton Museum
Old Town Hall, Market Place
☎ (0653) 5136

Contains extensive Romano-British collections from the Roman fort of Derventio and the settlements and villas in the vicinity. In addition there are displays of prehistoric and medieval material from Malton and district.

Open May–Sep, Mon–Sat 10–4, Sun 2–4; Oct–Apr Sat 1–3. (Closed Dec). Parties by arrangement.

30p (ch, pen & students 15p).

P (500 yds) ♿ (ground floor only) shop ✖

MALVERN
Hereford & Worcestershire
Map **3** SO74

Malvern Museum Abbey Gateway, Abbey Rd
☎ (06845) 67811

The museum is housed in one of only two buildings surviving from the Benedictine Monastery. Displays feature exhibits of the Malvern Hills, rocks of which are the oldest in England and Wales, and the history of Malvern traced from medieval to modern times.

Open Apr–Oct Mon–Sat 10.30–5; Sun 10.30–1 & 2–4.

20p (ch 5 10p).

P (400 yds) shop ✖

MAN, ISLE OF
Map **6**
See Ballaugh, Castletown, Cregneish, Douglas, Laxey, Peel, Ramsey & Snaefell Mountain

MANCHESTER
Gt Manchester
Map **7** SJ89

City Art Gallery Mosley St
☎ 061-236 9422

A sumptuous display of the city's treasures in an architectural masterpiece of the Greek Revival. Paintings by the Old Masters, Stubbs, Gainsborough, Turner, and the Pre-Raphaelites. Outstanding collections of decorative arts, furniture, and sculpture.

Open Mon–Sat 10–6. Sun 2–6.

Free.

P shop ✖

Gallery of English Costume
Platt Fields, Rusholme
☎ 061-224 5217

Famous costume collection displaying the changing styles of everyday clothes and accessories of the last 400 years or more, including contemporary fashion. The costume library is available to students on request.

Open daily (ex Tue) 10–6, Sun 2–6, Nov–Feb closes at 4 pm. Details not confirmed for 1986.

Free.

▲ (limited) ♿ (ground floor only) shop ✖

Gallery of Modern Art Arthenaum, Princess St (next door to City Art Gallery)

Modern British, European painting, sculpture, prints and decorative art, from Sickert to Hockney. Often replaced by temporary exhibitions.

Open Mon–Sat 10–6. Sun 2–6.

Free.

P shop ✖

Greater Manchester Museum of Science & Industry Liverpool Road Station, Castlefield
☎ 061-832 2244 for Museum

Steam and internal-combustion engines, machine tools, electrical exhibits, paper-making, printing and textile machinery and optical equipment among other exhibits. Stationary mill engines etc regularly demonstrated. Static display of railway locomotives and rolling stock. Bookshop. Steam train rides weekends during summer and BH.

Open daily, 10.30–5. Ch 11 only admitted if accompanied by an adult. (Closed Xmas.)

Free.

▲ ☕ Licensed ♿ shop ✖

John Rylands University Library of Manchester Deansgate
☎ 061-834 5343

Famous library, dating from 1851, containing over 3 million books, 17,000 manuscripts, extensive archival collections and c 600,000 titles in microform. Rare books division in the architecturally distinguished Rylands memorial building in Deansgate, holds regular exhibitions and lectures.

Open Mon–Fri 10–5.30, Sat 10–1 (Closed BH & Xmas–New Year).

Free.

▲ ✖ 🚌

Manchester Air & Space Museum
Liverpool Rd, Deansgate, Castlefield
☎ 061-833 9555

The aircraft exhibits are on the ground floor and the gallery, which goes right round the building providing an excellent view of the aircraft, has a series of displays which cover national and local aviation history and space exploration. The aircraft in the museum have been provided by the Royal Air Force Museum and the Aeroplane Collection Ltd. Among the aircraft included in the display are a Supermarine Spitfire Vb, a Roe Triplane replica, an Avro Shackleton AEW.2, a Bristol Belvedere HC.1 and a Bristol Sycamore HR.14.

Open Tue–Sat 10–6, Sun 1–6 & BH. Closed Xmas, Boxing Day & Good Fri.

Admission fee payable.

P (300 yds) ♿ shop ✖

Manchester Museum
The University, Oxford Rd.
☎ 061-273 3333

Contains exhibits of archaeology and natural history including an extensive collection from Ancient Egypt, rocks, minerals, fossils, coins and native craftsmanship and huge study collections of over 8 million specimens. Frequent temporary exhibitions, and lectures.

Open Mon–Sat 10–5; (Closed Good Fri, May Day & Xmas–New Year).

Free (Parking charge).

▲ ♿ shop ✖

Museum of Transport
Boyle St, Cheetham
☎ 061-273 3322

Exhibits include over fifty buses and other vehicles from the Manchester area plus displays of photographs, tickets and items of related interest. The Spring Transport Festival 22 & 23 Mar & Trans Lancs Rally 7 Sep.

Open Apr–Oct, Wed, Sat, Sun & BH 10–5. Parties at other times by arrangement.

50p (ch 5–15 & pen 25p). Family £1.25.

▲ ☕ ♿ shop

Whitworth Art Gallery University of Manchester, Whitworth Park
☎ 061-273 4865

Founded in 1889 by Royal Charter. The principal collections are British watercolours including work by Blake, Turner, the Pre-Raphaelites and 1939–45 War Artists; Continental water-colours including works by Cézanne, Van Gogh and Picasso; Old Master drawings and prints, including examples by leading Renaissance masters such as Pollaiuolo,

Mantegna and Dürer, and fine collection of Japanese prints; textiles, including the Whitworth Tapestry, designed by Paolozzi in 1968; historic wallpapers; and contemporary works of art. Frequent special exhibitions.

Open Mon–Sat 10–5, Thu until 9pm. (Closed Good Fri & Xmas–New Year).

Free.

 ⚫ 🔲 (licensed) & shop 🅧 (ex guide dogs)

MANNINGTON HALL GARDENS
Norfolk
Map **9** TG13

(2½m NE of Saxthorpe)
☎ Saxthorpe (026387) 284

Built in 1460 of flint and set in attractive gardens this moated manor house is still a family home. Rose festival 27–29 Jun '86.

Gardens open Jun–Aug, Wed–Fri 11–6; also Sun 2–5 May–Sep. Hall open by prior appointment only. Gardens £1 (accompanied ch 16 free pen 75p).

⚫ 🔲 卉 & (gardens only) shop & plants for sale 🅧 Ⓥ

MANORBIER
Dyfed
Map **2** SS09

Manchester
—
Mapledurham

Manorbier Castle
☎ (083482) 394 & 421 for enquiries when closed.

Mainly 13th-century, including chapel, hall and gatehouse, with 16th-century additions. Birthplace of 12th-century historian, Giraldus Cambrensis. Life-size wax figures in various parts of the castle.

Open Maundy Thu until Etr wk & Whit–Sep 10.30–5.30.

£1 (ch 30p, pen 50p).

P (200 yds) & (ground floor & gardens only) shop 🅧

MANSFIELD
Nottingham
Map **8** SK55

Museum & Art Gallery Leeming St
☎ (0623) 22561 & 646604

New display of William Billingsley porcelain, lustreware and Wedgwood. Water-colours of old Mansfield. Many temporary exhibitions. Natural history gallery.

Open Mon–Fri 10–5 & Sat 10–1 & 2–5.
Free.
P (160 yds) & shop 🅧

MAPLEDURHAM
Oxfordshire
Map **4** SU67

Mapledurham House
☎ Reading (0734) 723350
(Mr J.J. Eyston)

Elizabethan mansion set in unspoilt village beside River Thames. Built by the Blount family in the 16th century and restored by their descendant. Within the house are great oak staircases, well-proportioned rooms and moulded ceilings in white plasterwork, of the late Elizabethan period, collection of pictures and family portraits. (See following entry). River launches from Caversham, Reading (4m), when house is open (charter bookings arranged for parties).

Open Etr–Sep, Sat, Sun & BH 2.30–5. Party 30 + by arrangement Tue, Wed & Thu. Enquiries: Estate Office, Mapledurham House, Reading RG4 7TR.

✳ £1.60 (ch 80p).

⚫ 🔲 & (ground floor only) shop 🅧

An exciting new museum at the oldest passenger railway station in the world, in the heart of Britain's first Urban Heritage Park.

● POWER HALL-industrial power from the horse wheel to the jet engine, including locomotives, working waterwheel, beam engine and impressive mill engines.

● THE WAREHOUSE EXHIBITION-working displays of computers and textile printing and papermaking machinery.

● MUSEUM SHOP-Licensed Restaurant (home cooking). CAR PARK.

● 1830 STATION BUILDING with restored booking hall and Liverpool and Manchester Railway Exhibition.

● AIR AND SPACE GALLERY-(admission 50p for adults)

● ELECTRICITY GALLERY-opening March 1986

● SPECIAL EXHIBITION-MICROSCOPES IN MANCHESTER.

The Greater Manchester Museum of Science and Industry is at Liverpool Road, Castlefield, in central Manchester. OPEN EVERY DAY 10.30am–5.00pm. ADMISSION FREE. Telephone: 061-832 2244.

Mapledurham Watermill

☎ Reading (0734) 723350

Last working corn and grist mill on the Thames. Wheel, gearing and stones restored and used for grinding wholewheat flour which can be purchased. (See previous entry). The mill can be reached by river launch from Caversham Bridge, details obtained from the estate office as below.

Mill & riverside picnic area open Etr–Sep, Sat, Sun & BH 12–5.30. Also winter Sun 2–4. Party 30+ by arrangement any weekday. Enquiries: *Estate Office, Mapledurham House, Reading RG4 7TR.*

70p (ch 40p).

🅰 ⬛ 🎏 shop ✸

MARAZION

Cornwall
Map 2 SW52

St Michael's Mount

☎ (0736) 710507)

Offshore in Mount's Bay, reached on foot over causeway, or by ferry during summer only. Well-situated island-castle, with 14th-century chapel and collection of armour, pictures and furniture.

Open Nov–Mar, Mon, Wed, & Fri, guided tours at 11, 12, 2, 3 & 4; Apr–May, Mon, Wed & Fri 10.30–5.45 (last admission 4.45); Jun–Oct, Mon–Fri, guided tours from 10.30–4.45. Mar–May educational visits by prior arrangements, Tue only.

£2 (ch 90p).

⬛ (NT) (NGS)

MARGAM

West Glamorgan
Map 3 SS88

Margam Park (E of junc 38 M4)

☎ Port Talbot (0639) 881635

850 acres of open parkland and forest, full of natural and historic treasures including the Castle and Abbey ruins. Also there is the Margam Orangery, which is the largest building of its kind in Britain. Many other features include Wales' first sculpture park, the Coach House Theatre, gardens and waymarked walks, as well as an adventure playground and a herd of fallow deer. Large maze due to open 1986. Numerous events throughout the year.

Open Apr–Oct, Tue–Sun 10.30–8 (open Mon in Aug & BH); Nov–Mar, Wed–Sun 10.30–1hr before dusk. Subject to review.

✳ 60p (ch & pen 40p) (ch 5 & reg. disabled free). Party 10+.

🅰 ⬛ 🎏 ♿ shop

MARGATE

Kent
Map 5 TR37

Tudor House King St

☎ Thanet (0843) 225511

Mapledurham
Marypark

The oldest domestic building in Margate, dating from the early 16th century, displaying heavily moulded beams and an enriched plaster ceiling in an excellent state of preservation. Housed here is a small local history museum.

Open mid May–mid Sep, Mon–Sat 10–12.30.

25p (ch & pen 10p).

P shop ✸ (ex guide dogs)

MARKET BOSWORTH

Leicestershire
Map 4 SK40

Market Bosworth Light Railway

(5m NW on unclass road at Shackerstone station).

☎ Leicester (0533) 605748 & Tamworth (0827) 880754 wknds.

Regular train service (mainly steam) from Shackerstone to Market Bosworth. Extensive railway museum of small relics and collection of rolling stock on view.

Open Etr–Sep, Sun & BH 11–6; Oct–Etr Sun, 12–4.30 only.

Museum 40p (ch 20p). Return train fares including admission £1.35 (ch & pen 80p). Family Ticket £3.95. Details not confirmed for 1986.

🅰 ⬛ ♿ shop

MARKET HARBOROUGH

Leicestershire
Map 4 SP79

Harborough Museum Council Offices, Adam & Eve St

☎ (0858) 32468

Museum illustrating the Harborough area, particularly the town's role as a marketing and social focus, hunting centre and as a medieval planned town.

Open Mon–Sat 10–4.30; Sun 2–5. (Closed Good Fri & Xmas).

Free.

P ♿ (Sat, Sun & BH by arrangement) shop ✸

MARTIN MERE

Lancashire
Map 7 SD41

Wildfowl Trust

(W of A59 at Burscough Bridge station and signposted from A565 at Mere Brow)

☎ Burscough (0704) 895181

In a natural setting over 1500 colourful swans, geese and ducks from all over the world, plus 3 flocks of flamingos. 300-acre refuge with 20-acre lake overlooked by comfortable hides and visited by thousands of wild geese, swans, ducks and waders. The unique Norwegian log visitor centre, overlooks Swan Lake and

---

Flamingo Pool, and contains a coffee shop, gift shop, exhibition gallery and education complex. Nature trail for visually handicapped with free use of taped commentaries. Tarmac paths and free wheelchairs for disabled. Picnic areas. Binoculars for hire.

Open daily 9.30–5.30 or dusk. (Closed Xmas).

£2 (ch 4–16 £1, pen £1.20). Party 20+.

🅰 ⬛ 🎏 ♿ (ex gallery) shop ✸

MARWELL

Hampshire
Map 4 SU52

Marwell Zoological Park Colden Common

☎ Owslebury (096274) 406

Opened in May 1972, it is now established as one of Britain's major wild animal collections. In 100 acres of spacious enclosures, groups of rare animals thrive and breed. More than 1,000 animals from over 100 species are to be seen here, and new exhibits are constantly being added.

Open all year daily, (ex Xmas day), 10–6 (or dusk). Last admission 5pm or 1 hour before dusk (whichever is earliest).

Admission fee payable. Party.

🅰 ⬛ (licensed) 🎏 ♿ shop & garden centre ✸

MARYCULTER

Grampian *Aberdeenshire*
Map 15 NO89

Anderson's Storybook Glen

☎ Aberdeen (0224) 732941

Favourite nursery rhyme and fairy tale characters provide a fantasy world for children. While grown-ups can enjoy twenty acres of scenically attractive Deeside, full of lovely flowers, plants, trees and waterfalls.

Open Apr–Oct daily 10–7.

✳ £1.50 (ch 75p, pen £1).

🅰 ⬛ (licensed) ♿ shop & garden centre ✸

MARYPARK

Grampian *Banffshire*
Map 15 NJ13

Glenfarclas Distillery (1m W)

☎ Ballindalloch (08072) 257

One of the finest Highland Malt whiskies is produced here. There is an exhibition, museum, craft shop and visitor centre. Museum and exhibition now in French, German and Swedish.

Open all year Mon–Fri 9–4.30; Jul–Sep also Sat, 10–4. (Closed 25 & 26 Dec and 1 & 2 Jan).

Free.

🅰 ♿ (ground floor only) shop

MARYPORT
Cumbria
Map **11** NY03

Maritime Museum Shipping Brow, 1
Senhouse St
☎ (090081) 3738

*Material of local and general maritime
interest. Photographic display illustrating
Maryport's history.*

Open Mon, Tue, Thu–Sat 10–12 & 2–4.
Also Sun 2–4.30 (Etr–Sep). Details not
confirmed for 1986.

Free.

P shop ✘

MATLOCK
Derbyshire
Map **8** SK36

Riber Castle Fauna Reserve
☎ (0629) 2073

*19th-century castle and fauna reserve of
more than 20 acres on 853ft-high Riber
Hill. European birds and animals in near-
natural surroundings. Breeding colonies
of European Lynx, whose kittens can be
seen Jun–Sep. The Castle is also a Rare
Breeds Survival Trust Centre (No 10) with
collections of sheep, pigs, cattle, goats,
rabbits and poultry. There is also a nature
centre, model railway, motor and motor
cycle museum, children's playground and
garden centre.*

Open daily 10–5, 4 in winter, (Closed
Xmas day).

✽ £1.65 (ch 90p) Parties 20 + .

⚠ ⵣ ⌔ ⛋ shop & garden centre ✘ (in
animal section) Ⓥ

MATLOCK BATH
Derbyshire
Map **8** SK25

The Heights of Abraham
☎ Matlock (0629) 2365

*30 acres of landscaped woodland
situated high on the southern slopes
above the village of Matlock Bath.
Attractions include the Victorian Prospect
Tower on the summit of the Heights
offering an excellent vantage point from*
which to view Derbyshire and its
surrounding counties. Nestus Mine, which
is almost level throughout, easy to tour
and for the more adventurous Great
Masson Cavern, where visitors carry
hurricane lamps through long passages
veined with calcite and fluorspar.

Grounds & tower open all year 9–dusk.
Great Rutland Cavern & Nestus Mine Etr–
Oct 10–5; Great Masson Cavern Etr–Oct
Sun & BH; Aug daily. Parties by
arrangement.

Admission fee payable.

P ⵣ (licensed) ⌔ ⛋ shop

Peak District Mining Museum The
Pavilion
☎ Matlock (0629) 3834

*The history of the Derbyshire lead
industry. The museum illustrates geology,
lead mining and miners, lead smelting,
mining and quarrying today, by means of
static and moving display and an audio-
visual programme. Also a unique early
19th-century water pressure pumping
engine—the only one of its kind in the
British Isles.*

Open daily mid Feb–mid Oct & winter
wknds, 11–4 (later in summer) (Closed
Xmas day).

70p (ch 16, pen, students & disabled
45p). Party rates on application.

P (20 yds) ⛋ (ground floor only) shop

Temple Mine Temple Rd (off A6)
☎ Matlock (0629) 3834

*Old lead and fluorspar workings
reconstructed as in 1920s and 1930s with
tracks, tubs and electric light. Exhibits are
still being developed by volunteers.*

Open Etr–Oct daily 11–5. Nov–Etr Sat &
Sun only 2–4. Coach parties & school
groups should ring the Peak District
Mining Museum & make prior
arrangements.

60p (ch, pen & students 40p). Party rates
on application.

Shop ✘

MAWNAN SMITH
Cornwall
Map **2** SW72

Glendurgan
*Beautifully situated gardens near Helford
River inlet on road to Helford Passage.
Walled garden and maze.*

Open Mar–Oct Mon, Wed & Fri 10.30–
4.30. (Closed Good Fri).

£1.30
(NT)

MAYBOLE
Strathclyde *Ayrshire*
Map **10** NS20

Crossraguel Abbey (2m SW)
*A Cluniac monastery founded by Duncan,
Earl of Carrick in 1244. The extensive
remains are of high architectural
distinction and consist of the church,
claustral buildings, outer court with an
imposing castellated gatehouse and
abbot's house.*

Open, see end of gazetteer.
Closed Thu afternoon & Fri.

50p (ch & pen 25p).
⚠ ⛋ (AM)

MEIGLE
Tayside *Perthshire*
Map **11** NO24

Meigle Museum
*Housed in the old school, a magnificent
display of 25 sculptured monuments of
the Celtic Christian period, one of the
most notable assemblages of Dark Age
sculpture in Western Europe.*

Open see end of gazetteer. Closed Suns.

50p (ch & pen 25p).
(AM)

THE HEIGHTS OF ABRAHAM

The most exciting ride in England!
Travel by Cable Car high above the Derwent
Valley to the Tree Tops Visitor Centre.

Refresh yourself in the Coffee Shop or licensed
Restaurant and enjoy the spectacular views.

Come underground in the Great Rutland
Cavern - Nestus Mine and the
Great Masson Cavern experience the
atmosphere of these famous lead mines.

Climb the Prospect Tower for a unique
panorama of Derbyshire.

Telephone Matlock (0629) 2365

Matlock Bath, Derbyshire

MELBOURNE
Derbyshire
Map **8** SK32

Melbourne Hall
☎ (03316) 2502

Once lived in by Queen Victoria's famous Prime Minister Lord Melbourne, and inherited by Lady Palmerston, it is now the Derbyshire home of the Marquess of Lothian. The contents include an important collection of pictures and antique furniture. One of the most famous formal gardens in Britain.

Open Jun–Oct Weds 2–6. Also open for Prebooked parties (20 +) by appointment throughout the year. Gardens open Apr–Sep, Wed, Sat, Sun & BH Mons 2–6. Other times by appointment.

£1.50 (ch 16 75p). Family ticket available.

🅰 (Limited) 💷 & (ground floor & gardens only) shop ✗

MELROSE
Borders *Roxburghshire*
Map **12** NT53

Abbotsford House (2m W off A6091)
☎ Galashiels (0896) 2043

19th-century mansion on the River Tweed. Built by Sir Walter Scott and the place of his death. Contains his library and a collection of historical relics.

Open 3rd Mon in Mar–Oct, Mon–Sat 10–5, Sun 2–5.

✱ £1.30 (ch 16 60p). Party.

🅰 💷 & (ground floor & gardens only) shop ✗

Melrose Abbey

Probably the most famous ruin in Scotland, owing much of its modern fame to the glamour given to it by Sir Walter Scott. This was a beautiful Cistercian abbey, repeatedly wrecked during the wars of Scottish independence and notably by Richard II in 1385. Most of the ruins belong to the 15th-century reconstruction. The heart of Robert the Bruce is buried somewhere within the church.
Also **Abbey Museum** *housed in 15th- to 16th-century former Commendator's*

Melbourne
—
Menstrie

House, containing carved stones, Roman objects from the nearby fort of Trimontium, etc, and situated in the abbey grounds.

Open see end of gazetteer.

✱ £1 (ch & pen 50p).

(AM)

Melrose Motor Museum Newstead Rd
☎ (089682) 2624

One of the largest displays of motor vehicles in Scotland. The majority of cars are common models from the last 50 years, all in running order and where possible with original paintwork and plating. Also on display are motor cycles, bicycles, World War II military vehicles and other paraphernalia connected with motoring.

Open Jun–Sep 10.30–5.30. Also Etr, May & Oct by appointment (☎ St Boswells (0835) 22356).

✱ 75p (ch 25p). Party.

🅰 & shop ✗ (ex guide dogs)

Priorwood Garden
☎ (089682) 2965

Special garden with flowers for drying. Visitors centre adjacent to Melrose Abbey and 'Apples through the Ages' orchard walk.

Open 28 Mar–30 Apr & 1 Nov–24 Dec, Mon–Sat 10–1 & 2–5.30, May–Jun & Oct, Mon–Sat 10–5.30, Sun 1.30–5.30, Jul–Sep, Mon–Sat 10–6, Sun 1.30–5.30.

Donations.

(NTS)

MELTON MOWBRAY
Leicestershire
Map **8** SK71

Melton Carnegie Museum Thorpe End
☎ (0664) 69946

Museum illustrating past and present life of the area.

Open Etr–Sep, Mon–Sat 10–5, Sun 2–5; Oct–Etr, Mon–Fri 10–4.30, Sat 10.30–4, (Closed Sun, Good Fri, 25, 26 Dec & 1 Jan).

Free.

P (adjacent) shop ✗

MENAI BRIDGE
Gwynedd
Map **6** SH57

Museum of Childhood 1 Castle St
☎ (0248) 712498

The exhibits, many of which are rare and valuable, illustrate the habits and interests of children and families spanning 150 years. They include children's saving boxes; dolls; educational toys and games; pottery and glassware depicting and used by children; early clockwork toys, including trains, cars, and aeroplanes; music boxes; polyphons; magic lanterns and an art gallery full of paintings and prints of children, as well as early samplers and needlework pictures worked by children.

Open Week before Etr–Oct daily 10–6, Sun 1–5.

Admission fee payable.

P (150–200 yds) & (ground floor only) shop

Tegfryn Art Gallery Cadnant Rd
☎ (0248) 712437

A private gallery, standing in its own pleasant grounds near to shores of the Menai Straits. Exhibition of paintings by contemporary and prominent artists including many from North Wales. Pictures may be purchased.

Open daily 10–1 & 2–5. (Closed Mon Oct–Etr).

Free.

P (100 yds) & (ground floor only)

MENSTRIE
Central *Clackmannanshire*
Map **11** NS89

Menstrie Castle

16th-century fortress now restored, partly as modernised flats. It was the birthplace in 1657 of Sir William Alexander, the founder of Nova Scotia. The Nova Scotia Commemoration Rooms devised and furnished by the NTS are shown.

Open May–Sep, Mon 2.30–4.30, Wed 9.30–12, Thu 6–8.

20p (ch 10p) Honesty Box.

(NTS) & Clackmannan District Council.

MENTMORE
Buckinghamshire
Map **4** SP91

Mentmore Towers
☎ Cheddington (0296) 661881

Palatial Victorian mansion designed by Sir Joseph Paxton and the last surviving example of his domestic work in England, set in 80 acres of grounds. Former home of the Baron Meyer Amschel de Rothschild. Beautiful interiors with ornate gilt work, Rubens fireplace and magnificent banquet hall. Views of the Chilterns and the Aylesbury Vale can be seen from the windows of the house. It is now the British seat of the World Government of the Age of Enlightenment, founded by Maharishi Mahesh Yogi.

Open Suns & BH 1.45–4.

✱ £1.50 (ch & pen 75p).

Free introductory talks on Transcendental Meditation by Maharishi Mahesh Yogi every Wed evening at 8pm.

⚠ ✖

MERSHAM
Kent
Map **5** TR03

Swanton Mill
☎ Aldington (023372) 223

This restored mill won the 1975 European Architectural Heritage Year Award. The mill can be seen working and flour is on sale. Exhibition on top floor. Water garden. 3 acre garden & trout lake.

Open Apr–Sep, Sat & Sun 3–6.

£1 (ch 12 50p).

⚠ ♿ (ground floor & gardens only) garden centre. ✖

MERTHYR TYDFIL
Mid Glamorgan
Map **3** SO00

Brecon Mountain Railway Pant Station (2¾m NE, to the N of A465)
☎ Merthyr Tydfil (0685) 4854

A narrow-gauge steam railway operating into the Brecon Beacons National Park. Locomotives from three continents.

Opening times on application to The Brecon Mountain Railway, Pant Station, Merthyr Tydfil, Mid Glamorgan.

✱ Return fares £1.80 (ch 5–15 90p, under 5 free, pen £1.20). Party.
⚠ ☕ (licensed) ♿ shop

Cyfarthfa Castle Museum & Art Gallery
☎ (0685) 3112

Built by William Crawshay in 1825 the collections cover paintings, ceramics, coins, medals, silver and other objets d'art. Natural and local history, also a small Welsh kitchen.

Open weekdays 10–1 & 2–6, 4 on Fri & Oct–Mar. Sun 2–5. (Closed Good Fri, May Day, 25–26 Dec & 1–2 Jan).

10p (ch & pen 5p). Schoolparties free.

⚠ ⛼ ♿ (by arrangement) ✖

Garwnant Forest Centre
(5m N of Merthyr Tydfil off A470)
☎ (0685) 3060

A focal point for the many forest facilities in the Brecon Beacons forests, Garwnant relates the farming, water supply and forestry of the valleys. Forest trails and adventure play area.

Open Etr–Sep weekdays 10.30–4.45, BH 12–6. Apr, Sat & Sun 2–4, May & Sep 2–5, June 2–6 & Jul & Aug 1–6. Other times, telephone for details.

Free.

⚠ ⛼ ♿ shop

Joseph Parry's Cottage 4 Chapel Row
☎ (0685) 73117

Birthplace of the famous musician and composer Joseph Parry. Exhibition of his life and works and display of mementoes of Welsh male voice choirs. Open air museum with excavated section of Glamorganshire Canal and exhibits illustrating local industrial and social history.

Open Jun–Aug Mon–Fri & Sep–May Mon, Wed & Fri 1.30–4.30 (Closed BH).

Free.

⚠ shop

METHLICK
Grampian *Aberdeenshire*
Map **15** NJ83

Haddo House
(4m N of Pitmedden off B999)
☎ Tarves (06515) 440

Designed by William Adam in 1731 for the second Earl of Aberdeen. Much of the interior is 'Adam Revival' dating from about 1880. Country park run by Grampian Regional Council.

House open May–Sep daily 2–6, last admission 5.15. (Closed 10 & 11 May). Garden and park open all year 9.30–sunset.

£1.40 (ch 70p) garden by donation.

♿ shop, visitor centre & tearoom (May–Sep 11–6, Sun 2–6) (NTS)

MEVAGISSEY
Cornwall
Map **2** SX04

Folk Museum Earl Quay
☎ (0726) 843568

Occupying old boatbuilder's workshop dating from 1745, specialises in local crafts, seafaring, agricultural and mining items. Monthly exhibitions on loan from Plymouth Art Gallery.

Open Etr week 11–6; Etr–May 2–4; Jun–Sep 11–6.

20p (ch & pen 10p).

P (300 yds, on Quay) ♿ (ground floor only) shop ✖

Model Railway & International Model Collection
☎ (0726) 842457

British, Continental and American models run through a realistic layout which features urban and rural areas, an Alpine ski resort with cablecars and a Cornish china clay pit with refining plant. Over 2,000 models are on display.

Open 2 wks Etr, then Spring BH–Sep 11–5 (9pm during High Season); Winter Suns 2–5.

£1.10p (ch & pen 70p).

P (150 yards, on Quay) ♿ shop

MEY
Highland *Caithness*
Map **15** ND27

Castle of Mey Gardens
☎ Barrock (084785) 227

Castle built between 1566 and 1572 and is now a home of Her Majesty Queen Elizabeth, the Queen Mother. Fine views across the Pentland Firth towards the Orkneys. Gardens ***only*** *open.*

Open 17 & 25 Jul & 31 Aug (to be confirmed for 1986).

✱ 50p (ch & pen 30p).

⚠ ☕ ♿ ✖

MICKLETON
Gloucestershire
Map **4** SP14

Hidcote Manor Garden (½m SE)

Ten acres of small gardens, divided by hedges, herbaceous borders, old roses, rare shrubs and trees.

Gardens only open 29 Mar–Oct Sat–Mon, Wed & Th 11–8, no entry after 7pm or 1hr before sunset.

£2.40. Parties by prior written arrangement.

☕ shop ✖ (NT)

Kiftsgate Court Garden (½m S off A46, adjacent Hidcote NT garden)

Magnificently situated house with fine views and trees. The garden has unusual plants and shrubs, and a collection of old-fashioned roses including R Filipes Kiftsgate, the largest rose in England.

Open Apr–Sep Wed, Thu, Sun & BH 2–6.

£1.50 (ch 50p). Parties by appointment only.

⚠ ☕ (Whit Sun–Aug only) plants for sale ✖

MIDDLE CLAYDON
Buckinghamshire
Map **4** SP72

Claydon House
(off A413, entrance by North drive only)
☎ Steeple Claydon (029673) 349

Eighteenth Century house of the Verney family containing fantastic rococo carvings. Frequently visited by Florence Nightingale. Museum with mementoes of Crimean War.

Open 29 Mar–Oct, Sat–Wed, 2–6, BH Mon 1–6. Last admissions ½hr before closing. £1.70 (Mon & Tue, excluding BH Mons, £1.30).

⚠ 🎫 ♿ ✻ in house (NT)

MIDDLEHAM
North Yorkshire
Map **7** SE18

Middleham Castle
A 12th-century former seat of the Nevilles, with two-storeyed keep standing within 13th-century curtain walls.

Open, see end of gazetteer.
✷ 60p (ch 16 & pen 30p).
⚠ (AM)

MIDDLESBROUGH
Cleveland
Map **8** NZ42

Captain Cook Birthplace Museum
(3m S on A172 at Stewart Park, Marton)
☎ (0642) 311211

The museum illustrates the early life of James Cook and his voyages of discovery. Opened to mark the 250th anniversary of Cook's birth at Marton in 1728. Situated in spacious rolling parkland. Other attractions include an aviary of colourful parakeets including many rare breeds, a conservatory of tropical plants, and assorted animals and fowl in small paddocks.

Open summer 10–5.30, winter 9–4 (Closed Xmas day & New Years day).
✷ 30p (ch & pen 10p). Party.
P 🎫 ♿ shop ✻

Middle Claydon
—
Middle Woodford

Dorman Museum Linthorpe Rd
☎ (0642) 813781

Displays of local, social, industrial and natural history. A permanent display of regional and Linthorpe pottery together with a regular, varied programme of temporary exhibitions.

Open Mon–Fri 10–6; Sat 10–5. (Closed Xmas Day).

Free.

P (adjacent street) ♿ (ground floor only) shop ✻

MIDDLETON
Warwickshire
Map **4** SP19

Bainbridge Collection Middleton Hall
(off A4091 between Fazeley & the Belfry National Golf Centre)
☎ Clifton Campville (082786) 446

Comprehensive collection of agricultural equipment from 1850–1943. Very rare machines, some of which may be seen running. Set in magnificent pre 1550 Tudor barn and courtyard.

Open Apr–Sep Sat & Sun, plus BH & school holidays Wed–Sun 10.30–5.30 (2–5.30 Sun).

Admission fee payable.
⚠ ♿

MIDDLETON BY WIRKSWORTH
Derbyshire
Map **8** SK25

Middleton Top Engine House (½m S, signposted from B5036 Cromford/ Wirksworth road)
☎ Wirksworth (062982) 3204

Engine House with beam engine, built in 1829 for the Cromford and High Peak Railway, to haul wagons on cables up the Middleton incline. The visitor Centre tells the story of this historic railway. Here the

High Peak Trail which follows the óld Cromford and High Peak Railway is available for walkers and riders. Also cycle hire centre.

Open daily Apr–Sep & wknds Oct–Mar. (Visitor centre only). Engine House Suns 10.30–5 & 1st Sat in each month when engine is in motion. Bicycle Hire Jun–Aug daily; Apr, May, Sep, Oct & Nov open weekends & BH's.

✻ Engine working 40p (ch 20p). Engine static 25p (ch 10p). Party.

⚠ 🚻 shop

MIDDLE WALLOP
Hampshire
Map **4** SU23

Museum of Army Flying
Army Air Corps Centre
☎ Andover (0264) 62121 ext 421

An exciting new aviation museum featuring a hundred years of Army Flying, from the earliest days of man-carrying kites and balloons, to the missile firing jet helicopters of today. Many special displays covering WW1–RFC, the Glider operations of WW2, right up to the Falklands campaign. International Air Tattoo 11–13 Jul.

Open daily 10–4.30 (Closed Xmas).

£1.40 (ch, students & pens 70p), Scouts/ Cadets groups 40p. Parties 15+. Service & AAC/GPR/AOP Assoc—free.

⚠ 🎫 🚻 ♿ shop ✻ Ⓥ

MIDDLE WOODFORD
Wiltshire
Map **4** SU13

Heale House Gardens
☎ Middle Woodford (072273) 207

A charming Manor house where King Charles II hid after the battle of Worcester in 1651. The 8 acres of gardens provide a varied collection of plants, shrubs, musk and other roses in the formal setting of clipped hedges and mellow stonework. Notable in spring and autumn is the water garden planted with magnolias and acers, surrounding an authentic Japanese tea house and bridge.

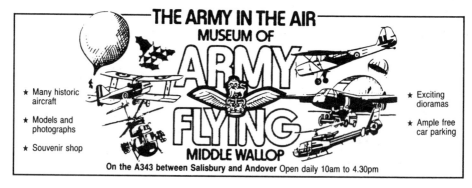

Open (gardens only) Etr–Autumn Mon–Sat & 1st Sun in the month & BH, 10–5.

✱ £1 (ch 14, accompanied free).

 ⚶ ♿

MILLOM
Cumbria
Map **7** SD18

Millom Folk Museum St Georges Rd
☎ (0657) 2555

All the exhibits are of a local character thus maintaining a true 'Folk Museum'. The main hall has a display connected with Hodbarrow Iron Ore Mines and Millom Iron Works together with items of mainly agricultural interest. There is also a replica of a blacksmith's forge, complete with tools, and a section dealing with natural history. Leading off the main hall is a full-scale model of a drift of the Hodbarrow Mine complete with the actual cage as used at the Moorbank Shaft. In an area behind the mine is the domestic section which houses a display of clothes, blankets and household goods, also a reconstruction of a miner's cottage.

Open Etr week; Spring BH–mid Sep, Mon–Sat 10–5, Sun 2–5. Details not confirmed for 1986.

✱ 35p (ch 5–16 20p, ch 5 Free). Party.

⚠ (30 yds) ♿ shop ⚒

MILLPORT
Great Cumbrae Island, Strathclyde *Bute*
Map **10** NS15

Museum of the Cumbraes Garrison House
☎ (0475) 530741

The museum tells the story of life on and around the Cumbraes and features many old photographs, including some of steamers which achieved fame on the Millport run.

Open Jun–Sep, Tue–Sat 10–4.30.
Free.

⚠ ♿

MILNATHORT
Tayside *Kinross-shire*
Map **11** NO10

Middle Woodford
Minster (Sheppey)

Burleigh Castle
A 16th-century tower house, with a courtyard enclosure and roofed angle tower, dating from 1582.

Open, see end of gazetteer. Application to key keeper.

Free.

(AM)

MILTON
Oxfordshire
Map **4** SU49

Milton Manor House
☎ Abingdon (0235) 831287

17th-century house with 18th-century wings and a walled garden.

Open Etr Sat–26 Oct, Sat, Sun & BH, 2–5.30pm.

£1.20 (ch 14 60p). Party 20 +.

⚠ ⚶ ♿ (ground floor) ❖

MINARD
Strathclyde *Argyll*
Map **10** NR99

Crarae Glen Gardens
☎ (0546) 86633

Woodland garden, set in a Highland glen. It includes rhododendrons, eucalyptus, rare trees and shrubs.

Open daily 9–6pm.

✱ £1 by collecting box (ch 16 free).

⚠ ⚶ Plant sales area

MINEHEAD
Somerset
Map **3** SS94

West Somerset Railway
☎ (0643) 4996

Steam and railcar trains run to various points including Minehead, Watchet and Bishops Lydeard. Maximum distance travelled is 40 miles.

Open daily Apr–Sep 9.30–6.30 & other days in off season. Tickets range fr 60p–£4.20 (ch 30p–£2.10). Special coach link between Taunton (town centre or railway station) and Bishops Lydeard provided for some trains.

⚠ ⚶ (licensed) ♿ shop

MINSTEAD
Hampshire
Map **4** SU21

Furzey Gardens
☎ Southampton (0703) 812464

8 acres of peaceful glades with winter and summer heathers, flowering trees and shrubs, many of which are rare, and spring bulbs. Also ancient cottage, 1560, now restored, where the work of 50 artists and 100 local craftsmen are displayed.

Open daily 10.30–5 (dusk in winter). (Closed Xmas).

✱ Gardens, cottage & gallery £1.25 (ch 5–14 75p). Nov–Feb, reduced admission charge. Party.

⚠ ♿ (ground floor only) shop ❖

MINSTER-IN-THANET
Kent
Map **5** TR36

Minster Abbey
☎ Thanet (0843) 821254

One of the oldest inhabited houses in Kent with some 11th-century work. Now home of a religious order.

Open all year, May–Oct, Mon–Fri 11–12 & 2–4.30, Sat & BH 3.30–5; Oct–Apr, Mon–Sat 11–12.

Free. (Alms box).

⚠ ♿ shop   •

MINSTER (Sheppey)
Kent
Map **5** TQ97

Minster Gatehouse Union Rd
☎ (0795) 872303 & 872903

This mediaeval gatehouse of one of Kent's earliest Benedictine nunneries is now converted to a museum of Island history featuring fossils, tools, costumes and photographs. Next to the Gatehouse →

CRARAE GLEN GARDEN
(CRARAE GARDEN CHARITABLE TRUST)

A paradise of flowering shrubs and rare trees on the shore of Loch Fyne, 10 miles south of Inveraray, Argyll, on the main A83 road.

Open to visitors daily, throughout the year 9am to 6pm
Admission (fixed charge). Children under 16 and car parking free.

PLANTS FOR SALE
at entrance 10am to 4.30pm, April to October.
Wholesale by application to Mr. J. MacKirdy.
Telephone — Office: (0546) 86633 Home: (evenings) (04995) 218

is a twin Abbey Church, founded in 674 and one of England's oldest places of worship.

Open beginning Jul–29 Sep daily (ex Thu) 2–5. Also Good Fri–Etr Mon, Spring BH. Sat–Mon & possibly wknds in Jun (please check) 2–5. Other times by Arrangement.

25p (ch 5p).

⚠ shop

MINSTER LOVELL
Oxfordshire
Map **4** SP31

Minster Lovell Hall

Ruined 15th-century structure associated with two strange legends including the Mistletoe Bough Chest.

Open, see end of gazetteer.

✱ 50p (ch 16 & pen 25p).

⚠ (AM)

MINTERNE MAGNA
Dorset
Map **3** ST60

Minterne House (on A352).
☎ Cerne Abbas (03003) 370

Large shrub garden landscaped in the 18th century with small lakes and cascades. Many varieties of Himalayan and Chinese rhododendrons, magnolias, azaleas and rare trees.

Open Apr–end of autumn colouring, daily 10–7.

£1 (ch 16 free).

⚠

MINTLAW
Grampian *Aberdeenshire*
Map **15** NK04

Aden Country Park (1m W Mintlaw off A950)
☎ (07712) 2857

230 acres of beautiful woodland set in open farmland. The grounds of a former Estate, the Park is the home of many varieties of plants and animals which can be explored by a network of footpaths including a specially developed nature trail. The semi-circular farmsteading is now home to the North East of Scotland Heritage Centre, providing an experience of estate life in the 1920s. Craft Workshops.

Park open all year. Buildings open mid May–Sep 12–6.

Free.

⚠ ⚲ (Table licence May–Sep) ⏚ ക (ground floor & gardens only) shop ✕

MISTLEY
Essex
Map **5** TM13

Mistley Towers

Twin, square porticoed towers, remaining features of church erected originally by Robert Adam c. 1776. Hall built about the

Minster (Sheppey)
Morecambe

same time of which only the Adam Lodges of 1782 still stand.

Towers accessible all reasonable times.

Free.

ക (exterior only) (AM)

MOFFAT
Dumfries and Galloway *Dumfriesshire*
Map **11** NT00

Ladyknowe Mill
☎ (0683) 20134

Small mill where visitors can see the garments being made. Showroom for the sale of woollens, tweeds and tartans.

Open May–Oct daily 8.30–5.30, Nov–Apr daily 10–4.

Free.

⚠ ⚲ (licensed) shop ✕

MONIAIVE
Dumfries and Galloway *Dumfriesshire*
Map **11** NX79

Maxwelton House
☎ (08482) 385

A stronghold of the Earls of Glencairn until 1611 and later the birthplace of Annie Laurie. Annie Laurie's Boudoir, Chapel and gardens can be seen.

Chapel, Apr–Sep daily 10–6; Gardens, Apr–Sep. Mon–Thu 2–5; Annie Laurie's Boudoir & Museum Jul & Aug, Mon–Thu 2–5. House by arrangement.

£1 (ch 10 free) reduction for pen.

⚠ ⏚ ക (ground floor & garden only).

MONKSILVER
Somerset
Map **3** ST03

Combe Sydenham Hall
☎ Stogumber (09846) 284

The house, built by Sir George Sydenham in 1580, was the home of Sir Francis Drake's wife Elizabeth and is now under restoration. A pleasant garden, woodland walks; also trout farm and tree nurseries.

Hall open 27–29 & 31 May & Jun–Sep Tue, Wed & Fri; Jul & Aug Mon–Fri, 1–4.30. Trout Farm open from 11am then as Hall plus Apr & Oct, Tue, Wed & Fri.

Admission fee payable.

⚠ ⚲ ⏚ ക ✕ (in house)

MONMOUTH
Gwent
Map **3** SO51

Monmouth Museum
Market Hall, Priory St
☎ (0600) 3519

Collections of Nelson relics and mementoes. Also local history centre of Monmouth.

Open Mon–Sat 10.30–1 & 2–5; Sun 2–5 (Closed Xmas & New Year).

50p (ch & pen 25p). Party. Educational groups free when booked in advance.

ക (ground floor only) shop ✕

MONTACUTE
Somerset
Map **3** ST41

Montacute House
☎ Martock (0935) 823289

Elizabethan house built 1588–1601 from Ham Hill stone by Edward Phelips. Fine old glass and panelling. Permanent collection of Tudor and Jacobean portraits from the National Portrait Gallery on view in the Long Gallery. Formal gardens.

Open 29 Mar–Oct, Wed–Mon 12.30–6, last admission to house 5.30. Gardens open daily. Parties by written appointment with the Administrator.

£2.20 (ch £1.10).

⚲ ക shop (NT)

MONTROSE
Tayside *Angus*
Map **15** NO75

Montrose Museum and Art Gallery
☎ (0674) 73232

Extensive collections covering local history from prehistoric times to local government reorganisation includes the maritime history of the port, the Natural History of Angus and local arts.

Open Apr–Oct Mon–Sat 10.30–1 & 2–5, Sun (Jul & Aug only) 2–5; Nov–Mar Mon–Fri 2–5, Sat 10.30–1 & 2–5.

Free.

P (100 yds) shop ✕ (ex guide dogs)

MORDIFORD
Hereford & Worcester
Map **3** SO53

Sufton Court
☎ Holme Lacy (043273) 268

Small Palladian mansion designed by James Wyatt. Completed c. 1780. Exquisite mouldings, fireplaces and doors. Antique china, lace, embroideries and water-colours. Park and grounds by Humphrey Repton.

Open 19 May–1 Jun & 18–31 Aug daily 2–5.30.

£1.

⚠ ക (ground floor & garden only) ✕

MORECAMBE
Lancashire
Map **7** SD46

Marineland
Stone Jetty, Promenade
☎ (0524) 414727

Dolphin and sea lion shows run continuously throughout the day. Also on show are turtles & alligators.

202

Fresh and marine fish both tropical and cold-water.

Open daily, Etr–Oct from 10.30am.

✳ £1.75 (ch & pen £1)

P (250 yds) shop

MORETON CORBET
Shropshire
Map **7** SJ52

Castle

Triangular group comprising keep of c. 1200, gatehouse altered in 1579, and notable Elizabethan range of the same date, all damaged by Parliamentary forces in 1644.

Open all reasonable times.

Free.

⚠ ⅄ (AM)

MORETON-IN-MARSH
Gloucestershire
Map **4** SP23

Batsford Arboretum (2m NW)
☎ (0608) 50722 & Blockley (0386) 700409 (wknds)

50 acres of privately owned gardens and arboretum. One of the largest and most comprehensive collections of trees in Europe.

Open Apr–Oct 10–5.

Morecambe
—
Morwellham

£1 (ch 16 & pen 50p). Party.

⚠ ⅏ ⅂ shop & garden centre

Sezincote (3m SW)

Water garden with trees of unusual size. The house of Indian style was the inspiration for the Brighton Pavilion.

House open May–Jul & Sep, Thu & Fri 2.30–5.30. Garden only all year (ex Dec) Thu, Fri & BH Mon 2–6 or dusk.

House & garden £2.50. Garden only £1.50 (ch 50p). Groups by appointment only.

⚠ (100 yds) ✖

MORPETH
Northumberland
Map **12** NZ18

Meldon Park (6m W on B6343)
☎ Hartburn (067072) 661

The house was built in 1832 by Dobson for the Cookson family and has been occupied by them up to the present time. Set in 10 acres of woodland with rhododendrons of many different colours.

Ground floor rooms only open to the public.

£1 (ch 50p) Party.

⚠ ⅖ ✖ ⓥ

MORWELLHAM
Devon
Map **2** SX46

Morwellham Quay Open-air Museum
(off A390 between Tavistock and Gunnislake)
☎ Tavistock (0822) 832766

Once the greatest copper port in Queen Victoria's Empire. Visitors can meet the blacksmith, cooper, assayer and servant girls, quay workers and coachmen dressed in period costume to recreate the bustling boom years in this picturesque old port. Ride underground into a copper mine and enjoy a heavy-horse-drawn wagonette ride along the Duke of Bedford's carriage way. Set in unspoilt country with riverside and woodland trails. Slide shows and other exhibits illustrating 1,000 years of history.

Open all year 10–6 (dusk in winter) last entry 4.30.

£3.20 (ch 5–18 £1.80, students & pen £2.20). Party.

⚠ ⅖ (licensed) ⅂ shop

CALDICOT CASTLE
Between Chepstow and Newport, just off the M4 (junctions 22 or 24, and signs from A48)

A restored Norman and mediaeval border castle, set in a Country Park, with ample parking, picnic and play space.

The Museum displays include furniture and costume; local history; relics from HMS Fondroyant, once Nelson's flagship. Regular temporary exhibitions. Free childrens worksheets available.

Open March — October inclusive, daily. School groups free (must book). Parties of 30+ reduced rates by arrangement.

Tel: Caldicot: 420241
Mediaeval Banquets — Tel. 421425.

Also visit:
Abergavenny Museum & Castle   Tel. 4282
Chepstow Museum   Tel. 5981
Monmouth—Nelson Museum   Tel. 3519

The Woodstock Tower and cannon from HMS Fondroyant

MOSELEY
Staffordshire
Map 7 SJ90

Moseley Old Hall
Built in Elizabethan times as half-timbered house, now encased in 19th-century brick, with interesting panelled rooms. Once the refuge (hiding hole and bed) of Charles II after Battle of Worcester in 1651.

Open Mar & Nov, Sun; Apr–Oct Wed, Sat, Sun also Etr, Spring & late summer BH 2–6.

£1.80 (ch 90p). Family ticket £5. Party.
ᴗ ᵭ shop ✗ (NT)

MOTTISFONT
Hampshire
Map 4 SU32

Mottisfont Abbey
A mainly 18th-century mansion with portions of former 12th-century priory. There is a fine Rex Whistler painting in drawing room and a walled rose garden.

Open 29 Mar–Sep. Grounds daily (ex Fri & Sat) 2–6. House (Whistler Room & Cellarium) Wed & Sun 2–6 (last admission 5).

Grounds Jun & Jul £1.30; Apr, May, Aug & Sep £1; House 30p extra.
(NT)

MOUSA ISLAND
Shetland
Map 16 HU42

Mousa Broch
The best preserved late prehistoric drystone tower in Scotland. It rises to a height of 40ft and, uniquely, is nearly complete.

Reached by boat from Leebottom, on Mousa Sound.

Open, see end of gazetteer. Apply keeper. Free.
(AM)

MUCHALLS
Grampian *Kincardineshire*
Map 15 NO89

Muchalls Castle
☎ Newtonhill (0569) 30217
17th-century castle, with fine fireplaces and plaster ceilings.

Open May–Sep, Tue & Sun 3–5.
30p (ch 10p).
ᴁ shop ✗

MUCHELNEY
Somerset
Map 3 ST42

Muchelney Abbey
☎ Langport (0458) 250664
15th- to 16th-century remains of Benedictine Abbey.

Open, see end of gazetteer. (Apr–Sep only).

┌─────────────────────┐
│   **Moseley**   │
│   —   │
│   **Nantwich**   │
└─────────────────────┘

✳ 50p (ch 16 & pen 25p).
ᴁ ᵭ (ground floor only) shop ✗ (AM)

MUCH WENLOCK
Shropshire
Map 7 SO69

Guildhall
☎ (0952) 727679
Striking half-timbered building dating from 1577, with beautiful oak panelling and furnishings.

Open Apr–Sep, Mon, Tue, Thu & Sat 11–12.30 & 2.30–5, Sun 2–5. (Closed 1st Thu of each month).

20p (ch 5 free, ch 5–16 & pen 10p).
P (50 yds) ✗

Much Wenlock Museum High St
☎ (0952) 727773
An interpretation of the history of the town and priory, including displays of geology, local natural history and local trades, houses in the old Market Hall.

Open 24 Mar–27 Sep, Mon–Sat 10.30–1 & 2–5, also Suns Jun–Aug 10.30–1 & 2–5.

35p (ch & pen free).
P ᵭ shop ✗

Wenlock Priory
Remains of a 13th-century abbey adjacent to chapter house, lavabo and transepts.

Only abbey ruins are open, see end of gazetteer.

✳ 50p (ch 16 & pen 25p).
ᴁ (AM)

MULL, ISLE OF
Strathclyde *Argyll*
Map 10 & 13
See **Craignure**

MUMBLES
West Glamorgan
Map 2 SS68

Oystermouth Castle
☎ Swansea (0792) 50821 ext 2815
Ruined gatehouse, chapel and great hall of 13th- to 14th-century date. Former stronghold of Braose family. Small park.

Open Apr–Sep daily 10.30–6; Sat & Sun 10–6.15, last admission 5.30. Oct–Mar, Mon–Fri 10–3.30 by appointment.

✳ 40p (ch, UB40 holders & pen 10p).
P ✗

MUNCASTER
Cumbria
Map 6 SD19

Muncaster Castle & Bird Garden
☎ Ravenglass (06577) 614 or 203

Seat of the Pennington family since 13th century and housing a fine collection of 16th- and 17th-century furnishings, pictures and embroideries. The garden has a famous collection of rhododendrons and azaleas, ornamental and tropical birds and Himalayan bears.

Open Good Fri–Sep, Tue–Sun & BH, House 1.30–4.30; Garden 12–5. Parties in the morning also, if booked in advance.

House & gardens £2.20 (ch 14 £1.10), Gardens only £1.10 (ch 14 70p). Party.

P ᴗ (licensed) ᵭ (ground floor) shop

Muncaster Mill
(1m NW on A595 by railway bridge)
☎ Ravenglass (06577) 232
Manorial mill on site dating from 1455. The mill race brings water from the River Mite ¾ mile to the 13ft overshot water wheel. The milling room contains three pairs of mill stones, two elevators, flour separators, and sack-hoist, all water-driven. Flour milled on premises for sale. Adjacent to, and served by, Ravenglass & Eskdale railway.

Open Apr, May & Sep, Mon–Fri & Sun 11–5; Jun, Jul & Aug 10–6. Party. Other times by appointment.

✳ 70p (ch 35p) Party.
ᴁ ᵭ (ground floor only) ✗

MUSSELBURGH
Lothian *Midlothian*
Map 11 NT37

Pinkie House
☎ 031-665 2059
A fine Jacobean building of 1613 and later, incorporating a tower of 1390. Fine painted ceiling in the long gallery. The house now forms part of the well-known Loretto School.

Open mid Apr–mid Jul & mid Sep–mid Dec, Tue 2–5.
Free.
ᴁ

MUTHILL
Tayside *Perthshire*
Map 11 NN81

Drummond Castle Gardens (1m N)
☎ (076481) 257
Beautiful formal gardens.

Gardens open Apr & Sep, Wed & Sun 2–6; May–Aug, daily 2–6. Details not confirmed for 1986.

✳ £1 (ch & pen 50p).
ᴁ ✗

NANTWICH
Cheshire
Map 7 SJ65

Churche's Mansion Hospital St
☎ (0270) 625933
An H-plan half-timbered mansion built in 1577 for Rychard and Margerye Churche. Restoration commenced in 1930 and continues to reveal the original fabric.

Open Apr Oct 10 4.

✱ 50p (ch 16 40p).

🄰 ⚓ (licensed) ⅋ (ground floor only) ✘

Dorfold Hall (1m W off A534)
☎ (0270) 625245

Attractive gabled house, dating from 1616, with fine panelling, plaster ceilings and furniture.

Open Apr–Oct Tue & BH Mon 2–5. Other times by appointment.

£1.50 (ch 75p).

🄰 ✘

NEATH
West Glamorgan
Map **3** SS79

Neath Abbey

Ruins of Cistercian (originally Savignac) abbey founded by Richard de Grainville in 1130.

Open see end of gazetteer.

60p (ch 16 30p).

🄰 (AM Cadw)

NETHER ALDERLEY
Cheshire
Map **7** SJ87

Nether Alderley Mill

15th-century mill, last worked in 1939. Preserved wooden waterwheels and machinery.

Open 30 & 31 Mar, Apr, May, Jun & Oct Wed, Sun & BH Mon 2–5.30, Jul–Sep, Tue–Sun & BH Mon 2–5.

£1.

(NT)

NETHER STOWEY
Somerset
Map **3** ST13

Coleridge Cottage
☎ (0278) 732662

Home of Samuel Taylor Coleridge from 1797 to 1800. His poem, The Ancient Mariner, was written here.

Open 29 Mar–Sep, Sun & Tue–Thu 2–5.

50p. Parties by arrangement with caretaker.

🄰 ✘ (NT)

NETHER WINCHENDON
Buckinghamshire
Map **4** SP71

Nether Winchendon House
☎ Haddenham (0844) 290101

Medieval house with Elizabethan and Georgian additions, containing portraits and maps belonging to Sir Francis Bernard, Governor of Massachusetts.

Open May–Aug, Thu 2.30–5.30, also 3–5 & 24–26 May; 7 & 8 Jun; 9 & 10 & 23–25 Aug. Parties 10+ by appointment throughout the year.

£1.30 (ch 12 70p) (pen 70p Thu only).

🄰 ⅋ (ground floor & garden only) ✘

Nantwich
—
Newby Bridge

NETLEY
Hampshire
Map **4** SU40

Netley Abbey

Extensive and beautiful remains of a Cistercian abbey founded in 1239.

Open any reasonable time.

Free.

🄰 ⅋ (AM)

NEW ABBEY
Dumfries and Galloway
Kirkcudbrightshire
Map **11** NX96

New Abbey Corn Mill

18th-century mill, in working order.

Open, see end of gazetteer.

✱ 50p (ch & pen 25p).

AM

Shambellie House Museum of Costume (½m N on A710)
☎ (038785) 375 or 031-225 7534
(National Museums of Scotland)

A costume collection, made by Charles Stewart of Shambellie, of European fashionable dress from the late 18th century to early 20th century. Mainly women's clothes and accessories although some children's and men's clothes; also fancy dress costume.

Open May–Sep Thu–Mon 10–5.30, Sun 12–5.30.

Free.

P shop

Sweetheart Abbey

One of the most beautiful monastic ruins in Scotland built by Lady Devorgilla of Galloway in memory of her husband John Balliol in 1273. In 1289 the Lady was buried in front of the high altar with the 'sweet heart' of her husband resting on her bosom.

Open see end of gazetteer.

✱ 50p (ch 25p).

🄰 ⅋ (AM)

NEWARK-ON-TRENT
Nottinghamshire
Map **8** SK85

Millgate Museum of Social & Folk Life
☎ Newark (0636) 79403

Collection reflecting the domestic, commercial and industrial life of the district from Victorian times onwards, including printing, with craft workshops, still being developed.

Open all year Mon–Fri 9–12 & 1–5, also Sat & Sun Apr–Sep 2–6.

Free.

🄰 shop ✘

Newark Museum Newark & Sherwood DC
☎ (0636) 702358

Local history, archaeology, natural history and art.

Open Mon–Wed, Fri & Sat 10–1 & 2–5, Thu 10–1, Apr–Sep also Sun 2–5.

Free.

P (100 yds) shop ✘

Newark Town Hall Market Pl
☎ (0636) 700200 & 700233

Designed by the architect John Carr in 1773, the town hall is perhaps one of the finest of all Georgian town halls. On display is the town's collection of silver gilt and silver plate, generally of the 17th and 18th centuries. Other items of interest are early historical records and various paintings including a collection by the artist Joseph Paul.

Open Mon–Fri, 10–12 & 2–4. (Closed BH Mon). Other times by appointment.

Free.

P (50 yds) ⅋ (ground floor only) ✘

Vina Cooke Collection of Dolls & Bygone Childhood The Old Rectory, Cromwell (5m N of Newark off A1)
☎ (0636) 821364

Large collection of Victorian and Edwardian dolls, including Vina Cooke handmade character dolls, prams, toys, dolls houses etc and costumes, all displayed in surroundings of 17th-century house.

Open daily 11.30–6, appointment advisable.

75p (ch 40p).

🄰 ⚓ (prior arrangement) ✘ Ⓥ

NEWBURY
Berkshire
Map **4** SU46

Newbury District Museum The Wharf
☎ (0635) 30511

In picturesque 17th and 18th century buildings. Displays include: Ballooning; Kennet and Avon Canal; Traditional Crafts; costume; Civil War battles of Newbury (with audio-visual). Local collections: archaeology, history, geology and birds. Also cameras, pewter and pottery. Temporary exhibitions throughout the year.

Open Apr–Sep, Mon–Sat (ex Wed) 10–6, Sun & BH 2–6. Oct–Mar, Mon–Sat 10–4 (Closed Sun & Wed).

Free.

P ⅋ (ground floor only) shop ✘ (ex guide dogs)

NEWBY BRIDGE
Cumbria
Map **7** SD38

Graythwaite Hall Gardens →

205

(4m N, on W side of Lake Windermere)
☎ (0448) 31248

7-acre landscaped garden with shrubs, azaleas, and rhododendrons.

Open Apr–Jun, daily 10–6.

75p (ch 14 free).

⚑

NEWBY HALL & GARDENS
North Yorkshire
Map **8** SE36

(4m SE of Ripon)
☎ Boroughbridge (09012) 2583

Late 17th-century house with additions and interior by Robert Adam, containing important collection of classical sculpture and Gobelin tapestries. The gardens cover some twenty-five acres, and include adventure gardens for children and a miniature railway.

Open Etr–Sep daily 1–5. Gardens open daily 11–5.30 (last admission 5). (Closed Mon ex BH Mon).

✸ £2.20 (ch £1.10, pen £2). Gardens only £1.40 (ch 90p) Party.

⚑ ⬛ (licensed garden restaurant) ⊞ ⚿ (ground floor only) shop ✗ ⓥ

See advertisement under Ripon.

NEWCASTLE EMLYN
Dyfed
Map **2** SN34

Felin Geri Mill (2m N on unclass rd off B4333 at Cwmcoy)
☎ (0239) 710810

Built in the 16th century, this is one of the last watermills in the UK using the original means of production to grind stone-ground wholemeal flour on a regular commercial basis. Visitors are shown all stages of production. There are wholemeal cookery demonstrations in the bakery during weekdays. There is also a mill museum and a water-powered sawmill.

Open Etr–Oct, daily 10–6.

£1.50 (ch 75p, under 5 free, pen 90p).

⚑ ⬛ ⊞ ⚿ (grounds & gardens only) shop

NEWCASTLE-UNDER-LYME
Staffordshire
Map **7** SJ84

Borough Museum The Brampton
☎ (0782) 619705

Local history, including Royal Charters, ceramics, dolls, display of firearms, and Victorian street scene.

Open Mon–Sat 9.30–1 & 2–6; Also Sun 2–5.30, May–Sep.

Free.

⚑ ⚿ (ground floor only) ✗

Hobbergate Art Gallery The Brampton
☎ (0782) 611962

Permanent collection of 18th- and 19th-

---

century English water-colours. Temporary exhibitions and picture loan scheme.

Open Tue-Fri 2–6, Sat 9.30–1 & 2–6 (Closed BH).

Free.

⚑ ⚿ (ground floor only) ✗

NEWCASTLE UPON TYNE
Tyne and Wear
Map **12** NZ26

Hancock Museum Barras Bridge
☎ (0632) 322359

One of the finest natural history museums in England. The geological displays and, more recently, John Hancock's magnificent collection of birds have been reinstated. New displays have also been prepared for the invertebrates. There are also ethnographical and Egyptian exhibits. Abels Ark gallery and Bewick room now open.

Open Mon–Sat 10–5; Also Sun 2–5, May–Sep

30p (ch & pen 15p) Party.

⚑ ⚿ (ground floor & gardens only) shop ✗

Laing Art Gallery Higham Pl
☎ (0632) 327734/326989

British paintings and watercolours from the 18th century to the present day with works by Reynolds, Turner, Burne-Jones and others including the Northumberland artist, John Martin. Also a collection of silver, ceramics and glass including a fine display of 18th-century enamelled glass by William Bailby of Newcastle. Temporary exhibition programme.

Open Mon–Fri 10–5.30; Sat 10–4.30; Sun 2.30–5.30.

Free.

P ⚿ shop ✗

Museum of Antiquities
University Quadrangle
☎ (0632) 328511 ext 3844/3849

The collection has been in the course of assembly since 1813, and was opened in its present form in 1960. Valuable collection of Roman and other antiquities, with models, reconstructions etc.

Open weekdays 10–5 (Closed Good Fri, 24–26 Dec & New Year's day & certain other PH's; telephone in advance).

Free.

P (600 yds) ⚿ (prior arrangement) shop ✗   •

Museum of Science & Engineering
Blandford House, West Blandford St
☎ (0632) 326789

Motive power (engine) gallery; Maritime

---

gallery; special exhibitions, educational activities, plus supporting displays.

Open Mon–Fri 10–5.30, Sat 10–4.30. (Closed Xmas & 1 Jan).

Free.

P ⚿ shop ✗ (ex guide dogs)

NEWCHAPEL
Surrey
Map **5** TQ34

London Temple Visitors Centre & Gardens
☎ Lingfield (0342) 833842

Pictures, films, and beautiful gardens.

Open daily (ex Mon) 10–7 or dusk.

Free.

⚑ ⚿

NEWENT
Gloucestershire
Map **3** SO72

Falconry Centre (1m SW on unclassified Clifford's Mesne Rd)
☎ (0531) 820286

Exceptional collection of birds of prey. Includes a museum, 'Hawk Walk' where trained birds may be seen, breeding aviaries and brooder room, and flying ground where birds are flown daily (weather permitting).

Open Mar–Oct daily (ex Tue) 10.30–5.30 (or dusk if earlier).

£1.95 (ch 3 free, ch 16 95p). Party 16+ (free guided tour).

⚑ ⬛ ⊞ ⚿ shop ✗

NEWHAVEN
East Sussex
Map **5** TQ40

Fort Newhaven Museum
☎ (0273) 513600

Restored Victorian fort built in 1860 to protect the area against invasion from abroad. Underground museum, gun emplacements, magazines, maze of underground tunnels and massive parade ground. Childrens assault course, amusements and public house.

Open daily 10–6. (Closed Xmas day).

£1 (ch, students & pen 60p). Party 10+.

⚑ ⬛ & public house ⊞ shop

NEWMARKET
Suffolk
Map **5** TL66

National Horseracing Museum
99 High St
☎ (0638) 667333

The great story of the development of horseracing in this country is told in the Museum's five permanent galleries, with changing displays each year. Temporary exhibitions, video programme of classic races.

Open 29 Mar–8 Dec Tue–Sat, (Mon in Aug also); 10–5, Sun 2–5 & BH's. →

Be there...

at a 2000 B.C. burial[1]; see a Roman fort being built[2]; step aboard a railway guard's van[3]; discover a glass arcade[4]; meet a hero of Gallipoli[5]; experience the Great Fire of Newcastle[6]; navigate the Tyne[7]; visit a pit-head[8]; stroll through an Edwardian house[9]; take a glass with Mr. Beilby[10]...

...and be back in time for tea.

In our Museums the emphasis is on action, participation and fun. Out are the endless, old fashioned glass cases you pored over in hushed silence. In are... professionally designed displays, working models to play with, complete period room settings to browse through and sound effects to complete the picture...

So take part in history and learn as you travel through the centuries.

TYNE AND WEAR COUNTY COUNCIL MUSEUMS

for time travellers

TYNE AND WEAR COUNTY COUNCIL-WORKING FOR YOU

£1.50 (ch, pen & students 75p). Party
20+.

P .⚏ 🍴 ᕑ shop ⋈ Ⓥ

NEW MILTON
Hampshire
Map **4** SZ29

Sammy Miller Museum Gore Rd
☎ (0425) 619696

*One of the largest collections of fully
restored motorcycles in Europe, some
extremely rare and many machines still
fully competitive. Also on display are
many interesting artefacts which
represent a link with motorcycling of a
bygone era. A constantly changing
collection.*

Open Apr–Sep daily 10.30–4.30. Oct–Mar
Sat & Sun 10.30–4.

£1 (ch 50p).

⚠ ᕑ (ground floor only) shop Ⓥ

NEWPORT
Dyfed
Map **2** SN04

Pentre Ifan Burial Chamber (3m SE)
*Remains of this chamber comprise
capstone and three uprights with semi-
circular forecourt at one end. Excavated
1936–37 when found to be part of a
vanished long barrow.*

Open all reasonable times.

Free.

(AM Cadw)

NEWPORT
Essex
Map **5** TL53

Mole Hall Wildlife Park Widdington
☎ Saffron Walden (0799) 40400

*Wildlife park with large collection of
animals and birds in pools and
enclosures. Set within grounds of part-
Elizabethan hall, not open to the public.*

Open all year (ex 25 Dec) 10.30–6 (or
dusk).

Admission fee payable.

⚠ ⚏ 🍴 ᕑ shop ⋈

Newmarket
—
Newtimber

NEWPORT
Gwent
Map **3** ST38

Museum & Art Gallery John Frost Sq
☎ (0633) 840064

*Archaeology and history of Gwent
including Roman finds from Caerwent and
Pontypool Japanned ware; section on
Chartist movement of 1838–40. Natural
history and geology. Also collection of
early English watercolours.*

Open Mon–Thu 9.30–5, Fri 9.30–4.30, Sat
9.30–4.

Free.

P (100 yds) ᕑ shop ⋈ (ex guide dogs)

Tredegar House & Country Park
Coedkernew
☎ (0633) 62275

*Former home of the Morgans, Lords of
Tredegar. Finest Restoration house in
Wales. Substantially remodelled during
the late 17th century but with medieval
wing remaining. Extensive grounds,
visitor centre, craft workshops, gardens,
carriage rides, orienteering course, fishing
and boating. Venue for 'Country Sports
Fair' 1 Jun, 'Services Spectacular' 16 & 17
Aug, 'Newport Show' 29–31 Aug &
'Vintage Car Rally' 14 Sep.*

Grounds open daily dawn–dusk. House
open daily Good Fri–last Sun in Sep Wed–Sun
& BHs (guided tours every 30 mins from
12.30–4.30).

✻ £1.20 (ch 60p, students, unemployed &
pen 90p). Family £2.50. Grounds free.

⚠ ⚏ (licensed) ᕑ shop Ⓥ

NEWPORT
Isle of Wight
Map **4** SZ48

Roman Villa Cypress Rd
☎ (0983) 529720 (Jun–Sep), other times
529963

---

*Villa built towards end of 2nd century and
discovered in 1926. Baths in good state of
preservation and several mosaic floors.*

Open Etr–Sep, Sun–Fri 10–4.30.

50p (ch & pen 25p). School parties.

P (200 yds) shop ⋈

NEW ROMNEY
Kent
Map **5** TR02

Romney, Hythe & Dymchurch Railway
☎ (0679) 62353

*Depot of 13½-mile-long Romney, Hythe
and Dymchurch railway, the world's
smallest public railway from Hythe,
through New Romney to Dungeness.*

Open daily Etr–Sep, also weekends in Mar
& Oct. For times & fares apply to: The
Manager, R.H. & D.R., New Romney
Station, New Romney, Kent.

Reductions for pen at wknds.

⚠ ⚏ (at New Romney & Dungeness
stations) shop

NEWSTEAD
Nottinghamshire
Map **8** SK55

Newstead Abbey
☎ Mansfield (0623) 792822

*Former Priory, founded in 12th century,
rebuilt as a house in the 16th and 17th
centuries, famous for its association with
Lord Byron, who lived here. Collections of
pictures and furniture.*

House open daily Etr–Sep 1.45–5. Garden
open daily 9.30–dusk.

✻ House 80p (ch 20p). Grounds &
gardens 70p (ch 20p).

⚠ (150 yds) ᕑ (gardens only) shop ⋈

NEWTIMBER
West Sussex
Map **4** TQ21

Newtimber Place
☎ Hurstpierpoint (0273) 833104

*Moated 17th-century house with
Etruscan-style wallpaintings.*

The National Horseracing Museum
99 High Street, Newmarket
Suffolk, CB8 8JL *(Telephone 0638 667333)*
The National Horseracing Museum, housed in the Regency
Subscription Rooms on the Newmarket High Street, was
opened by the Queen on April 30th 1983.
The great story of the development of horseracing in this
Country is told in the Museum's five permanent galleries, with
changing displays each year. Temporary Exhibitions, a video
programme of classic races and a Coffee Shop with a walled
garden are added attractions.
Opening Times:
Tues. to Sat. from 10:00 - 5:00 Sun. from 2:00 - 5:00
Closed Mondays except for Bank Holidays
June, July & August : Mon. to Sat. from 10:00 - 5:00
Sunday from 2:00 - 5:00
Admission: Adults £1.00 Children & OAP's 50p

House & gardens open May–Aug, 2–5.
£1 (ch 50p).

▲

NEWTON
Northumberland
Map **12** NZ06

Hunday National Tractor and Farm Museum
West Side (¾m N of A69)
☎ Stocksfield (0661) 842553

A collection of over 250 tractors and engines showing the development of agriculture from 1900 to the post-war period. It also includes small hand tools,

---

harness, dairy equipment and an 1835 Bingfield steam engine and thresher. The display area includes a narrow-gauge railway, a rebuilt 18th-century water powered corn mill with joiner's and blacksmith's shops, a farmhouse kitchen and many domestic items.

Open Jan–23 Apr daily ex Sat 10–4; 24 Apr–28 Sep daily 10–5; 29 Sep–Dec 10–4.

✳ £1.60 (ch & pen 60p) Party 20+.
▲ ⬚ (summer only) ⚓ ♿ (ground floor only) shop ✠

NEWTON ABBOT
Devon
Map **3** SX87

Bradley Manor
In deep valley of River Lemon. 15th-century house with chapel.

Open 2 Apr–Sep Wed 2–5; also Thu 3 & 10 Apr, 18 & 25 Sep 2–5. Last admissions 4.45.
£1.10.
(NT)

NEWTONGRANGE
Lothian *Midlothian*
Map **11** NT36

Scottish Mining Museum Lady Victoria
Colliery
☎ 031-663 7519

*After a working life of almost ninety years
the colliery is being restored and
developed as a museum. An exhibition in
the visitor centre portrays characters
involved in the creation and running of the
mine. The steam winding engine house
can also be visited. Newtongrange is the
largest surviving coal mining village in
Scotland. A self drive coal heritage trail
links the site to Prestongrange in East
Lothian.*

Open Tue–Fri 10–4.30, Sat & Sun noon–5.

✳ £1 (ch & pen 50p)

  ♨ 🏷 ᵭ (ground floor only) shop ✖

NEWTONMORE
Highland *Inverness-shire*
Map **14** NN79

Clan Macpherson House & Museum .
☎ (05403) 332

*Relics and memorials of the Clan Chiefs
and other Macpherson families. Prince
Charles Edward Stuart relics, including
letters to the Clan Chief (1745) and a letter
to the Prince from his father (The Old
Pretender). Royal Warrants, Green Banner
of the Clan, swords, pictures, decorations
and medals. Also James Macpherson's
fiddle, and other interesting historical
exhibits. Highland Games 1st Sat in
August.*

Open May–Sep Mon–Sat 10–5.30, Sun
2.30–5.30. Other times by appointment.

Free (Donation).

♨ ᵭ ✖

NEWTOWN
Isle of Wight
Map **4** SZ49

Old Town Hall

Restored 18th-century meeting house.

Open 30 Mar–Jul Mon, Wed, Thu & Sun
10.30–1 & 2–5; Aug Mon–Fri & Sun 10.30–
1 & 2–5.

40p (ch 20p)

(NT)

NORHAM
Northumberland
Map **12** NT94

Castle
☎ (07974) 2494

*Mid 12th-century keep, built by Bishop
Hugh Puiset, with later alterations, and
overlooking the River Tweed.*

Open, see end of gazetteer.

✳ 50p (ch 16 & pen 25p).

ᵭ (ex Keep). (AM)

Newtongrange
—
North Leigh

NORTHAMPTON
Northamptonshire
Map **4** SP76

Delapre Abbey
☎ (0604) 62129

*16th- to 19th-century house, with fine
porch, built on site of Cluniac nunnery.
Contains Northamptonshire Record Office
and HQ of Northamptonshire Record
Society.*

Abbey grounds open all year until dusk.
Wall garden open May–Sep only during
daylight. Certain parts of the interior
shown Thu only, May–Sep 2.30–5; Oct–
Apr 2.30–4.30.

Free.

♨ ✖ ♿

NORTH BERWICK
Lothian *East Lothian*
Map **12** NT58

North Berwick Museum
☎ (0620) 3470

*Small museum in former Burgh school
with sections on local and natural history,
archaeology and domestic life. Exhibitions
held throughout the summer.*

Open Jun–Sep Mon–Sat 10–1 & 2–5, Sun
2–5.

Free.

♨ ✖

Tantallon Castle (2m E on A198)

*A famous 14th-century stronghold of the
Douglases facing towards the lonely Bass
Rock from the rocky Firth of Forth Shore.
Nearby 16th- and 17th-century
earthworks.*

Open, see end of gazetteer. Closed Tue &
alternate Wed in Winter.

✳ £1 (ch & pen 50p).

♨ ᵭ (AM)

NORTH CREAKE
Norfolk
Map **9** TF83

Creake Abbey (1m N off B1355)

*Church ruin with crossing and eastern
arm belonging to a house of Augustinian
canons founded in 1206.*

Accessible any reasonable time.

Free.

(AM)

NORTHENDEN
Greater Manchester
Map **7** SJ89

Wythenshawe Hall Wythenshawe Park
☎ 061-236 9422

Inside this black and white half-timbered

---

*house are 17th-century panelled rooms
with oak furniture, an early 19th-century
library and a restored Georgian bedroom.
Recently discovered behind the panelling
is a rare example of Tudor wall painting.
The house is surrounded by beautiful
parkland with rare trees and shrubs,
horticultural centre, an aviary and walled
kitchen garden.*

Open Mon & Wed–Sat 10–6; Apr–Sep also
Sun 2–6.

Free.

♨ ᵭ shop ✖

NORTHIAM
East Sussex
Map **5** TQ82

Great Dixter
☎ (07974) 3160

*15th-century half-timbered house with
notable great hall, and fine gardens.*

Open Apr–12 Oct, & also 18, 19, 25, & 26
Oct Tue–Sun & BH Mon 2–5. Other times
by appointment. Gardens open 24 & 25
May, 25 Aug & Sun in Jul & Aug from
11am.

£1.60 (ch 14 40p). Gardens only £1 (ch
25p).

♨ ᷂ shop & garden centre ✖

NORTHLEACH
Gloucestershire
Map **4** SP11

Cotswold Countryside Collection,
Fosseway
☎ (04516) 715 during summer months,
Cirencester (0285) 5611 at other times

*Housed in the remaining buildings of the
Northleach House of Correction, one of a
group of 'country prisons' in
Gloucestershire. The museum tells the
story of rural life in the Cotswolds. Of
particular note is a unique exhibition of
Gloucestershire harvest-wagons. 'Below
Stairs' gallery of dairy, kitchen and
laundry.*

Open Apr–Oct Mon–Sat 10–5.30, Sun 2–
5.30 & BH's.

✳ 55p (ch 25p, students & pen 35p).
Party

♨ 🏷 (summer pm, wknds 2–5 & BH) ᷂
ᵭ (ground floor only) shop

NORTH LEIGH
Oxfordshire
Map **4** SP31

North Leigh Roman Villa

*Excavations of Roman villa occupied
between 2nd and 4th centuries and
reconstructed late in period. Tassellated
pavement and 2–3ft-high wall span.*

Open, see end of gazetteer. Apr–Sep
only.

✳ 30p (ch 16 & pen 15p).

♨ (AM)

NORTH LEVERTON
Nottinghamshire
Map **8** SK78

Windmill (½m W of village in minor road)
☎ Gainsborough (0427) 880200

*In 1813 the local farming community set
up a committee to build the four-sailed
tower mill which has been in use ever
since.*

Open most afternoons 2–4.

25p (ch 10p).

⚠ ♿ (ground floor only) shop

North Loverton
—
Northwich

NORTHWICH
Cheshire
Map **7** SJ67

Arley Hall & Gardens
(5m N of Northwich; 5m from M6 junc 19
and 20; M56 junc 9 and 10)
☎ (056585) 284 or 353

Early Victorian house, with private chapel

---

*by Salvin containing fine examples of
plasterwork, woodcarvings, pictures and
furniture. The gardens feature unusual
avenue of clipped ilex trees, walled
gardens, herb garden and scented
garden. Woodland walk. Farm animals.*

Open 28 Mar–5 Oct daily (ex Mon but
open BH) 2–5. Gardens Apr, May, Sep &
Oct 2–6, Jun–Aug 12–6.

✱ £2.10 (ch 8 free, ch 17 £1.05). Gardens
only £1.30 (ch 8 free, ch 17 65p).

⚠ ⬛ (licensed) ⟊ ♿ (ground floor only)
shop & plant sales Ⓥ

See advertisement on page 212

COTSWOLD COUNTRYSIDE COLLECTION

Award-winning museum for the
Cotswolds. The Lloyd-Baker
Collection of agricultural
history includes wagons, horse-
drawn implements and tools,
acquired by the nation for display
at Northleach. The museum's

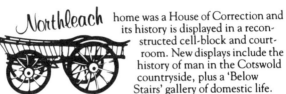

home was a House of Correction and
its history is displayed in a reconstructed cell-block and courtroom. New displays include the
history of man in the Cotswold
countryside, plus a 'Below
Stairs' gallery of domestic life.

Open Daily: 1st April – 29th September 1985. Telephone: Northleach 715 or Cirencester 5611

Great Dixter
Northiam, East Sussex

Here you can see a family
home in a timber-framed
hall well over 500 years
old, with antique furniture
and needlework. The
gardens, designed by
Lutyens, form a charming
setting. There is such a
wide variety of plants that
there will surely be
something new to you.
Many plants can be bought
in the nurseries. There are
two grass car parking
areas, good for a picnic.
Conducted tours of the
gardens by qualified guides
may be booked for groups
of any number up to 50 by
prior arrangement.
**Telephone 07974 3160 for
more information,
(or 3107 for plants).**

Lion Salt Works Marston (1½m NE off B5075)
☎ (0606) 2066
Inspect the pump house with original steam engine pumping brine from beneath the works. A non-working salt pan and stove have been restored to authentic condition. Original punching and shearing machine in restored smithy.
Open May–Sep, daily 2–5. Evening visits Wed & Thu fr 7pm for parties. (Subject to confirmation).
❉ 60p (ch 40p, pen 50p).
⚠ ♿ shop

Salt Museum London Rd
☎ (0606) 41331
Traces the history of the salt industry from Roman times.
Open Tue–Sat, Sun (Etr–Sep) & BH Mon 2–5. 10–5 Jul & Aug, (Closed Good Fri & Xmas).
❉ 50p (ch 25p) family £1.25.
⚠ shop ✘

Vale Royal Abbey Whitegate
☎ Sandiway (0606) 882164
The present stately home was constructed around the monastery of 1277, which survives the abbey of the same date. Still remaining are some fine carvings and panelling depicting various Royal visits. Beautiful beech-lined drive-approach from the south.
Open Apr–Sep, Sat, Sun & BH 11–4. (Closed Xmas).
£1 (ch 12 & pen 50p). Party.
⚠ ♿ (ground floor & gardens only) shop Ⓥ

NORTH WOOTTON
Somerset
Map 3 ST54

Wootton Vineyard North Town House
☎ Pilton (074989) 359
A vineyard set in the foothills of the Mendips, 3m from Wells, with 9000 vines specially imported from the Rhine and Alsace. The old farm buildings house a winery where fresh dry white wine is made. Visitors can walk in the vineyards

---

Northwich
Norwich

and wines may be purchased direct from the cellar.
Open Mon–Sat 10–1 & 2–5.
⚠ shop ✘

NORTON
Suffolk
Map 5 TL96

Norton Bird Gardens (nr Bury St Edmunds on A1088 off A45. Between Woolpit and Ixworth)
☎ Pakenham (0359) 30957
Collection of foreign birds and waterfowl etc. Aviaries well designed and planted to create natural conditions for the birds. Tropical house. Set in 4-acre garden with flowering bulbs, roses, herbaceous beds.
Open daily 11–6 (dusk in winter).
❉ £1.25 (ch 70p pen £1). Party.
⚠ 🚊 ♿ shop ✘ Ⓥ

NORWICH
Norfolk
Map 5 TG20

Bridewell Bridewell Alley
☎ (0603) 611277 ext 299
Flint-faced late 14th-century merchant's house, used as a prison from 1583 to 1828. Now interesting museum of local crafts and industries.
Open Mon–Sat 10–5, (Closed Good Fri, Xmas and New Year).
15p (ch 5p, students & unemployed 10p). 24 May–Sep 30p (ch 5p, students & unemployed 15p).
P (500 yds) shop ✘

City Hall St Peter Street
☎ (0603) 622233 ext 743
Civic Plate and Insignia dating from 1549 on show, also the Council Chamber.
Open Mon–Fri 10–4, visits by arrangement with the Director of Administration.

Free.
P ♿ (ground floor only) shop

Norwich Castle Castle Meadow
☎ (0603) 611277 ext 279
Restored 12th-century keep, now museum with a constantly changing pattern of exhibitions.
Open Mon–Sat 10–5, Sun 2–5, (Closed Good Fri, Xmas & New Year).
30p (ch 5p, students & unemployed 15p). 24 May–Sep 60p (ch 5p, students & unemployed 25p).
P (200 yds) 🚊 (licensed) ♿ shop ✘

Royal Norfolk Regiment Museum
Brittania Barracks, Brittania Rd
☎ (0603) 628455
Contains a fine collection of medals, uniforms and weapons, paintings, silver and trophies amassed by the Regiment.
Open Mon–Fri 9–12.30, 2–4 (Closed BH).
Free. (Donations).
P (50 yds) ✘

Sainsbury Centre for Visual Arts
University of East Anglia
☎ (0603) 56060
Houses Sir Robert and Lady Sainsbury's private art collection which was given to the University in 1973. European art of 19th and 20th centuries. Also African tribal sculpture, Oceanic traditional sculpture, North American and Pre-columbian art, Egyptian, Asian and European antiquities. Various other exhibitions during the year.
Open Tue–Sun 12–5. (Closed BH & University closure at Xmas).
Collections & exhibition 75p (students & pen 40p). Separately 50p (students & pen 25p).
⚠ 🚊 ♿ shop ✘

St Peter Hungate Church Museum
Princes St, near Elm Hill
☎ (0603) 611277 ext 296
Fine church (1460), with hammer-beam roof and good Norwich painted glass, now museum of church art. Brass rubbing centre.

Arley Hall and Gardens
Near Knutsford, Cheshire.

Magnificent award winning gardens of great variety.
Fine hall the home of the same family for over 500 years.
All set deep in the peaceful Cheshire countryside.

The Family Day Out at a Family Home

Signposted from roundabouts A556/M6 (Exit 19)
and A50/M6 (Exit 20)/M56 (Exit 9)

Telephone: Arley (056 585) 353, 284 or 203

Open Mon–Sat 10–5 (Closed Good Fri, Xmas & New Year day).

Free.

P (100 yds) ఈ shop ✖

Strangers' Hall Charing Cross
☎ (0603) 611277 ext 275

Late medieval merchant's house dating from 1320 and later, with furnished period rooms from early Tudor to late Victorian.

Open Mon–Sat 10–5 (Closed Good Fri, Xmas & New Year).

15p (ch 5p, students & unemployed 10p) 24 May–Sep 30p (ch 5p students & unemployed 15p).

P (500 yds) shop ✖

NOSTELL PRIORY
West Yorkshire
Map **8** SE41

Mid 18th-century mansion built by Paine in 1733, with Adam wing of 1766. Pictures, Chippendale furnishings, notable saloon and tapestry room. Lake in grounds.

Open: 29 Mar–Jun, Sep & Oct, Sat 12–5 & Sun 11–5: Jul & Aug Sat–Thu 12–5 & Sun 11–5 BH 11–5.

House, gardens & grounds £1.80, gardens & grounds only £1.

⚠ (50p) ♨ (NT)

NOTTINGHAM
Nottinghamshire
Map **8** SK53

Brewhouse Yard Museum Castle Boulevard
☎ (0602) 411881 ext 67 or 48

Housed in 17th-century buildings on a 2-acre site. The museum depicts daily life in the city in post-medieval times with period rooms and thematic displays. Unusual rock-cut cellars open showing their uses in the past. The museum contains material which can be handled or operated by the public. The cottage gardens contain unusual local plants.

Open all year 10–12 & 1–5, last admission 4.45pm, (Closed Xmas).

Free. Parties must book.

P (200 yds) ఈ (ground floor only) ✖ (ex guide dogs)

Canal Museum Canal St
☎ (0602) 598835

On ground floor and wharfage of 19th-century warehouse, the museum tells the history of the River Trent from the Ice Age to the present day. Includes local canal and river navigation, boats, bridges, archaeology etc.

Open Apr–Sep, Wed–Sun 10–12 & 1–5.45, Sun 1–5.45, Oct–Mar Wed, Thu & Sat 10–12 & 1–5, Sun 1–5.

Free.

P (300 yds) ఈ shop ✖

Castle Museum
☎ (0602) 411881

Mainly 17th-century with much restored

Norwich
—
Nunney

late 13th-century gateway. Now museum and art gallery. Conducted tours through underground passages.

Open summer 10–5.45; winter 10–4.45. Grounds open Mon–Fri 8–dusk, Sat, Sun, BH Mon 9–dusk. (Closed Xmas day).

✱ 20p (ch 10p) Sun & BH otherwise free.

P ♨ (licensed) ఈ shop ✖

Green's Mill and Science Centre
Belvoir Hill, Sneinton
☎ (0602) 503635

A partially reconstructed tower mill restored to working order with flour milled. The adjacent Science Museum contains working models and exhibits illustrating the importance to science of George Green, one time miller and distinguished mathematician.

Mill restoration due to be completed by Jan 1986. Open Wed–Sun 10–12 & 1–5, also BHs. (Closed Xmas day).

Free.

⚠ ఈ (ex mill) shop ✖

Industrial Museum
Courtyard Buildings, Wollaton Park
☎ (0602) 284602

Housed in 18th-century stable block are displays illustrating Nottingham's industrial history and in particular the lace and hosiery industries, together with exhibits on the pharmaceutical industry, engineering, tobacco industry and printing. New extensions house a mid 19th-century beam pumping engine, and heavy agricultural machinery. Outside yards display a horse gin from a local coalmine, Victorian street furniture etc.

Open Apr–Sep, Mon–Sat 10–6, Sun 2–6; Oct–Mar Thu & Sat 10–4.30; Sun 1.30– 4.30. 19th-century beam pumping engine in steam last Sun in each month & BH.

Free Mon–Sat, 20p (ch 10p) Sun & BH. (Ticket valid for both this and Natural History Museum, Wollaton Hall).

⚠ ఈ shop ✖

Museum of Costume and Textiles
43–51 Castlegate
☎ (0602) 411881

Displays include costume from 1730 to 1960 in furnished room settings of circa 1790, 1830, 1860, 1885, 1910 and 1935. Other rooms contain 17th-century costume and embroidery, the Lord Middleton collection, map tapestries of Nottinghamshire, dress accessories from 18th century to circa 1960, English, European and Asian embroidery, knitted, woven and printed textiles. Also there are exhibits of hand and machine made lace.

Open daily 10–5, (Closed Xmas day).

Free.

P (250 yds) shop ✖

Natural History Museum Wollaton Hall
☎ (0602) 281333 & 281130

Housed in imposing Elizabethan mansion by Robert Smythson, dating from 1580– 1588, and situated in large park with deer.

Open Apr–Sep, Mon–Sat 10–7, Sun 2–5; Oct, Mon–Sat 10–5.30, Sun 1.30–4.30; Nov–Mar, Mon–Sat 10–4.30, Sun 1.30– 4.30.

✱ Free weekdays, 20p (ch 10p) Sun & BH. (Ticket valid for both this and Industrial Museum).

⚠ ♨ Etr–Sep ♨ ఈ (ground floor & gardens) shop ✖

NUNEATON
Warwickshire
Map **4** SP39

Arbury Hall (2m SW)
☎ (0203) 382804

Unique Elizabethan and 18th-century house, containing fine plaster ceilings, furniture, pictures and china. The 17th-century stable block has a porch designed by Wren, housing a museum of veteran cycles. Rainbow Craft Fair 26 & 27 Apr.

Open Etr Sun–Sep, Sun & BH 2.30–5.30 (last admission 5) Jul & Aug also Tue & Wed. Gardens 1–6 (parties by special arrangement with Administrator, Arbury Estate Office, Windmill Hill, Astley).

✱ £1.50 (ch 80p) park & gardens only 80p (ch 40p).

⚠ ♨ ఈ (ground floor & gardens only) shop

Nuneaton Museum and Art Gallery
Riversley Park
☎ (0203) 326211 ext 473

A purpose-built structure, situated in a pleasant public park, it houses a permanent collection of ethnography, archaeology, the George Eliot Collection and a display of fine miniatures painted by May B Lee (Lady Stott). From Mar to May the Nuneaton Festival of Art is held here.

Open Summer Mon–Fri 12–7, Sat & Sun 10–7; winter 12–5 & 10–5.

Free.

P (100 yds) ఈ (ground floor only) shop ✖

NUNNEY
Somerset
Map **3** ST74

Nunney Castle

Moated structure modelled on French 'Bastille', built by Sir John de la Mere in 1373. Surrounded by one of the deepest moats in England.

Open any reasonable time.

Free.

ఈ (exterior only) (AM)

NUNNINGTON
North Yorkshire
Map **8** SE67

Nunnington Hall

16th- to 17th-century house with panelled hall and staircase. Carlisle Collection of miniature rooms on display.

Open Etr–Oct (Closed Good Fri) Tue–Thu, Sat & Sun 2–6 (Jul & Aug 12–6). BH Mon 11–6. Last admission 5.30.

£1.30.

P ⬛ shop (NT)

OAKHAM
Leicestershire
Map **4** SK80

Oakham Castle off Market Place
☎ (0572) 3654

Preserves a splendid Norman hall, with unique collection of presentation horseshoes.

Ground open daily 10–5.30 (4pm Nov–Mar). Great hall open Sun 2–5.30, Tue–Sat & BH 10–1 & 2–5.30. Nov–Mar close 4pm; (Closed Good Fri & Xmas). Magistrates Court in session on Mon.

Free.

P (100 yds) ♿ shop ✖ (in Hall)

Rutland County Museum Catmos St
☎ (0572) 3654

Local archaeology, especially Roman and Anglo-Saxon, craft tools and local history. Courtyard containing various farm wagons and agricultural implements. Temporary exhibitions.

Open Apr–Oct Tue–Sat & BH 10–1 & 2–5, Sun 2–5; Nov–Mar, Tue–Sat 10–1 & 2–5, (Closed Good Fri & Xmas).

Free.

P (adjacent) ♿ (ground floor only) shop ✖ (unless carried)

OAKHILL
Somerset
Map **3** ST64

The World of Models at Oakhill Manor
(Entrance by 'Mendip Inn' on A37)
☎ (0749) 840210

Nunnington — Okehampton

A country estate of 45 acres situated high in the Mendip Hills. The mansion is a fine example of one of England's smaller country houses set in eight acres of delightful gardens. Features one of the world's finest collections of models relating to transport, displayed in a furnished setting. Visitors are transported from the carpark on a miniature railway which covers ¾ mile with views of the surrounding hills plus 'N' gauge model electric railways and 'Dolores' the live miniature horse.

Open 27 Mar–2 Nov daily 11–5.

✳ £2.60 (ch 2–5 95p, ch 6–15 & pen £1.90) family ticket £6–£7. Party 25+.

♿ ⬛ 🍴 ♿ (ground floor & gardens only) shop ⓥ

OAKWELL HALL
West Yorkshire
Map **8** SE22

In Nova Lane, near Birstall Smithies (6m SE of Bradford)
☎ Batley (0924) 474926

Elizabethan moated manor house (1583), with Civil War and Brontë connections. It was 'Fieldhead', in Charlotte Brontë's novel Shirley. There is a recently opened Country Park complex.

Open all year Mon–Sat 10–5; Sun 1–5.

Free.

♿ 🍴 shop ✖

OBAN
Strathclyde *Argyll*
Map **10** NM83
See also **Barcaldine**

Caithness Glass Oban Glassworks, Lochavullin Estate
☎ (0631) 63386

Visitors can see the art of paperweight making. Large seconds shop.

Open all year Mon–Fri 9–5. Also Sat 9–12 noon May–Sep.

Free.

♿ ♿ shop ✖ (ex shop)

Dunstaffnage Castle
(3m N on peninsula)

A ruined four-sided 13th-century Campbell stronghold, with a gatehouse, two round towers and walls 10ft thick. Once the prison of Flora MacDonald.

Open see end of gazetteer. (Closed Thu afternoon & Fri in winter).

✳ 50p (ch & pen 25p).

♿ (AM)

Macdonald's Mill
(½m S of centre of Oban on A816)
☎ (0631) 63081

Exhibition of the Story of Spinning and Weaving, with demonstrations of this ancient Scottish industry. Also showroom containing modern products.

Open Mar–Oct Mon–Fri 9–7.30, Sat & Sun 9–5; demonstrations Mon–Fri only.

Free.

♿ ⬛ shop ✖

OGMORE
Mid Glamorgan
Map **3** SS87

Ogmore Castle

On River Ogmore with inner and outer wards and early 12th-century three-storeyed keep preserving hooded fireplace. West wall 40ft high, and dry moat around inner ward.

Open see end of gazetteer.

Free.

(AM Cadw)

OKEHAMPTON
Devon
Map **2** SX59

Museum of Dartmoor Life West St
☎ (0837) 3020

Unique museum, housed in an attractive old three storey mill together with a Dartmoor Tourist Information Centre in an

---

adjoining courtyard. Displays include, geology, prehistory, local history, farming, domestic life and industry. Craft and bookshops.

Open Etr–Oct, Mon–Sat 10.30–4.30. Other times by arrangement.

50p (ch 5–16 30p & pen 40p). Party.

▵ ᪲ (ground floor only) shop ⓥ

Okehampton Castle
(½m S in Castle Lane).

Chapel, keep and hall dating from 11th to 14th centuries, on northern fringe of Dartmoor National Park.

Open †, see end of gazetteer.

✳ 50p (ch 16 & pen 25p).

▵ (AM)

OLD BASING
Hampshire
Map **4** SU65

Basing House
☎ Basingstoke (0256) 67294

Ruins of a great Tudor palace built in 1530s on the site of four castles. Fine 16th-century Tithe Barn. Exhibition showing history of the site. Archaeological work in progress.

Open Apr, May & Sep wknd & BH 2–6; Jun–Aug, daily 2–6 (Closed Mon & Thu).

Admission fee payable.

P (½m) ᪲ (Sun & BH) ⌻ ᪲ (ground floor & gardens only) shop ⓥ

OLD DAILLY
Strathclyde *Ayrshire*
Map **10** NX29

Bargany Gardens (4m NE on B734 from Girvan)
☎ (046587) 227 or 274

Woodland walks, snowdrops, bluebells and daffodils. Fine display of azaleas and rhododendrons round lily pond in May and June. Autumn colours. Many ornamental trees. Plants for sale.

Gardens open Mar–Oct daily until 7pm (or dusk).

Contribution box.

▵ ⌻ ᪲

OLD DEER
Grampian *Aberdeenshire*
Map **15** NJ94

Deer Abbey

Remains of the Cistercian Abbey, founded in 1219, include the southern claustral range, the Abbot's House and the infirmary. The famous Book of Deer compiled in a former Celtic monastery on a different site is now in the University Library at Cambridge.

The ruins are accessible Apr–Sep Thu–Sat 9.30–7, Sun 2–7. (Closed winter).

50p (ch & pen 25p).

▵ (AM)

Okehampton — Osborne House

OLD WARDEN
Bedfordshire
Map **4** TL14

Shuttleworth Collection of Historic Aeroplanes and Cars Old Warden Aerodrome, 2m W from roundabout on A1, Biggleswade bypass
☎ Northill (076727) 288

A highly interesting collection of historical aircraft, cars, bicycles and other items of transport. There are special flying days, usually on the last Sunday in summer months, and other events.

Open daily 10.30–5.30 (last admission 4.45). Closed few days at Xmas.

£1.50 (ch & pen 75p). Special prices Flying days.

▵ ᪲ (licensed) ᪲ shop

Swiss Garden (2m W from roundabout on (A1) Biggleswade bypass)
☎ Bedford (0234) 63222 ex 30

An attractive garden dating from the early 19th century, with original buildings and artefacts. Interesting plants and trees, some quite rare.

Open Apr–Oct Wed, Thu, Sat, Sun (ex last Sun of each month), Good Fri & BH Mons 2–6 (last admission 5.15).

Admission fee payable.

▵ ⌻ ᪲ (gardens only) shop

OLD WHITTINGTON
Derbyshire
Map **8** SK37

Revolution House
☎ Chesterfield (0246) 32088

Old house, once known as Cock and Pynot (or Magpie) Inn, with 17th-century furnishings. Associated with the 1688 revolution.

Open May day–second Sun in Sep, Wed–Sun & BH Mon, 11–12.30 & 1.30–5.30.

Free.

P ✻

OLNEY
Buckinghamshire
Map **4** SP85

Cowper and Newton Museum Market Pl
☎ Bedford (0234) 711516

House where William Cowper lived from 1768 to 1786, now containing manuscripts of letters and poems, together with many personal possessions. Two small gardens open to visitors to the museum. Manuscripts available by previous arrangement. Exhibitions of lace and bobbins.

Open Etr–Oct Tue–Sat & BH Mon 10–12 & 2–5; Jun–Sep Sun 2.30–5; Nov–Etr Tue–

Sat 2–4; other times by prior arrangement with Curator.

50p (ch 7 30p & pen 40p). Party 12+.

P ex Thu ᪲ (prior arrangement) ᪲ (gardens only) shop ✻

ORFORD
Suffolk
Map **5** TM44

Orford Castle (on B1084)

Castle with three towers, incorporating remarkable 18-sided keep, built by Henry II, c.1165.

Open †, see end of gazetteer.

✳ 50p (ch 16 & pen 25p).

▵ (AM)

ORKNEY
Map **16**
See Dounby, Finstown, Kirkwall, Stromness, Westray

ORMESBY
Cleveland
Map **8** NZ51

Ormesby Hall

18th-century mansion with stables attributed to John Carr of York. Plasterwork, furniture and 18th-century pictures.

Open 29 Mar–Oct (Closed Good Fri). Wed, Sat, Sun & BH Mon 2–6. Last admission 5.30.

£1.

P (NT)

ORPINGTON
Gt London
(London plan 4 pages 174/175)

Priory Museum The Priory, Church Hill
Plan 4: **44** F1
☎ (0689) 31551

13th- to 14th-century clergy house with addition of 15th-century manor house. Now small museum of local interest and special exhibitions are held during year.

Open all year (ex Thu & Sun) 9–6 (5pm Sat) (Closed PH).

Free.

▵ ᪲ (ground floor only) ✻

OSBORNE HOUSE
Isle of Wight
Map **4** SZ59

(1m SE of East Cowes)

19th-century house, once Queen Victoria's home and where she died.

State apartments, Swiss Cottage and museum open Etr Mon–beginning of Oct, Mon–Sat 10–5, Sun 11–5.

Admission fee payable.

▵ (Dept. of Environment)

215

OSMOTHERLEY
North Yorkshire
Map **8** SE49

Mount Grace Priory (1m NW)
*Ruined 14th-century Carthusian Priory,
next to 17th-century house.*
Priory open see end of gazetteer.
✳ 60p (ch 16 & pen 30p).
⚠ (AM & NT) ·

OSTERLEY
Gt London (London Plan 4 pages 174/
175)

Osterley Park House
(off A4, Great West Rd) Plan 4: **42** B3
☎ 01–560 3918
*An Elizabethan mansion transformed into
an 18th-century villa. Elegant neo-
classical interior decoration designed by
Robert Adam. State apartment includes a
Gobelins tapestry ante-room, and a
dressing room decorated in the 'Etruscan'
style.*
House open all year daily ex Mon 11–5.
(Closed Good Fri, May day, 24–26 Dec & 1
Jan). Park open daily 10–8.
£1.60 (ch, pen & students 80p). Party
12+.
⚠ ⚗ ♿ (gardens only) ✘ NT & V & A
Museum

OSWESTRY
Shropshire
Map **7** SJ23

Old Oswestry (½m N)
*Iron Age hill fort covering 68 acres, with
five ramparts and elaborate western
portal. Abutted by part of prehistoric
Wat's Dyke.*
Accessible any reasonable time.
Free.
♿ (AM)

OTTERTON
Devon
Map **3** SY08

Otterton Mill
☎ Colaton Raleigh (0395) 68521 & 68031
A Devon mill mentioned in the Domesday

Osmotherley
—
Oxford

*Book, making wholemeal flour by water
power. Gallery with series of exhibitions
through the summer. Furniture making,
pottery, textiles, bakery and lace
exhibitions. 'Millhands' co-operative craft
shop. Falconry centre.*
Open daily Apr–Oct 10.30–5.30; Nov–Mar
2–5.
£1 (ch 50p). Party.
⚠ ⚗ (licensed) ♿ (ground floor only)
shop

OTTERY ST MARY
Devon
Map **3** SY19

Cadhay (½m from Fairmile, near junction
of A30 and B3167)
☎ (040481) 2432
Beautiful and historic house, built 1550.
Open Tue–Thu Jul & Aug, 25 & 26 May
and 24 & 25 Aug 2–6 (last admission 5.30).
£1.50 (ch 50p). Party 20+ by
appointment.
⚠ ♿ (ground floor only) ✘ (in house)

OUTWOOD
Surrey
Map **4** TQ34

Old Mill
☎ Smallfield (034284) 3458
*Fine example of post-mill dating from
1665, oldest working mill in England, one
of best-preserved in existence. Many
ducks, goats and horses wander freely in
its grounds and there is also a small
museum and collection of old coaches.*
Open Etr Sun–last Sun in Oct, Sun & BH
Mons only 2–6. Other days & evening
tours by arrangement.
60p (ch 14 30p). Party.
⚠ ♿ (ground floor & gardens only) shop

OWER
Hampshire
Map **4** SU31

Paulton's Country Park
☎ Southampton (0703) 814442
*140 acres of beautiful parkland and
extensive gardens at the edge of the New
Forest. Over 200 species of animals, birds
and wildfowl. Village life museum,
Romany museum, 10-acre lake, working
waterwheel, woodland walks and
adventure playground.*
Open all year 10–7 (or dusk). Last
admissions 5pm or 1 hour before dusk in
winter.
✳ £1.80 (ch 90p, pen £1.50).
⚠ ⚗ ♨ ♿ shop & garden centre ✘ ·

OXBOROUGH
Norfolk
Map **5** TF70

Oxburgh Hall
*A moated 15th-century and later building
with an 80ft turreted gatehouse and
French design parterre garden.*
Gatehouse, principal rooms and garden
open May–Sep Sat–Wed 1.30–5.30. Apr &
Oct wknds & BH Mon. BH Mons 11–5.30.
Closed Good Fri.
£1.80 (ch 90p) Party 15+.
✘ (NT)

OXFORD
Oxfordshire
Map **4** SP50

*Ancient and picturesque University city
on rivers Cherwell and Thames, dating
back to 8th century. **The University**, the
oldest in Britain, probably dates from
c. 1167 and consists of a large number of
colleges built over a period of several
centuries, many of which are among the
finest buildings of their age. Access to
some colleges is restricted to certain
times and details may be obtained from
the Official Information Bureau, Carfax
Tower.*

**Ashmolean Museum of Art and
Archaeology** Beaumont St
☎ (0865) 512651

Oxford

The oldest (1683) museum in the country, housed in C R Cockerell's building of 1845 (with later extensions). Its exhibits include archaeological items of British, European, Mediterranean, Egyptian and Near Eastern origins. Also exhibited are coins and medals of all countries and periods, located in the Heberden Coin Room; Italian, Dutch, Flemish, French, and English oil paintings; Old Master and modern drawings, watercolours, prints and miniatures; European ceramics; English silver; Chinese and Japanese porcelain; painting and lacquer; Tibetan art; Indian sculpture and paintings; Islamic pottery and metalwork; Chinese bronzes; casts from the antique and objects of applied art. Temporary exhibits throughout year.

Open all year Tue–Sat 10–4, Sun 2–4. (Closed Etr & during St. Giles Fair in early Sep, Xmas & 1 Jan).

Donations. Guided tours by arrangement.

P (200 yds at St. Giles & Gloucester Gn) & shop ✖

Museum of the History of Science Old Ashmolean Building, Broad St
☎ (0865) 243997

Contains the finest collection of early astronomical, mathematical and optical instruments in the world, which are housed in the Old Ashmolean Building, a fine example of 17th-century architecture, originally built to hold the collection of Elias Ashmole. One of the most distinguished parts of the present display is the series of Islamic and European astrolabes, once used for astronomical calculations. Other exhibits include early microscopes and other optical instruments, photographic apparatus, clocks and watches, air pumps etc. Of special interest are the penicillin material, H G J Moseley's X-ray spectrometer, and a prototype of Dr C R Burch's ultra-violet reflecting microscope made in 1946.

Open Mon–Fri (Closed BH, Xmas wk, & Etr wk) 10.30–1 & 2.30–4.

Free.

P (street, limited) bookstall ✖ 🚻

Museum of Oxford St Aldates
☎ (0865) 815559

Permanent displays of the archaeology and history of the famous university city from the earliest times to the present day. Temporary exhibitions. Facilities for parties.

Open all year Tue–Sat 10–5. (Closed Good Fri & Xmas).

Free.

Bookshop ✖

Rotunda Museum of Antique Dolls' Houses Grove House, 44 Iffley Turn, next to school. (2m from centre of Oxford, off A423)
☎ (0865) 777935

A collection of 50 dolls' houses dating from c1700–1900 together with their furnishings, kitchen implements, china, silver, food and dolls' house dolls, which reflect the changes in social life and the attitudes throughout the aforementioned period. Main appeal to collectors, **children under 16 are not admitted.**

Open Suns only 2.15–5.15 May–mid Sep. At other times by appointment only for parties 12+.

£1.25 (£1.50 on special openings for groups).

& & (ground floor only) ✖

St Edmund Hall
College of Oxford University
☎ (0865) 248180

This is the only surviving medieval hall and has a Norman crypt, 17th-century dining hall, chapel and quadrangle. Other buildings 18th- and 20th-century.

Open all year (Closed 23 Dec–1 Jan & 1–8 Apr).

Free.

P (600 yds) & ground floor only) ✖

University Arboretum
Nuneham Courtenay (5m SE on A423 just S of the village)
☎ (0865) 242737

50 acres of conifers and broad leaf trees.

Open Mon–Sat 8.30–5 & Sun 2–6. May–Oct.

Free.

& & ✖

University Private Botanic Garden High St (by Magdalen Bridge)
☎ (0865) 242737 →

Gardens of great botanical interest, founded in 1621, and the oldest in the country.

Open all year, weekdays 8.30–5, (9–4.30 Oct–Mar), Sun 10–12 & 2–6 (2–4.30 Oct–Mar). Greenhouses open daily 2–4. (Closed Good Fri & Xmas day).

Free.

P (300 yds in St. Clements Car Pk) ᕋ ✹

PACKWOOD HOUSE
Warwickshire
Map **7** SP17

(11m SE Birmingham on unclass road off A34)

Timber-framed 16th- to 17th-century house containing tapestry, needlework and furniture. Famous for remarkable mid 17th-century yew garden representing Sermon on the Mount.

Open Etr Sat–Mon 2–6; Apr–Sep, Wed–Sun & BH Mon 2–6; Oct Sat & Sun 2–5.

£1.50.

⚖ ✹ (NT)

PADSTOW
Cornwall
Map **2** SW97

Tropical Bird and Butterfly Gardens
Fentonluna Ln
☎ (0841) 532262

Established for years and continues to successfully breed many birds from all corners of the world. Gardens with sub-tropical plants, many of which are labelled. Heated walk-in Tropical House with free-flying birds. Walk through planted Butterfly House where the life cycle of the butterfly can be observed in summer. Also "Butterfly World", a comprehensive exhibition of the world's butterflies many displayed in their natural habitat.

Open all year 10.30–7, 5pm in winter. (Closed Xmas day).

✳ £1.75 (ch 80p & pen £1.40).

P (500 yds) ⚖ ⊞ shop & plant sales ⓥ

PAIGNTON
Devon
Map **3** SX86

Kirkham House
☎ (0803) 522775

Restored late 14th-century house, known as the Priests' House.

Open see end of gazetteer. Apr–Sep only.

✳ 30p (ch 16 & pen 15p).

P ᕋ (ground floor only) shop ✹ (AM)

Oldway
☎ Torquay (0803) 26244 ext 286 for bookings, Paignton (0803) 550711 enquiries

19th-century house containing replicas of rooms at the Palace of Versailles. Picturesque gardens. Tennis, putting & bowling.

House open: May–Sep, Mon–Sat, 10–1 &

Oxford
—
Parcevall Hall

2.15–5.15, Sun 2.30–5.30; winter Mon–Fri 10–1 & 2.15–5.15 (Closed Sat & Sun); closed occasionally for Council purposes.

Free.

⚠ ⚖ (summer only) ᕋ (ground floor & gardens only) ✹ (ex guide dogs)

Torbay Aircraft Museum Higher
Blagdon. (Off Totnes Rd A385, near Berry Pomeroy. About 2 miles from Paignton Zoo)
☎ (0803) 553540

Features over 18 complete aircraft dating from 1924 to 1954. Comprehensive indoor exhibition of aeronautics. Exhibitions include 'Heroes of the Battle of Britain' and the 'Red Baron'. Torbay model railway and 'Kenneth More Gardens'.

27 Mar–2 Nov 10–6 (summer), 5pm (winter) daily.

✳ £2.20 (ch 16 £1.10, under 5 free, pen £1.70). Party 20+.

⚠ ⚖ (licensed) ⊞ ᕋ shop ✹ kennels available ⓥ

Torbay and Dartmouth Railway
☎ (0803) 555872

Steam trains run for seven miles on former Great Western line from Paignton to Kingswear, stopping at Goodrington Sands and Churston, for ferry across to Dartmouth. Model railway exhibition at Paignton station.

Open Etr, BHs & Jun–Sep daily. Telephone for other dates in season.

✳ Return fare Paignton–Kingswear £2.80 (ch £1.80, pen £2.30). Other fares on application. Party.

⚠ (limited) ⊞ ᕋ shop

Zoological and Botanical Gardens
Totnes Rd
☎ (0803) 557479 & 527936

Third largest zoo in England approximately 75 acres of grounds, enhanced with tropical plants and shrubs, and over 1600 animals from all over the world. Among the main attractions are a breeding colony of Lar Gibbons on a large island on a lake, the baboon rock, monkey house, large tropical house, sub-tropical house, aquarium and reptile house. A large collection of peafowl roam the grounds. New family activity centre, The Ark. Also childrens' playground, miniature railway and new family activity centre. Various fayres and falconry displays.

Open, daily 10–6.30 (4.30pm in winter). Last admission 5 (4pm winter). Closed 25 Dec.

£2.40 (ch 3–14 £1.50, pen £2). Party 20+.

⚠ ⚖ (licensed) ⊞ ᕋ shop garden centre ✹ (kennels available) ⓥ

Strathclyde *Renfrewshire*
Map **11** NS46

Coats Observatory 49 Oakshaw St
☎ 041-889 3151

Dating from 1883 but recently renovated and installed with modern technology the Observatory has resumed a role of importance in the realms of astronomy and meteorology. There are displays relating to the history of the building, astronomy, meteorology and space flight.

Open Mon–Fri 2–5; Sat 10–1 & 2–5. Jan–Mar, Thu 7pm–9pm weather permitting. PH 2–5pm (Closed Xmas & New Year).

Free.

P (in street) shop ✹

Paisley Museum and Art Galleries
High St
☎ 041-889 3151

Collection illustrates local industrial and natural history of the town and district. Also a world-famous collection of Paisley shawls. The art collection has emphasis on 19th-century Scottish artists.

Open Mon–Sat, 10–5. (Closed PH).

Free.

P (street 200 yds) ᕋ (ground floor only) shop ✹

PAKENHAM
Suffolk
Map **5** TL96

Pakenham Water Mill Grimstone End
☎ Lavenham (0787) 247179

Fine 18th-century working watermill on Domesday site, complete with oil engine and other subsidiary machinery. Recently restored by Suffolk Preservation Society.

Open 29–31 Mar & then 3 May–28 Sep, Wed, Sat, Sun & BH 2.30–5.30. Other times by appointment.

60p (ch 30p) Ground flour for sale.

⚠ ⚖ ᕋ (ground floor & garden only) shop

PALNACKIE
Dumfries and Galloway
Kirkcudbrightshire
Map **11** NX85

Orchardton Tower

A rare example of a circular tower built originally by John Cairns in the late 15th century.

Open see end of gazetteer on application to the Key Keeper.

Free.

(AM)

PARCEVALL (PERCIVAL) HALL
GARDENS Skyreholme, North Yorkshire
Map **7** SE06

(8m SW of Pateley Bridge)
☎ Burnsall (075672) 214

Beautiful gardens of Elizabethan house, in

218

hillside setting east of the main Wharfedale Valley.

Open Etr–Oct, daily 10–6.

50p (ch 25p).

⛺ ⊓ ♿ (gardens only) 🚫🐕

PATELEY BRIDGE
North Yorkshire
Map **7** SE16

Nidderdale Museum
☎ Harrogate (0423) 711225 & 780426

A fascinating collection of exhibits in the original Victorian workhouse, illustrating the life and background of Dales folk. Items ranging from domestic, industrial and farming to photographic, costume and country crafts.

Open Etr–Spring BH, Sat & Sun, Spring Bank Hol–Sep, daily, Oct–Etr, Sun only 2–5.

Admission fee payable.

⛺ shop 🚫🐕

PEAKIRK
Cambridgeshire
Map **4** TF10

Wildfowl Trust
☎ Peterborough (0733) 252271

Over 600 ducks, geese and swans of over 100 different species in an attractive water garden. Magnificent flock of Chilean Flamingos, Trumpeter, Black-necked and Coscoroba swans, Andean geese and many other rare and unusual waterfowl. Visitor centre.

Open daily (ex 24 & 25 Dec), 9.30–5 (or dusk if earlier).

£1.60 (ch 4 free ch 80p, pen £1.20). Party 20+.

⛺ ☕ ⊓ ♿ shop 🚫🐕

PEEBLES
Borders *Peeblesshire*
Map **11** NT23

Kailzie (2½m SE on B7062)
☎ (0721) 22054

Extensive grounds with fine old trees. Burnside walk with bulbs, rhododendrons and azaleas. Walled garden with herbaceous and shrub rose borders. Pheasantry and waterfowl pond, also art gallery.

Open 28 Mar–12 Oct, daily 11–5.30.

90p (ch 35p).

⛺ ☕ (licensed, 11.30–5.30) ⊓ ♿ shop & plant sales

Neidpath Castle
☎ (0721) 20333

Spectacular position on Tweed. 14th-century stronghold interestingly adapted to 17th-century living. Successively owned by families of Fraser, Hay (Earl of Tweeddale), Douglas (Earl of March) and Wemyss (Earl of Wemyss & March).

Open 27 Mar–12 Oct, Mon–Sat 10–1 & 2–6, Sun 1–6 (last visitor 5.30), subject to the availability of staff.

75p (ch 14 20p, ch under 4 free, pen 50p).

⛺ shop 🚫🐕

PEEL
Isle of Man
Map **6** SC28

Peel Castle
On St Patricks Isle, facing Peel Bay
☎ Douglas (0624) 26262

The curtain wall and building date from the 10th century. The gatehouse featured as a location for Sir Walter Scott's novel Peveril of the Peak.

Open Etr weekend–Sep. Dates not confirmed for 1986.

✱ 40p (ch & pen 25p).

P (50 yds) shop

PEMBROKE
Dyfed
Map **2** SM90

National Museum of Gypsy Caravans
Commons Rd
☎ (0646) 681308

Fine collection of Gypsy caravans and representation of Gypsy life. Illustrated by caravans, carts, old photographs, tools and many other artefacts related to Romany life.

Open Etr–Sep, Sun–Fri 10–5.

✱ £1.20 (ch 60p, pen £1).

⛺ ♿ shop 🚫🐕

Pembroke Castle
☎ (0646) 684585

An impressive 12th- to 13th-century fortress with 80ft-high round keep.

Open Etr–Sep, daily 10–6. Oct–Etr, Mon–Sat 10–4. (Closed Sun in winter, Xmas and New Year's Day). Castle gates close ½hr before closing time.

✱ 70p (ch & pen 40p) ch under 5, mentally handicapped & physically handicapped (in wheelchair) free. Educational visits 25p.

P free, (100 yds) ♿ (ground floor & lawn only) shop

PENARTH
South Glamorgan
Map **3** ST17

Turner House
☎ Cardiff (0222) 708870

A small gallery holding temporary exhibitions of pictures and objets d'art from the National Museum of Wales and other sources.

Open Tue–Sat & BH Mons, 11–12.45 & 2–5, Sun 2–5. (Closed 24–26 & 31 Dec, 1 Jan, Good Fri & May Day).

Free.

P shop 🚫🐕

PENARTH FAWR
Gwynedd
Map **6** SH43
(3½m NE of Pwllheli off A497)

Part of house built probably in early 15th century preserving hall, buttery and screen.

Accessible at all reasonable times.

Free.

(AM Cadw)

PENDEEN
Cornwall
Map **2** SW33

Geevor Tin Mines
☎ Penzance (0736) 788662

A working tin mine with museum showing and illustrating the history of the tin mines of Cornwall. Guided tour available to see the tin treatment plant. A video film illustrates underground and surface techniques. 'Geevor Gala' August/September.

Open Apr–Oct, 10–5.30.

Museum 70p (ch 30p). Plant & Museum £1.50 (ch 75p).

⛺ ☕ ⊓ ♿ (ground floor & gardens only) shop

See advertisement on page 220

PENHOW
Gwent
Map **3** ST49

Penhow Castle
☎ (0633) 400800

This, the oldest inhabited castle in Wales, was originally a small border fortress and was the first home in Britain for the famous Seymour family. The building presents a fascinating picture of life from the 12th to 19th century and includes 12th-century ramparts, with views of three counties, 15th-century great hall with re-constructed screen and minstrels' gallery, 17th-century kitchen and a Victorian house-keeper's room.

Open Etr–Sep, Wed–Sun & BH Mon Tue 10–6 (last admission 5.15). Evening visits & Parties, by arrangement. 'Candlelit Tours' every Wed evening.

✱ £1.50 (ch 14 75p). Family ticket £3.75. Admission includes free audio-tour. (Children's and foreign language tours also available.) Party.

⛺ ⊓ shop 🚫🐕 Ⓥ

PENICUIK
Lothian *Midlothian*
Map **11** NT26

Edinburgh Crystal Visitor Centre
Eastfield Industrial Estate
☎ (0968) 75128

Tours around the factory allow visitors to see the various stages of the art of →

glassmaking including glass blowing, the 'lehr', cutting, polishing, engraving and sand etching. Audio-visual presentations.

Open Mon–Fri 9–3.30 (Closed Xmas, New Year & staff holidays).

Tours 75p (ch 25p).

⚠ ⬛ (licensed) 🚻 ♿ shop

PENMACHNO
Gwynedd
Map **6** SH75

Penmachno Woollen Mill
☎ Betws-y-Coed (06902) 545

Records date back to 1650 when the mill started as a Fulling Mill where cloth could be finished for local domestic weavers and flannel shirts for farmers and quarrymen were produced. During the 19th century power looms were introduced and these still make Welsh lightweight tweed today.

Open pre Etr–mid Nov daily 9–5.30 (Closed Sun am early & late season).

Free. Audio Visual of the 'The Story of Wool' 20p.

⚠ shop 🍴

Ty Mawr (3½m SW of Betws-y-Coed 2m W of Penmachno, at head of the little valley of Gwybernant) Approach roads unsuitable for large coaches.
☎ (06903) 213

The cottage is the birth place of Bishop William Morgan (born 1545) who translated the Bible into Welsh; his translation is considered a masterpiece and the foundation of modern Welsh literature. The Bishop Morgan nature trail covers approximately one mile to and from the house.

Open 28 Mar–26 Oct (May close Sep–Oct for restoration), Sun, Tue–Fri & BH Mon 12–5; (Last admission 4.45) Oct by appointment only.

40p (ch 20p). Party 20+.

⬛ 🍴 (ex guide dogs) (NT)

PENSHURST
Kent
Map **5** TQ54

Penicuik
—
Perth

Penshurst Place (On B2176)
☎ (0892) 870307

One of the outstanding stately homes of Britain and birthplace of Sir Philip Sidney in 1554. The world-famous chestnut-beamed Great Hall is the oldest and finest in England. The state rooms are splendidly furnished and the toy museum is much loved by children. There are extensive Tudor gardens. Leisure area includes a venture playground. Countryside exhibition and nature trail.

Open 28 Mar–1st Sun in Oct & BH Mons. Ground 12.30–6, House 1–5.30. Last entry 5pm.

✳ House & grounds; £2.40 (ch £1.10 pen £2) Grounds; £1.65 (ch 80p pen £1.30).

⚠ ⬛ (licensed) 🚻 shop 🍴

PENZANCE
Cornwall
Map **2** SW43

Penlee House, Penzance and District Museum Penlee Park
☎ (0736) 63625

The history and development of the district from earliest man to the 1980's. Exhibition of Town paintings.

Open all year, Mon–Fri 10.30–4.30 (Exhibition of Paintings closed 12.30–2.30). Sat 10.30–12.30 (Closed BH).

Free (Exhibition of Paintings charged for Jun–Sep).

P (150 yds, Wellfields Car Pk, Alverton St) ♿ (ground floor only) 🍴

Roland Morris's Maritime Museum 19 Chapel St, opposite the Admiral Benbow
☎ (0736) 3324

Exhibits hundreds of 'nautifacts' brought up by the diving teams of Roland Morris from the wrecks of Anson, Association, Romney, Eagle, Firebrand and Colossus. The display of the latter wreck depicting recovery of Lord Hamilton's 2,500-year-old

pottery. Gold and silver treasure was found on Association (The first treasure in British waters). Pieces of eight, golden Portuguese Reis, Louis D'or Guineas and half guineas and golden Reales. Man-o'-War display shows full scale section of 1730 warship with four decks including gun-decks.

Open Apr–Oct, daily 10–5.

✳ 80p (ch 50p).

P (300 yds) shop 🍴

PERTH
Tayside Perthshire
Map **11** NO12
See also **Scone**

Black Watch Regimental Museum
Balhousie Castle, Hay St
☎ (0738) 21281 ext 30

Treasures of the 42nd/73rd Highland Regiment from 1725 to the present day, including paintings, silver, colours and uniforms.

Open Mon–Fri 10–4.30 (Winter 3.30), Sun & PH's (Etr–Sep) 2–4.30. Other times & parties 20+ by appointment.

Free/donations.

⚠ shop 🍴

Branklyn Garden (on Dundee Rd, A85)
☎ (0738) 25535

Has been described as the finest garden of its size in Britain. Little more than two acres it is noted for its collection of rhododendrons, shrubs and alpines.

Open Mar–Oct, daily 9.30–sunset.

80p (ch 40p).

(NTS)

Caithness Glass
Inveralmond Industrial Est
☎ (0738) 37373

All aspects of glass making can be seen from the viewing gallery at this purpose-built visitors centre. Also a factory 'seconds' shop.

Open Mon–Sat 9–5, Sun 1–5 (11–5 Jul & Aug).

Free.

⚠ ⬛ (licensed) ♿ shop

GEEVOR
TIN MINING
MUSEUM
Pendeen • Penzance • Cornwall

● Open 1st April to 31st October 10am to 5.30pm.

● Guided tours of the working surface treatment plant producing tin concentrates — Monday to Friday 10.30am to 4.00pm except Bank Holidays.

Telephone (0736) 788662

Geevor Tin Mines plc

Elcho Castle
(5m SE on S bank of River Tay)
*A well preserved 16th-century stronghold
with wrought-iron window grilles.*

Open Apr–Sep wknds 9.30–7, Sun 2–7;
Oct–Mar weekdays 9.30–4, Sun 2–4.

50p (ch & pen 25p).

⚑ (AM)

Fair Maid's House North Port
☎ (0738) 25976

*Situated near the historic North Inch
where the battle of the Clans was fought
in 1396. In the 14th-century it became the
home of Simon Glover, a glovemaker
whose daughter Catherine was the
heroine of Sir Walter Scott's 'Fair Maid of
Perth'. The house was a guildhall for over
150 years. It was renovated in the 19th
century and is now a centre for Scottish
crafts. A recently uncovered wall is said to
be the oldest visible wall in Perth.
Changing exhibitions of paintings,
sculpture, tapestries etc.*

Open all year Mon–Sat 10–5.

Free.

P (close) ⛺ (ground floor only)

Huntingtower

*Formerly known as Ruthven Castle. A
castellated 15th-century and 16th-century
structure, with a painted ceiling. Famous
as the scene of the so called 'Raid of
Ruthven' in 1582.*

Perth
—
Peterculter

Open see end of gazetteer.

✳ 50p (ch & pen 25p).

(AM)

Perth Museum & Art Gallery
78 George St
☎ (0738) 32488

*Purpose-built to house collections of fine
and applied art, social and local history,
natural history and archaeology. Special
events monthly.*

Open Mon–Sat, 10–1 & 2–5.

Free.

⚑ shop ✄

PETERBOROUGH
Cambridgeshire
Map **4** TL19

**City of Peterborough Museum and Art
Gallery** Priestgate
☎ (0733) 43329

*Collections include local geology,
archaeology, natural history and articles
from former French prisoners' jail at
Norman cross. Also painting and a small
collection of ceramics and glass and
temporary exhibitions.*

Open May–Sep Tue–Sat 10–5; Oct–Apr
Tue–Sat 12–5. (Closed Good Fri & Xmas).

Free.

P (at Queensgate, 600 yds) shop ✄

Longthorpe Tower
*Fortified 13th- to 14th-century house,
which belonged formerly to the de Thorpe
family. Contains some rare wall paintings
of religious and educational subjects on
first floor.*

Open see end of gazetteer.

✳ 30p (ch 16 and pen 15p).

P (AM)

PETERCULTER
Grampian *Aberdeenshire*
Map **15** NJ80

Drum Castle (3m W)
☎ Drumoak (03308) 204

*The oldest part, the great square tower
dates from the late 13th century. A
charming mansion was added in 1619
enclosing a quadrangle. In 1323 King
Robert the Bruce gave a charter of the
Royal Forest of Drum to William de Irwin.
This family connection remained
unbroken until the death in 1975 of Mr H Q
Forbes Irvine who bequeathed the castle
and land to the NTS.*

Open May–Sep, daily 2–6, last admission
5.15. Grounds open all year 9.30–sunset;
by donation. —›

£1.40 (ch 70p).

🅰 (NTS)

PETERHEAD
Grampian *Aberdeenshire*
Map **15** NK14

Arbuthnot Museum and Art Gallery
St Peter St
☎ (0779) 77778

Specialises in local exhibits, particularly those relating to the fishing industry; including also Arctic and whaling specimens. Also a British coin collection which can be viewed by appointment.

Open Mon–Sat 10–12 & 2–5. (Closed PH's).

Free.

P (100 yds) shop 🍴 (ex guide dogs)

PETWORTH
West Sussex
Map **4** SU92

Petworth House

A large 17th- to 19th-century mansion situated in a great park. A notable picture gallery, 14th-century chapel, Grinling Gibbons carvings and grand staircase.

Open 29 Mar–Oct, Tue (ex following BH Mons), Wed, Thu, Sat, Sun & BH Mons, 2–6. Deer park open daily 9–sunset.

£2 Connoisseurs day on Tue, extra rooms shown £2.50.

🎫 (2.30–5.30) 🍴 (in house) (NT)

PEVENSEY
East Sussex
Map **5** TQ60

Old Minthouse High St
☎ Eastbourne (0323) 761251

Built in 1342 on a site which is reputed to have been a mint as long ago as 1076. The interior was constructed in 1542 by Dr Andrew Borde, then court physician to Henry VIII. It contains 18 rooms, open to the public, carvings, frescoes etc. Small museum.

Open all year Mon–Fri 9–5, Sat 10–4. (Closed Xmas, New Year & BH's ex Aug BH).

40p (ch 20p).

🅰 shop 🍴

Pevensey Castle

3rd-century Roman fort of Saxon Shore with Norman and 13th-century additions.

Open † see end of gazetteer.

✱ 50p (ch 16 & pen 25p).
🅰 ♿ (AM)

PICKERING
North Yorkshire
Map **8** SE78

Beck Isle Museum of Rural Life
☎ (0751) 73653

The museum contains a collection of exhibits illustrating the working life,

---

Peterculter
—
Plas Newydd

customs and pastimes of the local community during the past 200 years.

Open Apr–Oct, daily 10.30–12.30 & 2–5, Aug 10.30–7. Also open evenings for parties, by appointment only tel (0751) 73707.

60p (ch 16 30p).

P (300 yds) shop 🍴

North Yorkshire Moors Railway 'Moorsrail'
☎ (0751) 73535 (Talking timetable) or 72508 (Enquiries)

Operates through the heart of the North York Moors National Park between Pickering and Grosmont, a distance of 18 miles. Newtondale Halt, opened in 1981, is ideal for access to forest and walks.

Open Etr–early Nov with daily services from 3 May 10–6. 'Santa Trains' Dec. Further information available from Nymr, Pickering Station, North Yorkshire.

Return from £1.70 (ch 85p pen reduced).

🅰 (100 yds) ♿ 🚻 shop

Pickering Castle

Large 12th-century keep on mound between two baileys.

Open † see end of gazetteer.

✱ 60p (ch 16 & pen 30p).
🅰 (AM)

PICTON
Dyfed
Map **2** SN01

Graham and Kathleen Sutherland Foundation and Picton Castle Grounds
☎ Rhos (043786) 201 Grounds or 296 Gallery.

The gallery in a building in the castle grounds shows oil paintings, water-colours, works in mixed media, lithographs, etchings and aquatints. The extensive grounds provide walks through shrub gardens and woodland.

Castle **NOT** open. Grounds open Apr–Sep (ex Mon but open BH Mon), 10.30–6. Graham & Kathleen Sutherland Foundation Apr–Sep daily (ex Mon but open BH Mon) 10.30–5. Other times by arrangement.

✱ Garden £1 (ch & pen 50p), gallery 50p (ch & pen 30p).
🅰 🎫 🚻 ♿ shop

PITLOCHRY
Tayside *Perthshire*
Map **14** NN95

Faskally (2m NW)
☎ (0796) 3437

Incorporates woodland and lochside parking with picnic area and forest walk.

Open Apr–Sep, daily dawn–dusk.

Free.

🅰 🚻 ♿ 🐕

Pitlochry Power Station Dam and Fish Pass
☎ (0796) 3152

There is a permanent definitive exhibition of hydro-electricity, with audio-visual presentation. The Power Station is not open, but there is a viewing gallery in the exhibition area. Fish pass and observation chamber open during daylight hours.

Exhibition open Etr–Oct, daily 9.40–5.30.

50p (ch 30p, free if accompanied).

🅰 (Pitlochry Festival Theatre, ½m) shop 🍴

See advertisement under Edinburgh

PITMEDDEN
Grampian *Aberdeenshire*
Map **15** NJ82

Pitmedden Garden
☎ Udny (06513) 2352

A fine late 17th-century garden, now recreated. Sundials, pavilions and fountains. Elaborate floral designs. Also Museum of Farming Life. Rare breeds of livestock. Walks and Visitor Centre.

Gardens & grounds open all year daily 9.30–sunset. Museum open May–Sep, daily 11–6 (last admission 5.15).

Museum & garden £1.10 (ch 55p). Garden only 60p (ch 30p).

♿ (NTS)

Tolquhon Castle (2m NE off B999)

A late 16th-century quadrangular mansion now roofless and enclosing an early 15th-century tower. Fine gatehouse and courtyard.

Open see end of gazetteer.

✱ 50p (ch & pen 25p).
🅰 ♿ (AM)

PITSTONE
Buckinghamshire
Map **4** SP91

Pitstone Windmill (off B488)

One of England's oldest postmills, some of it part of original structure of 1627. Now restored and fully operative.

Open May–Sep, Sun & BH Mon 2.30–6.

30p (ch 15p).

(NT)

PLAS NEWYDD
Gwynedd
Map **6** SH56

(1m SW Llanfairpwll on A4080 to Brynsiencyn. Turn off A5 at Llanfairpwll on west end of Britannia Bridge)
☎ Llanfairpwll (0248) 714795

18th-century house by James Wyatt in unspoilt surroundings on the Menai Strait; uninterrupted views of the Snowdonia mountain range, beautiful lawn and parkland, fine spring garden. Rex

Whistler's largest wall painting and exhibition. Relics of the first Marquess of Anglesey, the Battle of Waterloo and the Ryan collection of military uniforms and headdresses.

Open 28 Mar–Sep, Sun–Fri 12–5 (last admission 4.30).

House & garden £1.70 (ch 60p). Garden only 90p (ch 50p). Party 20+.

⚠ 🚻 ♿ 🐕 (ex guide dogs) (NT)

PLAS-YN-RHIW
Gwynedd
Map 6 SH22
(on unclass road 4½m NE of Aberdaron)
☎ Rhiw (075888) 219

House with gardens and woodlands down to the sea on W shore of Porth Neigwl (Hell's Mouth Bay), small manor house, part medieval, with Tudor and Georgian additions; ornamental gardens with flowering trees and shrubs including sub-tropical specimens, divided by box hedges and grass paths, with stream and waterfall, rising behind to the snowdrop wood.

Open 28 Mar–28 Sep daily ex Sat 11–5 (last admission 4.45).

£1 (ch 50p). Party 20+.

⚠ 🐾 🐕 (ex guide dogs) (NT)

PLAXTOL
Kent
Map 5 TQ65

Old Soar Manor
Part of late 13th-century house joined to 18th-century farmhouse.

Open see end of gazetteer. Apr–Sep only.

✳ 30p (ch 16 & pen 15p).

P (AM & NT)

PLYMOUTH
Devon
Map 2 SX45

City Museum & Art Gallery
Drake Circus
☎ (0752) 264878

Collections of paintings and drawings, ceramics (especially Plymouth porcelain), silver; archaeology and local history. Cottonian collection of Old Master drawings, engravings and early printed books. Monthly exhibitions.

Open Mon–Fri 10–5.30 (Sat 5pm). (Closed Good Fri and 25 & 26 Dec).

Free.

P ♿ shop 🚻

Merchant's House Museum
33 St Andrews Street
☎ (0752) 264878

Large town house of 16th- and early 17th-century with many period features. Converted to Museum of Plymouth History.

Open all year Mon–Fri 10–5.30 (Sat 5pm), Sun (summer only) 3–5. (Closed Fri & 25–26 Dec).

Plas Newydd
—
Polperro

Admission fee payable.

⚠ shop 🚻

Prysten House Finewell St
☎ (0752) 661414 (Mon–Fri 9.30–1)

Old house in city, built 1490, former Priest's house of St Andrew's Church. Model of Plymouth 1620 and tapestries showing the story of the first Grammar School in Plymouth and the colonisation of America from Plymouth (the latter under construction). Herb display.

Open Apr–Oct Mon–Sat 10–4 (other times by appointment).

50p (ch & pen 25p) Party 15+.

P (50 yds) 🚻

Royal Citadel
Magnificent entrance gateway, dated 1670 and designed probably by Sir Thomas Fitz for stronghold commenced by Charles II in 1666. The remaining buildings from the fort include the Guard House, Governor's House and Chapel.

Open May–Sep. Guided tours daily 2–6pm. Winter access only by permission of Ministry of Defence. Enquire at Guardroom.

Free.

(AM)

Smeaton Tower The Promenade, Plymouth Hoe
☎ (0752) 66800 ext 4255

A former Eddystone Lighthouse, now rebuilt.

Open end Apr–early Oct. 10.30–1hr before sunset. Parties by appointment.

✳ 20p. Party 20+.

P (200 yds) 🚻

PLYMPTON
Devon
Map 2 SX55

Dartmoor Wild Life Park (3m NE at Sparkwell, N of A38)
☎ Cornwood (075537) 209

Set in 25 acres of Devonshire countryside is this collection of over 100 species of animals and birds. Special attractions include Siberian Tigers, six species of deer in a large natural enclosure and a timber-wolf pack in a woodland enclosure. Also donkey rides for children and falconry displays selected weekends.

Open daily 10–dusk.

✳ £2.40 (ch £1.20). Party.

⚠ ♿ 🚻 ♿ shop

Hemerdon House
☎ Plymouth (0752) 23816 (337350 weekends).

A small early 19th-century house

---

containing West Country paintings and prints with appropriate furniture and a library.

Open 5–26 May & 18–25 Aug 2–5.30.

£1.20.

⚠ ♿ (ground floor & gardens only)

Saltram House (S of bypass)
☎ Plymouth (0752) 336546

Tudor house refronted in the 18th century, with saloon and dining room (1768) by Robert Adam. Shrub garden with 18th-century summer house and orangery (1773) by Stockman. Art gallery in Chapel.

Open 28 Mar–Oct, house Sun–Thu & Good Fri & BH Sats 12.30–6. Garden daily 11–6 (ex Nov, Mar, daylight hours only). Other attractions Sun–Thu 11–6, last admission 5.30.

£2.40 Gardens only £1. Party.

♿ (licensed) ♿ shop (NT) & (NGS)

POCKLINGTON
Humberside
Map 8 SE84

Burnby Hall Garden & Stewart Collection
☎ (07592) 2068

Gardens with outstanding collection of water lilies in two lakes and fine rose garden. Museum contains sporting trophies and ethnic material from world-wide travels.

Gardens open Etr–Sep 10–6; Museum open Etr–May & mid Sep–end Sep, Sat & Sun 2–5; Jun–mid Sep daily 12.30–5.

✳ 60p (ch 10–16 20p, ch 10 free & pen 40p). Party 20+.

⚠ ♿ (same times as museum) 🐾 ♿
Plant sales

Penny Arcadia Ritz Cinema, Market Pl
☎ (07592) 3420

Museum comprising the World's most comprehensive collection of antique and veteran coin-operated amusement machines. Audio-visual screen show, stage presentation and guided tours by demonstrations.

Open May–Sep daily 10–5 (Jun–Aug), 2–5 (May & Sep). Other times by arrangement.

£1.20 (ch & pen 90p). Party.

P (in street) ♿ (ground floor only) shop Ⓥ

POLPERRO
Cornwall
Map 2 SX25

The Land of Legend and Model Village
☎ (0503) 72378

The Land of Legend offers a unique opportunity to catch many fascinating glimpses of old Cornwall presented in miniature. Animated models illustrate a glimpse of Cornwall's ancient traditions. The Model Village is a replica of old Polperro set amidst a garden of exotic and unusual plants. Photographic exhibition, with commentary (listening →

posts) giving history of Polperro and details of 1976 Flood disaster.

Open Mar–Oct, Sun–Fri 10–6 (Closes 9pm in the high season).

✳ 75p (ch 3 free, ch 15 & pen 55p).

P 🖵 ᵭ (ground floor & gardens only) shop Ⓥ

PONTEFRACT
West Yorkshire
Map **8** SE42

Pontefract Museum Salter Row
☎ (0977) 797289

Museum of Pontefract history also temporary exhibitions.

Open Mon–Sat, 10.30–12.30 & 1.30–5. (Closed BH).

Free.

P (200 yds) ᵭ ✘

PONTERWYD
Dyfed
Map **6** SN78

Bwlch Nant-Yr-Arian Forest Visitor Centre (3m W)
☎ (097085) 694 or Crosswood (09743) 404

Operated by the Forestry Commission in Rheidol to interpret the forest as part of the landscape, form of land use, traditional industry, part of local community, habitat for wild life and as a place for recreation and relaxation. Forest walks in the vicinity.

Open Etr–Sep, daily 10–5 (ex Sat) 12.30–5 (6pm in Jul & Aug).

Free.

P (100 yds) ⊞ ᵭ shop

Llywernog Silver-Lead Mine
(11m E of Aberystwyth on A44)
☎ (097085) 620

A mid 19th-century water-powered silver-lead mine located in the midst of the Welsh mountains. Restored to provide interpretive facilities for the bygone mining industry of the region. Way-marked trail system (the miner's trail), museum, audio-visual unit, underground drift mine and working machinery. Collections include the last Cornish Roll Crusher in Wales, jiggers, buddles and many water-wheels and other items. See restoration work actually going on and witness the reconstruction of a giant 50ft diameter overshot waterwheel dating from 1865.

Open daily Etr–Aug 10–6, Sep 10–5 & Oct 10–4, telephone for Oct dates.

£1.50 (ch 5–15 70p students & pen £1.20).

ᴀ 🖵 ⊞ shop

See advertisement under Aberystwyth

PONTYPOOL
Gwent
Map **3** SO20

The Valley Inheritance Park Buildings
☎ (04955) 52043

Polperro
—
Poolewe

Housed in the Georgian stable block of Pontypool Park House, the exhibitions and film tell the story of a South Wales Valley. Also temporary exhibitions.

Open Mon–Sat 10–5 & Sun 2–5. (Closed Xmas day). Details not confirmed for 1986.

✳ 60p (ch 5 free ch 16 30p pen & students 50p). Family ticket £1.20.

ᴀ ᵭ shop ✘

POOL
Cornwall
Map **2** SW64

Cornish Engines East Pool (on either side of A3047)

Impressive relics of the tin mining industry, these great beam engines were used for pumping water from 2000 ft deep and more, and for winding men and tin ore.

Open Apr–end Oct daily 11–6 or sunset if earlier (last admission 5.30).

£1.

shop (NT).

(There are two further engines preserved at working mines. These can only be visited when suitable arrangements are made in advance with the managers concerned. Levant Mine, 4m N of St Just – The Manager, Geevor Mine ☎ Penzance 788662; South Crofty Mine, Pool – The Manager, South Crofty ☎ Camborne (0209) 714821.)

POOLE
Dorset
Map **4** SZ09

Guildhall Museum Market St
☎ (0202) 675151 (ext. 3550)

The 18th-century Guildhall and Market House with displays illustrating the development of the town from the 12th-century to the present day. Children's area, audio-visual cinema, temporary exhibition gallery and the Poole Study Collection.

Open Mon–Sat 10–5, Sun 2–5 (ex Xmas, New Years day & Good Fri).

40p (ch 20p); combined ticket for Guildhall, Maritime & Scaplen's Court 70p (ch 30p).

P shop ✘

Maritime Museum Paradise St, The Quay
☎ (0202) 675151 (ext. 3550)

Town Cellars – 15th century Woolhouse, Oakleys Mill – 18th/19th century quayside grain and feed mill. Exhibitions trace the history of Poole's maritime community: the merchants and seamen; fishermen; shipwrights and allied craftsmen;

---

tradesmen of the port; through the tools of their trade and heirlooms, local boats, contemporary accounts and ship models. Gallery display of maritime art.

Admission times and charges as Guildhall Museum.

P shop ✘

Poole Aquarium Complex & Model Railway
☎ (0202) 687240

*Apart from the aquarium, it also includes Serpentarium, Craft Centre and National Model Museum. Also **Model Railway** '00' gauge scenic layout covering over 1000 square feet.*

Open all year, daily Nov–Mar 10.30–5; May & Oct 10.30–5.30, Jan–Sep 10–8.30. (Closed Xmas day).

£1.50 (ch 4–15 75p, pen £1.25). Discount ticket available with Aquarium.

P (on quay) 🖵 shop Ⓥ

Poole Park Zoo
☎ (0202) 745296

A small but well-equipped zoo, with a wide range of animals including small cats and a children's corner with lambs, goats, monkey's, otters and rabbits. Also parrots and parrot-like birds.

Open all year, daily 10–6 or sunset if earlier. (Closed Xmas day).

✳ £1 (ch 2–14, 50p) Party 20 + .

P (Poole Park) ⊞ ᵭ shop

Poole Pottery The Quay
☎ (0202) 672866

This well-known pottery was founded in 1873 and has been producing 'Poole Pottery' since 1921. The tour includes seeing pottery being made.

Open for tours Mon–Thu 10.15–11.50 & 1.15–3.50; Fri 10.15–11.30. (Closed BHs & Works Holidays).

✳ £1.55 (ch 80p).

P (100 yds) 🖵 shop Mon–Sat 9–5 (daily Jun–Sep until 9pm) ᵭ (gift shop & tea room only) shop ✘

Scaplen's Court High St
☎ (0202) 675151 ext 3550

A Medieval Merchant's House Kitchen – cooking and food preparation utensils, household cleaning and laundry equipemnt dating from the post-medieval period to early 20th century, can be found in the old kitchen buttery and pantry. John Scaplen's Best Parlour – now houses furniture, furnishings and other family possessions from the Victorian and Edwardian eras. Solar and first floor bedrooms – exhibitions which trace the domestic life of Poole throughout the centuries.

Admission times and charges as for Guildhall Museum.

P ᵭ (ground floor only) shop ✘

POOLEWE
Highland *Ross and Cromarty*
Map **14** NG88

Inverewe Garden
☎ (044586) 200

Remarkable garden, full of interest and beauty from Mar to Oct, at their best May to early Jun and containing rare and subtropical plants. Magnificent mountain background. Loch Maree lies to the south.

Open daily 9.30–sunset 28 Mar–5 May, 8 Sep–26 Oct Mon–Sat 10–5, Sun 12.30–5; 6 May–7 Sep Mon–Sat 10–6.30, Sun 12–6.30.

✹ £1.50 (ch 75p) Party.

⚠ (10p) ⚖ (ex 14–26 Oct) & (NTS)

PORTCHESTER
Hampshire
Map 4 SU60

Portchester Castle (off A27)

3rd-century Saxon shore fort with 12th-century keep in one corner and Assheton's Tower (1367) in another. Parish Church (1133) in south-west corner was church of Augustinian foundation moved later to Southwick.

Open † see end of gazetteer.

✹ 60p (ch 16 & pen 30p).

⚠ & (grounds & lower levels only) (AM)

PORT GLASGOW
Strathclyde Renfrewshire
Map 10 NS37

Newark Castle

Dates from the 15th and 17th centuries preserving a courtyard and hall; the hall carries an inscription of 1597. Fine turrets and remains of painted ceilings. Once home of the Maxwells.

Open see end of gazetteer. Key Keeper in winter.

✹ 50p (ch & pen 25p).

⚠ & (AM)

PORTHMADOG
Gwynedd
Map 6 SH53

Ffestiniog Railway
☎ (0766) 2340 or 2384 (Timetable and fares on request)

Historic narrow-gauge railway which originally carried slate from mines at Blaenau Ffestiniog to the sea at Porthmadog, with trucks running down from the quarries by gravity. Steam locomotives were introduced in 1863 and passengers were carried soon afterwards. Line closed in 1946 but reopened by enthusiasts to operate between Porthmadog and Blaenau Ffestiniog. Steam locomotives including unique Fairlie-type articulated locomotive. Observation and licensed buffet cars on most trains.

Daily service late Mar–early Nov and also 26 Dec–1 Jan & wknds Feb & Mar.

✹ Charges vary according to distance travelled. Max. third class fare Porthmadog to Ffestiniog £5.60 return.

⚠ (limited) ⚖ (licensed) & shop

Poolewe
—
Portsmouth

Ffestiniog Railway Museum
☎ (0766) 2340 or 2384

Located in Harbour Station and includes old four-wheeled hearse converted from quarryman's coach, one of the original steam locos (1863), historic slate wagon, model steam engine (1869), and maps and diagrams illustrating history of the well-known narrow-gauge railway.

Open Feb–Dec all weekends & Mar–Nov when train services operating (see Ffestiniog Railway).

Free.

⚠ ⚖ (licensed) & shop

Porthmadog Pottery Snowdon St
☎ (0766) 2785

Situated in what were the engine rooms of an old flour mill. Dates from 1862 and displays the history of pottery. A particular feature is the 1,300ft square mural, featuring the history of Porthmadog from the building of the Cob walls to reclaim land from the sea, to the loading of the locally built ketches with slate. Pottery can be seen being made and visitors can try to make a piece of pottery for themselves.

Open Apr–Oct Mon–Fri only, 9–5.30.

✹ 20p (ch free) incl illustrated guide to pottery. Potters Wheel 75p.

⚠ shop

PORTLAND
Dorset
Map 3 SY67

Portland Castle

Erected originally by Henry VIII and added to in 17th and 18th centuries.

Open Apr–Sep.

✹ 60p (ch 16 & pen 30p).

⚠ (AM)

Portland Museum 217 Wakeham.
☎ Portland (0305) 821804

Associated with Thomas Hardy's The Well-Beloved (Avice's cottage). Now a museum of local and historical interest. Regular temporary exhibitions.

Summer open daily 10–5.30 (Sun 11–5). Winter (Oct–May) open Tue–Sat 10–1 & 2–5.

Admission fee payable.

P (in road, 100 yds) & (ground floor & gardens only) shop

PORT LOGAN
Dumfries and Galloway Wigtownshire
Map 10 NX04

Logan Botanic Garden
☎ Stranraer (0776) 86231

An annexe of the Royal Botanic Garden in

Edinburgh, containing a wide range of plants from the warm, temperate regions.

Open Apr–Sep daily 10–5.

50p (admits car & all passengers).

⚠ ⚖ & shop ✖

PORTMEIRION
Gwynedd
Map 6 SH53

Portmeirion
☎ Porthmadog (0766) 770228

Delightful Italianate village, created by the late Sir Clough Williams-Ellis, set in its own wooded peninsula on the shores of Cardigan Bay. All its cottages are let as holiday accommodation and there are a number of shops selling a wide variety of goods, a children's playground and about a mile of sandy beaches.

Day visitors welcome 9.30–5.30, Etr–Oct. (Coaches by prior arrangement.)

£1.65 (ch 70p) Party 20 + .

⚠ ⚖ (licensed) & (ground floor & gardens only) shop ⓥ

PORT OF MENTEITH
Central Perthshire
Map 11 NN50

Inchmahome Priory
☎ Stirling (0786) 62421

The 13th-century ruins of the church and cloisters of an Augustinian house founded by Walter Comyn in 1238. Famous as the retreat of the infant Mary Queen of Scots in 1543. The ruins are situated on an island in the Lake of Menteith.

Open see end of gazetteer. Closed Thu & Fri in winter. Ferry subject to cancellation in adverse weather conditions, advisable to check.

✹ Ferry £1 (ch & pen 50p).

⚠ at ferry (AM)

PORTSMOUTH AND SOUTHSEA
Hampshire
Map 4 SZ69

Charles Dickens' Birthplace Museum
393 Old Commercial Rd
☎ (0705) 827261

A house of 1805 in which the famous novelist was born and lived for a short time, now restored and furnished to illustrate the middle-class taste of the early 19th-century. Also small display of items pertaining to his work.

Open Mar–Oct daily 10.30–5.30 (last admission 5).

✹ 50p (ch, pen & students 25p).

P shop ✖ (ex guide dogs)

City Museum & Art Gallery Museum Rd, Old Portsmouth
☎ (0705) 827261

Permanent displays of furniture and decorative art from the 17th–20th-century and a growing collection of 20th-century painting and sculpture also of history of Portsmouth social history. Also →

225

programme of frequently changing exhibitions which include major national touring shows.

Open daily 10.30–5.30, last admission 5. (Closed 24–26 Dec).

✳ 50p (ch, pen & students 25p).

⚠ ⬚ (licensed) ♿ (ground floor & gardens only) shop ✘ (ex guide dogs)

Cumberland House Natural Science Museum & Aquarium Eastern Pde
☎ (0705) 827261

Geology and natural history of the Portsmouth area including a full-size reconstruction of the dinosaur 'Iguanodon', fresh-water and marine aquaria and displays of local woodland, chalk down and marshland.

Open daily 10.30–5.30, last admission 5. (Closed 24–26 Dec).

✳ 50p (ch, pen & students 25p).

⚠ shop ✘ (ex guide dogs)

D-Day Museum & Overlord Embroidery
Clarence Esplanade (adjacent to Southsea Castle)
☎ (0705) 827261

A museum telling the story of D-Day from the viewpoints of people directly involved in the War on both sides in the form of pictures, plans, re-creations of wartime scenes, and examples of weapons, uniforms and vehicles. The centrepiece of the Museum is the 'Overlord Embroidery', a spectacular testimony to history's biggest sea-borne invasion – Operation Overlord.

Open daily 10.30–5.30. (Closed 24–26 Dec). Dates to be confirmed.

✳ £1.50 (ch, student & pen £1) including admission to Southsea Castle. Party.

⚠ ♿ shop ✘ (ex guide dogs)

Eastney Pumping Station
Henderson Rd, Eastney
☎ (0705) 827261

Beam Engine House contains a pair of Boulton and Watt beam engines and reciprocal pumps now restored to their original 1887 condition. Normally 'in steam' at weekends or operable on an electric drive at other times. Adjacent

---

Portsmouth

building of 1904 houses Crossley Gas Engines. Display 'Portsmouth – an Effluent Society?', describes the history of sewage pumping.

Open Apr–Sep daily 1.30–5.30; Oct–Mar first Sun in month 1.30–5.30 (Closed 24–26 Dec).

✳ 50p (ch, pen & students 25p). Persons under 18 must be accompanied by an adult.

⚠ shop ✘ (ex guide dogs)

Fort Widley Portsdown Hill Rd
☎ (0705) 827261

One of the ring of forts built by Lord Palmerston in the 1860s to counter the threat of a French invasion. It contains gun emplacements, mortar batteries, magazines and a labyrinth of underground tunnels within its massive structure. Commands panoramic views.

Open weekends & BH's only 1.30–5.30. Guided tours (last tour leaves 5pm).

✳ £1 (ch, pen & students 50p). Persons under 18 must be accompanied by an adult.

⚠ shop ✘ (ex guide dogs)

HMS Victory The Hard
☎ (0705) 822351 ext 23111

Nelson's famous flagship, still in commission, manned by regular serving officers and men of the Royal Navy and Marines, and being restored to the appearance she had before the Battle of Trafalgar in 1805. Navy Days 29–31 Aug.

Open Mar–Oct Mon–Sat 10.30–5.30 & Sun 1–5; Nov–Feb Mon–Sat 10.30–4.30 & Sun 1–4.30. (Closed 25 Dec).

Free.

P (500 yds) ⬚ (100 yds) ♿ (Lower Gun Deck) shop ✘

The Mary Rose HM Naval Base for enquiries: The Mary Rose Trust, Old Bond

---

Store, 48 Warblington St, Portsmouth PO1 2ET
☎ (0705) 750521

Henry VIII's warship, Mary Rose, raised from the Solent in 1982, presents a breathtaking spectacle in the heart of Portsmouth's historic Royal Dockyard. The hull has been turned into an upright position from the 60 degree angle at which she rested on the seabed and at which she lay in her dry dock workshop until July 1985. New viewing galleries allow visitors to watch the beginnings of the work to conserve the hull and replace many of the timbers removed during the years of excavation, including decks and cabins. Nearby, in a Georgian timber boathouse, an Exhibition features many of the 'treasures' of the Mary Rose . . . the everyday objects she carried into battle, manned and equipped for sea warfare. Also shown are re-creations of life on board and displays illustrating Tudor social and maritime history.

Open 2 Mar–Oct daily, 10.30–5.30 (last visitors 5) Nov–1 Mar daily, 10.30–5 (last visitors 4.30). (Closed Xmas day). The Naval Base is subject to security restrictions at short notice. It may also be necessary to close the Ship Hall at short notice for operational reasons, it is therefore advisable to check before visiting.

Combined ticket £2.50 (ch & pen £1.50) Family £6.50; Ship Hall £1.20 (ch & pen 50p) Family £2.70; Exhibition £1.70 (ch & pen £1.20) Family £4.50. Party.

P ⬚ ♿ (exhibition and one gallery of Ship Hall only) shop ✘

Round Tower Broad St, Old Portsmouth
☎ (0705) 827261

Dating from the early 15th century, this is the first permanent defensive work to be built in Portsmouth and commands the entrance to the Harbour. It now provides an excellent vantage point.

Open daily.

Free.

⚠ ✘ (ex guide dogs)

Royal Marines Museum Eastney
☎ (0705) 822351 ext 6133

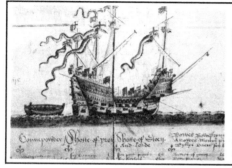

A chronological history of the Royal
Marines from 1664 to the present day.
Specialist displays of uniforms, badges,
Royal Marines' bands and medals,
including the complete collection of 10
Royal Marines VCs. A new display 'The
Royal Marines through the 70s into the
80s' opened in 1982 covering Northern
Ireland and the 'Arctic' commandos,
together with other aspects of Corps
activities over the past decade. A new
'Falklands' display was added in 1983.
Temporary exhibitions are a feature of the
museum. Museum is established in the
original Royal Marine Artillery Officers'
Mess, a superb example of Victorian
architecture and retains original
mouldings and fireplaces.

Open daily 10–4.30.

Free.

⚠ ⚒ (May–Sep) (ground floor & gardens
only) shop ✄

Royal Naval Museum H.M. Naval Base
☎ (0705) 822351 (ext 23868)

The only museum devoted exclusively to
the overall history of The Navy. Panorama
of Trafalgar (with sound effects). Relics of
Nelson, his officers and men. Uniforms,
medals, figureheads, ship models.
Displays on the 'Sailing Navy', the
'Victorian Navy', 'World War Two at Sea'
and the 'Modern Navy'.

Open daily 10.30–5. Closed 4.30pm
winter.

Admission fee payable.

P (500 yds) ⚒ ⚕ (ground floor only) shop
✄ coaches by prior arrangement

Southsea Castle & Museum
Clarence Esp
☎ (0705) 827261

Fort built in 1545 by King Henry VIII as part
of his national coastal defences. Contains
displays illustrating Portsmouth's
development as a military fortress,
aspects of naval history and the
archaeology of the area.

Open daily 10.30–5.30, (last admission
5pm). Closed 24–26 Dec.

✱ 50p (ch, pen & students 25p).
Combined ticket with D-Day Museum
£1.50 (ch, pen & students £1).

Portsmouth
—
Prescot

P (100 yds) ⚕ (ground floor only) shop ✄
(ex guide dogs)

Spitbank Fort
☎ Gosport (0705) 524551

Built in the 1860's as part of the coastal
defences against Napoleon this massive
fortress is built of granite and iron. The
interior is a maze of passages and has
over fifty rooms on two levels; a Victorian
cooking range is still in working order as
are the forge and a 402 foot deep well
from which fresh water is obtained. The
location of the fort one mile out to sea
provides a panoramic viewpoint of the
Solent.

Open Etr–Oct.

✱ £2 (ch £1) includes ferry charge. Boat
ride takes approx. 10mins, visitors should
allow at least 1 hour to look around.
Ferries depart from Gosport & Clarence
Pier.

P (available on shore) ⚒ shop

PORT SUNLIGHT
Merseyside
Map **7** SJ38

Lady Lever Art Gallery
☎ 051–645 3623

Pictures by famous English Masters in
addition to collections of English period
furniture, Chinese porcelain and
Wedgwood.

Open Mon–Sat 10–5 & Sun 2–5. (Good Fri,
24–26 Dec & 1 Jan).

40p (ch & pen 10p). Party 10+ £2.

⚠ ⚕ (ground floor only) shop ✄

POWDERHAM
Devon
Map **3** SX98

Powderham Castle (Entrance off A379
Exeter/Dawlish road)
☎ Starcross (0626) 890243

Seat of the Earls of Devon, built between

1390 and 1420, damaged in the Civil War,
restored and altered in the 18th and 19th
centuries. Fine furnishings and portraits
plus beautiful rose garden.

Open 25 May–11 Sep, Sun–Thu, 2–5.30
last admission 5pm. Connoisseurs day
Thu.

✱ £1.75 (pen £1.50, ch 8–16 £1 ch under 8
free). Thu £2 (pen £1.75 ch 8–16 £1.25 ch
8 free).

⚠ ⚒ ⚓ ⚕ (ground floor & gardens only)
shop ✄ Ⓥ

See advertisement on page 228

PRESCOT
Merseyside
Map **7** SJ49

Knowsley Safari Park
☎ 051-430 9009

Lions, tigers, elephants, rhinos, monkeys
and many other animals to be seen in
drive through reserves. Extra attractions
include children's amusement park and
pets corner.

Game reserves Mar–Oct. Other
attractions Etr–Sep. Daily 10–4.

✱ £5 per car (incl all occupants). No soft-
topped cars (Safari bus available). Coach
passengers £1.50 (ch 3–15 & pen 85p).

⚠ ⚒ (licensed) ⚓ ⚕ shop ✄ (in game
reserve, kennels available) Ⓥ

**Prescot Museum of Clock & Watch-
Making** 34 Church st
☎ 051-430 7787

An attractive 18th-century town house
contains exhibits about the clock, watch
and tool making industry of the area.
Display includes a reconstruction of part
of a traditional watch-maker's workshop,
examples of hand tools and machinery
used to make the many intricate parts of
watch and clock movements.

Open Tue–Sat & BH Mon, 10–5. Sun 2–5.
(Closed 24–26 Dec, New Year's day &
Good Fri).

Free.

P (100 yds) ⚕ (ground floor only) shop ✄
🚻

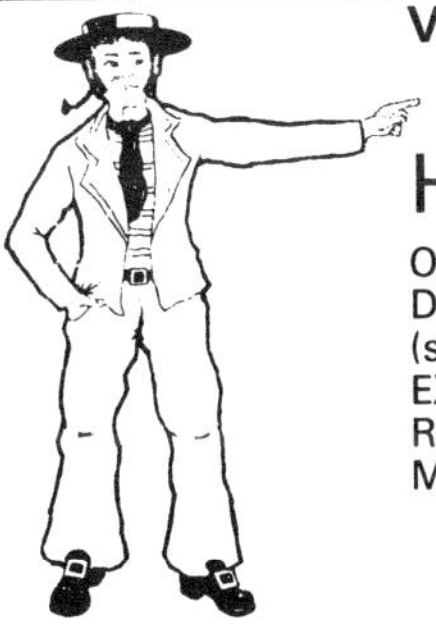

PRESTON
Lancashire
Map 7 SD52

Harris Museum & Art Gallery Market Sq
☎ (0772) 58248

*Impressive neo-classical building
containing extensive collections of Fine
and Decorative Arts. Includes paintings
by the Devis family, the Newsham
bequest of 19th-century paintings and
sculpture, and the Houghton bequest of
ceramics. Also social history and
archaeology collections together with
regular temporary exhibitions.*

Open Mon–Sat 10–5. (Closed BHs).

Free.

P (200 yds) ⚏ (Mon, Wed & Fri 10.30–
1.30) ዿ shop ✖ (ex guide dogs)

PRESTONPANS
Lothian *East Lothian*
Map 11 NT37

Scottish Mining Museum
Prestongrange
☎ 031-665 9904

*Oldest documented coal mining site in
Britain, with 800 years of history. Cornish
Beam Engine, Visitor centre, Exhibition
Hall, 16th-century Customs Port. Self-
drive Coal Heritage Trail to Lady Victoria
Colliery. It is a new independent twin-site
museum of coal mining in Scotland.*

Visitor centre open Mon–Fri 10–4, Sat &
Sun 12–5. Special steam days first Sun of
month Apr–Oct. Details not confirmed for
1986.

Free.

⚠ ዿ (ground floor only) ✖

PRESTWICH
Gt Manchester
Map 7 SD80

Heaton Hall Heaton Park (on A665)
☎ 061-236 9422

*The finest house of its period in
Lancashire and one of the finest in the
country. Designed for Earl of Wilton by
James Wyatt in 1772, the house has
magnificent decorated interiors and
commands panoramic views of
Manchester.*

Preston
—
Pudsey

Open Apr–Sep Mon, Wed–Sat 10–6 also
Sun 2–6. Details not confirmed for 1986.

Free.

⚠ ⚏ ዿ (ground floor only) shop ✖

PRISTON
Avon
Map 3 ST66

Priston Mill Priston Mill Farm
☎ Bath (0225) 23894

*Nature trail, children's play area and
watermill surrounded by beautiful
countryside and farm animals. 5 miles SW
of Bath. One of the only commercially
working Domesday Mills left in England.*

Open Etr–Oct, daily 2.15–5.

✳ 50p (ch 30p).

⚠ ♫ ዿ (ground floor & gardens only)
shop

PROBUS
Cornwall
Map 2 SW94

**County Council Demonstration
Garden, Arboretum & Rural Studies
Centre**
☎ Truro (0872) 74282 ext 3400

*Permanent displays of many aspects of
garden layout, plant selection and effect
of weather conditions. Plant, tree and
flower propagation. Exhibits of fruit, herbs
and vegetables. Emphasis on choosing
right foliage, flowers etc, to suit individual
requirements and environment. Historical
plant collection, Geological displays,
outdoor sculpture exhibition. For special
events see local press.*

Open May–Sep, Mon–Fri 10–5 also Sun 2–
6; Oct–Apr, Mon–Fri 10–4.30. Advisor on
duty Thu 2–5.

60p summer. 50p winter.

⚠ ♫ ዿ (ground floor & garden only) ✖

Trewithen Grampound Rd (on A390
between Probus and Grampound)
☎ St Austell (0726) 882418

Trewithen House *Guided tours round
this charming and intimate Cornish
country house built in 1720 and lived in
continuously by the same family.*
Trewithen Gardens *Internationally
renowned landscaped garden covering
some 20 acres with camellias, magnolias,
rhododendrons and many rare trees and
shrubs seldom found elsewhere.
Nurseries open all year.*

House open Apr–Jul only on Mon & Tue
including BHs 2–4.30. Gardens open Mar–
Sep, Mon–Sat including BH; 2–4.30.
(Opening dates to be confirmed for 1986).

✳ House (Guided Tour) £1.70. Gardens
Mar–Jun £1 (ch & pen 90p, ch 10 free);
Jul–Sep 90p (ch & pen 70p, ch 10 free).

⚠ ♫ ዿ (gardens only) shop garden
centre

PRUDHOE
Northumberland
Map 12 NZ06

Prudhoe Castle

*On River Tyne 12th- to 14th-century
stronghold of d'Umfravelles and Percys.
Keep stands in inner bailey and notable
example of gatehouse guards outside
bailey. Access to Pele Yard only.*

Open see end of gazetteer.

✳ 30p (ch & pen 15p; ch 16 not admitted
unless with an adult).
(AM).

PUDSEY
West Yorkshire
Map 8 SE23

Fulneck Moravian Museum 55–57
Fulneck
☎ (0532) or 571440

*This museum of Moravian exhibits and
Victoriana includes photographs,
furniture, 150 year-old fire engine, working
hand loom and spinning wheel.*

Open Mar–Oct, Wed & Sat 2–5. Other
times by appointment only.

25p (ch 15p).
 & shop

PULBOROUGH
West Sussex
Map **4** TQ01

Parham Park Gardens (3m SE off A283)
☎ Storrington (09066) 2021
Situated in a beautiful downland setting. Walled garden and pleasure grounds of an Elizabethan Mansion.
Open 30 Mar–5 Oct, Wed, Thu, Sun & BH, Gardens 1–6; House 2–6 (last entry 5.30pm).

Pudsey
—
Pusey

House & gardens £2.50 (pen £2 ch £1.50). Gardens only £1 (ch 75p). Party by appointment only.
 & ⏛ ⑂ & (gardens only) shop ✖ (in house)

PURSE CAUNDLE
Dorset
Map **3** ST61

Purse Caundle Manor
☎ Milborne Port (0963) 250400
Excellent example of medieval manor house, with great hall, chamber and gardens.
Open Etr Mon–28 Sep, Thu, Sun & BHs 2–5. By appointment at other times.
£1 (ch 30p).
 & & (ground floor & gardens only) ✖

PUSEY
Oxfordshire
Map **4** SU39

Pusey House Gardens
☎ Buckland (036787) 222 →

Parham House & Gardens
Pulborough, West Sussex

Grey stone Elizabethan House with an important collection of Elizabethan, Jacobean and Georgian portraits, fine furniture, carpets, tapestries and a profusion of rare needlework.

The Gardens include a beautiful walled garden with herbaceous borders, herb garden and orchard. Also Pleasure Grounds with mature trees, statuary and lake.

Open from Easter Sunday to first Sunday in October.
See gazetteer for details.

Probus, nr. Truro, Cornwall. (On A.390 between Probus and Grampound)

These gardens, covering some 20 acres, created in the early years of this century, are outstanding and internationally famous. Renowned for their magnificent collection of camellias, rhododendrons, magnolias and many rare trees and shrubs which are seldom found elsewhere in Britain. The extensive woodland gardens are surrounded by traditional parkland landscaped and planted in the 18th century and include an enchanting Walled Garden — the early rose and herb garden — contemporary with the house. Additionally there are the original water gardens which are currently being fully restored.

Open 1st March to 30th September, Monday to Saturday, 2 — 4.30 p.m. Closed Sunday.
Free car parking. Plants for sale. Dogs on leads. St. Austell (0726) 882418.
Head Gardener, St. Austell (0726) 882764. Wholesale orders welcomed.

Designed in 1748 with new garden terraces added in 1935 by Geoffrey Jellicoe. 20 acres of garden and lake, with herbaceous borders.

Gardens open 29 Mar–26 Oct, Tue–Thu, Sat, Sun & BH Mons, 2–6.

£1.30 (ch 11 free). Party.

⚠ ⚖ ᵴ garden centre ⓥ

QUAINTON
Buckinghamshire
Map **4** SP71

Buckinghamshire Railway Centre
Quainton Station (off A41)
☎ (029675) 450

One of the largest and most comprehensive collections of standard-gauge railways – industrial and main line. Many items were built in the last century. There are rides in a vintage steam train, a small relics museum and display of locomotives and rolling stock.

In steam every Sun from Etr–Oct 10–6, plus BH Mons. Special rallies held throughout the year.

✳ £1.60 (ch & pen 80p). Family ticket £4. BH & Rallies £1.90 (ch & pen 95p). Family ticket £4.75.

⚠ ⚖ ᵴ shop

QUATT
Shropshire
Map **7** SO78

Dudmaston
☎ (0746) 780866

In extensive parkland garden, a late 17th-century house with fine furniture, 17th-century flower paintings which belonged to Francis Darby of Coalbrookdale. Also modern pictures, water-colours and botanical art.

Open 30 Mar–Sep, Wed & Sun 2.30–6 (last admissions 5.30) Parties by appointment only.

£1.80. Garden only 80p. Party.

⚖ ᵴ shop ✖ (in house) (NT)

QUEENSFERRY (South)
Lothian West Lothian
Map **11** NT17

Dalmeny House
☎ 031-331 1888

Home of the Earl and Countess of Rosebery, magnificently situated on the Firth of Forth. Contains the Rothschild collection of superb 18th-century French furniture, porcelain and tapestries, early Scottish furniture, important 18th-century portraits and an exhibition of pictures and items associated with Napoleon. Old private apartments. Rosebery racing mementos. Woodland and shore walks.

Open May–Sep, Sun–Thu, 2–5.30 (last admission 5pm).

✳ £1.50 (ch 5–16 & students £1, pen £1.20). Party.

⚠ ⚖ ᵴ

Pusey
—
Ramsey

Hopetoun House
(2m W on unclassified road)
☎ 031-331 2451

Scotland's greatest Adam mansion and home of the 3rd Marquess of Linlithgow M.C. Magnificent reception rooms, pictures and furnishings. Beautiful spacious grounds with red and fallow deer, St Kilda sheep and nature trail. Views of the Forth Bridges.

Open Etr then 27 Apr–16 Sep daily 11–5.30.

✳ £2 (ch £1, students & pen £1.50). Family ticket £5.10.

⚠ ⚖ (licensed) ⊞ ᵴ (ground floor only) shop & garden centre ✖ (in house) ⓥ

Inchcolm Abbey Inchcolm Island (1½m S of Aberdour) (Access by ferry from South Queensferry Apr–Sep only)
☎ Dalgetty Bay (0383) 823332

Situated on a green island in the Firth of Forth, are the remains of an Augustinian Abbey, founded c.1123 by Alexander I. The well preserved monastic buildings include a fine 13th-century octagonal Chapter House and a 13th-century wall painting depicting a funeral procession of clerics.

Open see end of gazetteer. (Closed Wed pm & Thu in winter).

£1 (ch & pen 50p).

(AM)

QUEEN'S VIEW
Tayside Perthshire
Map **14** NN85

Tummel Forest Centre
☎ Pitlochry (0796) 3437

Exhibits show changes in the Tummel Valley since Queen Victoria's visit in 1866. Audio-visual programmes, forest walks and information desk.

Open Apr–Sep 9.30–5.30.

Free.

P (adjacent) ᵴ shop ✖

RADCLIFFE
Gt Manchester
Map **7** SD70

Radcliffe Tower Tower St, off Church St East
☎ 061-761 4021 ext 54 (enquiries to Bury Art Gallery & Museum)

Remains of medieval tower once part of a larger hall occupied by the Radcliffe family. Adjacent to medieval parish church.

Open at all times.

Free.

P (in nearby street) ᵴ (ground floor & gardens only)

RADCLIFFE-ON-TRENT
Nottinghamshire
Map **8** SK63

Holme Pierrepont Hall
(¾m W on unclass rd)
☎ (06073) 2371

Early brick Tudor manor house of medieval design built around 1500 and contains fine old timbering. The family furniture and portraits span 300 years, mostly of regional character. Victorian formal courtyard garden. Jacob sheep.

Open Etr Sun–Tue; Spring & Summer BHs Sun–Tue; Jun–Aug, Sun, Tue, Thu & Fri; Sep Suns only (2–6). Parties by appointment other times.

✳ £1.20 (ch 50p). Gardens only 25p.

⚠ ⚖ ᵴ (ground floor only) shop ✖

RAGLAN
Gwent
Map **3** SO40

Raglan Castle
Mainly 15th-century and noted for 'Yellow Tower of Gwent'. Built by Sir William Thomas and destroyed during the Civil War. Long Gallery added by Lord Worcester, was 126ft long. Castle has own bowling green.

Open † see end of gazetteer.

✳ 70p (ch 16 & pen 35p).

⚠ ⊞ shop (AM Cadw)

RAINTHORPE HALL
Norfolk
Map **5** TM29

(7½m S of Norwich)
☎ Swainsthorpe (0508) 470618

Fine Elizabethan manor house of brick and timber.

House open by appointment only. Garden open May–Sep Sun & BH 2–5.

£1 (ch & pen 50p).

⚠ ᵴ (ground floor & gardens only) garden centre ✖ ⓥ

RAMPTON
Nottinghamshire
Map **8** SK77

Sundown Pets Corner Treswell Rd
☎ (077784) 274

Created specially for young children, with pets and farm animals and animated nursery rhymes set amidst attractive gardens. There is also a 'play village', modern playground, unique life size 'toy jungle', Noahs Ark, pirate ship with rocks and caves, large sandpit and much more.

Open daily 10–7 or dusk. (Closed 25 & 26 Dec).

£1 (school parties & play groups 80p).

⚠ ⚖ & tea garden ⊞ ᵴ shop ✖

RAMSEY
Cambridgeshire
Map **4** TL28

Abbey Gatehouse

A 15th-century Benedictine ruin.

Open Apr–Oct Daily 10–5 (or dusk).

Free. (NT)

Ramsey Abbey

☎ (0487) 813285

House (now a comprehensive school) erected circa 1600 on the site of a Benedictine monastery, fragments of which still remain. An interesting mixture of architectural styles, reflecting its varied history, the house was extended and refurbished by architects Sir John Soane and Edward Blore in 19th century.

Open Sun 31 Mar–27 Oct 2–5.

Free.

🅰 ✖ (NT)

RAMSEY
Isle of Man
Map **6** SC49

'The Grove' Rural Life Museum
(on W side of Andreas Rd)
☎ Douglas (0624) 75522 or 25125

A Victorian house with a display of early agricultural equipment in the outbuildings.

Open early May–late Sep, Mon–Fri 10–5. Sun 2–5. (Closed Sat.)

✻ 35p (ch 10p).

🅰 ⬚ ⓺ (gardens only) shop ✖ (ex guide dogs)

RAMSGATE
Kent
Map **5** TR36

Ramsgate Motor Museum West Cliff Hall, West Cliff
☎ Thanet (0843) 581948

Display of over fifty cars and motor cycles dating from the 1900's, plus a three-wheeler section, stationary engines, petrol pump globes and old signs.

Open Apr–Nov daily & Dec–Mar Sun 10.30–6. Details not confirmed for 1986.

Admission fee payable.

P (20 yds) ⬚ ⅌ ⓺

Ramsgate Museum Ramsgate Library, Guildford Lawn
☎ Thanet (0843) 593532

A display of objects, pictures and documents illustrating the history and development of Ramsgate.

Open Mon–Sat; Mon–Wed 9.30–6, Thu & Sat 9.30–5 Fri 9.30–8. (Closed BH.)

Free.

P (100 yds) ⓺ (ground floor only) ✖

RAVENGLASS
Cumbria
Map **6** SD09

Ravenglass & Eskdale Railway
☎ (06577) 226

Narrow-gauge (15 inch) steam railway established in 1875 to carry iron ore. Now passenger line with steam and diesel

---

Ramsey — Reedham

locomotives, open and saloon coaches. Runs 7 miles from Ravenglass to Eskdale through beautiful scenery. Railway Museum at Ravenglass.

Trains operate 22 Mar–2 Nov daily; 22 Feb–16 Mar & 8–23 Nov wknds only. Museum and shops. ✻ Return fare £3.10 (ch 15 £1.60). Family ticket (2 adults & 2 ch) £8.

🅰 ⬚ ⅌ ⓺ shops ⓥ

RAVENSHEAD
Nottinghamshire
Map **8** SK55

Longdale Rural Craft Centre
(The Gordon Brown Collection)
☎ Mansfield (0623) 794858

Timbered buildings and narrow streets of bygone days, recreated at the centre, where workshops produce an extensive range of traditional crafts.

Open daily 9–6.

60p (ch 5 free, ch 30p, pen & disabled 45p).

🅰 ⬚ (licensed) ⓺ shop ⓥ

READING
Berkshire
Map **4** SU77

Blake's Lock Museum
☎ (0734) 55911 ext 2242 (Reading Museum & Art Gallery)

In an attractive Victorian building, the museum illustrates the history of industrial and commercial life in Reading, with a section on its waterways. There are reconstructions of a family baker, barbers and a printers workshop.

Open Wed–Fri 10–5; Sat & Sun 2–5. Parties by arrangement.

Free.

🅰 ⓺(ground floor only) ⅌ shop ✖

Museum & Art Gallery Blagrave St
☎ (0734) 55911 ext 2242

Noted especially for its exceptional collection of exhibits from Roman Silchester, but there are also items from the River Thames area, including a splendid Bronze Age torc from Moulsford. Also displays of local natural history and monthly changing exhibitions. See also: Silchester, Calleva Museum.

Open Mon–Fri 10–5.30 & Sat 10–5. (Closed Sun & BHs).

Free.

P shop ✖

Museum of English Rural Life
The University, Whiteknights Park, Shinfield Rd entrance
☎ Reading (0734) 875123 ext 475

Collection of highly interesting

---

agricultural, domestic and crafts exhibits.

Open Tue–Sat 10–1 & 2–4.30. (Closed BHs).

50p (ch free).

🅰 ⓺ shop ✖

REAY
Highland Caithness
Map **14** NC96

U.K.A.E.A. Dounreay Exhibition
(2m NE)
☎ Thurso (0847) 62121 ext 656

Information panels, models participatory displays and charts relating to fast reactors and nuclear energy generally. Housed in a former airfield control tower overlooking the plant which is conspicuous for its 135ft sphere and the prototype fast reactor.

Open May–Sep, daily 9–4.

Exhibition free. Public tours of the prototype fast reactor on the hour commencing at 12 noon. Tickets available from Exhibition or Wick & Thurso Tourist Information Centre.

🅰 ⓺ (ground floor only) ✖

RECULVER
Kent
Map **5** TR26

Roman Fort

Remains of 3rd-century Roman fort of the Saxon Shore on an even older site. Within its walls stand the towers of a Norman church left as a mariners' landmark.

Open see end of gazetteer. Apr–Sep only.

✻ 30p (ch 16 & pen 15p).

P (AM)

REDDITCH
Hereford & Worcester
Map **7** SP06

Forge Mill Museum Forge Mill, Needle Mill Ln
☎ (0527) 62509

The only remaining water-driven needle-scouring mill, with much of its machinery preserved from the 18th century.

Open Mon–Fri, 11–4.30; Sat 1–5; Sun & BH 11.30–5.

£1 (ch & pen 50p). Parties.

🅰 ⬚ ⅌ shop ✖

REEDHAM
Norfolk
Map **5** TG40

Pettitts Crafts, Gardens & 'Falabella'
☎ Great Yarmouth (0493) 700094

Peacocks, ornamental pheasants, birds of prey and parrots displayed. Waterfowl on show in gardens surrounded with picnic area. Art of feather craft and taxidermy usually being demonstrated and products are on sale. Putting green, crazy golf, donkey rides and large adventure playground. Particularly suitable for →

elderly and disabled with no difficult steps.

Open Etr–Oct, Mon–Fri 10–6, Sun 1–5.30.

£1.20 (ch 60p pen 90p). Party.

⚠ ⬛ 🚻 ♿ shop Ⓥ

REIGATE
Surrey
Map **4** TQ24

Priory Museum Bell St
☎ (07372) 45065

Contained in house, originally founded in 1235, and converted into Tudor mansion, of which the hall fireplace is the finest surviving relic. Palladian stucco of 1779 changed the face of the building and painted staircase by Verrio c 1710 is a notable example. House now used as school and part is a small museum with changing displays. Special exhibitions throughout the year.

Museum open Weds only in term time 2–4.30. Conducted tour if requested. Details not confirmed for 1986.

Free.

⚠ (coaches only) P (50 yds) ♿ (ground floor only) shop ✗

REIGATE HEATH
Surrey
Map **4** TQ25

Old Windmill
220 year-old mill, converted into a Church in 1882. Services (3pm on third Sun of each month between May and Oct). Restored in 1964.

Accessible all year daily, 10–dusk. Key available from Club house.

Free.

⚠ ✗ ⚏

RESTORMEL
Cornwall
Map **2** SX16

Restormel Castle (1m N of Lostwithiel off A390)
Comprises circular mound and gateway c 1100 with notable round keep built c 1200. Rectangular 13th-century chapel (AM) situated nearby

---

Reedham
–
Ribchester

Castle open † see end of gazetteer.

✳ 60p (ch 16 & pen 30p).

P (AM)

RETFORD (EAST)
Nottinghamshire
Map **8** SK78

National Mining Museum Lound Hall
(5m S on B6387)
☎ Mansfield (0623) 860728

Exhibits include locomotives, coal-face machinery, headgear, hand tools, lamps and electrical equipment. Engines in steam on Sundays. The modern Bevercotes colliery is adjacent to museum.

Open Tue–Sat 10–5.30 or dusk; Sun 2–5.30 or dusk.

£1 (ch 25p pen & unemployed 50p). School party 20p.

⚠ ♿ (ground floor only) shop Ⓥ

RHOOSE
South Glamorgan
Map **3** ST06

Wales Aircraft Museum
Cardiff (Wales) Airport
☎ (0222) 29880

Opened in 1977, this privately operated museum is situated adjacent to the airport. More than 20 aircraft, including a Viscount airliner and a Vulcan Bomber, can be inspected. Aircraft engines and aviation-related items, photographs, models and historical items. Children can sit in a Sea Hawk cockpit section.

Open Jun, Jul & Aug daily 11–5.30. Remainder of year open on Suns only 11–7 (or dusk).

✳ 80p (ch 6–16 & pen 40p, ch 6 & disabled free).

P (200 yds in Cardiff Airport) ⬛ (summer only) ♿ (ground floor only) shop Ⓥ

RHUDDLAN
Clwyd
Map **6** SJ07

Bodrhyddan Hall (1½m E on A5151)
☎ (0745) 590414

A 17th-century manor house (part earlier), with armour, furniture, and notable pictures set in fine grounds.

Open Jun–end Sept, Tue & Thu 2–5.30.

90p (ch 14 45p).

⚠ ⬛ ♿ (gardens only) shop ✗

Rhuddlan Castle
Begun 1277 by Edward I to a 'diamond' plan and showing round towers, gatehouses and 9ft-thick curtain walls.

Open see end of gazetteer.

✳ 60p (ch 16 & pen 30p).

⚠ shop (AM Cadw)

RHYNIE
Grampian Aberdeenshire
Map **15** NJ42

Leith Hall & Garden
(3¼m NE on B9002)
☎ Kennethmont (04643) 216

A house built round a courtyard with Jacobite relics and a fine rock garden. The earliest part dates from 1650. Extensive grounds.

House open May–Sep, daily 2–6, last visitors 5.15. Garden & grounds open all year 9.30–sunset.

House & gardens £1.40 (ch 70p). Grounds by donation.

(NTS)

RIBCHESTER
Lancashire
Map **7** SD63

Roman Museum & Fort
(5½m NE of Preston on B6245)
☎ (025473) 261

Site museum of the Roman Fort of Bremetennacum in an attractive village. Contains cavalryman's tombstone, coins, pottery, jewellery, inscriptions and a replica of the famous Parade Helmet, the original of which is in the British Museum.

Also unique collection of Celtic heads. Remains of Roman granary.

Open all year daily; Feb–May 2–5; Jun–Aug 11.30–5.30; Sep–Nov 2–5; Dec–Jan Sat only 2–5. Details not confirmed for 1986.

Admission fee payable.

P (300 yds) & shop

RICHBOROUGH
Kent
Map **5** TR36

Fort & Museum
Roman 'Rutupiae' and original fort of the Saxon Shore.

Open † see end of gazetteer.

✴ 60p (ch 16 & pen 30p).

⚠ & (AM)

RICHMOND
North Yorkshire
Map **7** NZ10

Georgian Theatre Royal Victoria Rd
☎ (0748) 3021
Built in 1788 this is the oldest theatre in the United Kingdom still in its original form. The museum contains playbills, photographs and the oldest complete set of painted scenery in the country.

Open May–Sep daily 2.30–5, Sat & BH 10.30–1.

60p (ch, students & pen 40p). Parties by appointment.

P (200 yds) shop ✗

Green Howards Museum
Trinity Sq, Market Place
☎ (0748) 2133
Covers history of famous regiment, including uniforms dating from 1688, weapons and special VC exhibition.

Open Feb Mon–Fri, 9–4.30; Mar Mon–Sat 9–4.30; Apr–Oct Mon–Sat 9–4.30 & Sun 2–4.30; Nov Mon–Sat 9–4.30.

✴ 50p (ch 25p).

P (300 yds)

& (ground floor only) shop ✗

Richmond Castle
Dates from 11th and 12th century, one of the earliest in England with massive curtain walls and splendid rectangular keep overlooking river Swale.

Open † see end of gazetteer.

✴ 60p (ch 16 & pen 30p).

P & (AM)

RIEVAULX
North Yorkshire
Map **8** SE58

Rievaulx Abbey
Magnificent Cistercian abbey begun about 1132, surrounded by wooded hills. Earliest large Cistercian nave in Britain. Extensive, well preserved monastic buildings.

Open † see end of gazetteer.

✴ 80p winter 40p (ch 16 & pen 40p, winter 20p).

⚠ (charge) & (AM)

Rievaulx Terrace
Half-mile-long terrace looking down on the ruined 13th-century abbey with views of Ryedale and the Hambleton Hills. There are two 18th-century garden temples and some remarkable fresco paintings by Burnici. Exhibition on English landscape design.

Open 29 Mar–Oct daily 10.30–6, last admission 5.30. (Closed Good Fri).

£1.20 (ch 60p).

⚠ (NT)

RIPLEY
Derbyshire
Map **8** SK35

Midland Railway Centre Butterley Station
☎ (0773) 47674
The centre not only operates a regular

---

steam-train passenger service, but also is the focal point for an industrial museum project depicting every aspect of the golden days of the Midland Railway and its successors. The working section of the line extends some 3 miles from Butterley Station to Ironville. Exhibits range from steam locomotives of 1866 to diesels of 1959, together with a large selection of rolling stock that spans the last 100 years.

Open for static display in season. Trains run weekends Mar–Dec & Wed in Jul daily Whit wk & 21 Jul–Aug. Timetable for 1986 not confirmed.

£1.90 (ch 95p). Family £4.75.

⚠ ☑ ╬ shop

RIPLEY
North Yorkshire
Map **8** SE26

Ripley Castle
☎ Harrogate (0423) 770152 (Estate Office)
Home of the Ingilby family since 1350 the present castle dates from the 16th and late 18th century, with gatehouse c 1450. Cromwellian associations, Royalist armour and weaponry and priest's hiding hole discovered in 1964. Fine gardens and grounds. British Beautiful Homes and Gardens Exhibitions 2–5 May.

Open Apr & May wknds, 11.30–4.30; Jun–2nd wk Oct, wknds & Tue–Thu, 11.30–4.30; Etr & BHs 11–4.30. Gardens, daily Etr–2nd wk in Oct.

✴ £1.80 (ch 90p, pen & unemployed £1.35, children with unemployed 70p). Gardens only 80p (ch 40p pen & unemployed 60p). Party.

⚠ ☑ & (ground floor & garden only) shop ⓥ

RIPON
North Yorkshire
Map **8** SE37

Fountains Abbey & Studley Royal Country Park (2m SW off B6265)
☎ Sawley (076586) 333
The largest monastic ruin in Britain founded by Cistercian monks in 1132. Extensive park with deer and landscape →

garden laid out in 1720–40 with lake, formal water gardens and temples. St Mary's church built by William Burges. Abbey & garden open all year. Open daily Jan–Mar & Oct–Dec 10–4, Apr–Jun & Sep 10–7, Jul & Aug 10–8. (Closed Xmas).

£1.50

P (50 yds) ⚲ & shop (NT)

Norton Conyers
☎ Melmerby (076584) 333

A Jacobean house with later additions. Associated with Charlotte Brontë. Believed to be one of the originals of Thornfield Hall in 'Jane Eyre'. Charlotte Brontë relics are on display together with a family collection of furniture, pictures and dresses. 18th-century walled garden.

Open 26 Jul–4 Aug daily; Jun–25 Jul & 4 Aug–7 Sep Sun only; BH Sun & Mon: 2–5.30.

£1.20 (ch 60p, pen 80p). Party.

⚠ & (ground floor only) shop & garden centre ✘

Prison and Police Museum St Marygate
☎ (0765) 3706

Displays and exhibits illustrating the twin themes of the museum and reflecting the history of the buildings.

Open 3 May–28 Sep Tue–Sun & BH Mon 1.30–4.30. Other times by appointment.

Ripon
—
Robertsbridge

✳ 50p (ch under 5 free, ch over 5 25p)
P shop

Wakeman's House, Museum & Tourist Information Centre
☎ (0765) 4625

House dates back to the 14th century, now a combined tourist information centre and museum of local and historical interest.

Open Etr then May Day–mid Sep, Mon–Sat 10–5 & Sun 1–5. Details not confirmed for 1986.

Admission fee payable.

P (30 yds)

RISELEY
Berkshire
Map **4** SU76

Wellington Country Park & National Dairy Museum (off A32 between Reading & Basingstoke)
☎ Heckfield (073583) 444

The Park comprises woods and meadows set around a lake in a peaceful rural

---

setting. Within the grounds is the National Dairy Museum showing the history of dairying, a collection of small domestic animals, and a miniature steam railway. Five nature trails are marked in addition to the opportunity for boating, fishing, windsurfing and other leisure activities.

Open Mar–Oct daily; Nov–Feb Sat & Sun; 10–5.30 (or dusk if earlier).

£1.50 (ch 70p). Party.

⚠ ⚲ ⊞ & shop

ROBERTSBRIDGE
East Sussex
Map **5** TQ72

Robertsbridge Aeronautical Museum
Bush Barn (1m N off A21)
☎ Lamberhurst (0892) 890386

On display are 29 engines, a Hurricane cockpit section complete with seat, radio, controls, instrument panel and Merlin engine, Lancaster rear turret, many aircraft components, documents, uniforms and associated items. There are at least 60 different types of aircraft represented, dating from First World War to the present day.

Open last Sun of each month (except Dec) 2.30–5.30. Other times by appointment.

Free.

⚠ ⚲ shop ✘ (guide dogs only) ♿

ROCHDALE
Gt Manchester
Map **7** SD81

Rochdale Pioneers Museums 31 Toad
Lane
☎ 061-832 4300 ext 287

*The Rochdale Pioneers' Memorial
Museum houses the original first shop
opened by the Rochdale Equitable
Pioneers Society on 21 December 1844,
marking the beginning of the world-wide
Co-operative movement. The shop
contains period furniture and equipment.
The rear room exhibits documents and
relics of the Pioneers, and tells their story
up to the 1944 Centenary of the Society.
Also displayed are documents and relics
relating to the formation of the Co-
operative Wholesale Society. The upper
floor contains a gallery of original
photographs of the Pioneers and of
events in the history of the Society and
the Museum. The Museum is operated by
the Co-operative Union, the National
Federation of British Co-operative
Societies.*

Open Tue–Sat 10–12 & 2–4.

✻ 25p (ch 10p)

P (20 yds) shop ✻

___

ROCHE ABBEY
South Yorkshire
Map **8** SK58
(1½m SE Maltby)

*Cistercian abbey founded in 1147 with
walls of north and south transepts still
standing to their full height. Fine
gatehouse lies to north-west of church.*

Open 15 Mar–15 Oct, Mon–Sat 9.30–6.30,
Sun 2–6.30. 16 Oct–14 Mar, wknds only
2–4.30.

Admission fee payable.

⚠ ⅁ (AM)

___

ROCHESTER
Kent
Map **5** TQ76

Charles Dickens Centre
Eastgate House, High St
☎ Medway (0634) 44176

*A display of Dickens characters with
clever use of sound and light.*

Open all year daily 10–12.30 & 2–5.30.
(Closed Good Fri, Xmas & 1 Jan).

£1.20 (ch, pen & students with card 60p).
Family £2.75. Party 20 + .

P (60 yds) shop ✻ ⓥ

Guildhall Museum High St
☎ Medway (0634) 48717

*A major portion of the building dates from
late 17th-century and has magnificent
decorated plaster ceilings. The
collections include local history,
archaeology, arms and armour, dolls toys
and Victoriana, models of local sailing
barges, fishing vessels, Shorts flying
boats and Napoleonic prisoner-of-war
work. The museum also houses the civic
plate, regalia and Archives of the city.*

Open daily 10–12.30 & 2–5.30 (Closed
Xmas, 1 Jan & Good Fri).

Free.

P (100 yds) ⅁ (ground floor only) shop ✻

Rochester Castle

*Commenced 1087 and retaining
remarkable storeyed keep dating from
1126 to 1139.*

Keep open † see end of gazetteer.

✻ 60p (ch 16 & pen 30p).

⚠ (AM).

___

ROCKBOURNE
Hampshire
Map **4** SU11

Roman Villa
☎ (07253) 445

*Excavation is still in progress on this site.
Museum has unique items of pottery and
jewellery and hoard of 7,717 coins. So far
73 rooms have been uncovered.*

Open Apr–Oct Mon–Fri 2–6, Sat, Sun &
BH 10.30–6; Jul & Aug daily 10.30–6.

✻ 50p (ch 30p).
⚠ ⅁ shop ✻

___

ROCKINGHAM
Northamptonshire
Map **4** SP89

Rockingham Castle
☎ (0536) 770240

*Elizabethan family home within walls of
Norman royal castle. Panoramic views of
four counties. Fine paintings, gardens and
associations with Charles Dickens. Also
there is a special exhibition on the Civil
War. 'Arnescote Castle' in BBC TV series
'By the Sword Divided'.*

Open Etr–Sep Thu, Sun, BH Mon &
following Tue 2–6. In Aug only also open
Tue 2–6.

£1.80 (ch £1). Gardens only £1. Party.
⚠ ⅁ ⌠ ⅁ (ground floor only) shop

___

ROCQUAINE BAY
Guernsey *Channel Islands*
Map **16**

Fort Grey
☎ Guernsey (0481) 26518

*Built as part of the Island's defences
against Napoleon on the site of an ancient
castle. It has recently been restored and
opened as a maritime museum, featuring
the wrecks on the treacherous Hanois
Reef nearby.*

Open May–15 Oct daily, 10.30–12.30 &
1.30–5.30.

50p (ch 20p, pen 25p). Party (schools
free) (see Castle Cornet, St Peter Port
entry).

P (100 yds) shop ✻ (ex guide dogs)

___

RODE
Somerset
Map **3** ST85

Tropical Bird Gardens
☎ Frome (0373) 830326

*17 acres of grounds planted with trees
and shrubs; ornamental lake and ponds
surround aviaries where more than 180
species of colourful birds are kept, many
of which are at liberty. Pets corner, tree
trail and clematis collection. Also natural →*

ROCKINGHAM CASTLE

"Arnescote" in the BBC TV series
"By the Sword Divided".

Built as a fortress by William the
Conqueror, and a family home
since 1530. Wonderful views
over four counties. Twelve acres
of gardens, Special Exhibition —
"Rockingham Castle and the
Civil War". Home-made cream
teas and gift shop make it a
great place to visit.

2 miles north of Corby Northamptonshire on A6003.
*Open:*Easter Sunday to September 30th Thursdays,
Sundays and Bank Holiday Mondays and Tuesdays
following. Also every Tuesday during August 2.00-6.00p.m.

history exhibition. Children under 14 must be accompanied by an adult.

Gardens open all year. (Closed Xmas day), summer 10.30–7 (last admission 6pm), winter 10.30–sunset.

✳ £1.85 (ch 95p & pen £1.50). Party 25 +.

 ⚠ 𝒟 (Summer only) ♿ (wheelchairs for hire) shop ✸ Ⓥ

ROLVENDEN
Kent
Map **5** TQ83

C M Booth Collection of Historic Vehicles
Falstaff Antiques, 63 High St
☎ Cranbrook (0580) 241234

Contains historic vehicles and other items of transport interest. The main feature is the unique collection of Morgan 3-wheel cars dating from 1913, plus the only known Humber tri-car of 1904, a 1929 Morris van, motocycles, bicycles.

Open Mon, Tue, Thu–Sat 10–6, & some Wed pm. Also some Suns & BH. (Closed Xmas day).

60p (accompanied ch 15 30p).

P 𝒟 shop

ROMSEY
Hampshire
Map **4** SU32
See also **Ower**

Rode
—
Rotherham

Broadlands (Main Entrance on A31 Romsey by-pass)
☎ (0794) 516878

Formerly the home of Lord and Lady Mountbatten, and the Victorian Prime Minister Lord Palmerston, it is now the home of Lord and Lady Romsey. It has long been famous as a centre of hospitality for royal and distinguished visitors. The 18th-century house is set in grounds landscaped by Capability Brown. Richly decorated interiors and fine works of art. The Mountbatten Exhibition and an audio-visual film show trace the eventful lives of Lord and Lady Mountbatten.

Open 27 Mar–Sep 10–5. (Closed Mon ex Aug, Sep & BH).

£2.70 (ch 12–16 £1.50, ch 12 free; pen, students & disabled £2). Party 15 +. The Mountbatten Exhibition only open Oct–Mar 86 Tue–Thu 10–4 for pre-booked parties.

 ⚠ 𝒟 ♨ ♿ (ground floor) shop ✸

ROTHBURY
Northumberland
Map **12** NU00

Cragside House & Country Park
(Entrance for cars 2m N on B6341)
☎ (0669) 20333

Victorian house designed for the first Lord Armstrong by Richard Norman Shaw, the first house in the world to be lit by electricity generated by water-power. Contains much of its original furniture, 900 acre Country Park.

Open: Country Park Good Fri–Sep daily 10.30–6; Oct daily 10.30–5; Nov–Mar Sat & Sun 10.30–4. House Good Fri–6 Apr daily; 7 Apr–end Apr Wed, Sat & Sun 2–6. May–Sep Tue–Sun & BH Mon 2–6; Oct Wed, Sat & Sun 2–5. Last admissions ½hr before closing.

House & Country Park £2.40. Country Park only £1. Party.

 ⚠ 𝒟 ♨ ♿ ✸ (in house) (NT)

ROTHERHAM
South Yorkshire
Map **8** SK49

Art Gallery
Brian O'Malley Library and Arts Centre, Walker Place
☎ (0709) 382121 ext 3569/3579/3549

Continuous programme of temporary exhibitions including, at times 19th- and 20th-century paintings from the museum collections and Rockingham pottery.

Open Mon & Wed–Fri 10–6, Sat 10–5. (Closed Sun, Tue, & BH).

GOVERNING OVERSEAS

STATE OCCASIONS

SOUTH EAST ASIA

Relive your memories of those incredible Mountbatten days.

Share the treasures and memories of the great house he loved... the riverside lawns he strolled... the history-making life he lived... a life recreated for you in a fascinating exhibition and film theatre. Then picnic in the spacious grounds... or lunch in the self-service restaurant. A day you can never forget.

_____VISIT_____

BROADLANDS
ROMSEY·HAMPSHIRE
All incl. admission. Open 27th March – end of Sept. 10am - 5pm.
(Closed Mon. except Bank Holidays until August). Tel: Romsey (0794) 516878.

Free.

🅰 🈂 (licensed) 👌 shop ✖

Museum Clifton Park
☎ (0709) 382121 ext 3519

*Late 18th-century mansion reputed by
John Carr of York. Contains 18th-century
furnished rooms, family portraits, period
kitchen. Displays of Victoriana, local
history, local Roman antiquities,
numismatics, glass and glassmaking,
church silver, 19th- and 20th-century
paintings. Also British ceramics, including
Rockingham, local geology and natural
history. Temporary exhibitions.*

Open Apr–Sep Mon–Thu & Sat 10–5, Sun
2.30–5; Oct–Mar Mon–Thu & Sat 10–5,
Sun 2.30–4.30. (Closed Fri).

Free.

🅰 👌 (ground floor only) shop ✖

ROTHES
Grampian *Moray*
Map **15** NJ24

Glen Grant Distillery
☎ (03403) 494

*Established in 1840. The whisky produced
here is regarded as one of the best, and is
used in many first-class blends as well as
being sold in a single Glen Grant Malt in
bottle. Traditional malt whisky methods of
distillation are used together with the
most modern equipment. Reception,
shop and Hospitality Bar.*

Open Etr–Sep 10–4.

Free.

🅰 shop ✖

ROTHESAY
Isle of Bute, Strathclyde *Bute*
Map **10** NS06

Ardencraig
☎ (0700) 4225

*Particular interest has been paid to
improving layout and introducing rare
plants into the garden. The greenhouse
and walled garden produce plants for use
in floral displays throughout the district. A
variety of interesting fish are to be found
in the ornamental ponds and the aviaries
contain many foreign species of birds.*

Open May–Sep Mon–Fri 9–4.30, Sat &
Sun 1–4.30.

Free.

🅰 🈂 👌 garden centre ✖

Bute Museum Stuart St
☎ (0700) 3380

*Contents are all from the island of Bute.
Natural history room contains exhibits of
birds, mammals and items from the
seashore. History room, has varied
collections of recent bygones including
models of Clyde steamers. There is a
collection of early Christian crosses.
Prehistoric section contains flints and
pots from two recently excavated
neolithic burial cairns. Recently mounted
comprehensive geological survey of*

Rotherham
Rufford

*Island of Bute. Details of nature trails on
the island are on sale.*

Open Apr–Sep 10.30–12.30 & 2.30–4.30;
Oct–Mar 2.30–4.30. (Closed Mon); Jun–
Sep Sun 2.30–4.30.

50p (ch 20p pen 30p).

P 👌 shop

Rothesay Castle

*13th-century moated castle with lofty
curtain walls, defended by drum towers
enclosing a circular courtyard.*

Open see end of gazetteer. Closed Fri am
& Thu in winter.

✱ 50p (ch 25p).

(AM)

ROTTINGDEAN
East Sussex
Map **5** TQ30

**Rottingdean Grange Museum & Art
Gallery**
☎ Brighton (0273) 31004

*Early Georgian house, remodelled by
Lutyens, now library, art gallery and
museum including Kipling exhibits and
part of the National Toy Museum.
Frequent temporary exhibitions.*

Open Mon, Thu & Sat 10–5; Tue & Fri 10–1
& 2–5. (Closed Wed). Details not
confirmed for 1986.

Free.

P (50 yds) shop ✖

ROUSHAM
Oxfordshire
Map **4** SP42

Rousham House (off A423)
☎ Steeple Aston (0869) 47110

*Attractive 17th- and 18th-century house
near River Cherwell, with Civil War
associations, fine pictures, furniture and
notable garden layout by William Kent.*

Open Apr–Sep, Wed, Sun & BH 2–4.30.
Gardens only all year, daily 10–4.30.

✱ House £1.50. Garden £1. Party by
arrangement. No children under 15.

🅰 ✖

ROWLAND'S CASTLE
Hampshire
Map **4** SU71

Stansted Park
☎ (070541) 2564

*A neo Wren house with ancient chapel,
walled gardens and theatre museum. Set
in attractive forest surroundings with
views along the longest beech avenue in
the south of England. Cricket matches are
played in front of the house on most
Sundays.*

237

Open 4 May–30 Sep, Sun, Mon & Tue 2–6
(last admission 5.30).

£1.60 (ch 12 80p, pen £1.20). Grounds,
chapel & tearoom only £1 (ch 12 50p, pen
80p). Parties by appointment.

🅰 🈂 👌 (some parts of ground floor &
gardens) shop & garden shop ✖

ROWLANDS GILL
Tyne and Wear
Map **12** NZ15

Gibside Chapel & Avenue
☎ (0207) 542255

*Repaired and rededicated in July 1966,
originally built by James Paine in 1760,
one of remaining buildings of 18th-
century landscape layout.*

Open Good Fri–Etr Mon 2–6 Apr–Sep,
Wed, Sat, Sun & BH Mons 2–6; Oct, Wed,
Sat & Sun 2–5. Other times by
appointment.

✱ 60p. Party.

🅰 (NT)

ROYSTON
Hertfordshire
Map **5** TL34

Royston Museum Lower King St
☎ (0763) 42587

*Former Chapel Schoolroom contains a
local history museum with displays
depicting the history of the town with
regular temporary exhibitions.*

Open Wed & Sat only 10–5.

Free.

P (250 yds) 👌 (ground floor only) shop ✖

RUDDINGTON
Nottinghamshire
Map **8** SK53

Ruddington Village Museum The
Hermitage, Wilford Rd
☎ Plumtree (06077) 2795

*The headquarters of the Ruddington local
History and Amenity Society, this
museum is housed in the village's oldest
building, occupied in medieval times.
Permanent displays of local
archaeological and folk material,
photographs, postcards and growing
collection of source material. Changing
exhibitions of historical interest.*

Open all year Tue 10.30–12, Fri 7.30–9pm.
Other times by appointment.

✱ 25p (ch 15p).

🅰 ✖

RUFFORD
Lancashire
Map **7** SD41

Rufford Old Hall

*Tudor and later (1662 and 1821) with fine
Great Hall and remarkable woodwork
including a rare example of a movable
screen.*

Open 26 Mar–2 Nov, Sat–Thu, Hall 1–6; →

gardens 11–6. Last admission 5.30. (Closed Good Fri).

Hall & gardens £1.40 (ch 70p) Garden 60p (ch 30p). Party.

⏛ ⅁ (gardens only) shop (NT)

RUNCORN
Cheshire
Map **7** SJ58

Norton Priory Museum Warrington Rd,
☎ (09285) 69895

Subject of largest excavation carried out by modern methods of any monastic site in Britain. Landscaped Priory remains including 12th-century undercroft with beautifully carved passage. St Christopher statue and Norman doorway are surrounded by seven acres of Georgian woodlands. It has the most comprehensive exhibition about medieval monastic life anywhere in Britain, an auditorium, and temporary exhibitions.

Open Mar–Oct Mon–Fri 12–5, Sat, Sun & BH 12–6; Nov–Feb daily 12–4. (Closed Xmas).

✱ 70p (ch under 5 free, ch 16 & pen 30p).

⚠ ⏛ ⇆ ⅁ (ground floor only) shop

RUSHTON
Northamptonshire
Map **4** SP88

Triangular Lodge
Curious three-sided lodge built 1593–96 by recusant Sir Thomas Tresham in the form of mystical and heraldic symbolism of the figure three. An inscribed Latin frieze encircles the building.

Open see end of gazetteer.

✱ 50p (ch 16 & pen 25p).

P ⅁ (grounds only) (AM)

RUSLAND
Cumbria
Map **7** SD38

Rusland Hall
☎ Satterthwaite (022984) 276

The house was built in 1720, and enlarged in 1845. It contains many unusual mechanical instruments including a grand piano and a mechanical organ. Varied collection of antiques. Early cinema projectors and photographic equipment on show also. Four acres of landscaped grounds of 18th-century style with peacocks, including rare whites. Demonstrations of mechanical music.

Open Etr–Sep Mon–Fri & Sun 11–5.

£1 (ch 16 50p).

⚠ ⇆ ⅁ (ground floor & gardens only) ✗

RUTHWELL
Dumfries and Galloway Dumfriesshire
Map **11** NY16

Duncan Savings Bank Museum
☎ Clarencefield (038787) 640

First Savings Bank founded here in 1810. Interior set in period furnishings around a

---

Rufford
—
St Agnes

---

peat fire and contains many early savings bank documents, four-lock security kist, collection of home savings banks from Great Britain and abroad, International Money Corner etc. Personal pencil drawings and historic papers dealing with the Runic Cross in Ruthwell Church.

Open daily, Summer 10–6, Winter 10–4. (Closed for Custodians Holiday), evenings by arrangement.

Free.

⚠ ⅁

Ruthwell Cross (off B724)
One of Europe's most famous carved crosses resting in the parish church in an apse built specially for it. The date is probably late 7th century and the 18ft-high cross is richly carved with Runic characters showing the earliest form of English in Northumbrian dialect.

Free. Key of church obtainable from the Key Keeper, Kirkyett Cottage, Ruthwell.

(AM)

RYCOTE
Oxfordshire
Map **4** SP60

Rycote Chapel (off B4013)
Small, well-restored 15th-century chapel consecrated in 1449 and visited by Princess Elizabeth in the reign of her sister Mary I and also by Charles I. Interior contains notable 15th-century benches and 17th-century pews. Barrel roof is noted for gilded-star decor cut originally from rare Continental playing cards.

Open see end of gazetteer.

✱ 30p (ch 16 & pen 15p).

⚠ ⅁ (AM)

RYDAL
Cumbria
Map **11** NY30

Rydal Mount
☎ Ambleside (0966) 33002

Family home of William Wordsworth from 1813 until his death in 1850. Incorporates a pre-1574 farmer's cottage. Now owned by a descendant and containing an important group of family portraits, possessions and books. Lovely setting overlooking Windermere and Rydal Water.

Open daily Mar–Oct 10–5.30; Nov–Feb daily 10–12.30 and 2–4. (Closed Wed).

Admission fee payable.

⚠ shop

RYE
East Sussex
Map **5** TQ92

Lamb House West St
An 18th-century house, home of Henry James from 1898 until his death in 1916. Attractive garden.

Three rooms open only Apr–Oct, Wed & Sat 2–6. Last admission 5.30.

✱ 80p.

(NT)

Rye Museum Ypres Tower
☎ (0797) 223254

A 13th-century three-storeyed fortification containing collections of Cinque Port material, medieval and other pottery from the Rye kilns, militaria, shipbuilding, dolls, toys and local history archives.

Open Etr–mid Oct, Mon–Sat 10.30–1 & 2.15–5.30, Sun 11.30–1 & 2.15–5.30 (last admission ½hr before closing time).

Admission fee payable.

✗

RYHOPE
(Nr Sunderland) Tyne and Wear
Map **12** NZ45

Ryhope Engines Museum
☎ Sunderland (0783) 210235

Twin beam engines (1868), restored by Ryhope Engines Trust.

Open Etr–end of year, Sat & Sun 2–5. Run under steam power Etr & BH Sat, Sun & Mon 11–5. May BH static only. Phone for odd steaming dates.

✱ Steam days 75p (ch 15p, pen 30p); static 30p (ch 15p).

⚠ ⏛ (Steaming days only) ⅁ (ground floor only) shop ✗

SAFFRON WALDEN
Essex
Map **5** TL53

Saffron Walden Museum Museum St
☎ (0799) 22494

Built in 1834, the museum houses collections of local archaeology, natural history, ceramics, glass, costume, furniture and toys. Ethnography, geology and local history. Special events include Walden's 750th anniversary celebrations with special exhibitions and events in grounds Apr–Sep. Reproductions of the Pepy's Mazer Bowl will be available.

Open Apr–Sep, Mon–Sat 11–5, Sun & BH 2.30–5; Oct–Mar Mon–Sat 11–4, Sun & BH 2.30–5. (Closed Good Fri and 24 & 25 Dec).

Free.

⚠ ⅁ (ground floor & gardens only) shop ✗

ST AGNES
Cornwall
Map **2** SW75

Wheal Coates Engine House
The engine house stands on the cliff between St Agnes and Chapel Porth and once housed an engine which provided the essential services of winding,

pumping and ventilation for the mine. An
important relic of the country's industrial
past.
(NT)

ST ALBANS
Hertfordshire
Map **4** TL10

City Museum Hatfield Rd
☎ (0727) 56679
Displays collections relating to natural
history and geology of south-west
Hertfordshire. Salaman collection of craft
tools with reconstructed workshops.
Open Mon–Sat 10–5. (Closed Sun, BH &
PHs).
Free.
⚠ shop ✠

Clock Tower Market Place
☎ (0727) 53301
Example of early 15th century curfew
tower, which provides fine views over the
city. Present structural repairs are hoped
to be completed by Etr 1986.
Open Etr–mid Sep, Sat, Sun & BH 10.30–
5.
✱ 20p (ch 6–12 10p ch 5 free if
accompanied).
P (200/300 yds) shop

Gorhambury House (entry via lodge
gates on A414).
☎ (0727) 54051
Late Georgian mansion designed 1777–
84 in modified classical style by Sir Robert
Taylor. Chippendale furniture, Grimston
portraits, 16th-century enamelled glass,
and Francis Bacon associations.
Open May–Sep, Thu 2–5.
£1.50 (ch & pen 80p) Party.
⚠ shop ✠

Kingsbury Watermill Museum
St Michael's Street. (Situated on the River
Ver ½m upstream from St Albans
Cathedral and Abbey, in the village of St
Michaels)
☎ (0727) 53502
16th-century corn mill with working
waterwheel, on 3 floors, with a collection
of old farm implements, and an art gallery.

St Agnes
St Andrews

Open Mar–Nov, Wed–Sat 11–6. Sun 12–6.
Dec–Feb Wed–Sat 11–5. Sun 12–5.
(Closed Mon & Tue & 25 Dec–2 Jan).
50p (ch 25p, pen & students 35p).
⚠ ⚌ shop ✠ ⇞

The Gardens of The Rose (Royal
National Rose Society's Gardens) (2m S
off Watford Rd in Chiswell Green Lane)
☎ (0727) 50461
Rose garden and trial ground for new
varieties. Over 30,000 plants in 1,650
varieties. Special roses, old fashioned
roses, modern roses and roses of the
future.
Open 14 Jun–28 Sep Mon–Sat 9–5, Sun &
BH 10–6.
£1.30 (accompanied ch free, registered
disabled 60p). Party 20+.
⚠ ⚌ (licensed) ♿ shop ⓥ

St Albans Organ Museum
320 Camp Rd
☎ (0727) 68979 or 51557
Contains a unique collection of
automatically operated organs and other
musical instruments. Records and
cassettes of some of the organs and other
instruments, also books on mechanical
musical instruments can be purchased.
Recitals Sun 2.15–4.30. Parties at other
times by appointment.
✱ 80p (ch 40p). Price includes tea.
⚠ (limited) ⚌ ♿ shop ✠ (ex guide dogs)

Verulamium Museum & Hypocaust
St Michaels
☎ (0727) 54659
Superb museum of Roman finds,
including tessellated pavements nearby,
as well as a Hypocaust.
Open Apr–Oct Mon–Sat 10–5.30, Sun 2–
5.30, Nov–Mar Mon–Sat 10–4 Sun 2–4.
60p (ch, students & pen 35p).
⚠ ♿ shop ✠

Verulamium Theatre St Michaels
☎ (0727) 54051
Roman theatre, built AD 140–150, used
for presentation of plays and other
functions.
Open daily 10–5. (Closed Xmas).
60p (ch 25p students 50p).
⚠

ST ANDREW
Guernsey, Channel Islands
Map **16**

**German Military Underground Hospital
& Ammunition Store**
La Vassalerie
☎ Guernsey (0481) 39100
The largest structural reminder of the
German occupation of the Channel
Islands. A concrete maze of about 75,000
sq ft, which took slave workers 3½ years to
construct, at the cost of many lives. It was
designed to accommodate 500 patients
but could in emergency have housed
many more. The hospital was only used
for about 6 weeks for German wounded
brought over from France soon after
D-Day, but the ammunition store, which
was larger than the hospital, was packed
tight with thousands of tons of
ammunition during its nine months of use.
Most of the equipment has been
removed, but there are still some signs of
previous use such as the central-heating
plant, some hospital beds and cooking
facilities.
Open Apr daily 2–4; May–Sep daily 10–12
& 2–5; Oct daily 2–4.
80p (ch 40p).
⚠ ♿ shop

ST ANDREWS
Fife Fife
Map **12** NO51

Castle
Ruined 13th-century stronghold where
Cardinal Beaton was murdered in 1546.
Open see end of gazetteer.
✱ 50p (ch 25p).
♿ (AM)

239

Cathedral (& Museum)

Remains of largest cathedral in Scotland, dating mainly from 12th and 13th centuries, and adjacent to St Rule's Church, the most interesting Romanesque church in Scotland. Large part of precinct walls survive, and also 14th-century pend **Museum** contains important collection of Celtic and medieval sculpture and artefacts, and fascinating array of later gravestones.

Open see end of gazetteer.

50p (ch 25p).

(AM)

ST AUSTELL
Cornwall
Map **2** SX05

Charlestown Visitor Centre
Charlestown (1¼m SE A3061)
☎ (0726) 73332

A visitor-centre incorporating Shipwreck Centre and Charlestown village life in bygone days.

Open Etr–Oct daily 10–6 (9pm in high season). Last admission 1 hour before closing.

£1.65 (ch 80p). Party.

⚠ ⚐ & shop

Wheal Martyn Museum
(2m N on A391)
☎ (0726) 850362

Open-air site museum of the china clay industry. Complete clay works of the last century have been restored; huge granite-walled settling tanks, working water-wheels and wooden slurry pump. 220ft pan kiln or 'dry', horse-drawn wagons, two steam locomotives from the industry, a fully restored 1914 Peerless lorry and the story of clay in Cornwall over two centuries shown in indoor displays. Also short slide and sound programme for visitors. Working Pottery, Nature trail and viewing area of a modern working claypit with spectacular views.

Open Etr–Oct, 10–6 (last admission 5, Oct 4).

✳ £1.70 (ch 85p, pen £1.40).

⚠ ⚐ ⊞ & (ground floor only) shop

ST BOSWELLS
Borders *Roxburghshire*
Map **12** NT53

Mertoun Gardens
☎ (0835) 23236

20 acres of beautiful grounds with delightful walks and river views. Fine trees, herbaceous plants and flowering shrubs. Walled garden and well preserved circular dovecot.

Open Apr–Sep Sat, Sun & BH Mon, 2–6 (last admission 5.30pm).

✳ 60p (ch 14 & pen 30p).

⚠ & (parts of garden only) ✖

St Andrews
—
St Ives

ST CATHERINE'S POINT
Isle of Wight
Map **4** SZ47

St Catherine's Lighthouse
☎ Niton (0983) 730284

Situated at St Catherine's Point, 136ft above the sea.

Open Mon–Sat only from 1pm–one hour before dusk, weather and other conditions permitting at visitors own risk. Free. Visitors are strongly recommended to write or telephone the Principal Keeper in advance. Cars not allowed within ¼m except on business. ✖

ST DAVID'S
Dyfed
Map **2** SM72

Bishop's Palace

Extensive remains of the principal residence of Bishops of St David's. Dates from 13th century with fine architectural detail.

Open see end of gazetteer.

✳ 60p (ch 16 30p).

shop (AM Cadw)

ST FAGAN'S
South Glamorgan
Map **3** ST17

Welsh Folk Museum
☎ Cardiff (0222) 569441

Open air branch museum of the National Museum of Wales, in grounds of 16th-century St Fagan's Castle (also open). Exhibits include woollen mill complete with machinery, old Welsh farmhouses, tannery and tollgate from mid Wales, chapel from Vale of Teifi and North Wales Quarryman's cottage. Craftsmen demonstrate their traditional crafts throughout the year.

Open weekdays 10–5, Sun 2.30–5. (Closed Good Fri, May Day, 24–26 Dec & New Year's day).

£2 (ch £1 & pen £1.50). Family ticket £5. Nov–Mar (excl Etr) £1 (ch 50p & pen 75p). Family ticket £2.50.

⚠ ⚐ (licensed) ⊞ & shop

ST FLORENCE
Dyfed
Map **2** SN10

Manor House Wildlife & Leisure Park
Ivy Tower
☎ Carew (06467) 201

Set in 12 acres of delightful wooded grounds and gardens. Collections of animals, including apes, monkeys and deer; a variety of tropical birds. Also children's adventure playground and

---

amusements, radio-controlled models. Giant astraglide slide and other attractions. Daily falconry displays (except Sat) on the main lawn.

Open Etr–Sep daily 10–6.

£1 (ch & pen 80p). Party.

⚠ ⚐ (licensed) ⊞ & shop ✖ Ⓥ

ST HELENS
Merseyside
Map **7** SJ59

Pilkington Glass Museum (on Prescot Rd, A58, 1m from town centre)
☎ (0744) 28882 ext 2499 or 2014

History of glassmaking from Egyptians to present day, with some of the finest examples of glass in the world. Various temporary exhibitions throughout the year.

Open Mon–Fri 10–5, Sat Sun & BH 2–4.30; (also open until 9 on Weds, Mar–Oct).

(Closed Xmas–New Year).

Free.

⚠ & shop ✖

ST HELIER
Jersey, Channel Islands.
Map **16**

The Jersey Museum
Pier Road
☎ Jersey (0534) 75940

Local collections relating to history, maritime biology, natural history, coins and medals, silver, law and order, photography, shipping and sport. Art gallery. Lillie Langtry displays. Victorian pharmacy and four period rooms. All set in large Georgian house.

Open all year, Mon–Sat 10–5.

80p (ch & pen 40p).

P (200 yds) shop ✖

ST HILARY
South Glamorgan
Map **3** ST07

Old Beaupré Castle (1m SW)

Ruined manor house, rebuilt in 16th century, with notable Italianate gatehouse and porch. Porch is three-storeyed and displays Basset arms.

Open at any reasonable time. (Closed Sun).

Free.

(AM Cadw)

ST IVES
Cambridgeshire
Map **4** TL37

Norris Museum The Broadway
☎ (0480) 65101

A comprehensive collection of Huntingdonshire local history, including fossils, archaeology and bygones, water-colours of local features, work in bone and straw by French prisoners at Norman Cross. Also Huntingdonshire lacemaking.

Open May–Sep Tue–Fri 10–1 & 2–5, Sat
10–12 & 2–5, Sun 2–5; Oct–Apr Tue–Fri
10–1 & 2–4, Sat 10–12. (Closed BH
wknds).

Free.

P (200 yds) shop

ST IVES
Cornwall
Map **2** SW54 (Park your car at Lelant
Station and take advantage of the park
and ride service. The fee includes parking
and journeys on the train between Lelant
and St Ives during the day).

**Barbara Hepworth Museum &
Sculpture Garden** Barnoon Hill
☎ Penzance (0736) 796226

*The museum is in the house lived in by
Dame Barbara Hepworth from 1949 to her
death in 1975. Sculpture by Dame
Barbara from 1929 to 1974 is on display in
the house and garden. Also to be seen
are many photographs, letters and other
documents showing the artist's career.
(Administered by Tate Gallery.)*

Open Oct–Mar Mon–Sat 10–4.30; Apr–
Jun & Sep 10–5.30; Jul & Aug Mon–Sat
10–6.30 also Sun 2–6.

50p (ch, students & pen 25p).

P (200 yds) shop

Barnes Museum of Cinematography

*Comprehensive collection of items
relating to history of cinematography and
photography.*

Open Etr–Sep Mon–Sat 11–1 & 2.30–5.

40p (ch 20p).

P

ST KEYNE
Cornwall
Map **2** SX26

Paul Corin's Mechanical Music Centre
Old Mill (St Keyne Station)
☎ Liskeard (0579) 43108

*One of the finest collections in Europe of
automatic musical instruments including
Fair organs, Orchestrions, Player pianos
and mighty Wurlitzer theatre organ.*

Open Etr week then May–Sep, daily 11–1
& 2–5.

St Ives
—
St Nicholas

✳ £1.75 (ch 75p).

 ⚠ ♿

ST LAWRENCE
Isle of Wight
Map **4** SZ57

Tropical Bird Park Old Park
☎ Ventnor (0983) 852583

*Over 400 exotic birds in unique walk-
through aviaries and around the
ornamental lake.*

Open Etr–Oct, 10–5; Oct–Etr, 12–4.
(Closed Xmas day).

✳ £1.20 (ch 5–16 80p, ch under 5 free &
pen £1).

⚠ ♿ (licensed) shop ✗ (in bird park)

ST MARGARET'S-AT-CLIFFE
Kent
Map **5** TR34

Pines Garden St Margaret's Bay (off
Beach Rd)
☎ Dover (0304) 853229

*A haven of rural peace. Gardens
comprising of a rockery, waterfall and
lake, together with a bog garden and a
variety of trees, shrubs, aquatic plants
and spring flowers.*

Open summer 10–7; winter 10–5.

Free.

⚠ ♿ ⊞ ♿ shop & garden centre

ST MARY'S
Jersey, *Channel Islands*
Map **16**

La Mare Vineyards
☎ Jersey (0534) 81491

*18th-century farm set in its own gardens
and surrounded by vineyards. Press
House and Cider House open to visitors.
Also children's playground.*

Open 9 May–Sep, Mon–Fri 10–5.30.

✳ 95p (ch 50p).

⚠ ♿ ⊞ ♿ shop ✗ ♿

ST MAWES
Cornwall
Map **2** SW83

St Mawes Castle
*Coastal blockhouse erected in 16th
century by Henry VIII. Faces Pendennis
Castle across Carrick Roads.*

Open † see end of gazetteer.

✳ 50p (ch 16 & pen 25p).

⚠ ♿ (grounds & ground floor only) (AM)

ST NEWLYN EAST
Cornwall
Map **2** SW85

Lappa Valley Railway
☎ Mitchell (087251) 317

*The 15in-gauge steam railway runs along
part of the old Newquay–Chacewater
GWR line. The train makes a round trip of
over two miles through scenic
countryside, and stops at East Wheal
Rose Halt where you can explore the site
of a famous old silver and lead mine. Five-
acre pleasure area which is accessible by
train only, with a boating lake, maze,
crazy golf, children's railway and play
area.*

Open 2 wks Etr fr Good Fri daily 11–5, rest
of Apr & Oct, Wed & Thu 11–5; May–mid
Jul, daily 10.30–5.30; mid Jul–9 Sep daily
10–6; 9–30 Sep daily 11–5.

£2 (ch £1 & pen £1.50).

⚠ ♿ (licensed) ⊞ shop.

ST NICHOLAS
South Glamorgan
Map **3** ST07

Dyffryn Gardens
☎ Cardiff (0222) 593328

*50 acres of gardens including rare trees
and shrubs. Various events throughout
the year.*

Open end Mar–end May & Sep daily 1–6;
late May–Aug daily 10–7; Oct weekends
only 1–6 (last admission 1 hr before
closing). →

✱ £1 (ch 16 accompanied free, unaccompanied & pen 50p). Party.

Ⓐ ⚏ 🎠 ♿ (gardens only) shop Ⓥ

ST OLAVES
Norfolk
Map 5 TM49

St Olaves Priory near Fritton Decoy

Remains of small Augustinian priory. Exceptional early example of brickwork dating from late 13th century or early 14th century.

Open see end of gazetteer. Apr–Sep only.

Free.

♿ (ground floor & grounds only) (AM)

ST OUEN
Jersey, *Channel Islands*
Map 16

Battle of the Flowers Museum
La Robeline, Mont des Corvées
☎ Jersey (0534) 82408

Contains exhibits which have appeared in the Jersey Battle of Flowers over the last 18 years. The tableaux executed in Harestails and Marram grass, represent scenes of wild and tame animals from all over the world.

Open Feb–Nov, daily 10–5.

80p (ch 50p pen 65p).

Ⓐ ♿ shop ✘

ST PETER
Jersey, *Channel Islands*
Map 16

Jersey Motor Museum St Peters Valley
☎ Jersey (0534) 82966

Contains fascinating collection of motor vehicles from the early 1900s, together with Allied and German military vehicles of World War Two, a Jersey Steam Railway section and Aero Engines etc. Also pre-war Jersey AA Box and collection of AA badges of all periods.

Open Mar–Nov, daily 10–5.

80p (ch 40p).

Ⓐ ⚏ (licensed) 🎠 shop

Le Moulin de Quetivel St Peters Valley
(on B58 off A11)
☎ Jersey (0534) 83193

There has been a water-mill on this site since 1309 when it was owned by the Crown. The granite-built mill was worked until the end of the 19th century, when it fell into disrepair. During the German Occupation it was re-activated for grinding locally grown corn. After 1945, the mill was again disused and a fire destroyed the remaining machinery, roof and internal woodwork. In 1971, the National Trust for Jersey began restoration of the mill and work was completed in 1979. The mill is producing stone-ground flour again. '

Open Apr–Sep, Tue & Wed 10–4.

St Nicholas
—
Salford

✱ 50p (ch 20p, free to members of Jersey or British National Trusts'). Coach parties by arrangement.

Ⓐ ♿ (ground floor only) shop ✘

St Peters' Bunker St Peters Village
(At junction of A12 and B41)
☎ Jersey (0534) 81048

An exhibition of Nazi German equipment and Occupation relics, housed in an actual German bunker, including uniforms, motorcycles, equipment, weapons, documents, photographs, various newspaper cuttings, badges, awards and insignia. This six-roomed bunker accommodated thirty-three men, and could be air and gas sealed in case of attack. One of the rooms contains an actual reconstruction with original bunk beds, and a store and rifle rack, as well as figures of soldiers asleep and on duty.

Open Mar–Nov, daily 10–5.

80p (ch 40p).

Ⓐ 🎠 shop

St PETER PORT
Guernsey, *Channel Islands*
Map 16

Castle Cornet
☎ Guernsey (0481) 21657

An ancient castle with buildings dating from 13th to 20th century and the scene of many battles. During the Civil War it was garrisoned by the Royalist governor of the island, Sir Peter Osborne, and although the island's people sympathised with Cromwell it was not until 15 Dec 1651 that this last Royalist stronghold surrendered to Parliamentary forces. In 1940 it was taken over by German troops and adapted to the needs of modern warfare. Today it is maintained as an ancient monument and houses the Spencer collection of uniforms and badges, the Museum of Guernsey's Own 201 Squadron Royal Air Force, the Royal Guernsey Militia Museum, Maritime Museum, Art Gallery and Armoury. Gun fired daily at mid-day.

Open Apr–Oct, daily 10.30–5.30.

£1 (ch 25p, pen 50p). Party. Schools free.

P (100 yds) ⚏ shop ✘ (ex guide dogs)

Guernsey Museum & Art Gallery
Candie Gardens
☎ Guernsey (0481) 26518

Opened in 1978, it is the island's first purpose-built museum. The exhibition depicts the story of the island and its people. It includes an audio-visual programme in the museum's own theatre and paintings in the Art Gallery. Special exhibitions are featured during the winter.

Open daily, 10.30–5.30 (winter 4.30).

70p (ch 25p, pen 35p). Party. Schools free.

P (100 yds) ⚏ 🎠 ♿ shop ✘ (ex guide dogs)

Hauteville House Maison de Victor Hugo, 38 Hauteville
☎ Guernsey (0481) 21911

Built c1800 and bought by Victor Hugo, the great French writer, in 1856 who lived there until 1870, the house contains a fine collection of china, paintings and tapestries.

Open Apr–Sep, daily 10–11.30, 2–4.30. Open once a day at 10.30 for one guided tour during closed season or by appointment. (Closed Sat & BH).

80p (ch, pen 40p, school parties free).

Ⓐ ♿ (ground floor only) shop ✘

SALCOMBE
Devon
Map 3 SX73

Overbecks Museum & Garden
Sharpitor (½m SW on unlcass rd)

An Edwardian house with a museum of local interest. Beautiful gardens.

Open 28 Mar–Oct, daily, 11–1, last admission 12.45 & 2–6, last admission 5.30. Garden always open.

Museum & gardens £1.30 gardens only £1. Parking charge refundable on purchase of entrance ticket.

Ⓐ shop (NT) (NGS)

SALFORD
Gt Manchester
Map 7 SJ89

Museum of Mining
Buile Hill Park, Eccles Old Rd
☎ 061–736 1832

In an attractive Georgian building, the museum has two reproduction coal mines a large gallery dealing with all aspects of coalmining and its history, and a gallery of mining art.

Open Mon–Fri 10–12.30 & 1.30–5; Sun 2–5. (Closed Sat, 24–26 Dec, 1 Jan & Good Fri). Details not confirmed for 1986.

Free.

Ⓐ shop ✘ (ex guide dogs)

Ordsall Hall Museum Taylorson St
☎ 061–872 0251

Half-timbered manor house, with later brick-built wing (1639), includes Tudor Great Hall, Star Chamber with 14th-century features and Victorian farmhouse kitchen. On upper floor are local and social history displays.

Open Mon–Fri 10–5, Sun 2–5. (Closed Good Fri, 25–26 Dec & New Years day).

Free.

P ♿ (ground floor only) ✘

Salford Museum & Art Gallery The Crescent, Peel Park.
☎ 061–736 2649

242

The ground floor displays a period street scene typical of a northern industrial town at the turn of the century. The first floor art galleries house a large collection of works by L S Lowry, as well as a regular series of temporary art exhibitions and displays of decorative arts.

Open Mon–Fri 10–1 & 2–5, Sun 2–5. (Closed 25–26 Dec, New Years day & Good Friday).

Free.

🔥 ⚓ ✻

SALISBURY
Wiltshire
Map **4** SU12

Mompesson House, Cathedral Close

Built 1701 with magnificent plaster work, furnished as the home of a Georgian Gentleman. Walled garden.

Open 29 Mar–Oct, Mon–Wed, Sat & Sun 12.30–6 or sunset if earlier.

£1.20

🔥 ⚓ ✻ (NT)

Old Sarum (2m N on A345)

First probably an Iron Age camp, later Roman 'Sorbiodunum' and finally site of Norman castle and cathedral town, foundations of which can be seen, together with small museum.

Open † see end of gazetteer.

✳ 50p (ch 16 & pen 25p).

🔥 (charge) (AM)

Regimental Headquarters & Museum of The Duke of Edinburgh's Royal Regiment The Wardrobe, 58 The Close
☎ (0722) 336222 ext 2683

Military exhibits of uniforms, weapons, militaria and medals laid out in four rooms in a building of great historic interest.

Open Apr–Oct, Sun–Fri, July & Aug daily; Nov–Mar Mon–Thu 10–5, Fri 10–4.30. (Last visitor 30 mins before closing). Also open BHs.

70p (ch 16 15p & pen 40p).

P (Cathedral Close) ⚓ (ground floor only) shop ✻ Ⓥ

Salford
—
Sandling

Salisbury & South Wiltshire Museum
The King's House, 65 The Close
☎ (0722) 332151

Winner Special Judges Award, Museum of the Year Award, 1985.

New galleries in a Grade 1 listed building: Stonehenge, Early man in Wessex, Old Sarum and Salisbury, the Pitt Rivers Collection, ceramics, pictures and costume. Temporary exhibitions including Spode (Jan–Apr), 125th Anniversary (Apr–Jul). Open day 18 May.

Open Mon–Sat 10–5 summer, Jul & Aug also Sun 2–5; Mon–Sat 10–4 winter. (Closed Xmas–New Year).

£1 (ch 20p, students, unemployed and pen 70p). From Apr 86 £1.25 (ch 30p, pen, students & unemployed £1). Party. Museum members free .

P (Cathedral Close) ⚐ (Apr–Sep) ⚓ (ground floor only) shop ✻

SALTCOATS
Strathclyde Ayrshire
Map **10** NS24

North Ayrshire Museum
☎ (0294) 64174

A museum located in the ancient former parish church, with interesting old churchyard gravestones. Exhibits portray local historical items, and early 19th-century interiors.

Open summer Mon–Sat 10–4, School hols 10–4.30; winter Thu, Fri & Sat 10–4.

Free.

P (50 yds) ⚓ (ground floor & gardens only)

SAMLESBURY
Lancashire
Map **7** SD63

Samlesbury Hall Preston New Rd
☎ Mellor (025481) 2010 & 2229

Restored half-timbered 14th-century Manor House administered and preserved by the Samlesbury Hall Trust. Sales of Antiques and Collectors items, crafts and exhibitions.

Open 17 Jan–23 Mar Tue–Sun 11.30–4; 25 Mar–19 Oct Tue–Sun 11.30–5; 21 Oct–14 Dec Tue–Sun 11.30–4.

80p (ch 16 40p). Party 20 + .

🔥 ⚐ ⚓ ⚓ (ground floor & gardens only) ✻

SANCREED
Cornwall
Map **2** SW42

Carn Euny Ancient Village (1m SW)

Iron Age village site with characteristic Cornish 'fogou', subterranean hiding hole, 66ft long with circular chamber.

Open any reasonable time.

Free.

🔥 (AM)

SANDFORD ORCAS
Dorset
Map **3** ST62

Manor House
☎ Corton Denham (096322) 206

Fine example of a mid Tudor manor house of Ham Hill stone, in original condition of about 1550. Fine collections of panelling, stained glass, furniture and pictures.

Open Etr Mon 10–6; May–Sep, Sun 2–6, Mon 10–6.

£1.10 (ch 16 50p). Party 10 + by prior arrangement.

🔥 ✻ (in house)

SANDLING
Kent
Map **5** TQ75

Museum of Kent Rural Life Lock Ln
☎ Maidstone (0622) 63936

On a 27-acre site close to the River Medway, the museum tells the story of the Kent countryside. Its farming history with exhibits of agricultural tools and machinery; outside crops and livestock important to the county. →

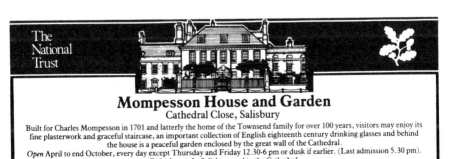

The National Trust

Mompesson House and Garden
Cathedral Close, Salisbury

Built for Charles Mompesson in 1701 and latterly the home of the Townsend family for over 100 years, visitors may enjoy its fine plasterwork and graceful staircase, an important collection of English eighteenth century drinking glasses and behind the house is a peaceful garden enclosed by the great wall of the Cathedral.
Open April to end October, every day except Thursday and Friday 12.30-6 pm or dusk if earlier. (Last admission 5.30 pm).
Refreshments In Salisbury and in the Cathedral.
Car Parking In Salisbury Cathedral Close (a charge is made by the Dean and Chapter). National Trust Shop in High Street.

Open Etr–mid Oct Mon, Tue & Thu–Sat 10–4.30, Sun 2–4.30. Coaches by appointment.

50p (ch 25p)

  ⚠ 𝓛 ㅠ ჭ (ground floor only) shop

SANDOWN
Isle of Wight
Map **4** SZ58

Museum of Isle of Wight Geology
Sandown Library, High St
☎ (0983) 404344

This museum, situated in the local library, houses a collection of fossils and exhibits of the island's geology.

Open Mon–Fri 10–5.30, Sat 10–4.30. (Closed Sun & BH).

Free.

P (200 yds) shop ✱

SANDRINGHAM
Norfolk
Map **9** TF62

Sandringham House, Grounds & Museum
☎ Kings Lynn (0553) 772675

Bought by Queen Victoria for the Prince of Wales in 1862, this royal mansion contains paintings of the Royal Family from 1845, also members of European Royal Families. Sculpture, china, ornaments and furniture.

Open 30 Mar–25 Sep. (Closed 21 Jul–9 Aug). Parties in Apr, May & Sep only except Sun & BHs.

House & grounds £1.80 (ch £1, pen £1.40). Grounds only £1.30 (ch 70p, pen £1).

⚠ 𝓛 ㅠ ჭ shop & garden stall ✱

Wolferton Station (down side)
☎ Dersingham (0485) 40674

On the Sandringham Estate, former Retiring Rooms built in 1898 specifically for, and solely used by kings and queens and their guests en route for Sandringham, can be seen. Fine oak panelling, original fittings, some of which are gold plated. Period railway posters, important small railway relics including Royal train furniture, and Queen Victoria's Travelling Bed (1828).

Open Apr–Sep & BH, Mon–Fri 11–1 & 2–6, Sun 2–6.

70p (ch 30p). Party 20 + .

⚠ ჭ shop

SANDTOFT
Humberside
Map **8** SE70

Sandtoft Transport Centre (15m E of Doncaster off M18/M180, A18/A161)
☎ Doncaster (0302) 530936

Developing national transport museum, primarily for the preservation and operation of trolleybuses, but also includes motorbuses and other items of transport interest. Over 60 vehicles from

---

Sandling
—
Scone

many parts of Britain and the Continent. Several trolleybuses are restored and operated on the centre's own overhead wiring circuit.

Etr–Sep, Sun & BHs, also Sat 26 Jul 12–6.

60p (ch & pen 30p). Family car £1.50.

⚠ 𝓛 ㅠ ჭ shop

SAXMUNDHAM
Suffolk
Map **5** TM36

Bruisyard Winery & Vineyard Church Rd, Bruisyard, between Framlingham and Peasenhall.
☎ Badingham (072875) 281

This ten-acre vineyard produces the estate-bottled Bruisyard St Peter wine. Children's play area.

Open May–mid Oct, daily 10.30–5.

£1.60 (accompanied ch 14 free, pen £1.50). Party 20+ by appointment. Conducted tour of winery every hour.

⚠ ㅠ ჭ shop ⓥ

SAXTEAD GREEN
Suffolk
Map **5** TM26

Windmill
on A1120

Fine 18th-century postmill, twice altered, the present superstructure dating from 1854.

Open Apr–Sep, Mon–Sat 9.30–6.30. (Closed Sun).

✳ 50p (ch & pen 25p).

⚠ (AM)

SCALLOWAY
Shetland
Map **16** HU33

Scalloway Castle

Erected by Patrick Stewart, Earl of Orkney, c 1600, and designed on the two-stepped plan.

Open, see end of gazetteer, on application to the key keeper.

Free.

(AM)

SCARBOROUGH
North Yorkshire
Map **8** TA08

Scarborough Castle

Fortified c 1140 by the Earl of Albermarle and rebuilt with a four-storey keep in 1155 by Henry II. Damaged in the Civil War and the 1914–18 War.

Open † see end of gazetteer.

✳ 60p (ch 16 & pen 30p).

⚠ (AM)

SCHOLAR GREEN
Cheshire
Map **7** SJ85

Little Moreton Hall (on E side of A34)

Splendid example of 16th-century half timbering, with moat and gatehouse, chapel, great hall, long gallery and collection of oak furniture.

Open Mar & Oct, Sat & Sun 2–6 or sunset; Apr–Sep daily (ex Tue) 2–6 or sunset.

£1.80 wknds & BH, £1.60 weekdays. Parties by prior arrangement.

𝓛 ჭ shop

(NT)

Rode Hall (1m NW)
☎ Alsager (09363) 3237

18th-century country house with Georgian stable block. Later alterations by L. Wyatt and Darcy Braddell.

Open Etr–mid Sep on Wed only 2–5. Also open Etr Mon, May Day, Spring BH & Late Summer BH & Sun in Jun also 2–5.

£1.

⚠ ჭ (ground floor & gardens only)

SCOLTON
Dyfed
Map **2** SM92

Scolton Manor Museum & Country Park (on B4329)
☎ Clarbeston (043782) 328

A late Georgian country mansion set in 40 acres of grounds, specially rich in fine trees and ornamental shrubs. A 'tree trail' and a nature trail are provided. The mansion, stables and large exhibition hall provide for a comprehensive display of the history and natural history of Pembrokeshire. Pembrokeshire Country Fair first Sat in Aug.

Museum open Jun–Sep only, Tue–Sun & BHs 10.30–6. Country Park open all year.

✳ 50p (ch 25p, ch under 5 free, pen, students & unemployed 25p). Party.

⚠ (400 yds) 𝓛 ㅠ ჭ (ground floor & gardens only) shop ✱

SCONE
Tayside *Perthshire*
Map **11** NO02

Scone Palace
☎ (0738) 52300

Home of the Earl of Mansfield. Famous in Scottish history as the 'Royal City of Scone'. A seat of government in Pictish times, the home of the Stone of Destiny until 1296 when Edward I removed it to Westminster Abbey; Scottish kings were crowned at Scone until 1651. A religious centre for more than 1,000 years. Present palace, largely rebuilt in 1803, incorporates part of the earlier 1580 palace. Fine collection of French furniture, china, 16th-century needlework, including bed hangings worked by Mary Queen of Scots, ivories and objets d'art. The Pinetum has one of the finest collections of rare conifers in the country, and the woodland garden displays rhododendrons and azaleas. Children's playground.

Open 28 Mar–13 Oct, Mon–Sat 10–5.30, Sun 2–5.30 (Jul & Aug 11–5.30). Special parties outside normal opening hours and during winter by arrangements.

House & grounds £2.20 (ch £1.80). Grounds only £1.10 (ch 90p). Family £8. Party 20+.

& (licensed) ⟷ & shop Ⓟ

SCUNTHORPE
Humberside
Map **8** SE81

Borough Museum & Art Gallery
Oswald Rd
☎ (0724) 843533

Exhibits cover prehistoric to recent history, natural history, period rooms and Ironstone workers' cottage, continuous programme of temporary exhibitions. Golden Jubilee Exhibition 10 Oct–Dec.

Open Mon–Sat 10–5, Sun 2–5. (Closed Xmas).

Free on weekdays. 10p (ch 5p) on Sat, Sun & BHs.

& & (ground floor only) shop ✘ (ex guide dogs)

Scone
Sedlescombe

Normanby Hall Normanby Country Park. (5m N on B1430)
☎ (0724) 862141 ext 297 (bookings)
720215 (enquiries)

A Regency mansion, built in 1825, and containing displays of costume and furniture. There are 350 acres of parkland with lawns, gardens, deer park and nature trails. The stable complex includes a Countryside Interpretation Centre and a pottery.

Open Apr–Oct, Mon & Wed–Sat 10–12.30 & 2–5.30, Sun 2–5.30; Nov–Mar Mon–Fri 10–12.30 & 2–5, Sun 2–5. (Closed Good Fri, Xmas, New Years day). Details not confirmed for 1986.

✱ 50p (ch & pen 20p).

& Ⓛ (late May–early Sep) ⟷ & (ground floor only) shop ✘ (ex guide dogs)

SEAVIEW
Isle of Wight
Map **4** SZ69

Flamingo Park Springvale
☎ (098371) 2153

Waterfowl and watergardens set in lovely

---

countryside overlooking the Solent. Many hundreds of birds which are tame and feed from the hand.

Open Good Fri–mid May daily 2–6; mid May–Sep daily 10.30–6 (last admission 5pm); Oct Wed–Sun 2–5.

✱1.40 (ch 3–15 £1 pen £1.20).

& Ⓛ ⟷ & shop ✘

SEDBERGH
Cumbria
Map **7** SD69

National Park Centre 72 Main St
☎ (0587) 20125

Visitor centre with interpretative display. Maps, walks, guides and local information available.

Open Apr–Oct, daily mid morning–late afternoon.

Free.

&

SEDLESCOMBE
East Sussex
Map **5** TQ71

Nortons Farm Museum & Farm Trail (4½m NW of Hastings on A21)
☎ (042487) 471.

Depicts the carthorse era with a fine display of carts, ploughs and handtools. The Farm Trail takes visitors round the →

fruit and arable farm, where cart horses are still used.

Open May–Sep 9–5.

Free.

▲ ☕ ╥ ✗

SELBORNE
Hampshire
Map **4** SU73

Oates Memorial Library & Museum & the Gilbert White Museum. The Wakes
☎ (042050) 275

Home of the Rev. Gilbert White, pioneer naturalist whose 'Natural History of Selborne' was written here. Also galleries devoted to Captain Oates, of Antarctic fame and to Frank Oates, explorer of Southern Africa. Extensive gardens.

Open Mar–Oct, Tue–Sun & BH 12–5.30 (last admission 5pm). (Closed Mon ex BH).

✱ 90p (ch 50p & pen 70p). Parties 10+ at other times by arrangement.

P ♿ (ground floor) shop ✗ (ex guide dogs) Ⓥ

SELKIRK
Borders *Selkirkshire*
Map **12** NT42

Bowhill (2½m off A708)
☎ (0750) 20732

Sedlescombe — Shaftesbury

For many generations the Border home of the Scotts of Buccleuch. The house contains an outstanding collection of pictures, porcelain and furniture, Monmouth's saddlery and relics, Sir Walter Scott's proofs and portraits, Queen Victoria relics. Adventure woodland play area, nature trail and pony trekking.

Open Grounds May–Aug; House 4 Jul–15 Aug Mon–Sat 12–5, Sun 2–6. Last entry to house 45 mins before closing.

£2 (ch 75p). Disabled free. Party 20+.

▲ ☕ (4 Jul–15 Aug wknds only May–3 Jul & 16–31 Aug) ╥ ♿ shop

Halliwells House Museum Halliwells Close, Market Pl.

☎ (0750) 20096

Housed in Selkirk's oldest surviving dwelling house, the museum recreates the building's past role as a house and ironmonger's shop. First-floor galleries tell the story of the Burgh's development.

Open Apr–Oct Mon–Sat 10–5, Sun 2–5; Nov–Dec, Mon–Fri 2–4.30. (Closed some lunchtimes).

✱ 50p (ch, unemployed & pen 25p). Party 10+. Nov–Dec free.

▲ ╥ ♿ (ground floor only) shop ✗ (ex guide dogs)

SEVENOAKS
Kent
Map **5** TQ55

Knole
☎ (0732) 450608.

Famous mansion of Sackvilles, one of the largest in England, begun in 1456 by Thomas Bourchier, Archbishop of Canterbury, with many early 17th-century additions. Notable state rooms with pictures and 17th- and 18th-century furnishings, Cartoon and Brown galleries.

Open 28 Mar–Oct, Wed–Sat & BH Mon including Good Fri 11–5, Sun 2–5; Extra rooms shown Fri (except Good Fri) no reductions for children. Last admission 1 hr before closing. House closed Nov–Mar. Garden open 1st Wed in month May–Sep.

£2 (ch £1); Gardens 50p (ch 25p). Park open free to pedestrians.

▲ (£2) (NT)

SHAFTESBURY
Dorset
Map **3** ST82

Abbey Ruins & Museum Park Walk
☎ (0747) 2910

The excavated foundations of Shaftesbury Abbey and a museum containing carved stone, decorated floor tiles etc, found on site.

Open Good Fri–Oct daily from 10am, last admission 6.30pm.

Admission fee payable.

P (200 yds) & shop garden centre

Local History Museum Gold Hill
☎ (0747) 2157

Small museum of needlework toys, agricultural and domestic items, fans, pottery and finds from local excavations. Fire engine of 1744.

Open Etr–Sep, daily 11–5, Sun 2.30–5 (other times by appointment).

25p (ch 10p).

P (500 yds public car park) & (ground floor & gardens only) shop ✹

SHALLOWFORD
Staffordshire
Map **7** SJ82

Izaak Walton Cottage
☎ Stafford (0785) 760278

The famous angler's restored cottage with a small museum and a period garden which is being established.

Open all year, mid Mar–Oct, Fri–Tue 12.30–5.30pm; winter wknds only 12.30–4.30pm.

20p (ch 10p).

A ♫ & shop

SHANKLIN
Isle of Wight
Map **4** SZ58

Shanklin Chine
☎ Isle of Wight (0983) 866432

A natural gorge of great scenic beauty, with a spectacular 45ft waterfall. Historic features. Rare flora and nature trail.

Open 27 Mar–22 May 9.30–5.30pm & 22 May–21 Sep, 9.30–10pm (illuminated at night, weather permitting) & 22 Sep–12 Oct 9.30–4.

50p (ch 14 20p, pen 40p). Party.

P (100 yds Esplanade & 200 yds Old Village) ♫ (licensed)

SHAP
Cumbria
Map **12** NY51

Shap Abbey
An abbey of the Premonstratensian order, dedicated to St Mary Magdalene, with buildings dating from 1201–1540, when abbey was dissolved.

Open any reasonable time.

Free.

P & (AM)

SHARDLOW
Derbyshire
Map **8** SK43

Shaftesbury
—
Sheffield Park Garden

Clock Warehouse London Rd
☎ Derby (0332) 792844

Exhibition situated in 200-year old canalside warehouse. It tells the story of the building of the English canal system in words, pictures, models and artefacts. Passenger boat trips, boats for hire and canal marina.

Open Apr–Oct, daily 9–5.30; Nov–Mar, weekends 10–4.

✹ 80p (ch 14 & pen 40p).

A ♫ (licensed) ♫ & (ground floor & garden only) shop

SHEBBEAR
Devon
Map **2** SS40

Alscott Farm Agricultural Museum
☎ (040928) 206

A remarkable collection of vintage farm tractors, ploughs, dairy and household implements, photographs and information on North Devon's agricultural past. Wallis and Steevens Traction Engine. Special exhibition of unique scale model of an Edwardian travelling fair and contemporary photographs and original circus posters.

Open Etr–Sep, daily 12–dusk.

Admission fee payable.

A & (ground floor only) shop

SHEFFIELD
South Yorkshire
Map **8** SK38

Abbeydale Industrial Hamlet
Abbeydale Road South
☎ (0742) 367731

One of the first examples of industrial archaeology to be preserved and made accessible to the public. The late 18th- and early 19th-century steel scythe works, with their machinery, show production from the raw material stage to the finished production. Abbeydale Working Days and Craft Fair, please contact for information.

Open Mon–Sat 10–5 & Sun 11–5.

80p (ch & pen 40p). (90p, ch & pen 45p on working days).

A ♫ (Apr–Oct) & (ground floor only) shop ✹

Bishop's House Meersbrook Park
☎ (0742) 57701

A 15th–16th-century yeoman's house, restored as a museum of local and social history. Educational facilities for schools and colleges.

Open all year, Wed–Sat 10–5, Sun 11–5. (Closed 24–26 Dec).

30p (ch 5–16 & pen 15p).

P (in road 15 yds) shop ✹ (ex guide dogs)

City Museum Weston Park
☎ (0742) 27226

A regional museum of geology, natural sciences, archaeology, and Sheffield area trades, including cutlery, plate and ceramics. Educational facilities for schools and colleges.

Open daily 10–5, Sun 11–5; Jun, Jul & Aug 10–8; Sun 11–8. (Closed 24–26 Dec).

Free.

shop ✹ (ex guide dogs)

Sheffield Industrial Museum (Kelham Island) Alma St
☎ (0742) 22106

The museum tells the story of Sheffields industrial development over the past 400 years. Displays include working machinery, film slide shows, workshops where traditional cutlery craftsmen carry on their trades and show the wide variety of goods made in Sheffield.

Open Wed–Sat, 10–5, Sun 11–5.

80p (ch & pen 40p, holders of UB40's free). Party 20 + . Evening visits by arrangement.

A ♫ & (ground floor only) shop ✹

Sheffield Manor Manor Ln
☎ (0742) 734697/27226

A ruined manor house which began as a medieval hunting lodge enlarged in the 16th century and between 1406 and 1616 principal seat of the Earls of Shrewsbury. The house fell into disrepair in the 17th century and in the early 1900s the site was cleared of all except the surviving 16th-century structures. Now undergoing restoration and archaeological excavation to recover information about the house and earlier hunting lodge.

Open May–Oct, Wed–Sun 10–6.30.

Opening hours subject to staff availability. (Closed Mon & Tue). Details not confirmed for 1986. For visitors safety, access to some parts of the site may be restricted.

Free.

P (in street) & (ground floor & gardens only) ✹ (ex guide dogs)

Shepherd Wheel Whiteley Woods
☎ (0742) 367731

An early water-powered cutler's grinding establishment.

Open Wed–Sat 10–12.30 & 1.30–5, Sun 11–12.30 & 1.30–5pm. (4pm Nov–Feb).

Free.

P (400 yds) &

SHEFFIELD PARK GARDEN
East Sussex
Map **5** TQ42

(5m E of Haywards Heath off A275)
☎ Danehill (0825) 790655

Magnificent gardens and lake-watered park of nearly 150 acres, laid out from the 18th to 20th century, they surround a house by James Wyatt. Rhododendrons, azaleas (May–Jun), notable trees and shrubs (autumn). →

Gardens open 29 Mar–9 Nov, Tue–Sat 11–6, Sun & BH 2–6 or sunset (Sun, Oct & Nov 1pm–sunset). Last admission 1hr before closing. (Closed Good Fri & Tue after BH).

£1.90 (ch £1) Apr & June–Sep. £2.50 (ch £1.30) May, Oct & Nov.

△ ⊥ (not under NT Management) shop ✕ (NT)

SHEFFIELD PARK STATION, BLUEBELL RAILWAY MUSEUM
East Sussex
Map **5** TQ42

Sheffield Park Station, Bluebell Railway Museum
(4½m E of Haywards Heath, off A275)
☎ Newick (082572) 2370

A station of the revived Bluebell Railway. Parade weekend 10 & 11 May. Vintage and Fair 7 Sep. Part of the station is a small museum of old railway relics and records.

Vintage steam trains run as follows: wknds throughout the year (Sun only in Dec, Jan & Feb); weekends and Wed in May and Oct, daily Jun–Sep, and daily during Easter week. Museum open 10.30am on days when trains run, on other days open only for limited viewing.

✱ Return fare £2.20. Museum 50p.
△ ⊥ ⊞ ঙ (most parts) shop

SHERBORNE
Dorset
Map **3** ST61

Sherborne Castle
☎ (0935) 813182
A 16th-century house built by Sir Walter Raleigh, home of the Digby family since 1617, with fine furniture, paintings, porcelain and items of historical interest. Twenty acres of grounds planned by 'Capability' Brown. Teas and refreshments in the Gothic dairy by a lake.

Open Etr Sat–Sep, Thu, Sat, Sun & BH 2–6.

✱ £2.20 (ch £1.10, pen £1.70). Grounds only £1.20 (ch 60p).

△ ⊥ ঙ (ground floor) shop ✕ (ex guide dogs)

Sheffield Park Garden
—
Sheringham

Sherborne Museum, Abbey Gate House Church Ln
☎ (0935) 813214
On show are a model of the Norman castle, a fine Victorian doll's house, local geological and Roman material, coloured photographs of the Sherborne Missal of 1400. Natural history section.

Open Apr–Oct, Tue–Sat 10.30–12.30 & 3–4.30, Sun 3–5; Nov–Mar, Tue & Sat only. 25p (ch 10p).

P (200 yds) ঙ (ground floor only) ✕.

Sherborne Old Castle
Ruined castle about half a mile east of the town was built by Roger, Bishop of Salisbury between 1107 and 1135.

Open † see end of gazetteer.

✱ 30p (ch 16 & pen 15p).
△ (AM)

Worldwide Butterflies & Lullingstone Silk Farm Compton House.
(Entrance on A30, 2½m W)
☎ Yeovil (0935) 74608
Unique example of butterfly farm in stately home and grounds. Collections from across the world. Natural jungle with living exotic butterflies and tropical palmhouse. Extended facilities include a new Butterfly I louse, vintage tractors and fire engine. Also the home of the Lullingstone Silk Farm which produced unique English-reared silk for the last two coronations, the Queen's wedding dress and for the Princess of Wales.

Open 28 Mar–Oct 10–5.

Admission fee payable.
△ shop ✕ ⓥ

SHERBORNE St JOHN
Hampshire
Map **4** SU65

The Vyne (½m NE)

An early 16th-century house with additions by John Webb in 1654 including the earliest classical portico and showing diaper brickwork. Pleasant garden with a small lake.

Open 29 Mar–mid Oct, Tue–Thu, Sat & Sun 2–6. BH Mon 11–6. (Closed Tue following BH).

£1.70 (ch 80p). Gardens only 80p.

⊥ (in the Old Brewhouse 2.30–5.30) ✕ (NT)

SHERINGHAM
Norfolk
Map **9** TG14

North Norfolk Railway Sheringham Station
☎ (0263) 822045
A collection of steam locomotives and rolling stock, some undergoing or awaiting restoration, including several industrial tank engines and ex-Great Eastern Railway main-line engines. Rolling stock includes suburban coaches, Brighton Belle, Pullmans and directors' private saloons and vintage buffet saloon. Model railway. Souvenirs and bookshop. Museum of railwayana, Steam-hauled trains to operate weekends, Etr, Spring Bank Hol, then every Sun & certain weekdays throughout summer, daily in Aug until Sep.

Open Etr–Sep, daily 10–5 (or later).

✱ 30p (ch & pen 15p). Steam trains £1.70 return (ch & pen 90p). Party.

△ ⊥ ⊞ ঙ (ground floor only) shop

Sheringham Hall
(½m W of town, off A149)
☎ (0263) 823074
Regency mansion and park, by Humphry Repton. Magnificent rhododendron woods (1 mile drive).

Park and rhododendron woods open May–Jun Mon–Sat, 10–6; Sun 2–6 (mid May–mid Jun). House open by written appointment only.

£1 (ch 50p)
△ ▥

Sherborne Castle
Built by Sir Walter Raleigh 1594

Home of the Digby family (17th-century Earls of Bristol) since 1617. A fascinating fully-furnished historic home in a beautiful setting of lake, woods and parkland with ruins of the old castle in the background. Described by Alexander Pope in 1722 as a 'phantasy castle — so peculiar and of so uncommon kind that it merits a more particular description'. Situated 1 mile to the east of the attractive town of Sherborne, with its ancient abbey, almshouses and 2 castles. For details of the opening times see the gazetteer entry.

SHETLAND
Map 16

See Mousa Island, Scalloway, Sumburgh

SHIPLEY
West Sussex
Map 4 TQ12

Belloc's Mill King's Mill
☎ Coolham (040387) 310

A fine example of a smock mill (1879, restored 1957) in full working order. Hillaire Belloc, the writer, lived here from 1906–53.

Open for conducted tours May–Oct, first weekend in month 2.30–5.30. Also Etr Mon & Aug BH. Parties at other times by written appointment to Mrs A. E. Crowther, 13 Church Close, Shipley, Horsham, West Sussex RH13 8PJ.

50p (ch 5–16 20p).

P (100 yds) shop

SHIPTON
Shropshire
Map 7 SO59

Shipton Hall (6½m SW of Much Wenlock on B4378.)
☎ Brockton (074636) 225

A beautiful Elizabethan manor house in picturesque Corvedale setting. There is an attractive walled garden, medieval dovecote and old parish church.

Open May–Sep, Thu 2.30–5.30; Sun 2.30–5.30 Jul & Aug; also 30 & 31 Mar, 4, 5, 26, 27 May, PH wknds, 24, 25 Aug.

£1 (ch 14 50p). Party 20+.

▲ & (ground floor & gardens only) shop

SHOREHAM-BY-SEA
West Sussex
Map 4 TQ20

Marlipins
☎ (07917) 62994 (Sussex Archaeological Society)

A Norman and later flint building, possibly a warehouse, now a maritime and local history museum.

Open May–Sep, Mon–Sat 10–1 & 2–5. Sun 2–5.

Free. (Donation boxes).

P (100 yds) shop

SHORWELL
Isle of Wight
Map 4 SZ48

Yafford Water Mill Farm Park
☎ Isle of Wight (0983) 740610

Situated in attractive surroundings with a large mill pond and stream. The 19th-century mill contains much of the original machinery. There is also a collection of farm implements, wagons and tractors. Children's playground.

Open Etr–Oct daily 10–6.

£1.10 (ch & pen 60p). Party.

Shetland
—
Sidmouth

▲ ⬚ (licensed) ⊞ & (ground floor & gardens only) shop & garden centre

SHOTTERY
Warwickshire
Map 4 SP15

Anne Hathaway's Cottage
☎ Stratford-upon-Avon (0789) 292100

Anne Hathaway, Shakespeare's wife, was born in this thatched and timbered Elizabethan cottage.

Open Apr–Oct weekdays 9–6, Sun 10–6 (5pm in Oct); Nov–Mar weekdays 9–4.30, Sun 1.30–4.30. Last admission 20 mins before closing. (Closed Good Fri am, Xmas & New Years day am).

£1.20 (ch school age 50p). Combined ticket to all five Shakespearian properties £3.80 (ch £1.50). School & Student party rates.

P (150 yds) ⬚ (summer only) shop (except guide dogs)

SHREWSBURY
Shropshire
Map 7 SJ41

Bear Steps St Alkmund's Sq
☎ (0743) 56511

Recently restored, timber framed, 14th-century cottage with shops and meeting hall.

Open Mon–Sat 10–5.

Free.

P (150 yds) shop

Clive House Museum
☎ (0743) 54811

An 18th-century town house occupied by the 1st Lord Clive during his period as Mayor of Shrewsbury in 1762. Now houses fine collections of Shropshire pottery and porcelain, church silver, watercolours, and Museum of the 1st The Queen's Dragoon Guards.

Open Mon–Sat 10–5.

Free.

shop

Rowley's House Museum Barker St
☎ (0743) 61196

Fine adjoining half-timbered and brick buildings containing Roman remains from Wroxeter, art, local history, natural history and costume displays.

Open Mon–Sat 10–5; Sun mid May–mid Sep 12–5.

✳ 30p (ch 15p)

P (200 yds) shop

Shrewsbury Castle & Regimental Museum of the Kings Shropshire Light Infantry Castle St
☎ (0743) 52255 ext 267

Norman castle dating from 1083 and rebuilt by Edward I. Altered by the famous engineer Thomas Telford and open to the public since 1924. Now in 1985 opened as the Regimental Museum of the Kings Shropshire Light Infantry, the Shropshire Yeomanry and The Shropshire Royal Horse Artillery.

Open Etr–Oct daily 10–5; Oct–Etr Mon–Sat 10–4.

£1 (ch 40p).

P (150 yds) ⊞ shop

SHUGBOROUGH
Staffordshire
Map 7 SJ92

Shugborough Hall & Staffordshire County Museum
(5m E of Stafford off A513)
☎ Little Haywood (0889) 881388

Mansion built 1693–1810 including work by Samuel Wyatt. Plasterwork, pictures, fine collection of French furniture, mementoes of Admiral George Anson (1697–1762). Notable landscaped grounds feature Chinese house in neo-Grecian style by James 'Athenian' Stuart. Riverside gardens. Museum exhibits include social history, crafts, agriculture and Park Farm with rare livestock.

Open 15 May–26 Oct Tue–Fri & BH Mon 10.30–5.30, Sat & Sun 2–5.30. Museum & Park Farm only open winter, Tue–Fri 10.30–4.30 & Sun 2–4.30.

Museum & gardens £1 (ch 50p). House £1 extra (ch 50p). Park Farm 80 p (ch 50p).

▲ ⬚ & (ground floor only) shop (NT)

SIDMOUTH
Devon
Map 3 SY18

Sidmouth Museum
☎ (03955) 2363

An elegant Georgian house, next to parish church.

Open Etr–Oct Mon–Sat 10.30–12.30 & 2.30–4.30, Sun 2.30–4.30. Otherwise by appointment.

25p (ch 5–16 10p).

P (250 yds)

Vintage Toy & Train Museum 1st floor, Fields Dept Store, Market Pl
☎ (03955) 5124 ext 34

Exhibits of many toys, games and children's books covering 50 years (1925–75) including the first and last Dinky Toy, Hornby Gauge 'O' trains and Minic clockwork vehicles.

Open 24 Mar–1 Nov, Mon–Sat 10–5. (Closed BH)

70p (ch 3–14 30p)

P ⬚ shop

249

SILCHESTER
Hampshire
Map **4** SU66

Calleva Museum
☎ (0734) 700362 (mid-day, evenings & wknds).

Dealing with the Roman town of Calleva Atrebatum, this small museum includes panels of photographs, maps and other illustrative materials as well as actual objects excavated here, in order to present a brief account of life in the nearby walled Roman town (see **Reading Museum***).*

Accessible daily 9–sunset.

Free.

P & ✗

SILSOE
Bedfordshire
Map **4** TL03

Wrest Park Gardens
Notable 18th-century garden layout with formal canals and alterations by Capability Brown. Baroque early 18th-century banqueting house by Thomas Archer and Bowling Green House by Betty Langley.

Gardens and part of house open Apr–Sep, Sat, Sun & BH 9.30–6.30.

60p (ch & pen 30p)

& ⚏ (AM)

SINGLETON
West Sussex
Map **4** SU81

Weald & Downland Open Air Museum
☎ (024363) 348

A museum of rescued historic buildings from SE England that have been re-erected together with displays of traditional crafts and rural industries. Exhibits cover the 14th–19th centuries and include Medieval Houses, Agricultural Buildings, Tudor Market Hall, a Blacksmiths Forge, Charcoal Burner's Camp, Village School and a working Watermill. Situated in a beautiful Downland setting.

Silchester
—
Skelton

Open Apr–Oct daily 11–5. Nov–Mar Wed & Sun 11–4.

✳ £1.60 (ch 90p, pen £1,20). Party 15 + .

& ⚏ ⊞ & (ground floor only) shop

SISSINGHURST
Kent
Map **5** TQ73

Sissinghurst Castle Garden
(1½m NE of town)
☎ Cranbrook (0580) 712850

Beautiful gardens, created by the late V Sackville-West. Gardens famous for roses in Jun and Jul.

Gardens open 28 Mar–12 Oct Tue–Fri 1–6.30; Sat, Sun & Good Fri 10–6.30 (last admission 6pm).

£2.50 (ch £1.30) Tue–Sat; £3 (ch £1.50) Sun.

⚏ shop ✗ (NT)

SITTINGBOURNE
Kent
Map **5** TQ96

Dolphin Yard Sailing Barge Museum
Crown Quay Lane
☎ Maidstone (0622) 62531

Original sail loft, forge, shipwrights, also sailmakers' and riggers' tools. Barges being restored on site. Models, plans, prints etc.

Open Good Fri–Oct Sun also BH Mon 11–5.

50p (ch 16 & pen 25p).

& ⚏ & (ground floor only) shop.

SIZERGH
Cumbria
Map **7** SD48

Sizergh Castle
14th-century pele tower incorporated in a house dating from the 15th to 18th centuries.

Open 30 Mar–Oct, Sun, Mon, Wed & Thu 2–5.45; Garden open 12.30. (Closed Good Fri).

Castle & garden £1.40 (ch 70p). Garden only 60p (ch 30p). Party.

(NT)

SKEGNESS
Lincolnshire
Map **9** TF56

Church Farm Museum Church Road South
☎ (0754) 66658

Farmhouse and outbuildings restored to show the way of life of a Lincolnshire farmer at the end of the 19th century. Farm implements and machinery, domestic and household equipment. Re-erected timber-framed cottage. Re-erected barn provides temporary exhibition area. Craftsmen at work during weekends in summer. Craft week 1–7 Jul.

Open May–Oct, daily 10.30–5.30.

40p (ch 18 & pen 20p).

& ⚏ & (ground floor & gardens only) shop

Skegness Natureland Marine Zoo
North Pde, The Promenade
☎ (0754) 4345

Specialises in keeping sea lions, seals and penguins. Also a tropical house, aquarium and a Floral Palace of exotic plants with tropical birds in free flight. The zoo also cares for baby seals that have been washed up on nearby beaches. Pets Corner, Wild Fowl Pool, tropical butterflies and an Animal Brass Rubbing House.

Open Apr–Jun & Sep 10–5 (Jul & Aug 10–7.30); Oct–Mar 10–4.30. (Closed Xmas day).

✳ £1.20 (ch & pen 60p). Party.

P (100 yds) ⚏ & shop

SKELTON
Cumbria
Map **12** NY43

Hutton-in-the-Forest
☎ (08534) 500

14th-century pele tower, with later additions between the 17th–19th

---

WEALD&DOWNLAND A fascinating collection of rescued historic buildings from S.E. England, reconstructed in a beautiful Downland setting. Exhibits include 14th, 15th, 16th and 17th century houses, Tudor Market Hall, 17th century Treadwheel, Blacksmith's Forge, 18th century Barns and Granary, Toll Cottage, Charcoal Burners Camp, 19th century village school. The Lurgashall Watermill is in regular operation producing stone ground flour. The Museum is continuously developing and new buildings are regularly being re-erected. The Museum's magnificent 40 acre site contains picnic sites and light refreshments are available.

Open.   Apr - Oct. Daily 11-5 (last admission 5).
Nov - Mar, Weds, Suns and Bank Holidays only 11-4pm
Parties by arrangement.
Tel: Singleton 348 for further Information.

centuries. The house contains contemporary tapestries, pictures and furnishings. Gardens include fine specimen trees, an ornamental lake and a nature trail.

Open 4 & 5 May, 22 May–14 Sep Thu, Fri & Sun, 1–4. Grounds open daily, dawn–dusk. Parties all week.

£2 (ch accompanied free of charge, pen £1.50) Grounds £1 (ch 50p).

 ⚠ ⬩ ⬩ (ground floor only) shop ✗ (in house)

SKENFRITH
Gwent
Map **3** SO42

Skenfrith Castle (7m NW of Monmouth on B4521)

13th-century Marcher keep within a towered curtain wall, the work of Hubert de Burgh. One of the three 'trilateral' castles of Gwent.

Open at all reasonable times.

Free.

(AM Cadw & NT)

SKIDBY
Humberside
Map **8** TA03

Skidby Windmill (on A164)
☎ Hull (0482) 882255

Well preserved mill of 1821 which is being established as a milling museum. Black tarred tower and white cap form prominent local landmark.

The mill is operated on alternate Sun May–Sep. Open Tue–Sat 10–4, Sun 1–4 Oct–Apr Mon–Fri 10–4.

Admission fee payable.

P shop ✗

SKIPTON
North Yorkshire
Map **7** SD95

Craven Museum Town Hall, High St
☎ (0756) 4079

Contains collection dealing especially with the Craven district. There are

Skelton
—
Smailholm

important exhibits of folk life, lead mining and prehistoric and Roman remains.

Open Apr–Sep Mon, Wed–Fri 11–5, Sat 10–12 & 1–5, Sun 2–5; Oct–Mar Mon, Wed–Fri 2–5, Sat 10–12 & 1.30–4.30. Open some BHs & PH phone to check.

Free.

P (100 yds)

George Leatt Industrial & Folk Museum High Corn Mill, Chapel Hill
☎ (0756) 2883

Old mill, four storeys high, to which Victorian machinery is being added and where milling has been carried out since the 12th century. Two waterwheels, a turbine of 1912, and a winnower which took a prize in 1884, are all operational. Flour milling, collection of horse traps, carts, etc. Textile section.

Open most Wed, Sat & Sun at visitor's own risk from 2 pm. Parties at other times by arrangement only.

✳ 20p (ch 14 10p).
P ⬩ (ground floor only)

Skipton Castle High St
☎ (0756) 2442

One of the most complete and well preserved medieval castles in the country. Fully roofed and with enchanting Tudor courtyard.

Open daily 10–7, Sun 2–7 or sunset if earlier. Last admission 1hr before closing. (Closed Good Fri & Xmas day).

£1 (includes illustrated tour sheet in English, French and German) (ch 18 50p + free badge, ch 5 free). School parties booked in advance 50p, inclusive of guide's services.

P shop.

SKYE, ISLE OF
Highland Inverness-shire
Map **13**

See Armadale, Colbost, Dunvegan, Kilmuir

SLEDMERE
Humberside
Map **8** SE96

Sledmere House
☎ Driffield (0377) 86208

Georgian house with Chippendale, Sheraton and French furnishings. Park and gardens by Capability Brown.

Open 5–8 Apr & Suns to 5 May. Daily until 29 Sep (ex Mon & Fri), 1.30–5.30. Also BH Mons. Last admission 5 pm.

Admission fee payable.

 ⚠ ⬩ ⬩ shop ✗ (in house)

SLIMBRIDGE
Gloucestershire
Map **3** SO70

Wildfowl Trust (off A38 and M5 junction 13 or 14)
☎ Cambridge (Glos) (045389) 333

Founded by Sir Peter Scott. Slimbridge is the world's largest and most varied collection of swans, geese and ducks, all of which can be studied at close quarters. The collection includes six flocks of flamingoes, the largest collection of these birds in the world. First class viewing facilities are available and, in winter, towers and hides provide remarkable views of hundreds of wild swans and thousands of wild geese and ducks. Facilities and Nature Trail for visually handicapped with taped commentaries. Permanent exhibitions and a Tropical House. Exhibition Hall.

Open daily 9.30–5 or dusk if earlier. (Closed 24 & 25 Dec).

£2.50 (ch £1.20, ch 4 free, £1.80). Party 20 + .

 ⚠ ⬩ (licensed) ⋔ ⬩ shop ✗

SMAILHOLM
Borders Roxburghshire
Map **12** NT63

Smailholm Tower (1½m SW Smailholm)
Classic Scottish tower-house, probably erected in the 15th century. Exhibition →

THE MOST NATURAL PLACES TO GO TO AT ANY SEASON

Visit the Wildfowl Trust
ARUNDEL Sussex   PEAKIRK Cambridgeshire
SLIMBRIDGE Gloucestershire WASHINGTON Tyne/Wear
MARTIN MERE Lancashire
WELNEY Cambridgeshire
CAERLAVEROCK Dumfries (open 16 September) to 30 April

In summer see the famous collections, in spring see the young cygnets, goslings and ducklings and from September to April see the thousands of wild geese, swans and ducks.
For further information send SAE to the Wildfowl Trust, Slimbridge, Glos GL2 7BT. Tel: Cambridge (Glos) 333

251

'Minstrelsy of the Scottish Border', a fascinating display of costume figures and tapestries.

Open see end of gazetteer on application to Key Keeper in winter.

50p (ch 25p).

(AM)

SMALLHYTHE
Kent
Map **5** TQ82

Smallhythe Place
☎ Tenterden (05806) 2334

Dame Ellen Terry's former half-timbered 16th-century home with a museum and barn theatre.

Open 29 Mar–Oct, Sat–Mon, Wed & Thu. (Closed Good Fri).

£1.10 (ch 60p).

✹ (NT)

SNAEFELL MOUNTAIN
Isle of Man
Map **6** SC38

Murray's Museum The Bungalow (Junction A14 and A18)
☎ Laxey (0624) 719

Contains an interesting collection of over 100 veteran and vintage motor cycles dating from 1902 to 1960, in addition to ancient arms and musical instruments and hundreds of bygones of yesteryear. A further 150 machines can be seen by appointment only.

Open 25 May–25 Sep, daily 10–5.

£1 (ch & pen 50p). Party.

⚠ ⬚ shop

SOMERLEYTON
Suffolk
Map **5** TM49

Somerleyton Hall (off B1074)
☎ Lowestoft (0502) 730224

Magnificent Tudor to Jacobean mansion rebuilt in Anglo-Italian style in 1846. Superb furniture, tapestries, pictures. Heritage display and Grinling Gibbons carvings. There are 12 acres of grounds with famous maze and miniature railway.

Open 7, 8 Apr; 5, 6 May & 26 May–29 Sep, Thu, Sun & BH 2–5.30; Tue & Wed also in Jul & Aug.

Garden only on all other days ex Sat's, 2–5.30.

Admission fee payable.

⚠ ⬚ ⛩ ⛫ shop ✹

SOTTERLEY
Suffolk
Map **5** TM48

Sotterley Agricultural Museum
Alexander Wood Farm
☎ Brampton (050279) 257

Collection of agricultural items, cars and motor cycles. Blacksmith's shop, household utensils and farmhouse

---

Smailholm
—
South Harting

kitchen. Events include British Motor Cycle Exhibition Spring BH.

Open Etr–Oct (Sun & BH) 1–6.

60p (ch 14 & pen 30p).

⚠ ⬚ ⛩ ⛫ shop

SOUDLEY
Gloucestershire
Map **3** SO61

Dean Heritage Museum & Craft Centre
Camp Mill
☎ Dean (0594) 22170

Set around a tranquil mill pond in a beautiful wooded valley the unique Heritage of the Forest of Dean is portrayed through permanent and temporary museum displays, audio-visual presentation, the Living World display, nature trails and smallholding. Archaeological exhibition with dig in progress, working craftspeople and adventure playground.

Open Apr–Oct daily 10–6; Nov–Mar 10–5.

✻ £1 (ch, student, unemployed & pen 50p).

⚠ ⬚ ⛩ ⛫ (ground floor & garden only) shop ✹

SOUTHAMPTON
Hampshire
Map **4** SU41

Art Gallery
Civic Centre, Commercial Rd
☎ (0703) 223855 ext. 2769

18th- to 20th-century English paintings. Continental Old Masters of 14th- to 18th-century. Modern French paintings. Collection of sculpture and ceramics. Of special interest are paintings and drawings of the 'Camden Town Group'. Particularly good collection of contemporary British paintings and sculpture. Temporary exhibitions.

Open Tue–Fri 10–5, Sat 10–4, Sun 2–5. (Closed 25–27 & 31 Dec).

Free.

P (metered) ⛫ shop ✹ (ex guide dogs)

Bargate Guildhall Museum
Above Bar
☎ (0703) 224216

The medieval North gate of the city. The upper floor, once a guildhall, is used to house short term displays on special themes.

Open Tue–Fri 10–12 & 1–5, Sat 10–12 & 1–4, Sun 2–5. (Closed 25–27 & 31 Dec & BH).

Free.

P (100 yds) shop ✹

God's House tower Winkle St.
☎ (0703) 220007 & 224216

Early fortified, sea-defensive, building dating from 1300's. Now a museum of Southampton's archaeology from Bronze Age to medieval times.

Open Tue–Fri 10–12 & 1–5; Sat 10–12 & 1–4; Sun 2–5.

Free.

P shop.

Southampton Hall of Aviation Albert Rd South
☎ (0703) 35830

Examples of historic aircraft featuring the Sandringham Flying Boat (prominent in opening up the Empire's air routes), one of the last Spitfires (Mark 24) ever produced and the Supermarine S6A. There are also other aircraft and coverage of aviation production and engineering in the South of England.

Open Tue–Sat & BH Mon 10–5; Sun 2–5. (Closed Good Fri & Xmas).

Admission fee payable.

⚠ ⬚ shop ✹

Tudor House Museum Bugle St, St Michael's Sq
☎ (0703) 224216

A restored, half-timbered 16th-century house, containing a museum of antiquarian and historical interest, social and domestic history, some costume and jewellery. Tudor garden reached through the museum.

Open Tue–Fri 10–5; Sat 10–4; Sun 2–5. (Closed 25–27 & 31 Dec & BH Mon).

Free.

P (150 yds) ⛫ (ground floor & garden with help) shop ✹

Wool House Maritime Museum
Town Quay
☎ (0703) 223941 & 224216

This 600-year-old building, once a wool warehouse, has buttressed stone walls and old roof timbering. Houses an interesting maritime museum.

Open Tue–Fri 10–1 & 2–5, Sat 10–1 & 2–4, Sun 2–5. (Closed 25–27 & 31 Dec).

Free.

P (100 yds) ⛫ (ground floor only) shop ✹

SOUTH HARTING
West Sussex
Map **4** SU71

Uppark (1m S on B2146)

A notable pedimented red brick mansion designed by Talman c1690 with original wallpapers and curtains of 1750. Victorian 'below stairs' rooms. Beautiful downland setting and views.

Open 30 Mar–Sep Wed, Thu, Sun & BH Mons 2–6 (last admission 5.30).

£1.70.

✹ (NT)

SOUTH MOLTON
Devon
Map **3** SS72

Castle Hill (3½m W on A361)
☎ Filleigh (05986) 227

Palladian mansion built c1729. Fine 18th-century furniture, tapestries, porcelain and pictures. Ornamental garden, shrub, woodland garden and arboretum.

Open Apr–Oct by appointment for conducted tours by owners for parties of 20 or more.

£2 per person Garden only 50p (can be seen any time by telephoning Estate Office ☎ (05986) 336).

⚠ 🚫

Quince Honey Farm
☎ (07695) 2401

Exceptional exhibition of wild honey bees, in this large working honey farm. Behind glass the bees can be seen in their natural habitats, unique opening hives which reveal the centre of the colony with the bees working undisturbed.

Open daily, Etr–Oct 8–6; Nov–Etr 9–5.

£1.50 (accompanied children free).

⚠ Ⓢ ₤ ♿ (ground floor only) shop

South Molton Museum Town Hall, Market St
☎ (07695) 2951

Part of the Guildhall, a stone-fronted building c1743 entered through open arcaded frontage. Local history, old charters, weights and measures, pewter, old fire engines, giant cider press. Monthly art craft, and educational exhibitions.

Open Apr–Nov Mon (ex Oct & Nov) Tue, Thu & Fri 10.30–12.30 & 2–4; Wed & Sat 10–12. (Closed BH).

Free.

P (200 yds) ♿ shop 🚫

SOUTHPORT
Merseyside
Map **7** SD31

Atkinson Art Gallery Lord St
☎ (0704) 33133 ext 129

South Molton
‒
South Shields

19th- and 20th-century oil paintings, watercolours, drawings and prints 20th-century sculpture. Also visiting exhibition programme.

Open all year, Mon, Tue, Wed & Fri 10–5; Thu & Sat 10–1.

Free.

P (300 yds) shop 🚫

Botanic Gardens Museum
Church Town (situated in public park)
☎ (0704) 27547

Collections of local history, natural history, 18th- and 19th-century china, a display of the local shrimping industry; and a rare example of an early dug-out canoe from the nearby Martin Mere. Also Ainsdale National Nature Reserve display reconstructed. Victorian parlour and Cecily Bate collection of dolls.

Open all year Tue–Sat & BH Mon 10–6 (5pm Oct–Apr), & Sun 2–5 (Closed Mon, Good Fri, 25 Dec & 1 Jan also Fri following BH Mon).

Free.

P (50 yds) ♿ (ground floor) shop 🚫

Model Village & Model Railway
The Promenade
☎ (0704) 42133

Set amidst a variety of trees, shrubs and plants with lake and waterfalls. Model and figures on a scale of 1:12 as well as a working 3″ gauge railway.

Open Mar–Oct, daily 9.30–5.30 (weather permitting).

✳ 90p (ch 45p, pen 60p). Party 20+.

P (50 yds) ₤ ♿ shop

Steamport Transport Museum
Derby Rd
☎ (0704) 30693

Ex-British Rail locomotives and several industrial locomotives. 1000ft of standard gauge track, connects the museum to the British Rail system. Also on display are

---

local buses, tramcars, traction engines and other vehicles in what is possibly the largest preservation centre of its type in north-west England. Special events Etr, May Day, Spring & Aug BH.

Oct–Apr Sat & Sun 2–5; May–Sep Sat & Sun 11–5; Jun wkdays 1–5, Jul & Aug 11–5 & first 2 wks Sep 1–5. Also BH periods.

£1 (ch 60p pen 80p). Steam days £1.20 (ch 70p, pen £1). Inclusive of train rides.

⚠ ₤ (Sun) ♿ shop

Southport Zoo Princes Park
☎ (0704) 38102

A varied collection, within an area of 3½ acres. Large and small mammals, duck and flamingo pools, and assorted aviaries. New aquarium, reptile house, alligator beach and mandrill house. New extension including room for educational lectures etc.

Open all year (ex 25 Dec) 10–6 in summer, 10–4 in winter.

Admission fee payable.

P ₤ ➕ ♿ shop

SOUTH SHIELDS
Tyne & Wear
Map **12** NZ36

Arbeia Roman Fort & Museum
Baring St
☎ (0632) 561369

Roman fort at the easternmost end of the Hadrianic frontier, displaying fort defences, stone granaries, gateways, headquarters building, tile kilns and latrine. Museum contains site finds and interpretation.

Open May–Sep Mon–Fri 10–5.30, Sat 10–4.30 & Sun 2–5; Oct–Apr Mon–Fri 10–4 & Sat 10–noon (Closed Sun).

Free.

⚠ ♿ shop

South Shields Museum & Art Gallery
Ocean Rd
☎ (0632) 568740

The museum shows the archaeology, history and natural history of South Shields. A maritime display includes a section on the evolvement of the lifeboat →

and local shipbuilding. The art gallery features a programme of changing exhibitions.

Open Mon–Fri 10–5.30, Sat 10–4.30, Sun 2–5. (Closed Good Fri & 25 & 26 dec).

Free.

P (500 yds) & shop ✗

See advertisement under Newcastle-upon-Tyne

SOUTH WALSHAM
Norfolk
Map **9** TG31

Fairhaven Garden Trust
☎ (060549) 449

The gardens contain a beech walk with spring flowers, rhododendrons, a water garden and walks beside a private broad. The King Oak is said to be 900 years old. The waterways are spanned by small bridges; many rare shrubs and plants. Bird Sanctuary may be visited at certain times by arrangement with the warden.

Open 28 Mar–11 May, Sun & BH's; 14 May–7 Sep, Wed–Sun & BH's; 14–28 Sep Sun only: 2–6.

80p (ch & pen 50p).

🅰 🖵 &

SOUTHWICK
Northamptonshire
Map **4** TL09

Southwick Hall (between Oundle (A605) & Bulwick (A43))
☎ Oundle (0832) 74013 & 74064

Manor house, retaining medieval building dating from 1300, with Tudor rebuilding and 18th-century additions. Exhibitions Victorian and Edwardian life; musical instrument workshop; collections of agricultural and carpentry tools, named blocks and local archaeological finds and fossils.

Open 28 May–21 Aug Wed, also Etr Sun & Mon, BH Sun & Mon & 13 Apr 2.30–5. Other times by arrangement.

£1.20 (ch 60p, pen 75p).

🅰 🖵 & (ground floor & gardens only) ✗

SOUTHWOLD
Suffolk
Map **5** TM57

Southwold Museum
Bartholomew Green

Formerly known as Dutch Cottage Museum, it contains relics of Southwold light railway and also illustrations of local history.

Open Spring BH–30 Sep, daily. Also Etr Mon & May Day BH, 2.30–4.30. Other times by appointment.

Donations accepted.

P (limited)

SPALDING
Lincolnshire
Map **8** TF22

South Shields
—
Stalham

Springfields Gardens
☎ (0775) 4843

Unique 25-acre spring flower spectacle on eastern outskirts of the town (A151). More than a million bulbs, with lawns, lake, glasshouses and Summer Rose Gardens with over 12,500 rose bushes in 100 varieties. Flower parade 3 May Exhibition of floats 3–6 May.

Open 28 Mar–30 Sep daily 10–6.

£1.20 (ch free). Special events £1.50.

🅰 🎋 & shop & garden centre ✗ ⓥ

SPEKE
Merseyside
Map **7** SJ48

Speke Hall
☎ 051-427 7231

Grand example of 16th-century half-timbering with interior courtyard. Great hall, 16th- and 17th-century plasterwork and Mortlake tapestries.

Open Apr–Sep, Mon–Sat 10–5, Sun 2–7 & BH 10–7; Oct–Mar, Mon–Sat 10–5, Sun 2–5 (last visitor 1hr before closing). (Closed Good Fri, 24–26 Dec & 1 Jan).

✳ 60p (ch 30p). Prices subject to review. Party.

🅰 🖵 (Etr & summer afternoons only) ✗
(NT & Merseyside County Museums)

SPETCHLEY
Hereford and Worcester
Map **3** SO85

Spetchley Park Gardens
☎ (090565) 213 & 224

Fine gardens and park, surrounding early 19th-century mansion, with red deer and lake with wildfowl. Gardens cover 30 acres and include many unusual trees and shrubs.

Gardens only shown Apr–Sep, Mon–Fri 11–5, Sun 2–5.30; BH Mons 11–5.30. Other days by appointment. Garden centre within gardens open same hours.

£1.20 (ch 60p).

🅰 🖵 (Sun & BH Mons only) & garden centre ✗

SPROATLEY
Humberside
Map **8** TA13

Burton Constable Hall (1½m N)
☎ Skirlaugh (0401) 62400

Elizabethan house, built 1570 with 18th-century state rooms and 200 acres of parkland landscaped by Capability Brown. Camping and caravanning park. Seasonal fishing. Steam Rally & Country

Fair–Jun, Light Aircraft Rally August BH & Crafts at Home Sep.

Hall Etr Sun–Sep, Sun & Mon 1–5; Aug also Tue–Thu. Grounds Etr Sun–Sep, daily noon–5.

House £1.20 (ch 60p, pen 70p).

🅰 🖵 🎋 & (ground floor only) shop ✗ ⓥ

STAFFORD
Staffordshire
Map **7** SJ92

Art Gallery The Green
☎ (0785) 57303

Art gallery showing temporary exhibitions of contemporary art, craft and photography. Craft shop selling a wide range of fine work from British craftsmen. Garden Festival Craft Exhibition mid Jun–Sep.

Open all year, Tue–Fri 10–5, Sat 10–4.

Free.

P (multi-storey 100 yds) shop ✗ (ex guide dogs)

STAGSDEN
Bedfordshire
Map **4** SP94

Stagsden Bird Gardens
☎ Oakley (02302) 2745

A breeding centre for many species of birds, including owls, cranes, pheasants, waterfowl and old breeds of poultry. Also fine collection of shrub roses.

Open all year daily (ex 25 Dec), 11–6 or dusk.

£1.30 (ch 4–15 60p pen £1).

🅰 🖵 🎋 & shop ✗

STAINDROP
Co Durham
Map **12** NZ12

Raby Castle
☎ (0833) 60202

Principally 14th-century with 18th- and 19th-century alterations. Fine pictures from English, Dutch and Italian schools. Carriage Collection. Red and fallow deer in Park. Also about 5 acres of gardens.

Open 29 Mar–Jun, Wed & Sun 2–5; Jul–Sep, Sun–Fri 2–5. Park and gardens only open 1–5.30. Last admission 4.30.

Castle £1.80 (ch & pen £1); Park & Gardens 75p (ch & pen 50p). Party.

🅰 🖵 🎋 & (ground floor only) shop ✗

STALHAM
Norfolk
Map **9** TG32

Sutton Wind Mill
(2m SE on unclass road)
☎ (0692) 81195

The tallest windmill in the country with nine floors plus the cap floor. Built in 1789 the milling machinery is complete and there is access to all floors including the top outside stage. An extensive collection

254

of bygones is displayed in the museum area.

Open Apr–mid May 1–6; mid May–Sep 9.30–6 daily.

85p (accompanied ch 45p).

🅰 ⬆ shop 🍴

STAMFORD
Lincolnshire
Map **4** TF00

Brewery Museum All Saints St
☎ (0780) 52186

A complete Victorian steam brewery in attractive stone buildings with coopered vats, shining coppers and displays of Victorian working life. Brewers dray, cooperage, corking machines, a boof and flogger. Souvenir shop and bar with antique beer engine.

Open Apr–Sep, Wed–Sun 10–4 and BH Mon. (Closed Wed in BH weeks).

✳ £1.20 (ch & pen 60p) Party 12 + .

P (50 yds) ⬆ (licensed) & (ground floor only) shop ⓥ

Burghley House (1m SE)
☎ (0780) 52451

England's greatest Elizabethan house. Contains painted ceilings, silver, fireplaces, largest private collection of Italian Old Masters, Verrio's masterpiece, the Heaven Room, a miracle of perspective. Burghley horse trials held in Sep. Nearby Barnack Church has Saxon Tower and 13th-century font.

Open Good Fri–5 Oct daily 11–5.

✳ £2.75 (ch £1.50). Party.

🅰 ⬆ (licensed) shop 🍴 ⓥ

Stamford Museum Broad St
☎ (0780) 55611

Museum illustrating the history and archaeology of Stamford. Also has the original clothes of famous fat man Daniel Lambert on display with those of the American midget General Tom Thumb. Temporary exhibitions throughout the year. Special exhibition to commemorate 900th anniversary of Domesday.

Open May–Sep Tue–Sat 10–5, Sun 2–5; Oct–Apr Tue–Sat 10–12.30 & 1.30–5.

Stalham
Stirling

20p (ch 10p).

P (300 yds)

STANSTED MOUNTFITCHET
Essex
Map **5** TL52

Windmill
☎ Bishop's Stortford (0279) 812096

Red-brick tower-mill of 1787 (restored 1966, new sails 1985), with machinery and furnishings intact. 65ft high.

Open 2.30–7 on first Sun in month from Apr-Oct, every Sun in Aug. Also on Etr, May, Spring & late Summer BH (Sun & Mon). Other times by telephone application to committee secretary.

40p (ch 14 20p).

🅰 (20 places) shop 🍴

STANWAY
Gloucestershire
Map **4** SP03

Stanway House
☎ Stanton (038673) 469

Built of limestone and standing in an attractive Cotswold village this Jacobean manor has fine furnishings. Set in parkland with gatehouse and tithe barn.

Open Jun–Aug, Tue & Thu 2–5.

£1.50 (ch 75p, pen £1.25) Party.

🅰 ⬆

STEVENAGE
Hertfordshire
Map **4** TL22

Benington Lordship Gardens
Benington
☎ Benington (043885) 668

An Edwardian terraced garden of seven acres overlooking lakes and parkland. On the site of a Norman castle, the keep and moat can still be seen. There is also a Victorian folly. Spectacular double

---

herbaceous borders, spring rock-and-water garden, rose garden and green house display.

Open 23 Feb; 2 Mar; Etr Mon, May & Aug BH's. May–Jul, Wed & Sun; Aug, 1st Sun & 1st Wed (Sun 2–5 & Wed 10–5).

£1 Wed & Sun, other times £1.20. Parties by appointment.

🅰 ⬆ (Sun only) garden centre 🍴

Stevenage Museum St George's Way
☎ (0438) 354292

This museum, in the undercroft of the parish church of St George, tells the Story of Stevenage from the present day back to earliest times. Temporary exhibitions.

Open all year Mon–Sat 10–5 (Closed BH).

Free.

P (multi-storey 50 yds) & shop 🍴

STICKLEPATH
Devon
Map **2** SX69

Sticklepath Museum of Rural Industry & Finch Foundry Trust
☎ Okehampton (0837) 840286

Once corn mill and cloth mill, later converted to edge-tool factory and grinding house. Among the exhibits are two water-powered 'tilt' hammers, unique in the West Country, and other machinery driven by three separate water-wheels. Demonstrations of machinery and water-wheels in motion daily. Parties by appointment: apply to Secretary.

Open all year, daily 11–5

£1 (ch 50p).

🅰 ⏚ & (ground floor only) shop

STIRLING
Central *Stirlingshire*
Map **11** NS79

Cambuskenneth Abbey

Founded in 1147 by David I, this abbey was the scene of Bruce's important parliament of 1326. It is also the burial place of James III and his wife.

Open see end of gazetteer. Apr–Sep only.

50p (ch & pen 25p).

(AM)

RABY CASTLE (The Lord Barnard)

The only Stately Home in County Durham open to the public. Mainly 14th-Century Castle with 18th- and 19th-Century interior; superb Medieval Kitchen; tapestries and furniture; paintings of English, Dutch and Flemish Schools. Fine collection of carriages. Large garden.

Open Easter Saturday — end September. Easter Sat, Sun, Mon, Tues; Wed and Sun — April, May, June. May Bank Holiday — 3, 4, 5, 6 May, Spring Bank Holiday, 24, 25, 26, 27 May. Daily (ex Sat) July, August, September.

Castle open 2 - 5 p.m. Park and Gardens open 1 - 5.30 p.m.
Last admission 4.30 p.m.

Staindrop, Darlington, Co Durham. Tel Staindrop (0833) 60202

Mar's Wark Broad St

A partly ruined Renaissance mansion with a gatehouse enriched by sculptures. Built by the Regent Mar in 1570.

Open at all times.

Free.

(AM)

The Museum of the Argyll & Sutherland Highlanders
☎ (0786) 75165

Situated in King James V Palace of Stirling Castle. Fine collection of regimental silver and plate, colours, pipe banners, paintings and uniform. Also medals, covering period from Waterloo to present day.

Open Etr–Sep, Mon–Sat 10–5.30, Sun 11–5; Oct Mon–Fri 10–4.

Free.

P (300 yds) ⬛ shop ✘

Stirling Castle Upper Castle Hill

This royal castle is the strategic centre of Scotland. Little remains earlier than 16th-century when the Palace, Great Hall and Chapel Royal were built. The fortifications were refurbished at the time of the Jacobite uprisings.

Open 5 Jan–Mar & Oct–Dec, Mon–Sat 9.30–5.05, Sun 12.30–4.20; Apr–Sep, Mon–Sat 9.30–6, Sun 10.30–5.30. Last admission 45 mins before closing.

£1.20 (ch & pen 60p).

⚠ (AM)

Stirling Castle Visitors Centre
☎ (0786) 62517

Exhibition and shop in restored old building overlooking River Forth near the castle. Audio-visual presentation of the history of Stirling Castle.

Open Feb–Sep, Mon–Sat 9.30–5.15, Sun 10.30–4.45. Oct–Dec, Mon–Sat 9.30–4.20, Sun 12.30–3.35.

Charge for audio visual.

⚠ ⬛

Stirling Smith Art Gallery & Museum
40 Albert Pl, Dumbarton Rd
☎ (0786) 71917

Stirling
—
Stoke-on-Trent

Stirling's Story—A permanent display of the history of Stirling from William Wallace to the present day. Lively programme of exhibitions throughout the year.

Open Wed–Sun 2–5 (10.30–5 Sat).

Free.

P (in Street) ⬥ shop ✘ (ex guide dogs)

STOBO
Borders Peeblesshire
Map **11** NT13

Dawyck Botanic Garden (Royal Botanic Garden, Edinburgh) on B712, 8m SW of Peebles
☎ (07216) 254

Impressive arboretum, noted for collection of trees, shrubs and bulbs. House not shown.

Open Apr–Sep, daily 9–5.

✱ 50p per car.

⚠ ✘

STOCKTON-ON-TEES
Cleveland
Map **8** NZ41

Preston Hall Museum Yarm Rd
(2m S A19)
☎ (0642) 602474 (weekends: 781184)

Museum illustrates Victorian Social history and collections include costume, arms, armour and period rooms. Also 19th-century reconstructed street with working blacksmiths and farrier.

Open all year, Mon–Sat 9.30–5.30, Sun 2–5.30. Last admission 5 pm. (Closed Good Fr, Xmas & New Year).

Free.

⚠ (charged) ⬛ 🕀 ⬥ (ground floor & gardens only) shop ✘ (ex guide dogs)

STOKE BRUERNE
Northamptonshire
Map **4** SP74

Stoke Park Pavilions
☎ Roade (0604) 862172

Twin 17th-century pavilions, attributed to Inigo Jones, remains of Stoke Park, burnt in 1884 and subsequently rebuilt.

Exteriors of pavilions and gardens shown. Sun Jun; Sat & Sun, Jul & Aug 2–6. Any other times by appointment only.

Admission fee payable.

⚠ ⬥

Waterways Museum
☎ Northampton (0604) 862229

Former corn mill, situated near a flight of locks on the Grand Union Canal, records the fascinating canal story of over two centuries. Old narrow boat on show.

Open Jan–Etr Tue–Sun 10–4; Etr–Oct daily 10–6; Oct–Dec Tue–Sun 10–4 (Closed Xmas). Enquiries to Curator.

✱ £1 (ch & pen 50p). Family ticket £2.25.

⚠ ⬥ (ground floor & gardens only) shop ✘

STOKE-ON-TRENT
Staffordshire
Map **7** SJ84

Chatterley Whitfield Mining Museum
(Nr Tunstall)
☎ (0782) 813337

Guided tours of the mine workings 700ft below ground. On the surface are exhibition galleries, lamproom, steam winding engines, colliery canteen and museum shop.

Open daily 9.30–5.30, last tour 4 (in summer). (Closed Sat winter).

£3.10 (ch £2, students & pen £2.50). Family tickets £9.20; prices & dates to be confirmed.

⚠ ⬛ ⬥ (surface only) shop ✘ (underground)

City Museum & Art Gallery
Bethesda St, Hanley
☎ (0782) 273173

Exhibits include one of the largest and finest collections of ceramics, with the emphasis on Staffordshire pottery and porcelain. A changing programme of temporary exhibitions. →

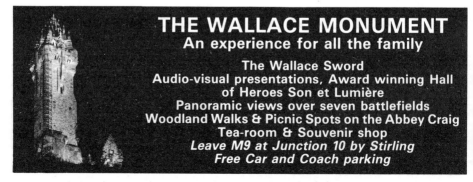

THE GREATEST SHOW OF '86
FESTIVE·FLORAL·FANTASTIC FUN·

Join in the fun with thousands of attractions for all the family, never mind the weather — more than 10 acres under cover.

Leaflets and tickets at post offices from April 1986 onwards or at the Festival entrances. There's so much going on, you'll want to visit again and again . . . .

THE BIGGEST SPECTACULAR FESTIVAL IN EUROPE . . . RUNS FOR A WHOLE SIX MONTHS, FROM 1st MAY TO 26th OCTOBER

REAL VALUE FOR MONEY

Adults	£4·50
Children/OAP/Student/ Unemployed	£3·00

CHILDREN UNDER 5 — FREE

Special discounts for groups and multi-visit tickets

SPECIAL PRICES

Fabulous Family 5 Ticket
2 CHILDREN FREE! 2 Adults and up to 3 Children — only £12 all in!
Ask at your Post Office for details.

CABLE-CARS, TRAIN RIDES

FESTIVAL EXPO 86
20 changing exhibitions — from antiques to electronics

LAKES, BRIDGES, CASCADES, FABULOUS LANDSCAPES

80 COLOURFUL THEME GARDENS — THE FINEST YOU'VE EVER SEEN

SEE THE £1 MILLION GREENHOUSE 2000

50 CONTINUOUS HORTICULTURAL SHOWS IN THE GIANT FESTIVAL HALL

VISIT THE FESTIVAL FARM, MARINA AND MARKET

EUROPE'S MOST SPECTACULAR FESTIVAL

Phone Festivaline (0782) 274777 NOW For recorded information

NATIONAL GARDEN FESTIVAL
STOKE·ON·TRENT · STAFFORDSHIRE
OPEN EVERY DAY 10.00am-DUSK
1st MAY — 26th OCTOBER 1986

SEE YOU THERE!

PATRON HER MAJESTY THE QUEEN

☆ EASY TO REACH ☆

Situated midway between Birmingham and Manchester, the National Garden Festival is at the heart of the country's communication network. Easily accessible by road and rail, the M6 Motorway is a few minutes away and London is just a two-hour train journey. Parking couldn't be easier and there are special facilities for coach travellers.

☆ 80 GLORIOUS GARDENS ☆

Every Garden an experience in itself. Take the traditional Pergola Walkway; discover the Chess Garden with its own giant pieces, see an ingenious sunken garden, stunning bedding displays and many, many more gardens of great beauty and interest.

Step from the past to the future and back again, from early Monastic Gardens through Tudor Times and right back up to date in a garden of Fun for the Eighties.

Sample the styles of China, Holland and Italy in the INTERNATIONAL AREA, or stay cool in the Hereford Cider Garden with its own bowling green. Themes abound, from a Kenyan Village to English Conservation — see them all.

Open Mon–Sat 10.30–5, Sun 2–5. (Closed Xmas wk & Good Fri).

Free.

P (200 yds) 🍽 (licensed) & shop ✠

Ford Green Hall
Ford Green Rd Smallthorne
☎ (0782) 534771

A timber-framed farmhouse built in about 1580 for the Ford family. Brick wings were added in the early 1700's. Furnished with items and utensils used by a farming family from the 16th- to the 19th-century. Guided tours only (45 mins)

Open Mon, Wed, Thu & Sat 10–12.30 & 2–5, Sun 2–5. (Closed Xmas & New Year).

Stoke-on-Trent

Last admission 45 mins before closing.

Free.

⚠ shop ✠

Gladstone Pottery Museum
Uttoxeter Rd, Longton (2m SE of Stoke-on-Trent, on A50)
☎ (0782) 319232

A Victorian pottery, still complete with old warehouses, workshops and four bottle

---

ovens. Traditional skills may be seen in action. Historical, Tile, Sanitary and Colour galleries. Pottery for sale.

Open Mon–Sat 10.30–5.30; Sun & BH 2–6; 9pm Wed Apr–Sep for booked parties. (Closed Xmas day).

£1.50 (ch 16 70p, students & pen £1). Reduced family ticket £3.

⚠ 🍽 shop

National Garden Festival
☎ (0782) 289788

164 acres of spectacular gardens, exhibitions, displays and special events.

Open May–26 Oct daily 10–dusk.

GLADSTONE

the living and working Pottery Museum

The Story of the British Potteries

— *displayed* in colourful galleries of tableware, tiles and sanitaryware —
— *housed* in an early Victorian Potbank complete with spectacular Bottle Ovens —
— *demonstrated daily* by skilled Craftsmen making and decorating ware.

Uttoxeter Road, Longton, Stoke-on-Trent telephone (0782) 319232 Or 311378

Invest in the original at factory prices.

Ever since Josiah Spode first created fine bone china at the end of the 18th century, the products that bear his name have been prized above all the others. Today you can still tour the Spode factory, on

BY APPOINTMENT TO
HER MAJESTY QUEEN ELIZABETH II
MANUFACTURERS OF CHINA
SPODE STOKE-ON-TRENT

the very site where he made his momentous discovery, and find genuine bargains in beautiful fine bone china, cookware, earthenware, giftware and figurines.

The reward of years of experiment. Josiah Spode's and the world's first successful piece of bone china

Spode

FACTORY SHOP & TOURS

Church Street, Stoke-on-Trent. Tel: 0782 46011
Shop open: Monday-Thursday 8.30am to 5.00pm, Friday 8.30am to 4.00pm, Saturday 9.00am to 1.00pm.
Factory Tours available twice daily, Mon-Fri. Ring the Tours Organiser for details.

£4.50 (ch, students, pen & unemployed £3) Family ticket £12. party 20 +.

& .Ⴑ (licensed) ⊞ ᕇ shop ✗ (ex guide dogs) ⌕

See advertisement on page 257

The Sir Henry Doulton Gallery
☎ (0782) 85747

A tribute to Sir Henry Doulton, the gallery contains pottery treasures and artistry representing over 150 years. Nearly 300 figures, some rare and some very early pieces. Displays by outstanding artists, experimental ceramic and exhibits demonstrate the great variety of the Royal Doulton tradition accompanied by archive material, sketches, pattern books and medals.

Mon–Fri 9–12.30 & 1.30–4.15. Tours by appointment. £2 per person. Party 30 +. (Closed factory holidays).

Free.

& shop ✗

Spode Church St
☎ (0782) 46011

1½hr tour of the factory includes mouldmaking and plate making, decorating and gilding. The museum displays a wide range of Spode ware and the Spode Seconds Shop is housed in a quaint old building that was here in the first Spode's day.

Stoke-on-Trent
—
Stone

Tours of factory and museum Mon–Thu 10–2 & Fri 10–1.30 by appointment only (ex factory holidays). Shop Mon–Thu 8.30–5, Fri 8.30–4, Sat 9–1.

75p.

P (limited) .Ⴑ shop ✗

Trentham Gardens
(2m SW edge of town, on A34)
☎ (0782) 657341

Gardens and lake landscaped by Capability Brown and its elegant architecture designed by Sir Charles Barry. The 800 acre estate offers woodland walks and other leisure attractions.

Gardens open daily Etr–mid Sep 9am–dusk. Special events throughout season.

Admission fee payable.

& .Ⴑ (licensed) ᕇ

STOKESAY
Shropshire
Map 7 SO48

Stokesay Castle Craven Arms
☎ Craven Arms (05882) 2544

Fortified manor house of the 13th century. Oldest surviving examples of its kind in a romantic setting with a quaint Elizabethan gatehouse.

Open 5 Mar–Oct daily (ex Tue) 10–6 (10–5 Mar & Oct). Also Nov wknds only 10–dusk & wkdays (party bookings only). Last admission ½hr before closing.

80p (ch 15 40p).

& ᕇ (ground floor & gardens) shop ✗

STOKE-SUB-HAMDON
Somerset
Map 3 ST41

Stoke-sub-Hamdon Priory

A 15th-century Ham-Hill stone house, once a chantry and retaining original screens and part of great hall.

Open daily 10–6.

Free.

& (NT)

STONE
Hereford & Worcester
Map 7 SO87

Stone House Cottage Gardens
☎ Kidderminster (0562) 69902

Sheltered one-acre walled garden full of rare wall shrubs, climbers and interesting herbaceous plants. Adjacent nursery with large selection of unusual plants. →

STOKESAY CASTLE, Craven Arms, Shropshire
Owned by Sir Philip and Lady Magnus-Allcroft

A Fortified Manor House of the 13th Century.
The oldest and most complete surviving example of its kind in England in a romantic setting with a quaint and delightful Elizabethan Gatehouse.

Three quarters of a mile from Craven Arms on the A49.

Open First Wednesday in March. Daily **except Tuesday** 10am — 5pm. April to September. Daily except Tuesday 10am — 6pm. October. Daily **except Tuesday** 10am — 5pm November. Weekends only 10am — dusk. Monday to Friday — party bookings only.
Note: last admissions half an hour before closing time.
Closed During December, January and February
Admission Adults 80p Children under 15 years 40p. Party bookings in advance.
No reduced rates for parties. Toilets. Free Car Park.
The Custodian, Stokesay Castle, Craven Arms, Shropshire SY7 9AH
Telephone Craven Arms 2544

Garden & nursery open Mar–Nov Wed–Sat 10–6. (Also Suns 25 May, 22 Jun, 13 Jul and Late summer BH Mon. in aid of the National Garden Scheme). Coaches by appointment only.

50p (in collection box for charity).

⚠ ♿ nursery ✘ (NGS)

STONEHAVEN
Grampian Kincardineshire
Map **15** NO88

Dunnottar Castle (1½m S off A92)
☎ (0569) 62173

On a headland facing the North Sea, dates from late 12th to 18th century. The Scottish regalia kept here for safety in the 17th century.

Open Mon–Sat 9–6, Sun 2–5 (Closed Sat Nov–Mar).

Admission fee payable.

⚠

Stonehaven Tolbooth Old Pier, The Harbour
☎ Peterhead (0779) 77778

Once a 16th-century storehouse of the Earls Marischal, later used as a prison. Now a fishing and local history museum.

Open Jun–Sep Mon, Thu, Fri & Sat 10–12 & 2–5; Wed & Sun 2–5.

Free.

P (50 yds, limited) ♿ (Ground Floor only) shop ✘ (ex guide dogs)

STONEHENGE
Wiltshire
Map **4** SU14
(off A344)

Prehistoric monument dating from two periods. The encircling ditch bank and Aubrey holes are late neolithic. The stone circles consisting sarsen stones around horseshoe of trilithons encompassing the blue stones, with an altar stone, are probably of early Bronze Age date.

Open see end of gazetteer, also open Sun all year from 9.30 am.

✱ £1 (ch & pen 50p).

⚴ (AM) ⓥ

Stone
—
Stowe

STONOR
Oxfordshire
Map **4** SU78

Stonor House and Park (4m NW of Henley-on-Thames on B480)
☎ Turville Heath (049163) 587

The home of Lord and Lady Camoys and occupied by the Stonor family for the past 800 years. originally built in c1190, the house contains examples of some of the earliest domestic architecture in Oxfordshire. The beautiful gardens behind the house have commanding views of the park. Craft Fair Late Summer BH weekend.

Open Etr Sun–28 Sep, Wed, Thu & Sun (Sat in Aug) 2–5.30, also BH Mon 11–5.30. Tue, parties only. Last admission 5pm.

✱ £1.70 (ch 14 free, ch 14–18 & pen £1.40). Party 12+.

⚠ ⚴ ♿ (ground floor only) shop ⓥ

STOURBRIDGE
West Midlands
Map **7** SO98

Hagley Hall
(2½m SSE, of A456 at Hagley)
☎ Hagley (0562) 882408

18th-century Palladian house, the family home of the Lytteltons, completed in 1760. Fine Rococo plasterwork by Francesco Vassali. Family portraits, 18th-century furniture and Lyttelton papers. The park was re-landscaped in the 18th century. Horse Trials 30 & 31 Mar, Country Fair 1 June & MG Rally 10 Aug.

House & Park open daily (ex Sat) Jul–Aug, also all BH Mon & Sun 2–5 (last admission).

£1.75 (ch & educational visits 75p, pen £1.25). Park only 75p.

⚠ ⚴ (licensed) ⚓ ♿ shop ✘ (in house) ⓥ

Thomas Webb Crystal Dennis Hall, King William St, Amblecote
☎ (0384) 392521

The museum is housed in one of the largest rooms of 18th-century Dennis Hall and contains a fascinating variety of glassware, including superb examples of the work of well known artists and craftsmen such as George and Thomas Woodall, William Fritsche, Jules Barbe, John Thomas Fereday and many others. There are also numerous interesting documents which are reminders of the long and illustrious history of Thomas Webb Crystal. During the conducted factory tour visitors will see many of the glassmaking and hand cutting techniques used for almost 150 years.

Open Mon–Fri 10–4 (last factory tour 3pm). (Closed BH).

Free.

⚠ ⚴ shop ✘

STOURHEAD
Wiltshire
Map **3** ST73

Stourhead House & Pleasure Gardens (At Stourhead, off B3092)
☎ Bourton (Dorset) (0747) 840348

An 18th-century house by Colen Campbell with paintings and Chippendale furniture. There are notable mid- 18th-century lake-watered grounds laid out by Henry Hoare, which show contemporary garden temples, forming one of Europe's most famous landscapes.

House open 29 Mar–Apr & Oct Mon–Wed, Sat & Sun 2–6; May–Sep Mon–Thu, Sat & Sun 2–6. Garden open daily all year 8am–7pm or dusk is earlier.

House £1.80, Gardens £1.50, Dec–Feb 80p (ch reduced rates). Party 15+.

⚠ ⚴ ♿ shop & information room ✘ (NT)

STOWE
Buckinghamshire
Map **4** SP63

Stowe House Landscape Garden
☎ Buckingham (0280) 813650

Fine 18th-century mansion, now a public

---

school. Splendid grounds, with statuary and garden temples.
Open 28–31 Mar; 19 Jul–7 Sep; Aug BH, 11–6. Other times by appointment.
60p (ch & pen 40p).
▲ ⬚ ⊞ ⓖ (ground floor only) shop

STOWMARKET
Suffolk
Map **5** TM05

Museum of East Anglian Life
☎ (0449) 612229
An open-air museum on an attractive river valley site. Large collections of

---

Stowe
—
Strata Florida Abbey

---

agricultural tools and machinery, horse-drawn vehicles and domestic items. Reconstructed buildings including watermill, windpump and smithy plus craft workshop interiors. Traction engine and Suffolk Punch horse on display.
Open 28 Mar–26 Oct, Mon–Sat 11–5 & Sun 12–5.
£1.50 ch £1, pen & students £1.20). Party.

▲ ⬚ (Sun & daily, school summer holidays) ⊞ ⓖ (ground floor only) shop

STRATA FLORIDA ABBEY
Dyfed
Map **3** SN76
(6m NW of Tregaron on unclass road off B4343)
Remains of church and cloister of Cistercian abbey founded in 1164.
Open see end of gazetteer.
✳ 50p (ch & pen 25p).
▲ shop (AM Cadw)

STOWE SCHOOL, nr. BUCKINGHAM

18th Century House. Former home of the Dukes of Buckingham and Chandos.
Superb landscaped gardens with largest collection of garden buildings in England.
Open:
Saturday 19th July to Sunday 7th September, also Good Friday, Saturday, Sunday and Easter Monday.
Adults 60p. Children & OAP's 40p.
Special rates for coaches.
(Tel: 0280 813650).

261

STRATFIELD SAYE
Hampshire
Map **4** SU66

Stratfield Saye House
☎ Basingstoke (0256) 882882

Home of the Dukes of Wellington. Built in 1630 the house was bought by the nation for the first Duke of Wellington in 1817, after his victory over Napoleon Bonaparte at the Battle of Waterloo. Contains a unique collection of paintings, prints, furniture and various mementoes of the first Duke including the Great Duke's magnificent funeral carriage weighing 18 tons and standing 17 feet high. Also the Wellington exhibition showing the life and times of this great soldier and statesman. In the grounds are gardens, wildfowl sanctuary and the grave of Copenhagen, the Duke's famous charger ridden at the Battle of Waterloo.

Open Etr & wknds in Apr, May–28 Sep daily (ex Fri), 11.30–5. Enquiries: The Wellington Office (SH), Stratfield Saye, Reading RG7 2Bt.

£2.50 (ch £1.25). Party.

⚠ ⌷ (licensed) & shop ✖

For details of the Wellington Country Park see under **Riseley.**

STRATFORD-UPON-AVON
Warwickshire
Map **4** SP15

Arms & Armour Museum
Poet's Arbour, Sheep St
☎ (0789) 293453

Private collection of arms, armour and accoutrements ranging from about 1400 to the beginning of the First World War. Some 800 pieces exhibited, including guns, rifles, pistols, crossbows, swords, bows and arrows and armour.

Open daily 9.30–5.30. (Closed Xmas & New Year).

£1.20 (ch 12–16, pen & students 80p; ch 12 free if accompanied). Party 15+.

P (300 yds) & (ground floor only) ⓥ

Halls Croft Old Town
☎ (0789) 292107

Stratfield Saye
—
Stratford-upon-Avon

Tudor house with walled garden, former home of Shakespeare's daughter Susanna. Exhibition 'Dr John Hall and the medicine of his time.'

Open Apr–Oct weekdays 9–6 (5pm in Oct) Sun 10–6 (5pm in Oct); Nov–Mar weekdays 9–4.30 (last admission 20 mins before closing) (Closed Good Fri am Xmas & New Year's day am).

80p (ch 30p). Combined ticket to all five Shakespearian properties £3.80 (ch £1.50) School & student party rates.

P (in street) & (ground floor & gardens only) shop ✖ (ex guide dogs)

Harvard House High St
☎ (0789) 204507

An ornate half-timbered house, dating from 1596, the former home of the mother of John Harvard who founded Harvard University in the USA.

Open Apr–Sep weekdays 9–1 & 2–6, Sun 2–6; Oct–Mar certain weekdays 10–1 & 2–4.

✱ 75p (ch 16 & students 25p).

P (100 yds) shop ✖

New Place & Nash's House
Chapel St
☎ (0789) 292325

Foundations of the house (destroyed in 1759) where Shakespeare spent the last five years of his retirement and died in 1616. Picturesque knot garden, an Elizabethan replica. Furniture and local history in adjacent Nash's House.

Open Apr–Oct weekdays 9–6 (5pm in Oct) Sun 10–6 (5pm in Oct); Nov–Mar weekdays 9–4.30 (last admission 20 mins before closing) (Closed Good Fri am, Xmas & New Year's day am).

80p (ch 17 30p). Combined ticket to all five Shakespearian properties £3.80 (ch £1.50). School & student party rates.

P (in street) & (ground floor & gardens only) shop ✖ (ex guide dogs)

Royal Shakespeare Company Gallery
Royal Shakespeare Theatre, Waterside
☎ (0789) 296655 ext 215

Permanent and temporary exhibition of costumes, photographs, paintings and other theatrical material.

Open Mon–Sat 9–7, Sun 12–5.

✱ 50p (ch, students & pen 25p). Backstage & gallery tour £1.50 (ch, students & pen £1) available at set times.

⚠ ⌕ shop ✖

Shakespeare's Birthplace Henley St
☎ (0789) 204016

A half-timbered house, the birthplace of the poet in 1564. Contains numerous exhibits. Shakespeare's birthday celebration 26 April (property closed am).

Open Apr–Oct wkdays 9–6 (5pm in Oct) Sun 10–6 (5pm in Oct); Nov–Mar wkdays 9–4.30, Sun 1.30–4.30) (last admission 20mins before closing) (Closed Good Fri am, Xmas & New Years day am).

£1.30 (ch 60p). Visiting BBC costume exhibition £1.50 (ch 60p). Combined ticket to all five Shakespearian properties £3.80 (ch £1.50) School & student party rates.

P (Windsor St, 100 yds) & (ground floor & gardens only) shop ✖ (ex guide dogs)

Stratford upon Avon Motor Museum
1 Shakespeare St
☎ (0789) 69413

Housed in a former church and school, vintage cars and motorcycles are displayed in a setting of the Roaring Twenties, the Golden Age of Motoring. Exotic sports- and grand touring cars.

Open Apr–Oct daily 9.30–6; Nov–Mar 10–4. (Closed Xmas day).

✱ £1.25 (ch 13–19 & pen 75p) Family ticket £3.

P & shop

World of Shakespeare 13 Waterside
☎ (0789) 69190

The atmosphere of Elizabethan England is recreated here with 25 life-size tableaux combining dramatic light and sound techniques and original music. Stratford-upon-Avon Festival July.

Open daily Oct–Apr 9.30–5, May–Sep 9.30–7pm. (Closed Xmas)

✱ £1.75 (ch pen & students £1.25 ch 6 free). Family (2 adults & 4 ch) £6. Party 10+.

P (5 mins walk) ♿ shop 🐕 Ⓥ

STRATHPEFFER
Highland *Ross & Cromarty*
Map **14** NH45

Strathpeffer Station Visitor Centre
☎ (0997) 21618

The Centre comprises various craft workshops where visitors can watch goods being produced. There is also an excellent 30 minute audio-visual programme which tells the visitor about Strathpeffer and the wildlife of the Highlands. Strathpeffer Victorian Days mid June. Strathpeffer Highland Games early August.

Open Etr–Sep 10am–5pm & 8pm 10pm. Audio visual programme screened every evening (ex Sat) 8.30pm & 9.15pm. Tourist Information Office open May–Sep.

Audio visual programme 95p (ch 40p).

△ ♿ (ground floor only) shop

STREET
Somerset
Map **3** ST43

The Shoe Museum (C & J Clark Ltd), High St
☎ (0458) 43131

The museum is housed in the oldest part of the factory and contains shoes from Roman times to the present, Georgian shoe buckles, caricatures and engravings of shoemakers, costume illustrations and fashion plates, shoe machinery, hand tools, advertising material and 19th century documents and photographs illustrating the early history of the firm from the founding in 1825 by Cyrus Clark.

Open Etr Mon–Oct, Mon–Sat 10–4.45. Winter months by appointment only.

Free.

P (200 yds) ♿ (main floor only) shop 🐕

STROMNESS
Orkney
Map **16** HY20

Stromness Museum Alfred St
☎ (0856) 850025

Founded by the Orkney Natural History Society in 1837. Includes birds, shells, fossils, butterflies, whaling, fishing and items on Hudson's Bay and the German fleet in Scapa Flow.

Open Mon–Wed, Fri & Sat 11–12.30 & 1.30–5, Thu 11–12.30, in Jul & Aug open from 10.30 am. (Closed Sun, local PH & 3 wks Feb–Mar).

✱ 20p (ch 5p).

△ ♿ (ground floor only) shop 🐕

Pier Arts Centre
☎ (0856) 850209

Collection housed in warehouse building on its own stone pier. Also galleries for visiting exhibitions and children's work. Arts library and reading room in adjacent house.

Open Tue–Sat 10.30–12.30 & 1.30–5, Sun & Mon 2–5 (Jul & Aug only).

Free.

P (50 yds) ♿ (ground floor only) 🐕

STROOD
Kent
Map **5** TQ76

Temple Manor Knight Rd (½m SW Rochester Bridge)
☎ Medway (0634) 718743

Once part of a large medieval farm the Manor was built in 1240 by the Knights Templar, an order of celibate soldiers, founded to protect the Holy Land. This surviving building was probably used to house distinguished visitors.

Open see end of gazetteer. Apr–Sep only.

✱ 30p (ch 16 & pen 15p).

△ ♿ (grounds only) shop 🐕 (AM)

STROUD
Gloucestershire
Map **3** SO80

Stroud District (Cowle) Museum
Lansdown
☎ (04536) 3394

The exhibits cover geology, archaeology, local crafts, industrial archaeology (including local mills and houses), and farmhouse household equipment. A full-length model of the dinosaur Megalosaurus is on display.

Open Mon–Sat 10.30–1 & 2–5. (Closed BHs & other days, possibly Tue/Wed following BHs).

Free.

P (in street) ♿ shop 🐕

STRUMPSHAW
Norfolk
Map **5** TG30

Strumpshaw Hall Steam Museum
Old Hall (¾m S)
☎ Norwich (0603) 714535

Collection of steam vehicles including beam engine (running), showman's road engine, portable and stationary steam engines, steam wagon and fairground organ. Train runs Wed and Sun. Steam Engine rally 16 June & Strumpshaw Park Rally & Fun weekend Late Summer BH.

Open 21 May–1 Oct, daily (ex Sat) 2–5. Train runs Wed & Sun 3pm.

£1 (ch over 5 50p).

△ ☕ ⛱ ♿ shop

STUDLEY
Oxfordshire
Map **4** SP51

Studley Priory Hotel (off B4027)

Original priory founded in 12th century and sold after Dissolution to John Croke, whose descendants owned it for over 300 years. West range was altered to form Elizabethan manor Used to portray home of Sir Thomas More in film A Man for all Seasons. *Studley Prior is now a hotel, open all year, but visitors most welcome.*

STYAL
Cheshire
Map **7** SJ88

Quarry Bank Mill & Styal Country Park
(2m NW of Wilmslow near M56 Exit 6, off
B5166)
☎ Wilmslow (0625) 527468

*An 18th-century cotton mill housing a
working museum with three floors of
textile machinery and demonstrations of
hand spinning and weaving. Restored
Victorian iron waterwheel. Country Park
and Village, Apprentice House and
woodlands. Museum of Year Award 1984.*

Open all year Tue–Sun & BH Mons (ex
Jun–Sep daily): Jan–Mar & Oct–Dec 11–4;
Apr–Sep 11–5. (Closed Xmas).

£2, from 1 June £2.20 (ch £1.30, from 1
June £1.50). Family ticket.

⚠ ᴒ (licensed) 🎋 shop ✹ (NT) ⓥ

SUDBURY
Derbyshire
Map **7** SK13

Sudbury Hall
☎ (028378) 305

*A fine brick 17th-century house with
plasterwork ceilings, murals by Laguerre
and some Grinling Gibbons' carving.
Museum of childhood.*

Open Apr–Oct, Wed–Sun & BH Mons, 1–
5.30 or sunset (last admission 5pm).
(Closed Good Fri & Tue after BH Mons).

£2. (Thu & Fri £1.50). Party. Small charge
for Museum.

⚠ ᴒ (12.30–5.30) ♿ (museum & grounds
only) shop ✹ (ex in grounds) (NT)

SUDBURY
Suffolk
Map **5** TL84

Gainsborough's House
Gainsborough St
☎ (0787) 72958

*The birthplace of Thomas Gainsborough
(1727–88), the portrait and landscape
painter. Contains a display of 18th-
century furniture and china together with
a loan collection of paintings by
Gainsborough and his contemporaries.*

Styal
—
Sunderland

*Print workshop in former coach house in
garden. Exhibition programme.*

House open Tue–Sat 10–5, Sun & BH
Mons 2–5; (4pm Oct–27 Mar) (Closed
Good Fri & Xmas–New Year).

50p (ch, students & pen 25p). Party.

P (10 yds) ♿ (ground floor only) shop

SUFFOLK WILDLIFE PARK
Suffolk
Map **5** TM58
(2½m S of Lowestoft)
☎ Lowestoft (0502) 740291

*A wide selection of animals and birds and
a miniature steam and diesel passenger
railway.*

Open daily.

✱ £1.60 (ch 80p, pen 95p) Party.

⚠ ᴒ 🎋 ♿ shop dog park

SULGRAVE
Northamptonshire
Map **4** SP54

Sulgrave Manor
☎ (029576) 205

*Lawrence Washington, wool merchant
and twice Mayor of Northampton, bought
Sulgrave Manor in 1539 and it was here
that George Washington's direct
ancestors lived until 1656 when his great
grandfather, John, emigrated to Virginia.
The house which exists today differs
somewhat from the one which Lawrence
Washington built—his was larger—but
parts which remain of the original include
the porch and screens passage, the
Great Hall and the Great Chamber. Relics
of George Washington which can be seen
at Sulgrave include signed documents,
portraits, his saddle-bags and velvet
coat—even a lock of his hair. Guided tour
for all visitors.*

Open all year (ex Jan), daily (ex Wed)
10.30–1 & 2–5.30 (closes 4pm Oct–Dec,
Feb & Mar).

£1 (school children 50p).

⚠ shop ✹ (in manor)

SUMBURGH
Shetland
Map **16** HU30

Jarlshof Prehistoric Site

*Remarkable Bronze Age, Iron Age, Viking
and medieval settlements. The 17th-
century Laird's House is the 'Jarlshof' of
Scott's novel* The Pirate.

Open, see end of gazetteer. (Closed Tue
& Wed afternoons).

✱ 50p (ch 25p).

(AM)

SUNDERLAND
Tyne and Wear
Map **12** NZ35

Grindon Close Museum Grindon Ln
☎ (0783) 284042

*Edwardian period rooms, including
chemist's shop and dentist's surgery.*

Open Mon–Wed & Fri 9.30–12.30 & 1.30–6
(5pm Tue), Sat 9.30–12.15 & 1.15–4; Jun–
Sep also Sun 2–5. (Closed 1 Jan, 5–8 Apr,
4 & 6 May, 24 & 26 Aug, 25 & 26 Dec).

Free.

⚠ shop ✹

Museum & Art Gallery Borough Rd
☎ (0783) 41235

*On display are examples of local pottery
and glass. Local archaeology, history,
regional natural history and geology. 15th-
to 19th-century silver, models of
Sunderland-built ships.*

Open Mon–Fri 10–5.30, Sat 10–4, Sun 2–
5, BH Mon 10–5. (Closed New Years day,
Good Fri, May Day BH & Xmas).

Free.

P (50 yds) ᴒ (10–4.45 Mon–Fri, 10–12
Sat) ♿ shop ✹

Monkwearmouth Station Museum
North Bridge St
☎ (0783) 77075

*Land transport museum in classical
station of 1848. The booking office,
platform areas and footbridge have all*

been restored and there is an outdoor area with rolling stock. Displays inside the museum deal with transport in north-east England with a display showing the evolution of British steam locomotives.

Open Mon–Fri & BHs 10–5.30, Sat 10–4.30, Sun 2–5. (Closed Good Fri, 25 & 26 Dec & 1 Jan).

Free.

 ⚠ ㅎ shop ✹

See advertisement under Newcastle-upon-Tyne

SUTTON-AT-HONE
Kent
Map **5** TQ57

St John's Jerusalem Garden

Garden surrounding fine 13th-, 16th-and 18th-century house (not open). Only the walls and former chapel of the original buildings remain. The River Darent borders the garden.

Garden and former chapel shown Apr–Oct, Wed 2–6 (last admission 5.30pm).

40p. (NT)

SUTTON CHENEY
Leicestershire
Map **4** SP39

Bosworth Battlefield Ambion Hill Farm (2½m S of Market Bosworth)
☎ Leicester (0533) 871313 ext 645

Historic site of battle in 1485, between Richard III and future Henry VII. Comprehensive interpretation of Battle with extensive Visitor Centre including exhibitions, models, film theatre and newly illustrated Battle Trails which guides visitors around the area where the battle actually took place. Special Sunday events are held Jul–Sep, details on application.

Trail open all year during daylight hours. Visitor Centre open 26 Mar –26 Oct, Mon–Sat 2–5.30, Sun & BH Mon & Tue 1–6. Other times by appointment.

Visitor Centre £1 (ch & pen 60p). Party.

⚠ (charged) ⛪ ♨ ㅎ shop ✹ (in centre)

Sunderland
—
Swansea

SUTTON-CUM-LOUND
Nottinghamshire
Map **8** SK68

Wetlands Waterfowl Reserve & Exotic Bird Park Off Loundlow Rd
☎ Retford (0777) 818099

Collection of waterfowl including ducks, geese, swans and flamingos on two lagoons covering some 32 acres. Home to many species of wild birds, plants and trees.

Open daily 10–6 or dusk if earlier . (Closed Xmas day).

£1.20 (ch pen & disabled 60p). Party 20 + .

⚠ ⛪ ♨ ㅎ (ground floor only) shop ✹

SUTTON-ON-THE-FOREST
North Yorkshire
Map **8** SE56

Sutton Park (on B1363)
☎ Easingwold (0347) 810249

Early Georgian house containing fine antique furniture, paintings and porcelain room. Grounds with Georgian Ice House, lily canal and superb gardens, woodland walks and nature trail.

Open 28–31 Mar, 6, 13, 20 & 27 Apr; then 4 May–5 Oct Tue, Sun & BHs, 1.30–5.30 (last admission 5).

House & gardens £1.60 (ch 60p, pen £1.25). Gardens only 75p (ch 30p, pen 65p) Party 20 + .

⚠ ⛪ ㅎ (gardens only) shop ✹

SWAINSHILL
Hereford and Worcester
Map **3** SO44

The Weir

Cliff garden walks, with fine views of the River Wye and the Welsh hills.

Spring gardens only open 30 Mar–10 May, Sun–Fri; 11 May–Oct, Wed & BH Mon 2–6.

✳ 50p. (NT)

SWALLOWFIELD
Berkshire
Map **4** SU76

Swallowfield Park
☎ 01-836 1624 (Country Houses Association)

18th-century remodelling of house built in 1689. Special features include Baroque door case or gateway and oval stucco decorated vestibule containing the arms of the Clarendon family c1700. Walled garden of about 4 acres containing a variety of flowering shrubs, roses and many interesting trees.

Open May–Sep Wed & Thu 2–5. Last admission 4.30. Coaches by arrangement.

50p (ch 25p).

⚠ ㅎ (ground floor & gardens only) ✹

SWANAGE
Dorset
Map **4** SZ07

Swanage Railway Station House
☎ (0329) 425800

As part of the reconstruction of the railway serving the Isle of Purbeck steam rides of approximately one mile are available. Exhibition/museum coach on display with model railway.

Open Jul–early Sep daily; Etr–Jun, Sep & Oct Sun 11–5.30. Santa Specials Dec.

80p (ch 5 free, ch 5–14 50p) return. Party.

⚠ ⛪ ㅎ shop

SWANSEA
West Glamorgan
Map **3** SS69

Glynn Vivian Art Gallery & Museum
Alexandra Rd
☎ (0792) 55006

Contains work of British and French masters and contemporary British artists. Also collections of Continental and Swansea porcelain and pottery. Major contemporary exhibitions. Education service and craft outlet. →

Open wkdays 10.30–5.30. (Closed 25, 26 Dec & 1 Jan).

Free.

P shop ✗

Maritime & Industrial Museum, Swansea Museums Service
South Dock
☎ (0792) 50351

Contains complete working woollen mill in continuous production. Displays relating to the industry and the Port of Swansea and its environment. Transport exhibits, steam locomotives which run on some Saturdays throughout the season.

Open daily 10.30–5.30 (Closed 25, 26 Dec & 1 Jan).

Free.

P ঙ shop ✗

University College of Swansea & Royal Institution of South Wales Museum
Victoria Rd
☎ (0792) 53763

Founded in 1835 the museum contains archaeological finds of local interest. Swansea and Nantgarw china and pottery, natural and local history displays, including a reproduction of a 19th-century Welsh kitchen; the history and future of the Lower Swansea Valley.

Open Tue–Sat 10–4.30. (Closed Good Fri, Xmas holiday period & New Years day).

✻ 30p (ch, pen & students 15p, ch 10p if accompanied by adult, ch 5 free).

⚠ shop ✗ (ex guide dogs)

SWARTHMOOR
Cumbria
Map 7 SD27

Swarthmoor Hall
☎ Ulverston (0229) 53204

Elizabethan and later; the former home of George Fox, founder of the Quakers. The house is now administered by the Society of Friends.

Open mid Mar–mid Oct Mon–Wed & Sat 10–12 & 2–5; Thu & Sun by arrangement only; mid Oct–mid Mar by appointment only.

Free.

⚠ ঙ (ground floor only) ✗

SWINDON
Wiltshire
Map 4 SU18

Great Western Railway Museum
Faringdon Rd
☎ (0793) 26161 ext 3131

Interesting collection of locomotives and other exhibits relating to the Great Western Railway. Locomotives include the historic 'Dean Goods' and 'Lode Star', and a replica of the broad gauge locomotive 'North Star'. Temporary exhibitions change monthly.

Open weekdays 10–5, Sun 2–5. (Closed Good Fri, 25 & 26 Dec).

Swansea
—
Tamworth

✻ 70p (ch, pen & unemployed 35p). Party (Charge includes admission to the Railway Village Museum).

P (100 yds) ঙ (ground floor only) shop ✗

Richard Jefferies Museum
Coate Farm (off A345)
☎ (0793) 26161 ext 3130

Birthplace in 1848 of Richard Jefferies, the nature writer, and now a museum exhibiting literature relating to local wildlife written by Jefferies and Alfred Owen Williams.

Open all year, Wed, Sat & Sun 2–5. (Closed Xmas).

Free.

P (Day House Ln, 20 yds) shop ✗

Railway Village House 34 Faringdon Rd (adjacent to GWR museum)

Re-furbished as it was at turn of the century.

Open Mon–Fri 10–1 & 2–5; Sun 2–5 only. (Closed Good Fri & Xmas).

✻ 30p (ch pen & unemployed 15p). Party. Free with entry to GWR Museum.

P (in street) shop ✗

Museum & Art Gallery Bath Rd
☎ (0793) 26161 ext 3129

Contains a small collection of items of local interest and an art gallery. Visiting exhibitions alternate with pictures by 20th-century artists.

Open Mon–Sat 10–6, Sun 2–5. (Closed Good Fri, 25 & 26 Dec).

Free.

P (50 yds) shop ✗

SWINFORD
Leicestershire
Map 4 SP57

Stanford Hall (1m E)
☎ Rugby (0788) 860250

William and Mary house, on River Avon, built in the 1690s with antique furniture and paintings, and replica of Percy Pilcher's flying machine of 1898. Old forge and walled rose garden; motor cycle museum; Sun crafts centre; nature trail and fishing. A number of car and motorcycle rallies held throughout the season.

Open Etr–Sep, Thu, Sat & Sun 2.30–6; also BH Mon & Tue; house 2.30–6; grounds, museum, craft centre, shop & cafeteria open 12–6. Conducted tours.

House and grounds £1.70 (ch 80p). Thu £1.40 (ch 65p) Grounds only 90p (ch 40p) Thu 60p (ch 25p). Museum 75p (ch 35p) party 20+.

⚠ ⬚ shop

SYMONDS YAT (WEST) (near Ross-on-Wye)
Hereford & Worcester
Map 3 SO51

Jubilee Maze & Museum of Mazes
☎ (0600) 890655

Superbly presented maze and gardens where you have the opportunity to meet the men who built the maze, Edward and Lindsey Heyes. The garden was designed by Julian Dowle. Also here is the world's first museum of mazes depicting the history of the maze.

Open Etr wknd in Oct, daily ex Fri, 11–6 (last admission 5.30). Illumination of Maze & garden Etr Sat & Sun & twice wkly Jul & Aug, 7.30pm.

Admission fee payable.

⚠ ⚓ ✗ ⓥ

TALLEY
Dyfed
Map 2 SN63

Talley Abbey

The abbey was founded towards the end of the 12th century probably by Rhys ap Gruffydd for Premonstratensian canons.

Open see end of gazetteer.

✻ 30p (ch 16 & pen 15p).

⚠ (AM Cadw)

TAL-Y-CAFN
Gwynedd
Map 6 SH77

Bodnant Garden (8m S of Llandudno and Colwyn Bay on A470. Entrance ½m along Eglwysbach road).
☎ Tyngroes (049267) 460

Magnificent collection of rhododendrons, camellias, magnolias, shrubs and trees. Situated above the River Conwy it extends for 80 acres and enjoys magnificent views of the Snowdonia range.

Open 15 Mar–Oct, daily 10–5.

£1.60 (ch 80p). Party 20+.

P ⬚ ঙ ✗ (ex guide dogs) (NT)

TAMWORTH
Staffordshire
Map 4 SK20

Tamworth Castle & Museum
The Holloway
☎ (0827) 64222 ext 389 (or 63563 at weekends)

Norman 'Motte and Bailey' Castle. The 12th-century Shell Keep houses a local history museum. Excavated 13th-century Medieval Gatehouse. 15th-century Great Hall with late medieval timbered roof. Jacobean state apartments with fine woodwork, furniture and heraldic friezes. Haunted room and staircase. Castle Pleasure grounds and swimming pool. Spring Fair held during May.

Open Mon–Thu & Sat 10–5.30, Sun 2–5.30 (last tickets 5pm). Details not confirmed for 1986.

266

✱ 65p (ch 20p, unaccompanied ch & pen 40p).
P (Lady Bridge Car Ok) sales point ✖

TANGMERE
West Sussex
Map **4** SU90

Tangmere Military Aviation Museum
Tangmere Airfield
☎ Chichester (0243) 775223

A wide-ranging collection of photographs, paintings, documents, models, maps, uniforms, aircraft parts and relics related to Tangmere and the air war in this corner of England.

Open Mar–early Nov, 11–5.30.

80p (ch 30p)

🅰 ♿ shop

TARBOLTON
Strathclyde *Ayrshire*
Map **10** NS42

Batchelors' Club
☎ (0292) 541424

A 17th-century house, taking its name from the society which Robert Burns and his friends founded there in 1780. Period furnishings. Contains a small museum.

Open Etr–Oct, daily 10–6, other times by appointment.

✱ 60p (ch 30p).

(NTS)

TARFSIDE
Tayside *Angus*
Map **15** NO57

The Retreat (1m E)
☎ (03567) 236 & 254

Former shooting lodge, with museum of local country life and handicrafts.

Open Etr–May, Sun only 2–6, Jun–Sep, daily 2–6. Other times for Parties on application to Curator.

50p (ch 12 20p). Subject to review.

🅰 ♿ ♿ (ground floor only) shop ✖

TARLETON
Lancashire
Map **7** SD42

Leisure Lakes
☎ Hesketh Bank (077473) 3446

Boating lake set in 90 acres of picturesque woodland and heath setting with sailboard facilities, picnic areas and pleasant walks. The sandy beaches are ideal for children. UK Hovercraft Racing Championship during May and a model seaplane event during June.

Open all year 8am–8pm. Caravans welcome.

✱ 50p (ch 35p). Sun & BHs £2 per car including passengers. Tents & caravans £2, dinghys & canoes £1.50, fishing £1.60, sailboarding.

🅰 ♿ (licensed) shop

TATTERSHALL
Lincolnshire
Map **8** TF25

Tattershall Castle
☎ Coningsby (0526) 42543

The mid-15th-century, 100ft high brick keep of a fortified house. The Marquess of Curzon recovered the stone Gothic fireplace in 1911.

Open Mon–Sat, Apr–Sep 11–6.30, Nov–Mar 12–6 (or sunset). Sun 1–6.30 (or sunset). (Closed Xmas).

£1.30 (ch 60p).

🅰 shop (NT)

TAUNTON
Somerset
Map **3** ST22

Hestercombe Gardens
(3m N of Taunton off A361 near Cheddon Fitzpaine)
☎ (0823) 87222

Late 19th-century house, now the headquarters of the Somerset Fire Brigade. The gardens, originally planned in 1905 by Sir Edwin Lutyens and

---

Gertrude Jekyll, are at present being restored to their original condition.

Open every Tue–Thu 2–5, also 25 May, 29 Jun & 27 Jul.

Donations.

🅰 ♿ (only served on Suns end June & Jul)

Poundisford Park Poundisford (3½m S, signposted off B3170 north of Corfe)
☎ Blagdon Hill (082342) 244

Fine lived in Tudor house on an intimate scale in beautiful surroundings. Elizabethan plaster ceilings, good furniture, china and glass, family picture, costumes and needlework. Period garden, with unusual plants and 17th-century gazebo.

Open May–18 Sep Wed & Thu (also Fri Jul & Aug); May, Spring & Aug BH: 11–5. Parties by appointment throughout the year.

✱ £1.50 (ch 10–16 & disabled 60p, accompanied ch 10 free). Garden only 25p. Prebooked Party 15+.

🅰 ♿ (licensed, meals for parties by arrangement ☎ 566) ♿ (ground floor & gardens only) shop ✖

Sheppy's Three Bridges (3½m SW, A38)
☎ Bradford-on-Tone (082346) 233

A traditional Farm Cider Makers which has been commercially producing cider since 1925. Today the farm has 20 acres of standard and 22 acres of bush orchards; there is also a farm and cider museum.

Open Mon–Sat, 8.30–dusk, Sun (Etr–Xmas only) 12–2.

Free (ex bookable guided tours for Party 20+ £1.50).

🅰 ♿ (ground floor only) shop

Taunton Castle
☎ (0823) 55504

*Containing **Somerset County Museum & Somerset Military Museum**. Partly 13th-century structure, associated with Judge Jeffreys' 'Bloody Assize' of 1685. County Museum houses exhibits of local archaeology, natural history, geology, glass ceramics, bygones, costumes and dolls. Military Museum contains relics of →*

267

the Somerset Light Infantry from 1685–1959.

Open Mon–Fri (also Sat in summer) 10–5. Closed BHs.

40p (ch & pen 15p). Charges under review.

⚠ & (ground floor only) ✖

TAYNUILT
Strathclyde Argyll
Map **10** NN03

Bonawe Iron Furnace (¾m NE off B845)
An 18th-century Highland blast-furnace making cast-iron. The most complete in Britain, the works exploited the plentiful Forest of Lorne to provide charcoal for fuel.

Open Apr–Sep, Weekdays 9.30–7 & Sun 2–7. (Closed in winter).

50p (ch & pen 25p).

⚠ (AM)

TEMPLE SOWERBY
Cumbria
Map **12** NY62

Acorn Bank Garden
Walled and herb gardens, with spring bulbs and herbaceous plants.

Open Mar–Oct, daily incl Good Fri 10–5.30.

60p (ch 30p).

✖ (NT)

TENBY
Dyfed
Map **2** SN10

Tenby Museum
☎ (0834) 2809

Notable collection of geological specimens, seashells and cave deposits. Picture gallery, topography and other works of art. Two new galleries to house special or visiting exhibitions.

Open Etr–Oct, daily 10–6, Jul–15 Sep also evenings 7–9pm. Nov–Apr probably Mon–Sat, am only, not confirmed.

✳ 40p (ch 10p). School Parties by appointment Free.

P (Castle Sq 100 yds, Harbour Car Pk 120 yds) shop ✖ 🚻

Tudor Merchant's House Quay Hill
Good example of gabled 15th-century Architecture, ground floor of which is now National Trust Information Centre.

Open Etr Sun–Sep, Mon–Fri 10–1 & 2.30–6. Sun 2–6.

£1 (ch 50p).

P ✖ (NT)

TENTERDEN
Kent
Map **5** TQ83

Tenterden & District Museum
Station Rd
☎ (05806) 3605

Taunton
—
Thoresby

A local history museum, displaying the building and history of Tenterden, of the Cinque Ports, and the surrounding Weald of Kent. Also corporation records and insignia, local trades and industries, agricultural implements and hop gardens. The 'Tenterden Tapestry' and the Col. Stephens' collection of Light Railway material also exhibited.

Open Etr–Oct, daily 2–5. (10–5 Fri & Sat from Jun–Sep). Nov–Mar, Sat & Sun only 2–4. Guided tours by arrangement and at other times if required.

Admission fee payable.

P & (ground floor only) shop (dogs at attendant's discretion)

TETBURY
Gloucestershire
Map **3** ST89

Chavenage (2m NW)
☎ (0666) 52329

Unspoilt Elizabethan house (1576) with Cromwellian connections, containing some 17th-century, and earlier, stained glass, furniture and tapestries.

Open May–Sep, Thu, Sun & BH (incl Etr Mon) 2–5. Other times by appointment.

£1.50 (ch 75p). 'Friends of Historic Houses' free.

⚠ & (ground floor only) coaches by appointment

THAXTED
Essex
Map **5** TL63

Thaxted Windmill
☎ (0371) 830366

A fine tower mill built in 1804. It has five floors and most of the original machinery is intact. The sails and fantail have been re-erected. A rural museum has been established on the first two floors.

Open May–Sep Sat, Sun & BHs 2–6. Special opening times for parties can be arranged.

30p (ch 10p).

P (5 mins walk) shop ✖

THETFORD
Norfolk
Map **5** TL88

Ancient House Museum White Hart St
☎ (0842) 2599

An early Tudor timbered house with collections illustrating Thetford and Breckland life, history and natural history. Series of occasional, temporary exhibitions.

Open Mon–Sat 10–5 (Closed 1–2 Mon); Spring BH–Sep only Sun 2–5. (Closed Good Fri, Xmas & New Years day).

20p (ch 5p, students 10p) Spring BH–Sep. Other times 10p (ch & students 5p).

P (100 yds) shop ✖

Thetford Castle
One of the original motte and bailey castles, at 80ft, perhaps the largest still in existence. This represents the earliest form of castle, before masonry was added.

Accessible at any time.

Free.

Thetford Priory
Extensive remains of Cluniac monastery founded at beginning of 12th century. The 14th-century gatehouse of priory stands to its full height.

Open any reasonable time.

Free.

⚠ & (AM)

Warren Lodge
(2m NW of town, on B1107)
Remains of a two-storey hunting lodge in 15th-century flint with stone dressings.

Open any reasonable time.

Free & (AM)

THIRSK
North Yorkshire
Map **8** SE48

Osgodby Hall (5m E off A170)
☎ (0845) 597534

A small elegantly proportioned Jacobean manor house, nestling under Hood Hill. The walled forecourt is unchanged since construction in 1640, with its gate pillars, terrace and porch. The spacious interior contains a fine, broad staircase of the early 17th-century and also interesting oak panelling.

Open Etr–24 Sep, Wed & BH Mons, 2–5.30.

£1 (ch 50p).

⚠ & (ground floor only) shop ⓥ

THORESBY
Nottinghamshire
Map **8** SK67

Thoresby Hall
☎ Mansfield (0623) 822301

A great Dukeries mansion, in the heart of Sherwood Forest, dating from 1864–75, the only Dukeries mansion open to the public still occupied by descendants of the original owners. Fine state apartments and terraces. Deer Park. Special events include Antiques and Craft Fairs.

Open Etr Sun & Mon, then May–Aug, BH & Sun 1–5. Coach & school parties by appointment only on Wed & Thu, May–Aug.

House & garden £1.70 (ch 80p). Garden only 50p (ch 20p).

⚠ ⏛ shop

THORNBURY
Devon
Map **2** SS30

Devon Museum of Mechanical Music
Mill Leat (on unclassified road 5m NE of Holsworthy)
☎ Milton Damerel (040926) 378 or Shebbear (040928) 483

A fascinating collection of old mechanical musical instruments, from a tiny music box to a Dutch Street organ. Continuous demonstration.

Open Etr–Oct, daily 10.30–12.30 & 2–5.
£1.20 (ch 16 80p, pen £1). Party 25 +.
&

THORNHILL
Dumfries and Galloway *Dumfriesshire*
Map **11** NX89

Drumlanrig Castle (4m NW off A76 on west bank of River Nith)
☎ (0848) 30248

17th-century castle in pink stone. It contains a celebrated collection of paintings, silver and Bonnie Prince Charlie relics. Woodland walks, picnic areas and adventure playground.

Open May–25 Aug daily ex Fri, 1.30–5 May–Jun (11–5 in Jul & Aug) ex Sun, 2–6.
Last entry 45 minutes before closing.
Castle & grounds £2 (ch £1, pen £1.50).
Grounds only £1.
& ⚓ ⛩ & shop ✻ (in castle) ⓥ

THORNTON
Humberside
Map **8** TA11

Thornton Abbey

Displays a magnificent example of a 14th-century gateway approached across a dry moat spanned by a long bridge with arcaded walls and circular towers.

Open see † end of gazetteer.
✱ 50p (ch 16 & pen 25p).
& (AM)

THURNHAM
Lancashire
Map **7** SD45

Thornbury
—
Tintagel

Thurnham Hall
(5m S of Lancaster on A588).
☎ Lancaster (0524) 751766

Dating from the 13th-century, with part 16th-century additions. The Great Hall contains fine Elizabethan plaster work, Jacobean panelling and fine Jacobean staircase. There is also a priest's room, a priest hide and a 19th-century private chapel. In the Chapel there is the Turin Shroud exhibition.

Open Etr–Oct, Mon–Thu & Sun 2–5.30.
Admission fee payable.
& (limited), P (30 yds) ⚓ & (ground floor only) shop ✻

THURSFORD GREEN
Norfolk
Map **9** TF93

Thursford Collection
(6m NE Fakenham)
☎ Thursford (032877) 238

The collection includes showmen's engines, traction engines, ploughing engines and 2ft-gauge steam railway. Wurlitzer cinema organ, fairground organs, street and barrel organs, also farm machinery. Live musical shows given each day. Midsummer musical evenings Tue at 8pm through summer on Wurlitzer cinema organ by the country's leading organists. Savage's Venetian Gondola switchback ride and children's playground.

Open Etr–Oct, daily 2–5.30, Nov, Mar–Etr Sun only 2–5.
✱ £2 (ch 4–15 90p, pen £1.75). Party.
& ⚓ ⛩ & shop ✻ ⓥ

See advertisement on page 270

TILBURY
Essex
Map **5** TQ67

Thurrock Riverside Museum Civic Sq
☎ (03752) 79216

Illustrates the history of the River Thames and the people of its riverside. Ship and barge models, photographs, etc.

Open Tue–Fri 10–1 & 2–5.30, Sat 10–1 & 2–5. Advisable to telephone beforehand.
(Closed Mon, Sun & BHs).
Free.
P (street) & ✻

Tilbury Fort

Dates from the reign of Henry VIII and was the scene of the review by Queen Elizabeth I of the army raised to resist the Spanish Armada. Later altered and restored.

Open see end of gazetteer.
✱ 60p (ch 16 & pen 30p).
& & (exterior, fort square & magazines) (AM)

TILFORD
Surrey
Map **4** SU84

Old Kiln Agricultural Museum
Reeds Rd
☎ Frensham (025125) 2300

Collection of farm implements and machinery of the past, and examples of the crafts and trades allied to farming. Larger exhibits are displayed in the pleasant garden and woodland surroundings, covering some ten acres. Smithy, wheelwright's shop, hand tools etc, are housed in the old farm buildings. 'Rustic Sunday' 27 July (11–6).

Open Apr–Sep, Wed–Sun & BH 11–6.
£1 (ch 14 50p).
& ⛩ & shop ⓥ

TINTAGEL
Cornwall
Map **2** SX08

Tintagel Castle

Remains of a mid 13th-century castle, later abandoned and divided by subsequent erosion into two portions. There are also some remains of a Celtic →

DRUMLANRIG CASTLE

Magnificent 1680s Castle in pink sandstone whose fine rooms are filled with historic treasures – Exciting Adventure Woodland Play Area, Nature Trail & Picnic Areas. Tea Room & Gift Shop. Working Craft Centre. Pre-booked parties over 20 –special rates. Wheelchair access.

Dumfriesshire home of the Duke of Buccleuch & Queensberry K.T.
Dumfriesshire, 3m North of Thornhill off A76, 16m SW of A74 at Elvanfoot.

1986 SEASON
1st May to **25th August.**
Open daily (except Fridays).
May and **June** 1.30 to 5pm.
July and **August** 11am to 5pm.
Sundays throughout 2 to 6pm.
Last open day 25th August.
Last entry ¾ hour before closing time.
Telephone (0848) 30248.

monastery dating from the 5th century to the 9th century.

Open † see end of gazetteer.

✱ 80p (ch 16 & pen 40p).

P (Tintagel Village) (AM)

Old Post Office
A former 14th-century manor house, with a hall and an ancient slate roof.

Open Apr–Oct, daily 11–6 or sunset.

80p.

P (NT)

TINTERN
Gwent
Map 3 SO50

Tintern Abbey
Extensive remains of a fine 13th-century church founded for monks of the Cistercian Order in 1131.

Open † see end of gazetteer.

✱ 90p (ch 16 & pen 45p)

⚠ (AM Cadw)

TINTINHULL
Somerset
Map 3 ST51

Tintinhull House
Modern formal garden surrounding an attractive 17th-century house, with fine pedimental façade.

Tintagel
—
Titchfield

Open 29 Mar–Sep, Wed, Thu, Sat & BH Mons 2–6 (last admission 5.30).

£1.50.

⚠ (NT)

TISBURY
Wiltshire
Map 3 ST92

Wardour Castle (2m SW of Tisbury)
☎ (0747) 870464

Built by James Paine in 1768 and restored in 1960 for Cranborne Chase School, contains a notable stairway with two semi-circular flights.

Open provisionally, 21 Jul–6 Sep, Mon, Wed, Fri & Sat 2.30–6.

£1.10 (ch 14 70p). Party 12 + .

⚠ ✖

Wardour Old Castle (2m SW)
Built in 1392 by John Lord Lovel, with additions by Robert Smythson after 1570. Damaged after the Civil War.

Open † see end of gazetteer.

✱ 50p (ch 16 & pen 25p) Party.

⚠ ♿ (grounds only) (AM)

TITCHFIELD
Hampshire
Map 4 SU50

Carron Row Farm Museum
Segensworth Rd
☎ (0329) 43169 or 45102

Once part of the grounds of nearby Titchfield Abbey, the museum and its adjoining land can give the whole family an enjoyable day out. A collection of agricultural implements and rural craft tools are displayed in the picturesque 17th-century barn. Included in the wide range of exhibits are examples of carts, wagons and ploughs, a farm kitchen and a blacksmith's shop. An interesting exhibit is an 1841 manually operated horse-drawn fire-engine that used to be stationed at Titchfield. There is also a small flock of St Kilda sheep, a narrow-gauge railway and fishponds. Pets corner. Shire Horses and miniature Shetlands parade most Sundays. Blacksmiths forge. Carp fishing available in the ponds.

Open Etr–Oct 10.30–5.30. (Closed Mon & Tue in Apr, May & Oct ex BH).

£1.25 (ch & pen 75p).

⚠ 🚗 🎋 shop ⓥ

Titchfield Abbey
Also known as 'Place House'. The surviving picturesque gatehouse of a 13th-century abbey converted into a mansion by the Earl of Southampton, Lord

---

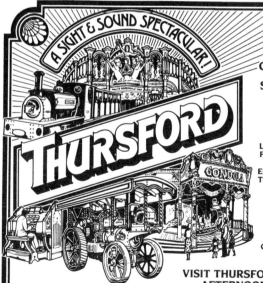

Chancellor of England, during the 16th century and showing fine Tudor chimneys.

Open see end of gazetteer.

✱ 30p (ch 16 & pen 15p).

P ර් (AM)

TIVERTON
Devon
Map **3** SS91

Tiverton Castle
☎ 01-493 4164 & 3024

Historic fortress of Henry I founded 1106. Notable medieval gatehouse, clock museum, Joan of Arc gallery and Chapel of St Francis.

Open Etr–Sep, Sun–Thu 2.30–5.30. Private visits by arrangement.

£1.50 (ch, pen & students £1).

⚠ ර් (ground floor & gardens only) ✖ (in castle).

Tiverton Museum
St Andrew Street, near Town Hall. (Entrance from public car park)
☎ (0884) 256295

Comprehensive museum housed in a restored 19th-century school containing numerous local exhibits; a Victorian laundry, two water-wheels, costume gallery, industrial gallery covering the Grand Western Canal and local trades, natural history and wartime rooms. Heathcoat Lace gallery featuring 19th-century lace making machine and other relics of Heathcoat Lace Making Factory. Agricultural section includes a collection of farm wagons and a complete smithy. A large railway gallery houses the GWR locomotive No. 1442, and other railway relics.

Open Mon–Sat 10.30–4.30. (Closed BH & 23 Dec–1 Feb).

Free.

P (100 yds) ර් (ground floor only) shop ✖ (ex guide dogs)

TOLLAND
Somerset
Map **3** ST13

Titchfield
—
Tongwynlais

Gaulden Manor
(1m E of Tolland Church)
☎ Lydeard St Lawrence (09847) 213.

Small historic manor originating from the 12th-century, past home of the Turberville family, immortalised by Thomas Hardy, and of the Wolcotts of the USA and still lived in. Magnificent plaster ceiling and fine antique furniture. Herb and bog garden. Plants are for sale.

Open Etr Sun & Mon, then 4 May–Jun Sun & Thu, Jul–14 Sep Sun Wed & Thu, also BH 2–5.30.

✱ Admission to House and garden £1.50 (ch 13 70p). Garden only 70p.

⚠ 🎞 ර් (ground floor only) shop & garden centre ✖ coaches by appointment. ⓥ

TOLPUDDLE
Dorset
Map **3** SY79

Tolpuddle is remembered for its martyrs, agricultural workers sentenced to transportation in 1834 for uniting to resist a wage reduction. A hundred years later, the TUC built a museum of six cottages named after 'The Martyrs'. Among the village's other memorials is the Martyr's Tree (NT), the old sycamore under which it is thought that they met.

Museum open daily 9–6.
☎ Puddletown (030584) 237.

TOMINTOUL
Grampian *Banffshire*
Map **15** NJ11

Tomintoul Museum The Square
☎ Forres (0309) 73701

Reconstructed farm kitchen and blacksmiths shop, harness displays, local landscape and wildlife displays. Exhibition "Scotland's Disappearing Wildlife" for one month in summer.

Open Apr, May & Oct Mon–Sat 9–5.30; Jun & Sep Mon–Sat 9–6, Sun 2–6; Jul & Aug Mon–Sat 9–7, Sun 11–7. Details not confirmed for 1986.

Free.

⚠ ර් shop ✖

TONBRIDGE
Kent
Map **5** TQ54

Tonbridge Castle
☎ West Malling (0732) 844522

Late 12th-century curtain walls, with a ruined shell keep and a round-towered early 13th-century gatehouse. Nature trail through Castle grounds.

Open daily 28 Mar–6 Apr, 3–6 & 24–27 May, then 24 Jul–14 Sep. Open weekends only 12–27 Apr, 10–18 May & 31 May–20 Jul 11.30–1 & 2–5.30.

65p (ch & pen 35p). Ch 12 must be accompanied. Parties by prior arrangement.

P (50 yds) shop ✖

TONGLAND
Dumfries and Galloway
Kirkcudbrightshire
Map **11** NX65

Tongland Tour
☎ Kirkcudbright (0557) 30114

Tour of SSEB Galloway hydro-electricity scheme. It includes video presentation and a visit to the dam and power station at Tongland. A fish ladder is an added attraction.

Open May–Sep Mon–Sat 10, 11.30, 2, 3.30, by telephone appointment.

Free.

Visitors taken to power station from Kirkcudbright by minibus
P (in Kirkcudbright) ✖ (ex at discretion of guides) 🚐

TONGWYNLAIS
South Glamorgan
Map **3** ST18

Castell Coch
Small 13th-century castle restored 1875–90 by 3rd Marquis of Bute and his →

Tiverton Castle
Ancient Fortress of the Earls of Devon, Founded 1106.

Notable medieval gatehouse and towers; with fine furniture and pictures; Joan of Arc gallery; Chapel of St. Francis; international clock collection.

1986 Opening
Easter to end September each afternoon
2.30 - 5.30pm
EXCEPT Fri and Sat.

Party bookings at special rates.
Tel. (01493) 4164 - 3024

architect William Burges. Notable for its interior decorations, conical roofs and splendid hillside setting.

Open † see end of gazetteer.

✳ 90p (ch 16 & pen 40p).

🅰 ⊞ shop (AM Cadw)

TOPPESFIELD
Essex
Map 5 TL73

Toppesfield Museum of the Working Horse Gainsford End
☎ Great Yeldham (0787) 237150

Wheelwright's shop, Blacksmith's shop, sawpit, harness maker's shop, horse-drawn vehicles and agricultural implements.

Open first wknd Apr–last wknd Sep, Sat & Sun, also Oct Sun only 2–6. Last admission 5pm. Groups by appointment.
75p (ch 35p under 5 free).

🅰 ⊒ ⊞ ♿ shop ⓥ

TOPSHAM
Devon
Map 3 SX98

Topsham Museum 25 The Strand
☎ (039287) 3221 or 3437

Estuary museum, overlooking the River Exe, depicting Topsham's maritime history and trade. Late 17th century house, with rooms of that period (opening summer 1986). One of the Dutch style houses along the Strand.

Open fr Jun, Mon, Wed, & Sat 2–5.
50p (ch 30p).
P (400 yds). ♿ (ground floor & gardens)
⊒ ✖ 🍴.

TORPHICHEN
Lothian West Lothian
Map 11 NS97

Torphichen Preceptory

This was the principal seat of the Knights of St John. The central tower and transepts of their church still remain. The nave, now the parish church, was rebuilt in the 18th century.

Open see end of gazetteer. (Closed Fri & alternate Wed).
50p (ch & pen 25p).
P (AM)

TORPOINT
Cornwall
Map 2 SX45

Antony House (2m NW off A38)

Fine largely unaltered mansion of 1711–21 in brick and stone, in extensive grounds overlooking the Rhynher. Panelled rooms with portraits and old furniture.

House open Apr–Oct, Tue, Wed, Thu & BH 2–6.
£1.90.
(NT)

Tongwynlais
—
Totnes

TORQUAY
Devon
Map 3 SX96

Aqualand Beacon Quay, Torquay Harbourside
☎ (0803) 24439

The largest aquarium in the west country which specialises in tropical marine fish. There is also a splendid exhibition of local marine life, as well as tropical freshwater fish, a pair of otters from Asia, and turtles from Florida.

Open Apr–Oct, daily 10–10pm. Admission fee payable. Party 15 + .
🅰 shop

Babbacombe Model Village
Babbacombe
☎ Torquay (0803) 38669

In four acres of beautiful, miniature landscaped gardens, this attractive model village contains over 400 models and 1200 ft of model railways.

Open daily Etr–Oct 9am–10pm; Nov–Etr 9–5 (Closed Xmas day).
Admission fee payable.
🅰 ♿ shop & garden centre

Kents Cavern The Caves, Wellswood (1¼m NE off B3199)
☎ (0803) 24059

Caves of natural beauty and prehistoric interest where visitors are guided along pathways through the labyrinth of passages and beautifully illuminated grottoes. Stalacites and stalagmites abound, formed by the mineral content of the water. A tour of the cavern takes 30–40 minutes.

Open all year, daily (ex Xmas day) from 10am.
Tours of the Caves every few minutes with guides.
✳ £1.20 (ch 14 60p, pen £1).
🅰 ⊒ (during season) shop

Torquay Museum 529 Babbacombe Rd
☎ (0803) 23975

The museum has a new Natural History Gallery with exciting finds from Kent's Cavern. Pictorial records section, local archaeology, ceramics, and many exhibits concerning rural life in the West country are featured.

Open all year Mon–Fri, also Sat Mar–Oct, 10–4.45. (Closed Good Fri, Xmas & New Year).
50p (ch & pen 25p).
🅰 (limited) shop ✖

Torre Abbey The Kings Drive
☎ (0803) 23593

A 12th-century monastery, parts of which

---

were converted during the 18th century into a private house, which displays interesting pictures and furniture. Abbey ruins and Tythe Barn (Spanish Barn) nearby. Local Art Society exhibitions and touring exhibitions.

Open Etr–Oct, daily 10–5, winter parties by appointment.
✳ 50p (pen 25p accompanied ch free).
🅰 ⊒ (late May–early Sep) ✖ (in house)

TORRIDON
Highland Ross and Cromarty
Map 14 NG85

Countryside Centre (at junction of A896 and Diabeg road)
☎ (044587) 221

Amid some of Scotland's finest scenery. Audio-visual presentations on wild life and static display at nearby Mains of the life of the red deer; also collection of live animals.

Both open Jun–Sep, Mon–Sat 10–6, Sun 2–6. Ranger/naturalist service.
✳ Deer Museum 35p (ch 15p). Audio-visual display by donation.
(NTS)

TORRINGTON, GREAT
Devon
Map 2 SS41

Dartington Glass Factory
☎ Torrington (0805) 22321

Apart from the factory tours there are viewing galleries that overlook the manufacturing and processing areas, plus tape and slide presentations.

Open Mon–Fri 9.30–10.30 & noon–3.25. Tours at regular intervals (Closed Xmas, 1st wk May & BH's).
✳ 75p (ch under 5 free, ch 5–12 & pen 50p)
🅰 ⊒ ⊞ shop (Mon–Fri 9–5, Sat 10–4) ✖

Rosemoor Garden Trust
(1m SE of town on B3220)
☎ Torrington (0805) 22256

Species and hybrid rhododendrons, shrub roses and ornamental trees and shrubs planted since 1959. There is also a peat garden, a scree garden, dwarf conifer collection, and an arboretum.

Open Apr–Oct daily. Nursery 8–5 daily.
£1 (ch 50p, pen 80p). Party.
🅰 ⊒ (Sun, Wed, BH & parties by arrangement) ⊞ ♿ garden centre.

TOTNES
Devon
Map 3 SX86

Bowden House
☎ (0803) 863664

Parts of the house date back to the 9th-century, today it is a fine example of Tudor and Queen Anne architecture. The Grand Hall is decorated in Neo Classical

---

Baroque style and the Great Hall is adorned with 18th and 19th-century muskets. Set in twelve acres of grounds that are particularly attractive in the spring. The family and guides wear Georgian costumes.

Open Etr–25 Sep Tue–Thu also BH Sun & Mon. House 2–4.30, Grounds noon–6

£1.60 (ch under 5 free, ch 5–10 40p, ch 10–16 80p) Grounds 60p (ch 5–10 20p, ch 10–16 40p)

⚠ ⛾ ✖ (in house)

Devonshire Collection of Period Costume 10a High St
☎ (0803) 862423

The Devonshire Collection is an entirely voluntary organisation administered by a Trust. A selection of costumes and accessories from the collection are exhibited each summer to illustrate a particular theme.

Open Spring BH–1 Oct, Mon–Fri 11–5 & Sun 2–5.

50p (ch 16 10p, pen 25p).

P (200 yds) ✖ 🚻 (ex by appointment)

Guildhall off High St
☎ (0803) 862147

Gabled and colonnaded 16th-century building, which has been in use since 1624, now housing council chamber. There is also a Court Room and Mayor's Parlour. Relics on show include Saxon coins minted locally.

Open Etr–Sep, Mon–Fri 9.30–1 & 2–5; Oct–Etr by appointment.

✻ 25p (ch 10p).

P (50 yds)

Totnes Castle

A ruined 13th- and 14th-century castle with a shell keep and curtain walls.

Open † see end of gazetteer.

✻ 50p (ch 16 & pen 25p).

⚠ (AM)

Totnes Motor Museum Steamer Quay
☎ (0803) 862777

Private collection of vintage, sports and racing cars, most of which are currently raced and cover a 60-year span.

Open Etr–Oct, daily 10–5.30.

✻ £1.50 (ch £1) Family ticket £4.

⚠ ⛾ (ground floor only) shop

Totnes Elizabethan Museum 70 Fore St
☎ (0803) 863821 (Feb–Oct) 862147 (Nov–Jan)

Four-storey, partly half-timbered house, dating from circa 1575, with cobbled courtyard. Now a museum of furniture, domestic objects, toys, dolls, costumes and archaeology, computer exhibition.

Open Apr–Oct, Mon–Fri 10.30–1 & 2–5.30. (Reduced hours in winter).

40p (ch 16 20p).

P ⛾ (ground floor & garden only) shop

Totnes
—
Trewint

TOTTON
Hampshire
Map **4** SU31

Eling Tide Mill
☎ (0703) 869575

One of the few remaining mills still using tidal energy to grind wheat into flour. The present mill has been restored to full operational condition and is open to the public as a working museum, though there has been a mill here for about 900 years. It is usually possible to grind flour for demonstration purposes on alternate weekends. Stoneground wholemeal and wheatmeal flour are on sale.

Open Etr–Sep, Wed–Sun 10–4. Nov–Etr Mon–Fri 10–4. (Closed Xmas wk) Details not confirmed for 1986.

80p (ch & pen 50p). Party.

P shop ✖ coaches by appointment only.
ⓥ

TRAQUAIR
Borders Peebleshire
Map **11** NT33

Traquair House (1m S of Innerleithen on B709)
☎ Innerleithen (0896) 830323

Scotland's oldest inhabited, and most romantic house, dating back to the 10th century. Twenty-seven English and Scottish kings have stayed here. Rich in associations with Mary, Queen of Scots, and the Jacobite Risings. Contains fine collection of historical treasures. Unique 18th-century brew-house licensed to sell own beer. Newly planted maze. Woodland walks, 5 craft workshops. Traquair Fair 2 & 3 Aug (subject to confirmation). Croquet available. Children's play area.

Open 24 Mar–19 Oct 1.30–5.30, ex during Jul, Aug & first two weeks in Sep when open 10.30–5.30. Last admission 5.

House & grounds £1.90 (ch 90p). Grounds only 60p. Prices subject to review.

⚠ ⛾ (licensed) 🚻 ⛾ (ground floor & gardens only) shop

TREFRIW
Gwynedd
Map **6** SH76

Trefriw Woollen Mill
☎ Llanrwst (0492) 640462

Woollen mill dating from 1859. All stages of woollen manufacture can be seen, including blending, carding, spinning, dyeing, warping, weaving and tailoring, also hydro-electric turbines. Large shop selling own products. Demonstration of hand spinning and weaving and machine knitting Jun–Sep.

Open Mon–Fri 9–5.30. Shop also open Sat 10–4 (Mill closed BH & 2 weeks Xmas).

Free except for school parties which must be pre-booked.

P (opposite) ⛾ (Jun–Sep) ⛾ (shop only) shop ✖ (in mill)

TRELISSICK GARDEN
Cornwall
Map **2** SW83
(4m S of Truro, on B3289)

A beautiful woodland park at the head of Falmouth Harbour, growing rhododendrons and sub-tropical plants. Large shrub garden. Plants available at shop.

Gardens shown Mar–Oct, Mon–Sat 11–6, Sun 1–6.

£1.50.

⛾ (in Trelissick Garden Barn 11–6) (NT & NGS)

TRERICE
Cornwall
Map **2** SW85
(3m SE of Newquay on unclass road off A3058)

A picturesque Elizabethan house, displaying unusual curly gables, contemporary fireplaces and plaster ceilings. Museum of lawn mowers in the barn.

Open Apr–Oct, daily 11–6, last admission 5.30.

House £2. Party.

⛾ (11–6) (NT)

TRETOWER
Powys
Map **3** SO12

Tretower Court & Castle

Remains of a 14th- to 15th-century Welsh fortified manor house, with nearby ruined Norman and 13th-century castle noted for its cylindrical keep.

Open see end of gazetteer.

✻ 60p (ch 16 & pen 30p).

⚠ shop (AM Cadw)

TREWINT
Cornwall
Map **2** SX28

Wesley's Cottage (near Altarnun)
☎ Pipers Pool (056686) 572

Small 18th-century Methodist shrine, well-restored in 1950. John Wesley came here six times between 1744 and 1762. Annual Wesley Day service is held. Also Sun services in summer. Interesting testaments and period furnishings are on display. Wesley Day celebrations 24 May.

Open all year, daily 9–dusk.

Free.

P (10 yds) ⛾ (ground floor only) ✖

TRING
Hertfordshire
Map **4** SP91

The Zoological Museum Akeman St
☎ (044282) 4181

A branch of the British Museum (Natural History) specialising in mounted specimens of mammals, birds, insects and shells. These are from the Zoological collections of Lional Walter, Second Baron Rothschild who opened the museum to the public in 1892.

Open Mon–Sat 10–5, Sun 2–5. (Closed Good Fri, May Day, 24–26 Dec & 1 Jan).
Free.

⚠ ♿ (ground floor only) shop ✘ (ex guide dogs)

TRINITY
Jersey *Channel Islands*
Map **16**

Zoological Park
☎ Jersey (0534) 61949

Founded in 1959 by Gerald Durrell and headquarters of the Jersey Wildlife Preservation Trust. Its purpose is to breed animals critically endangered in the wild. Families include gorilla, orang-utan, snow leopard, and many others.

Open daily May–Sep 10–6, Oct–Apr 10–5. (Closed Xmas day).

✱ £2 (ch & pen £1).
⚠ ☕ shop ✘

TROUTBECK
Cumbria
Map **7** NY40

Townend

Fine 17th-century yeoman's house, containing carved woodwork and furnishings of the Browne family.

Open 26 Mar–2 Nov, Tue–Fri & Sun also BH Mon 2–6 or dusk if earlier.

£1.10 (ch 55p).
(NT)

TRURO
Cornwall
Map **2** SW84

Tring
—
Twickenham

County Museum & Art Gallery River St
☎ (0872) 72205

Interesting display illustrating the history of the county. The mineral collection is world-famous. Collections of pottery, pewter, old-master drawings, Japanese ivories and lacquer-work.

Open Mon–Sat 9–5, Library closes 1–2; (Closed BH's).

Admission fee payable.
P shop ✘

Killiow Country Park Kea (2m SW Truro off A39)
☎ (0872) 72768

A superb parkland setting with lake and extensive gardens and woodland walks including a nature trail. Sanctuary for rare breeds of farm animals, working Shire horses, coach carriage and harness displays, horse power farm museum, rural displays with working pottery and weaving shop, pets corner and adventure playground. Beautifully preserved Georgian and Elizabethan buildings.

Open daily Apr–1 Oct 1.30–6 (ex Sun, BH & 2 Jun–1 Oct when open 10.30–6pm). Details not confirmed for 1986.

✱ £1.60 (ch 60p, pen £1). Party.
⚠ ☕ ⛽ ♿ shop garden centre ✘

TUNBRIDGE WELLS
Kent
Map **5** TQ53

Tunbridge Wells Museum & Art Gallery Civic Centre
☎ (0892) 26121 ext 171

Local and natural history, and Tunbridge ware. Collections of toys, dolls and domestic bygones.

Open Mon–Fri 10–5.30 & Sat 9.30–5. (Closed Sun, BH & Tue after spring & summer BH's, and Etr Sat).

Free.
P (multi-storey 200 yds) ✘

TUTBURY
Staffordshire
Map **8** SK22

Tutbury Castle
☎ Burton-on-Trent (0283) 812129

A medieval ruin of the 'motte and bailey' type. A fine view can be seen from the North Tower. The oldest part is the 12th-century chapel in the courtyard. On two occasions it was the prison of Mary Queen of Scots. In the grounds are wildlife, Jacob sheep and nature trails.

Open Apr–Oct daily 10–6.

50p (ch & pen 25p).
⚠ ☕ (Sat, Sun & BH Mon) ♿ (ground floor only) shop

TWICKENHAM
Gt London
(London plan 4 pages 174/175.)

Marble Hill House Marble Hill Park Richmond Rd London plan 4: **34** B2
☎ 01-892 5115

An example of English Palladian school of architecture standing in a wooded park near the River Thames. Built 1724–9 for Henrietta Howard, mistress of George II and later Countess of Suffolk. Georgian paintings and furniture; Italian paintings in the Great Room by G. P. Panini.

Open Mon–Thu, Sat & Sun 10–5 (4pm Nov–Jan). (Closed 24 & 25 Dec).

Free.
⚠ ☕ (Apr–Sep) ♿ (ground floor & gardens only) shop ✘

Orleans House Gallery Riverside London plan 4: **41** B2
☎ 01-892 0221

Original Orleans House, in which Louis Phillippe, Duc d'Orléans, King of the French 1830–48, lived in exile in early 19th century. It was demolished in 1927. Surviving octagonal room, designed by James Gibbs in c 1720, has exquisite plasterwork.

Open Tue–Sat 1–5.30 (4.30pm Oct–Mar) Sun & BH 2–5.30 (Oct–Mar 2–4.30).

(Closed 25 & 26 Dec and Good Fri). Woodland gardens open all year, daily 9–dusk.

Free.

🚫 ♿ (ground floor only) ✚ 🚗 (in car park)

TWYCROSS
Leicestershire
Map **4** SK30

Twycross Zoo Park (1½m NW off A444)
☎ Tamworth (0827) 880250

Collection of large animals, especially noted for its range of primates, including gorillas, orang-utans and chimpanzees. Modern reptile house. Butterfly house. Numerous exotic birds.

Open daily from 10am. (Closed Xmas day).

✳ £2 (ch £1 pen £1.50).

🚫 (charge) 🍽 (licensed in summer only) 🎠 ♿ shop ✚ ⓥ

TYNEMOUTH
Tyne and Wear
Map **12** NZ36

Tynemouth Priory & Castle
A 16th-century ruin, with the towers, gatehouse and keep erected to defend the nearby 11th- to 13th-century Priory.

Open † see end of gazetteer.

✳ 60p (ch 16 & pen 30p).

🚫 (charge) (AM)

TYWYN
Gwynedd
Map **6** SH50

Narrow-Gauge Railway Museum Wharf Station
☎ (0654) 710472

An interesting small museum displaying a number of locomotives and wagons.

Open Etr–Oct, Mon–Fri 10–5, Sat & Sun 11–5. (6pm Jul & Aug). Nov–Mar open by arrangement.

30p (ch 14 10p).

P (100 yds) 🍽 (at Wharf Station) ♿ (ground floor only) shop ✚

Twickenham
—
Ugbrooke

Talyllyn Railway Wharf Station
☎ (0654) 710472 or 711297 (Talking Timetable)

The oldest 2ft 3in gauge railway in the world. Steam operated. Built 1865 and became first railway to be saved by a voluntary preservation society. Runs 7¼ miles, from Tywyn to Nant Gwernol.

Regular daily 24 Mar–28 Sep; 30 Sep–2 Nov Tue–Thu, Sat & Sun also 26 Dec–1 Jan daily. Details for 1986 to be confirmed. Timetables available.

✳ Fares for return journey £2.80. Family (2 adults + 1 child) £6.50 (2 adults + 2 children £7).

P (100 yds) 🍽 🎠 ♿ (on trains by prior arrangement) shop

UCKFIELD
East Sussex
Map **5** TQ41

Beeches Farm Buckham Hill
(1½m W of town on Isfield Rd)
☎ (0825) 2391

16th-century farmhouse with gardens, lawns, sunken garden, borders and yew trees. Wide views.

Gardens open all year, daily 10–5; House open by appointment only.

✳ Conducted tour 75p. Gardens only 20p (ch 12 10p). Party.

🚫 shop coaches by appointment

UDDINGSTON
Strathclyde Lanarkshire
Map **11** NS66

Glasgow Zoo
☎ 041-771 1185/6

Birds, mammals, and reptiles housed in spacious new enclosures and buildings. Other attractions include ample picnic sites and children's shows.

Open all year, daily 10–5 (or 6pm depending on season).

£1.80 (ch, pen, students & unemployed £1.10, ch 3 free). Party.

🚫 🍽 🎠 ♿ shop ✚

UFFCULME
Devon
Map **3** ST01

Coldharbour Mill
Coldharbour (½m SW off B3391)
☎ Craddock (0884) 40960

18th-century working mill museum producing knitting wool and woven cloth. Features include a large steam engine and water wheel together with a collection of interesting machinery and artefacts relating to West Country worsted and woollen manufacture. Knitting wool and cloth can be purchased.

Open May–Aug daily 11–5; Mar, Apr, Sep & Oct Mon–Fri 11–5 & Sun 2–5; Nov–Feb Wed–Fri & Sun 2–5. Also Etr Sat.

Admission fee payable.

🚫 🍽 (licensed) 🎠 shop

UFFINGTON
Oxfordshire
Map **4** SU38

Castle & White Horse
Iron Age hill fort situated on the ancient Ridgeway at a height of more than 700ft on the Berkshire Downs. Below it, cut in the chalk, is the famous White Horse.

Both accessible any reasonable time.

Free.

🚫 (AM)

UGBROOKE
Devon
Map **3** SX87

Ugbrooke (1½m SE on unclass road)
☎ Chudleigh (0626) 852179

Ancestral home of the Lords Clifford of Chudleigh. Grounds designed by Capability Brown. Fine collection of embroideries from the 16th century to present day. Added attractions include Pets Corner, adventure playground and trailer rides around the lakes. →

Open 25 May–6 Sep daily; House open 2–5. (Grounds 12.30–5.30. (Last admission 5pm).

£1.50 (ch 80p). Grounds only 50p. Party 20+ (by prior arrangement).

⚠ 🍽 (licensed) ⌇ ♿ shop

ULEY
Gloucestershire
Map **3** ST79

Uley Tumulus (1m N)

Known as Hetty Pegler's Tump, this long barrow, 120ft by 85ft, has a chamber approached by means of a deep forecourt. The chamber forms part of a gallery grave.

Accessible any reasonable time.

Free.

(AM)

ULVERSTON
Cumbria
Map **7** SD27

Conishead Priory Priory Rd
☎ (0229) 54029

A 19th century Gothic mansion just south of the Lake District on the shores of Morecambe Bay. The house is surrounded by 70 acres of woods and gardens with a marked woodland trail to the bay.

Open Etr–Sep Sat, Sun & BH 2–5; also Wed & Thu, Jul & Aug.

House tours £1. Grounds free.

⚠ 🍽 ♿ (ground floor & gardens only) shop

Cumbria Crystal Lightburn Rd
☎ (0229) 54400

Using a fine full-lead crystal, the factory specialises in glassware based on 18th-century design made by traditional hand-blowing and hand-cutting techniques. Visitors welcome in factory. Factory shop where glass can be purchased at substantial discounts.

Open all year, factory Mon–Fri 8–4; shop Mon–Fri 9–5, Sat 10–4. Details not confirmed for 1986.

✳ 40p (ch & pen 10p) includes 20% discount voucher to spend in shop.

P (in street) ♿ shop 🍽

UPMINSTER
Gt London
Map **5** TQ58

Tithe Barn Agricultural & Folk Museum
Hall Ln
☎ Hornchurch (04024) 47535

15th-century thatched timber building contains large selection of old agricultural implements, craft and farm tools, domestic bygones and items of local interest, over 2,000 exhibits in all.

Open 5 & 6 Apr, 3 & 4 May, 7 & 8 Jun, 5 & 6 Jul, 2 & 3 Aug, 6 & 7 Sep, 4 & 5 Oct; 1.30–6.

Ugbrooke
—
Waddesdon

Free.

⚠ ♿ shop 🍽

UPNOR
Kent
Map **5** TQ77

Upnor Castle

A restored castle of 1561 designed originally as a River Medway blockhouse. Queen Elizabeth I reviewed the fleet here in 1581.

Open see end of gazetteer. Apr–Sep only.

✳ 50p (ch 16 & pen 25p).

P (AM)

UPPERMILL
Lancashire
Map **7** SD90

Saddleworth Museum & Art Gallery
High St
☎ Saddleworth (04577) 4093

Art gallery with many fine exhibitions. Museum with exhibits of local interest and model of the Roman Fort of Castelshaw, in early section gallery. Story of domestic textile industry featuring weaver's cottage, early mill equipment, including power loom working on textile weekends. Permanent transport exhibition. Boat trips on canal.

Open daily 2–5.

40p (ch & pen 10p).

⚠ 🍽 ⌇ ♿ (ground floor only) shop 🍽

UPTON CRESSETT
Shropshire
Map **7** SO69

Upton Cressett Hall
☎ Morville (074631) 307

Elizabethan manor house, gatehouse and gardens in beautiful countryside. 14th-century Great Hall with medieval garden, peacocks and delightful, small Norman church.

Open May–Sep, Thu 2.30–5. Parties by appointment throughout the year.

£1 (ch 50p). Party.

⚠ ⌇ ⓥ

UPTON HOUSE
Warwickshire
Map **4** SP34

(7m NW of Banbury on A422)

17th-century house with fine collection of paintings, porcelain, tapestries and furniture. Terraced gardens.

Open Apr–Sep, Mon–Thu 2–6 (last admission to house 5.30pm). Also 10–11, 17–18 May; 26–27 July; 2–3, 9–10, 16–17 Aug.

£1.90. Grounds only 95p.

(NT)

USK
Gwent
Map **3** SO30

Gwent Rural Life Museum Malt Barn,
New Market St
☎ Tredunnock (063349) 315 or (02913) 2285

Award-winning collection of farm tools, machinery, wagons and domestic items.

Open Apr–Sep daily (ex Sat & Sun am) 10–12.30 & 2–5; Mar & Oct Mon–Fri & Sun pm. Winter Mon–Fri (Closed Xmas).

75p (ch & pen 25p). Party.

P (100 yds) ♿ (ground floor & yard only) ⓥ

VENTNOR
Isle of Wight
Map **4** SZ57

Museum of the History of Smuggling
Botanic Gardens
☎ Isle of Wight (0983) 853677

A unique underground museum showing methods of smuggling over a 700-year period to the present day. Adventure playground. The 'Isle of Wight Smuggling Pageant' a week in middle of June.

Open Etr–Sep, daily 10–5.30.

80p (ch 7–14 & pen 50p, accompanied ch 7 free). Botanic Gardens free.

⚠ 🍽 (licensed) ⌇ shop

VERWOOD
Dorset
Map **4** SU00

Dorset Heavy Horse Centre Brambles Farm (1½m NW, signposted from Verwood)
☎ (0202) 824040

Home of some of the finest champion Shire, Percheron, Clydesdale and Suffolk horses. Also displayed are farm wagons and farm implements. Plaiting, Harnessing and driving demonstrations.

Open Apr–Oct daily 10–6; Jan–Mar & Nov by arrangement only. (Closed Dec). Parades at 11.30, 2.30 & 4 pm.

✳ £1.60 (ch 3–14 & pen £1.10). Party.

⚠ 🍽 ⌇ ♿ shop ⓥ

WADDESDON
Buckinghamshire
Map **4** SP71

Waddesdon Manor (6m NW of Aylesbury, gates off A41)
☎ Aylesbury (0296) 651282

A French Renaissance-style château built in 1874–89 for Baron Ferdinand de Rothschild. Rich in French royal decorative art and English 18th-century portraits. Extensive grounds with aviary, deer and play area for young children. Also costume exhibition featuring the wardrobe of a lady in 1860's.

Open 19 Mar–19 Oct. House: Mar, Apr,
Oct, Wed–Fri 2–5, Sat & Sun 2–6; May–
Sep, Wed–Sun 2–6. Grounds Wed–Sat
from 1pm (11.30am Sun). Good Fri & BH
Mons, House & Grounds 11–6. (Closed
Wed after BH). Children under 10 not
admitted to House.

House & grounds (including Good Fri)
£2.20. Fri (ex Good Fri) additional rooms
80p extra. Grounds only £1 (ch 25p).

△ ♫ shop & produce stall (NT)

WAKEFIELD
West Yorkshire
Map **8** SE32

Wakefield Art Gallery Wentworth Ter
☎ (0924) 370211 ext 8031. (After 5 & Sat
(0924) 375402)

*Good collection of modern paintings and
sculpture including works by Henry
Moore, Barbara Hepworth, Jacob Epstein,
Graham Sutherland, Ben Nicholson etc.
Temporary exhibitions.*

Open all year, Mon–Sat 10.30–12.30 &
1.30–5. (Closed BH).

Free.

P (100 yds) ✘

Wakefield Museum Wood St
☎ (0924) 370211 ext 7190. (After 5 & Sat
(0924) 361767)

*Archaeology, social history displays.
Waterton Collection of natural history
specimens. Temporary exhibitions.*

Open all year Mon–Sat 10.30–12.30 &
1.30–5. (Closed BH).

Free.

P (100 yds) ✘

WALKERBURN
Borders *Peeblesshire*
Map **11** NT33

Scottish Museum of Woollen Textiles
Tweedvale Mill
☎ (089687) 281 and 283

*Museum contains a variety of objects
connected with the Scottish woollen
industry.*

Open Mon–Sat 10–5, Sun 12–4.30; Etr–
Oct.

25p (ch & pen 15p) family ticket 50p.

△ ♫ & shop ✘

WALL
Staffordshire
Map **7** SK10

Roman Remains

*Remains of baths and posting stations
and a museum of excavated finds from
the Roman station of 'Letocetum' at the
junction of Watling and Ricknield Streets.*

Open see end of gazetteer. Apr–Sep only.

✹ 30p (ch 16 & pen 15p).

△ (AM & NT)

WALSALL
W Midlands
Map **7** SP09

Jerome K Jerome Birthplace Museum
Belsize House, Bradford St
☎ (0922) 21244 ext 3115

*Birthplace of Jerome K Jerome, now
restored as a museum, housing
documents and memorabilia of the
author. One room is a reconstruction of an
1850's parlour.*

Open Tue–Sat 10–5. (Closed Sun, Mon &
BH's).

Free.

P shop ✘

Museum & Art Gallery
Central Library, Lichfield St
☎ (0922) 21244 ext 3124

*Garman Ryan collection including
important works by Blake, Degas, Van
Gogh and Epstein. Regular loan
exhibitions. Local history museum.*

Open Mon–Fri 10–6 & Sat 10–4.45.
(Closed Sun & BH's).

Free.

P (200 yds) & shop ✘

WALSINGHAM
Norfolk
Map **9** TF93

Walsingham Abbey Grounds
☎ (032872) 259

*Contains site of the Shrine of Our Lady
and the remains of an Augustinian Priory.*

Abbey grounds open 25 Wed Apr. Wed,
Sat & Sun May–Sep (also Mon & Fri Aug).

Admission fee payable.

P (50 yds) & shop

Shirehall Museum Common Pl
☎ (032872) 510

*Almost perfect Georgian courtroom with
its original fittings, including prisoners'
lock-up. Local museum includes a display
on the History of Pilgrimage. Also a
Tourist Information Centre.*

Open daily, 27 Mar–Sep 11–1 & 2–4; Oct,
Sat & Sun only.

20p (ch 5p, students & UB40s 10p).

△ shop ✘

WALTHAM ABBEY
Essex
Map **5** TL30

Hayes Hill Farm Stubbins Hill Ln
☎ Nazeing (099289) 2291

*A traditional style farmyard where visitors
can see most farm animals in their natural
surroundings. Centrepiece of the farm is a
restored 16th-century barn.*

Open weekdays 10 4.00, wknds & BH
10–6.

£1 (ch 60p). Party.

△ ♫ & shop

**Waltham Abbey Gatehouse, Bridge &
entrance to Cloisters**

*14th-century gatehouse with separate
carriage and pedestrian entrances.
Harold's Bridge is also 14th-century.
Cloister entrance dates from 12th-
century. In the historic Norman and later
Abbey Church nearby is an undercroft
museum.*

Open at any reasonable time.

Free.

△ (AM)

WALWICK
Northumberland
Map **12** NY97

Chesters Roman Fort & Museum
(½m E)

*Roman fort designed for a garrison of 500
cavalry. Extensive ruins of bath house.
Museum houses Clayton collection of
items excavated from local forts such as
'Cilurnum'.*

Open † see end of gazetteer.

✹ 80p (ch 16 & pen 40p), winter 40p
(ch 16 & pen 20p).

△ ♫ (AM)

WANDLEBURY RING
Cambridgeshire
Map **5** TL45

(4m SE of Cambridge off A1307)

*On the summit of the low Gog Magog
Hills, the remains of an Iron-Age hill fort
which once comprised a double rampart
and ditch, 1,000ft in diameter; about 110
acres of the hills have been protected by
the Cambridge Preservation Society.*

Open daily.

Free, but donations are welcome.

△ shop 'dog run'

WANLOCKHEAD
Dumfries and Galloway *Dumfriesshire*
Map **11** NS81

Museum of Scottish Lead Mining
(on B797 at N end of Mennock Pass)
☎ Leadhills (06594) 387

*Conserves, displays and interprets the
physical and documentary history of lead
mining in Scotland. Indoor museum and
library. 1½-mile Visitor Walkway, including
an 18th-century lead mine, links a variety
of mining and social structures.*

Open Etr–end Sep, daily 11–4. Last visit
of mine 3.30pm.

Museum 50p (ch 5–16 20p). Mine 50p (ch
5–16 20p). Party.

△ ♫ & shop ✘

WANSFORD
Cambridgeshire
Map **4** TL09

Nene Valley Railway Wansford Station
(just off southbound carriageway of A1,
8m W of Peterborough).
☎ Stamford (0780) 782921, talking
timetable. Other enquiries Stamford
(0780) 782854.

*Standard-gauge steam railway running
between Wansford and Peterborough.
International array of steam locomotives
and stock. Small museum. Special events
arranged throughout the year.*

Open Etr–Oct, Sat, Sun also Wed & Thu
Jun–Aug. Also open for BH's & Christmas
Specials every weekend during Dec.

£2.50 (ch, disabled & pen £1.15) return.

⚠ ⏤ 卅 (Orton Mere) ᗙ shop

WANTAGE
Oxfordshire
Map **4** SU48

Vale & Downland Museum Centre
The Old Surgery, Church St
☎ (02357) 66838

*A lively museum centre with displays on
the geology, archaeology and local history
of the Vale of the White Horse and the
town of Wantage. Temporary exhibitions
and local craft demonstrations
occasionally.*

Open Tue–Sat 10.30–4.30 & Sun 2–5.

Free.

P (Civic Hall Car Pk, 500 yds) ⏤ 卅
ᗙ(ground floor only) shop

Kingston Lisle Park
(4½m W off B4507)
☎ Uffington (036782) 223

*The home of Mrs Leopold Lonsdale. The
central part of the mansion was built in
1677 and the wings were added in the
19th century. Items on display include
letters which belonged to Field Marshal
Lord Raglan, Commander-in-Chief of the
Crimea.*

Apr–Aug Thu & BH Sat–Mon 2–5. Parties
at other times by arrangement.

✳ £1.50 (ch 80p). Party 10 + .

⚠ (BHs & prebooked) ᗙ garden
centre 卅

WARKWORTH
Northumberland
Map **12** NU20

Warkworth Castle

*Built between 11th and 14th centuries
with a gatehouse and a great keep,
probably built by the 1st Earl of
Northumberland. Old bridge over River
Coquet and rare bridge tower.*

Open † see end of gazetteer.

✳ 60p (ch 16 & pen 30p).

⚠ ᗙ (except Keep). (AM)

Warkworth Hermitage

Interesting 14th-century hermitage with a

┌─────────────────────────┐
│   **Wansford**   │
│   —   │
│   **Washford**   │
└─────────────────────────┘

*small chapel cut in solid rock. Access by
rowing boat from nearby castle.*

Open see end of gazetteer.

✳ 30p (ch 16 & pen 15p).

P (at castle) (AM)

WARRINGTON
Cheshire
Map **7** SJ68

**South Lancashire Regiment (PWV)
Regimental Museum**
Peninsula Barracks, Orford
☎ (0925) 33563

*Military museum of South Lancashire
Regiment from 1717 onwards.*

Open all year Mon–Fri 9–3, also for parties
evenings & wknds by arrangement.

Free.

P (150 yds) 卅

WARWICK
Warwickshire
Map **4** SP26

Lord Leycester Hospital High St
☎ (0926) 491422

*Lovely, half-timbered building, built in
1383, and adapted for its present use by
the Earl of Leicester in 1571. It is still a
home of rest for ex-servicemen and their
wives. Guildhall, Great Hall, Chapel,
Courtyard & Regimental Museum of
Queens Own Hussars.*

Open all year Mon–Sat 10–5.30, summer;
10–4, winter. (Closed Good Fri & Xmas
day). Last admission ½hr before closing.

£1 (ch 14 50p, pen 75p). Party 20 + .

⚠ (20 yds) ⏤ (Etr–Sep) ᗙ (ground floor
only) shop

St John's House
Coten End (Junction of A429 & A445
E of town)
☎ Leamington Spa (0926) 493431 ext
2021. For Regimental Museum (0926)
491653

*Fine 17th-century house rebuilt by the
Stoughton family on the site of an old
hospital. It is now a branch of the County
Museum (domestic scenes, costume, and
musical instruments), Victorian
schoolroom. Includes the museum of the
Royal Warwickshire Regiment on the first
floor.*

Open all year, Tue–Sat & BH 10–12.30 &
1.30–5.30, Sun (May–Sep only) 2.30–5.

Free.

⚠ limited & P (St Nicholas Pk 200 yds)
ᗙ (ground floor only) shop

Warwick Castle off Castle Hill
☎ (0926) 495421

Famous 14th-century and later castle,

---

*overlooking the River Avon. Guy's Tower
(1394) and Caesar's Tower (1356) flank an
imposing gatehouse. Exhibition areas
include the Great Hall, State rooms,
dungeon and torture display. Armoury,
Clocktower and Barbican, Guy's Tower
Rampart Walk and Ghost Tower. The
Mound. 'A Royal Weekend Party–1898' by
Madame Tussaud's in the Private
Apartments. Special Events on Sunday
afternoons (Apr–Aug). Peacock gardens.
Medieval Banquets throughout the year.*

Open all year (ex Xmas day) 10–5.30 (4.30
Nov–Feb).

£3.50 (ch £2.25 pen £2.75). Family ticket
£10.

⚠ ⏤ (licensed) 卅 ᗙ (garden only) shop
卅

Warwick Doll Museum
Oken's House, Castle St
☎ (0926) 495546 & 491600

*Half-timbered Elizabethan house, the
16th-century birthplace of Thomas Oken,
a benefactor of the town. Now a doll
museum containing the Joy Robinson
Collection of antique and period dolls, and
toys.*

Open Mar–Nov, daily 10.30–5. Dec–Feb
wknds only, 10.30–5.

70p (ch, students & pen 50p).

P (limited) shop 卅 coaches by
appointment

Warwickshire Museum Market Pl
☎ (0926) 493431 ext 2500

*17th-century Market Hall now a museum
displaying the geology, history and
natural history of Warwickshire. Notable
for the Sheldon tapestry map of
Warwickshire, habitat displays and giant
fossil plesiosaur. Temporary exhibitions
throughout the year and children's holiday
activities during the summer and
Christmas. 150th Anniversary Celebration
including exhibition in summer.*

Open Mon–Sat 10–5.30. Suns (May–Sep
only) 2.30–5.

Free.

P (50–200 yds) 卅 shop

Warwickshire Yeomanry Museum
The Court House, Jury St
☎ (0926) 492212

*Display of military exhibits, includes
uniforms, medals, militaria and weapons
dating from 1794 to 1945. Also selected
items of silver from the Regimental
collection. There is also a very fine display
of paintings and pictures covering the
same period.*

Good Fri–end of Sep Fri, Sat & Sun & BHs
10–1 & 2–4.

Free.

P (½ mile at wknds) ᗙ (gardens only) 卅

WASHFORD
Somerset
Map **3** ST04

Cleeve Abbey

Ruined 13th-century Cistercian house noted for gatehouse, dormitory and refectory with traceried windows, timbered roof and wall paintings.

Open † see end of gazetteer.

✱ 60p (ch 16 & pen 30p).

⚠ ⛫ (ground floor & grounds only) (AM)

WASHINGTON
Tyne and Wear
Map **12** NZ35

Washington Old Hall
☎ ...

Mainly early 17th-century, the seat of the Washington family, now restored with period furniture.

Open Good Fri–6 Apr daily 11–5, 7 Apr–end Apr Wed, Sat & Sun 11–5. May–Sep 11–5, (closed Fri); Oct Wed, Sat & Sun 11–5; Nov–Mar by appointment.

✱ £1. Party.

⚠ (NT) ⓥ

Wildfowl Trust
☎ 091–416 5454

A waterfowl park on the N bank of the River Wear. 103 acres with a comprehensive collection of the world's waterfowl in attractive landscaped surroundings, including a refuge of 70 acres for wild birds, which can be viewed

---

Washford
—
Watford

from a number of public hides. Attractive log cabin visitor centre, souvenir and natural history bookshop, inside viewing gallery giving excellent view over part of main collection area. Lecture theatre where free natural history films shown most days and by special arrangement at weekends.

Open all year daily 9.30–5.30 or dusk if earlier. (Closed Xmas eve and day).

£1.80 (ch 80p, ch 4 free, pen £1.20). Party 20 + .

⚠ ⛫ ♨ ⛫ shop ✗

WATERPERRY
Oxfordshire
Map **4** SP60

Waterperry Gardens & Horticultural Centre
(2m NE Wheatley on unclass rd)
☎ Ickford (08447) 226 & 254

Peaceful gardens and nurseries in 80-acre estate surrounding 18th-century Waterperry House. Fine herbaceous borders and beds—featured on 'Gardeners' World', rock garden, riverside walk, shrub borders, lawns and fine trees.

Herbaceous, alpine, shrub, fruit nurseries and glasshouses provide all-year-round plants and produce for sale at garden shop. Church of Saxon origin and historical interest in grounds with famous old glass, brasses and woodwork. Open in aid of 'National Gardens Scheme' and 'Gardener's Sunday' 8 Jun and 10 Aug.

Gardens open all year ex Xmas & New Year & during 'Art in Action' preparation and event 17–20 Jul. Apr–Sep 10–5.30, wknds 10–6. Oct–Mar 10–4. Coach parties by prior booking only.

80p (ch 10–16 40p, pen 65p) Mar–Oct; (40p Nov–Feb). Party.

⚠ ⛫ garden centre, coaches by appointment ⓥ

WATFORD
Hertfordshire
Map **4** TQ19

Watford Museum 194 High St
☎ (0923) 32297

Museum describing the history of the Watford area from earliest times to the present day. There are special features on brewing and printing together with a display of wartime Watford based on the 'Dads Army' series written by Jimmy Perry from his Watford experience. A good art gallery and a constantly changing programme of exhibits. →

Open Mon–Sat 10–5 (Closed Xmas & New Years Day).

Free.

⚠ ⅄ shop ✖ (ex guide dogs)

WEEM
Tayside *Perthshire*
Map **14** NN85

Castle Menzies
☎ Aberfeldy (0887) 20982

Fine and historically important example of a 16th-century Z-plan fortified tower house of transitional type. Seat of the Chiefs of Clan Menzies and now under restoration. It houses a small museum. Music recitals at times.

Open Apr–Sep, weekdays 10.30–5, Sun 2–5.

£1 (ch 30p, pen 50p).

⚠ ⅄ (ground floor only) shop ✖ ⓥ

WEETING
Norfolk
Map **5** TL78

Weeting Castle
A ruined 11th-century fortified manor house, situated in a rectangular enclosure and preserving slight remains of a three storeyed cross-wing.

Open any reasonable time.

Free.

⚠ (AM)

WELLS
Somerset
Map **3** ST54

Bishop's Palace
☎ (0749) 78691

The early part of the Palace, the Bishop's Chapel and the ruins of the banqueting hall date from the 13th-century. The undercroft remains virtually unchanged from this date. State Rooms with Long Gallery contain portraits of former Bishops. Ringed with fortifications and a moat, access is gained through a 14th-century gatehouse.

Open Etr–Oct, Thu & Sun, most Weds, & also daily in Aug 2–6 (last admission 5.30).

✱ £1 (ch 14 30p).

P (Market Sq 60 yds) ⅃ ⅄ (ground floor & gardens only) shop ✖ coaches by appointment

Wells Museum 8 Cathedral Green
☎ (0749) 73477

This museum illustrates the history, archaeology and natural history of Wells and the Mendip Hills. Art exhibitions held during the summer.

Open all year; Sep–23 Mar, Wed, Sat & Sun 2–4.30; 24 Mar–28 Sep daily 11–5. (Closed Xmas/New Year).

✱ 30p (ch 16 10p).

P (in street 2hr limit) ⅄ (ground floor only) shop ✖

Watford
—
West Bromwich

WELLS-NEXT-THE-SEA
Norfolk
Map **9** TF94

Wells & Walsingham Light Railway
(Wells Station Sheringham Rd (A149): Walsingham Station, Egmere Rd)

The longest 10¼ inch gauge railway in Britain. A 4 mile journey between Wells and Walsingham. The line is noted for its display of wild flowers and butterflies.

Open Good Fri–Sep daily.

£1 (ch 60p). Return £1.50 (ch £1).

⚠ ⓥ

WELNEY
Norfolk
Map **5** TL59

The Wildfowl Trust Pintail House, Hundred Foot Bank
☎ Ely (0353) 860711

A popular 850 acre wild fowl refuge on the Ouse marshes. Winter home of some 3000 migratory swans and vast numbers of wild geese and ducks. In spring alive with nesting duck, redshank, snipe, ruff, black-tailed godwit etc. Spacious observatory, numerous hides and, on winter evenings, a floodlit lagoon containing hundreds of wild Bewick's Swans.

Open daily 10–5. Evening visits Nov–Feb & May–Aug for parties (prior booking). (Closed Xmas eve & day).

£1.40 (ch 4 free, ch 70p & pen £1). Party 20+.

⚠ ⅄ shop ✖ ⓥ

WELSHPOOL
Powys
Map **7** SJ20

Powis Castle (1m S of Welshpool, pedestrians' access from High St (A490). Cars turn right 1m along A483, Newton Rd. Enter by 2nd drive gate on right)
☎ Welshpool (0938) 4336 (Administrator) or 2952 (Head Gardener)

Medieval castle containing the finest country house collection in Wales. Built c.1200 by Welsh princes, Powis has been beautified by successive generations of Herberts and Clives, the most famous of whom is 'Clive of India'. The Powis gardens are of the highest horticultural and historical importance.

Open 29 Mar–13 Apr, May, Jun & Sep, Wed–Sun 1–6. Jul–Aug Tue–Sun 1–6. BH 11.30–6. Last admission 5.30.

House & Garden £2 (ch 75p). Party 20+.

⚠ ⅃ ⅄ shop ✖ (ex guide dogs) (NT)

Powysland Museum Salop Rd
☎ (0938) 4759

Museum of archaeology and local history.

Open Mon–Fri 11–1 & 2–5; Sat 2–4.30. (Closed Wed in winter).

Free.

P (200 yds) shop ✖

Trelydan Hall (2m N on A490)
☎ (0938) 2773

Wales' most beautiful Tudor home stands on the site of an ancient hospice and Roman Villa, near Offa's Dyke, set in 12 acres of walled gardens and woodland walks. Restored Tudor rooms, wine cellars and attic priest holes. Candlelight dinners, great log fires, harp music and song and traditional Welsh clog-dancing during great annual Xmas festival (Nov and Dec).

Open all year for pre-booked parties only.

⚠ ⅄ (ground floor & gardens only) shop ✖

WEMBLEY
Gt London
Map **London plan 4** pages 174/175.
Wembley Stadium
London plan 4 **56** B4
☎ 01-903 4864

Britain's number one stadium built in 1923, it holds 100,000. Home of the England football team-venue for annual Cup Final and World events. Tour comprises 15-minute audio-visual show, visit to dressing rooms, Royal Box and retiring rooms, a walk up Player's tunnel to pitch complete with sound effects.

Tours on the hour 10–3, 4 in summer (ex 1pm).

(Closed Xmas, New Years day, Thu & days before, during and after a major event).

✱ £2.50 (ch 16 & pen £1.50) Party 20+.

⚠ ⅄ (by prior booking) shop ✖ ⓥ

WENDRON
Cornwall
Map **2** SW63

Poldark Mine (on B3297)
☎ Helston (03265) 3173

Three levels of a Cornish tin mine open to the public with nine museums and a cinema programme on Cornish mining history. One-hour tours given. At the surface are restaurants, shops, gardens and children's amusements. Around the lawns is the West Country's largest collection of working antiques, including a forty-foot high beam engine.

Open Jul–Aug 10–9; Apr, May, Jun, Sep & Oct 10–6.

£2.50 (ch £1.50, pen £2.20).

⚠ ⅃ ⅊ ⅄ (gardens only) shop ⓥ

WEST BROMWICH
West Midlands
Map **7** SP09

Oak House Oak Rd
☎ 021-553 0759

Half-timbered 16th-century house, the

280

result of three separate building phases. The rooms display superb period furnishings and furniture. An Elizabethan garden is at the front of the house.

Open Apr–Sep Mon–Sat 10–8 (ex Thu 10–1 & Sun 2.30–8). Oct–Mar Mon–Sat 10–4.

Free.

P (50 yds) & (ground floor & gardens only) ✗

WESTBURY
Wiltshire
Map **3** ST85

Chalcot House (2¼m SW off A3098)
☎ Chapmanslade (037388) 466

Small Palladian-type villa now believed to have been designed by the great Elizabethan architect, Robert Smythson and built by builder of Longleat, Maynard. Collection of modern pictures, Carolingia and Boer war memorabilia.

Open Jul & Aug only, 2–5 daily. Other times by appointment.

£1.50 (ch free).

⚠ ✗

WESTBURY-ON-SEVERN
Gloucestershire
Map **3** SO71

Westbury Court Garden

A unique example of a 17th-century water garden layout, with pavilions, the earliest survivor of its kind in England.

Open 29 Mar–Oct Wed–Sun & BH Mon 11–6.

£1 (ch 50p).

✗ (NT)

WEST CLANDON
Surrey
Map **4** TQ05

Clandon Park (On A247)
☎ Guildford (0483) 222482

An 18th-century house, built by Leoni for the 2nd Lord Onslow, with fine plasterwork and a fine collection of furniture and pictures.

Open 29 Mar–mid Oct incl BH Mon 2–6. (Closed Mon, Fri & Tue following a BH Mon).

£1.70.

⚠ ⅃ (licensed) & (ground floor & gardens) shop ✗ (NT)

WEST DEAN
West Sussex
Map **4** SU81

West Dean Gardens
☎ Singleton (024363) 301

30 acres of gardens with specimen trees, pergola, summer houses, wild garden and a recently restored walled garden. A Museum of the Garden has also been created with tools and implements, including antique lawnmowers.

West Bromwich
—
Weston-super-Mare

Open Apr–Sep, daily 11–6 (last admission 1hr before closing).

£1 (ch 50p, pen 90p). Party 12 + .

⚠ ⅃ ⅊ & (gardens only) shop & garden centre ✗

WESTERHAM
Kent
Map **5** TQ45

Quebec House (off A25)
☎ (0959) 62206

A 16th- to 17th-century house once the home of General Wolfe. Exhibition.

Open Mar, Sun 2–6; 28 Mar–Oct Mon–Wed, Fri & Sun 2–6 (last admission 5.30pm).

£1.20 (ch 60p).

P (in road, 100 yds) ✗ (NT)

Squerryes Court
☎ (0959) 62345 or 63118

Manor house, c.1681. Owned and occupied by Wardes for 250 years. Fine pictures, china, tapestries and period furniture. Very attractive grounds with lake, azaleas and rhododendrons.

Open Apr–Sep Wed, Sat & Sun, also Suns in Mar & BH 2–6. Last entry to house 5.30pm.

House & grounds £1.40 (ch 14 70p); Grounds only 70p (ch 14 35p). Party.

⚠ (forecourt) ⅊ (weekend) & (gardens only) shop

WEST HOATHLY
West Sussex
Map **5** TQ33

Priest House
☎ Sharpthorne (0342) 810479 (Sussex Archaeological Society)

A 15th-century house, now a small interesting folk museum.

Open Apr–Oct, Mon–Sat 11–5, Sun 2–5. Admission fee payable. Party.

P

WEST MALLING
Kent
Map **5** TQ65

St Leonard's Tower

The surviving part of the former castle or fortified manor house belonging to Bishop Gundulph.

Open any reasonable time.

Free.

& (grounds only) (AM)

WESTONBIRT
Gloucestershire
Map **3** ST88

Westonbirt Arboretum
☎ (066688) 220

Includes splendid examples of rare specimen, temperate, broadleaved, trees. Now incorporated in a 600-acre Forestry Commission estate.

Accessible daily 10–8 or sunset.

✻ 70p (ch & pen 40p). 19 Oct–10 Nov £1 (ch & pen 50p).

⚠ ⅊ (Apr–mid Nov) ⅃ & shop

WESTON PARK
Staffordshire
Map **7** SJ81

(7m W of junction 12 on M6 & 3m N of junction 3 on M54)
☎ Weston-under-Lizard (095276) 207

A fine mansion of 1671. Notable collection of pictures, furniture and tapestries. Fine gardens and vast parkland by Capability Brown. Three lakes, miniature railway, butterfly farm and woodland adventure playground and aquarium. Studio pottery. Special exhibitions and events within the grounds including Horse trials & Point-to-Point. Air Display 20 July. Town & Country Fayre 24/25 Aug, Midland Game Fair 13/14 Sep.

Open Apr, May & Sep wknds, & BHs. Jun & Jul daily ex Mon & Fri. Daily in Aug. Grounds 11–5, House 1–5.

Grounds £1.70 (ch & pen £1.20). House 75p (ch & pen 50p).

⚠ ⅃ (licensed) ⅃ & shop ✗ (in house) ⓥ

See advertisement on page 282

WESTON RHYN
Shropshire
Map **7** SJ23

Tyn-y-Rhos-Hall Museum of Victoriana
(2m W near Bron-y-Garth on unclass rd)
☎ Chirk (0691) 777898

Small manor house, fully furnished in the style of the late 19th century. Many interesting items including a painting of Charles I; also worthy of note is the family chapel.

Open May–Sep, Wed, Thu, Sat & Sun 2.30–6.

✻ £1 (ch 15 50p).

⚠ ⅃ & (ground floor only) ✗ ⓥ

WESTON-SUPER-MARE
Avon
Map **3** ST36

Woodspring Museum Burlington St
☎ (0934) 21028

The museum is housed in the old workshops of the Edwardian Gaslight Company. Around a central courtyard are displays of the Victorian Seaside Holiday, an old chemist's shop, a dairy, a lion fountain with Victorian pavement mosaic and a gallery of wildlife in the district. Other exhibits include Mendip minerals and mining, transport from penny farthing to Weston Autogyro, cameras, a display →

281

of Peggy Nisbet dolls and the Dentist in 1900. Display featuring 'The Weston-super-Mare Story'. Changing exhibitions held in the Art Gallery.

Open Mon–Sat, 10–5. Closes 1–2 Nov–Feb. (Closed Good Fri, Xmas & New Year).

Free.

⚠ (1 hour limit) or P (⅓ mile Locking Rd) 🎱 ♿ (ground floor only) shop ✖

WESTRAY
Orkney
Map **16** HY44

Noltland Castle
Late 16th-century ruined castle which was never completed. It has a fine hall, vaulted kitchen and a notable winding staircase.

Open at all reasonable times on application to Key Keeper.

Free.

(AM)

WEST RUNTON
Norfolk
Map **9** TG14

Norfolk Shire Horse Centre
☎ (026375) 339

A collection of Draught horses and nine breeds of mountain and moorland ponies; horse-drawn machinery, waggons and carts. In addition photographic displays of draught horses past and present. A talk, harnessing and working demonstration twice daily. Video film show. Riding school activities.

Open Etr week & 3 May–Sep, Sun–Fri, daily in Aug, 10–5. Shire Horse demonstrations 11.15 & 3.15. School Parties by appointment Etr–Spring BH.

£1.25 (ch & pen 75p). Party.

⚠ 🎱 ✝ ♿ shop ⓥ

WEST STOW
Suffolk
Map **5** TL87

West Stow Anglo Saxon Village West Stow Country Park
☎ Culford (028484) 718

Weston-super-Mare
—
Weymouth

A unique reconstruction of a pagan Anglo-Saxon village, rebuilt on the site of the excavated settlement dated AD 500. The houses have been reconstructed using the same techniques, tools and building materials, as were used in the original farming village. Situated in the 125 acre West Stow Country Park. Open day 22 Jun.

Open Apr–Oct, Tue–Sat 2–5, Sun & BH 11–1 & 2–5.

40p (ch 20p). Party.

⚠ 🎱 ♿ (ground floor & gardens only) shop

WESTWOOD
Wiltshire
Map **3** ST85

Westwood Manor
A beautiful 15th- to 17th-century house showing fine Jacobean plasterwork. Modern topiary garden.

Open 30 Mar–29 Sep, Sun & Mon 2–6.

£1.50.

⚠ (NT)

WEST WYCOMBE
Buckinghamshire
Map **4** SU89

West Wycombe Park
☎ High Wycombe (0494) 24411

Rebuilt for Sir Francis Dashwood, c1765, and situated in a fine park containing garden temples by Capability Brown and Humphry Repton. Notable furnishings and painted ceilings.

House & grounds open Jun, Mon–Fri; Jul & Aug, Sun–Fri 2–6. Grounds only also open Etr, May Day & Spring BH Sun & Mon, 2–6. (Closed Good Fri).

£2. Grounds only £1.20.

(NT) & (NGS)

West Wycombe Caves
☎ High Wycombe (0494) 24411

Built between 1748 and 1752. The caves are said to have been used as a meeting place for the Hell Fire Club. The entrance to the caves is half way up West Wycombe Hill, and consists of a large forecourt with flint walls, from which a brick tunnel leads into the caves.

Open 5 Mar–24 May, wkdays 1–6; 28 May–8 Sep, Mon–Sat 11–6; 10 Sep–30 Oct Mon–Sat 1–5. Also Sun & BH Apr–Oct 11–6. Nov–Mar, Sat & Sun only 1–5.

£2 (ch & pen £1). Party 20 + .

⚠ 🎱 ✝ shop & garden centre ✖

West Wycombe Motor Museum
Cockshoot Farm, Chorley Rd
☎ High Wycombe (0494) 443329

A museum for motor enthusiasts and children with a changing exhibition of historic cars, bikes, stationary engines and nostalgia set in beautiful 18th-century timbered barns where the essence is on quality rather than quantity. Colour video films and free quiz for children.

Open Apr–Nov Suns 11–6, also wkdays Jul & Aug 2–5. Other times by arrangement.

95p (pen 75p & ch 50p). Party 20 + .

⚠ 🎱 ✝ shop

WEYHILL
Hampshire
Map **4** SU34

The Hawk Conservancy
☎ (026477) 2252

A specialist collection of birds of prey of the world, including hawks, falcons, eagles, owls, vultures and kites. Birds are flown daily, weather permitting.

Open daily Mar–Oct from 10.30am (last admission spring & autumn 4pm, summer 5pm). Details not confirmed for 1986.

✳ £1.50 (ch 14 75p, pen £1). Children must be accompanied by an adult.

⚠ 🎱 shop ✖

WEYMOUTH
Dorset
Map **3** SY67

The Earl and Countess of Bradford invite you to visit

WESTON PARK
the leading historic home of the West Midlands
Breathtakingly beautiful 17th Century House ★ Studio Pottery
★ Aquarium ★ Nature & Architectural Trails ★ Picnic Areas
★ Weston Park Railway ★ Special Events Programme ★
Cafeteria & Licensed Restaurant ★ Museum of Country
Bygones. Butterfly Farm.
Caravan Rally park ★ Gourmet Dinners ★ Conference and
Promotional Events throughout the year.
**For brochure containing details of opening times telephone Weston-under-Lizard (095276) 207.
Weston-under-Lizard is 6 miles west of Junction 12 on M6 and 3 miles north of Junction 3 on M54.**

Sea Life Centre Lodmoor Country Park
☎ (0305) 788255

Britain's largest, most exciting marine life display. Hundreds of fish and sea creatures can be explored from the 'Ocean Tunnel', 'Cliffwalk', 'Island Walkway' and 'Rockpool Touch Tanks'. Also a 'Theme Unit' showing Man's involvement with the oceans and the 'Blue Whale Splash Pool' with adventure playground.

Open end Feb–Dec daily 10–5 (later in summer).

✳ £1.75 (ch & pen £1). Party.

⚠ 🄩 ⬧ shop ✘

Tudor House 3 Trinity St
☎ (0305) 789742

An early 17th-century house which has been restored and refurbished to typify the harbourside house of a middle-class family of the period.

Open Weds, Jun–Sep 2.30–4.30. (Last tour 4.30 pm). Also 1st Sunday in the month all year, 2.30–4.

25p (ch 10p, students 15p).

P (limited 100 yds) ✘

Weymouth Museum Westham Rd
☎ (0305) 774246

An illustrated survey of the history of Weymouth and Portland. Numerous temporary exhibitions including 'I do like to be beside the seaside', an exhibition of traditional seaside entertainments.

Open summer, daily Mon–Fri 10–8, Sat 10–5.30, Sun 10.30–4.30; winter, daily ex Sun 10–5 (1pm Wed).

Admission fee payable.

P (100 yds) ⬧ shop

WHALLEY
Lancashire
Map **7** SD73

Whalley Abbey
☎ (025482) 2268

The Abbey ruins are in delightful gardens reaching down to the river. Guided tours for parties. Craft centre. Open-air service and 'Its a Knockout' competition 26 May and 'Open Day' 25 August.

Open daily, 10–dusk. Craft Centre Etr–Sep 11.30–4.30.

50p (ch 4 free, ch 13 & pen 25p). Party 12+.

⚠ 🄩 (parties only) ⌭ ⬧ (gardens only) shop

WHIPSNADE
Bedfordshire
Map **4** TL01

Whipsnade Park Zoo
☎ (0582) 872171

Open-air zoo situated on edge of Chilterns. Over 2,000 animals and birds can be seen in near natural surroundings in the 500-acre park. Children's zoo, water mammals exhibit displaying dolphins.

Weymouth
—
Whittington

Cars may drive round the zoo at an extra charge. A zoo train operates in the park according to demand. Steam Railway runs through White Rhino enclosure Apr–Oct.

Open Mon–Sat 10–6, Sun & BH 10–7 or sunset. (Closed Xmas day).

£2.85 (ch 5–15 £1.40, pen £1.15).

⚠ (main carpark outside Zoo free) 🄩 shop ✘ Coaches not admitted into park Jul, Aug & BHs

WHITBY
North Yorkshire
Map **8** NZ81

Whitby Abbey

Considerable remains of fine church dating from the 13th century. Damaged by shell fire during the 1914–18 war.

Open † see end of gazetteer.

✳ 50p (ch & pen 25p).

⚠ (AM)

Whitby Museum Pannett Park
☎ (0947) 602908

The museum portrays the history of the town. Next door is the Pannett Art Gallery.

Museum & Art Gallery open May–Sep, Mon–Sat 9.30–5.30, Sun 2–5; Oct–Apr, Mon, Tue, Thu & Fri 10.30–1, Wed & Sat 10.30–4, Sun 2–4; BH's, normal opening times. (Closed Xmas & New Year hols).

30p (ch 16 15p).

P (in road & 200 yds) shop ✘

WHITE CASTLE
Gwent
Map **3** SO41

(7m NE of Abergavenny on unclass road N of B4233)

An impressive 12th- to 13th-century Marcher stronghold situated on a hill, with a gatehouse and towers, erected by Hubert de Burgh.
The finest of the trio of trilateral castles of Gwent. For the other two see **Grosmont** and **Skenfrith**.

Open see end of gazetteer.

✳ 50p (ch 16 & pen 25p).

⚠ (AM Cadw)

WHITEHAVEN
Cumbria
Map **11** NX91

Whitehaven Museum & Art Gallery
Market Pl
☎ (0946) 3111 ext 307

Lower gallery devoted to approximately 20 exhibitions per year. The upper gallery features local history and Whitehaven-made pottery. Slide/tape shows usually featured in upper gallery.

Open Mon, Tue & Thu–Sat 10–5. (Closed BH).

Free.

P (50 yds) ⬧ (ground floor only) shop ✘ (ex guide dogs)

WHITHORN
Dumfries and Galloway Wigtownshire
Map **10** NX44

Whithorn Priory

This site is associated with the 5th-century mission at St Ninian. The ruins are scanty but the Norman doorway of the nave is notable. Group of early Christian monuments, includes the Latinus stone dating from the 5th century.

Open see end of gazetteer.

50p (ch & pen 25p).

(AM)

WHITNEY-ON-WYE
Hereford and Worcester
Map **3** SO24

Cwmmau Farmhouse, Brilley

Early 17th-century timber-framed and stone-tiled farmhouse.

Open Etr, Spring, May & Summer BH, Sat–Mon 2–6; other times by previous written appointment with the tenant.

80p.

⌭ (only by previous arrangement) (NT)

WHITTINGHAM
Northumberland
Map **12** NU00

Callaly Castle (Grounds & Gardens)
(2m W Entrance by west lodge only)
☎ (066574) 663

A 17th-century mansion incorporating 13th-century tower, with later alterations. Interesting pictures and furnishings and saloon with 18th-century plasterwork.

Open 4 May–16 Jun & 6 Jul–15 Sep, Sat, Sun & BH 2.15–5.30 (last tour 5pm). Other days for parties on application to the Estate Office, Callaly Castle, Alnwick or telephone. Dates to be confirmed.

Admission fee payable.

⚠ ⬧ (ground floor & gardens only) ✘

WHITTINGTON
Staffordshire
Map **7** SK10

Whittington Barracks, Staffordshire Regiment Museum
☎ (0543) 433333 ext 229

An interesting museum displaying details of the Regiment's battle honours; captured trophies, weapons old and new, uniforms past and present, and a special display of medals.

Open Mon–Fri 8.30–4.30; Sat, Sun & BH by appointment only.

Free.

⚠ ⬧ shop ✘

283

WICHENFORD
Hereford and Worcester
Map **3** SO76

Dovecote

17th-century half-timbered, black and white dovecote.

Open daily until sunset.

20p.

(NT)

WICK
Highland *Caithness*
Map **15** ND34

Caithness Glass Harrow Hill
☎ (0955) 2286

All aspects of glass blowing on view. There is also a factory seconds shop.

Open Mon–Fri 9–5: Sat 9–1 (4.30 May–Sep).

Free.

⚠ ☕ ♿ shop ✖ (ex shop)

Castle of Old Wick

A four storeyed ruined square tower, known also as Castle Oliphant, probably of 12th century.

Accessible except when adjoining rifle range is in use.

Free.

(AM)

Wick Heritage Centre
19–27 Bank Row
☎ (0955) 4179

A complex of four houses, yards and outbuildings, in the 'Telford' planned area of the town, near the harbour. The museum illustrates history from Neolithic times, with emphasis on the fishing industry in the 19th and 20th centuries.

Open Etr 10.30–12.30 & 2–5; Jun 2–5; Jul & Aug 10.30–12.30 & 2–5; Sep 2–5, then Sat & Sun 2–5. Details not confirmed for 1986.

Admission fee payable.

⚠ ✖

WIGHT, ISLE OF
Map **4**

Places of interest are indicated on location map 4. Full details will be found under individual placenames within the gazetteer.

WILDERHOPE
Shropshire
Map **7** SO59

Wilderhope Manor (off B4371)

A fine 16th-century house with 17th-century plaster ceilings. Views of Corvedale. Leased to Youth Hostels Association.

Open 30 Mar–Sep, Wed & Sat; Oct–Mar, Sat only 2–4.30.

80p.

(NT)

WILDFOWL TRUST
See **Arundel, Caerlaverock, Martin Mere, Peakirk, Slimbridge, Washington** and **Welney**.

WILLENHALL
West Midlands
Map **7** SO99

Lock Museum
Willenhall Library, Walsall St
☎ Walsall (0922) 21244 ext. 3115

The aim of the museum is to interpret all aspects of the locksmith's trade and the people who are employed in it, from the earliest times to the present day and from all over the world. There are locks on display to demonstrate the main developments over the years of lock mechanisms and range from padlocks no bigger than a finger nail to 32lb heavyweights, from mechanisms more akin to fine ornaments to the harsh reality of the prison asylum lock.

Open Mon, Tue, Thu & Fri 9.30–6, Sat 9.30–12.30 & 2–4.30. (Closed Wed, Sun & BH).

Free.

P shop ✖

WILLOUGHBRIDGE
Staffordshire
Map **7** SJ73

Dorothy Clive Garden

200-year-old gravel quarry converted into woodland garden, with daffodils, rhododendrons, and azaleas. Water and rock gardens. Rare trees and shrubs over 7 acres.

Open daily Mar–Nov, 11–7.30 (or dusk).

75p (ch 20p).

⚠ ♿

WILMCOTE
Warwickshire
Map **4** SP15

Mary Arden's House
☎ Stratford-upon-Avon (0789) 293455

The picturesque, half-timbered, Tudor childhood home of Shakespeare's mother. Farming museum in barns.

Open all year (ex 24–26 Dec, New Years Day am, Good Fri am); Apr–Oct, weekdays 9–6 (5pm Oct), Sun 10–6 (5pm Oct); Nov–Mar, weekdays only 9–4.30.

£1 (ch 17 40p). Inclusive tickets to all five Shakespearian properties £3.80 (ch £1.50).

⚠ shop ✖ (ex guide dogs)

WILMINGTON
East Sussex
Map **5** TQ50

Priory
☎ Alfriston (0323) 870537 (Sussex Archaeological Society)

Remains of a 13th-century Benedictine foundation now housing a small agricultural museum.

Open mid Mar–mid Oct Mon & Wed–Sat 11–5.30 Sun 2–5.30 (last entry 5pm).

Admission fee payable. Party.

P Ⓥ

WILTON (near Marlborough)
Wiltshire
Map **4** SU26

Wilton Windmill (½m, NE on unclass rd off A338)
☎ Marlborough (0672) 870268

A 150 year old mill which has stood idle since the 1920s now fully restored as a working windmill capable of grinding flour. Volunteer guides show visitors round the mill. Wholemeal flour, stoneground at the windmill, may be purchased.

Open Etr–end Sep on Suns & BHs only from 2–5. Parties at other times by arrangement.

✱ 60p (ch 30p).

⚠ ⊼ shop ✖

WILTON (near Salisbury)
Wiltshire
Map **4** SU03

Wilton House
☎ Salisbury (0722) 743115

A magnificent 16th to 19th-century house by Inigo Jones, Holbein and James Wyatt. Home of the Earls of Pembroke for over 400 years. It contains a world-famous collection of paintings, furniture and sculpture, in state apartments, including the great double and single 'cube' rooms. Exhibition of 7,000 miniature model soldiers, palace doll house and 400 sq ft working model railway. Unparalleled settings of lawns and Cedars of Lebanon. 'Fine Art and Antiques Fair' 14–16 March.

Open 25 Mar–12 Oct Tue–Sat & BH 11–6, Sun 1–6 (last admission 5.15pm).

£2.40 (ch 16 £1.20, students, pen & party 20+ £1.60). Grounds only 90p (ch 60p).

⚠ ☕ (licensed) ♿ shop & garden centre ✖

Wilton Royal Carpet Factory Craft Exhibition
☎ Salisbury (0722) 742733

The oldest carpet factory in the world, it is now possible to visit an exhibition of the old carpet making crafts and also tour the modern factory.

Open Mon–Fri 10–4. (Closed BH's & factory hols).

£1.50 (reduced rates for ch, students & pen).

⚠ ☕ shop ✖

WIMBORNE MINSTER
Dorset
Map **4** SZ09

Kingston Lacy House & Park (1½m W on B3082)
17th-century house remodelled by Sir Charles Barry in 1835; one of the finest private picture collections in the country with works by Van Dyck, Lely, Titian, Rubens, Reynolds and Velasquez.

Open 28 Apr–Oct, Sat–Wed 2–6, Park noon–6. Last admission ½ hour before closing.
£2.50.
📽 shop (NT)

Priest's House Museum High St
☎ (0202) 882533 or 886604
Has on view a wealth of exhibits of local interest including Roman objects from local excavations. Garden open to public.
Open Etr Mon–Sep, Mon–Sat, 10.30–12.30 & 2–4.30. Other dates as announced locally. Special exhibition at Xmas.
30p (ch 10p).
P 🎋 ᕒ (ground floor & gardens only) ✖

WIMPOLE
Cambridgeshire
Map **4** TL35

Wimpole Hall (8m SW of Cambridge at junct of A14 and A603)
☎ Cambridge (0223) 207257
A large 18th-century country mansion with Lord Harley's library. Soane's yellow drawing room and the chapel painted by Thornhill. The park was landscaped by Capability Brown, Repton and Sanderson Miller.
Open 29 Mar–26 Oct Tue–Thu, Sat, Sun & BH Mon 2–6.
£1.90 (ch 95p). Party 15 + .
📽 ᕒ wheelchairs available (NT)

Wimpole Home Farm
☎ Cambridge (0223) 207257
When built in 1794 the Home Farm was one of the most advanced agricultural enterprises in the country. The Great Barn, now restored, holds a display of farm machinery and implements of the kind used by Wimpole over the past two centuries. The parkland is now grazed by rare breeds of livestock, once common in the 18th and 19th centuries and there are paddocks for viewing these animals at the farm. Special children's corner.

Wimborne Minster
—
Winchcombe

Open 29 Mar–26 Oct, daily (ex Mon & Fri) 10.30–5. Open BH Mons. (Closed Good Fri).
£1.50 (ch 75p). Party.
🅰 📽 🎋 ᕒ shop ✖ (ex guide dogs) (NT)

WINCHCOMBE
Gloucestershire
Map **4** SP02

Simms International Police Collection
Town Hall
☎ (0242) 602925
The Folk Museum exhibits 17th & 18th century agricultural and domestic items, old newspapers, documents and Winchcombe 'folk' items. Exhibition of Winchcombe pottery in June. The Police Museum houses one of the largest and most notable collections of helmets, badges, uniforms, weapons, equipment and documents from both Britain and other countries including Canada, Monaco, Japan and USA.
Open end of Mar–Oct, 10–5. (Closed Sun except BH).
30p (ch & pen 20p). Family £1. Party.
P (50 yds) ᕒ

Sudeley Castle & Gardens
☎ (0242) 602308
Home and burial place of Queen Katherine Parr. Buildings date mainly from →

For an interesting day out visit the famous
Wilton Royal Carpet Factory
SEE how the skills developed for over 300 years in the manufacture of quality carpets in today's factory. Also visit our Exhibition of traditional carpet crafts to see how carpets were made at various times in history. Audio-Visual display too! We are located 3 miles west of Salisbury on the A36. Guided tours morning and afternoon throughout the year. For details, booking etc., RING SALISBURY (0722) 742733.

15th century. Art collection contains Turners, Constables etc. Antique furniture, porcelain, tapestries. Collection of Victorian photographs and letters. '400 Years of Toys'–largest private collection of toys on public view in Europe. Extensive gardens. Children's log fortress. Waterfowl collection.

Open Apr–Oct daily, grounds 11–5.30, castle and museum 12–5.

✱ £2.80 (ch £1.60, pen £2.40).

⚠ ⚗ (licensed) ⊓ shop & garden centre ✗

WINCHELSEA
East Sussex
Map **5** TQ91

Winchelsea Museum
☎ (07976) 257
Located in the restored 14th-century court hall, the museum contains a collection illustrating the history of this Cinque Port.

Open May–Sep, weekdays 10.30–12.30 & 2.30–5.30, Sun 2.30–5.30. Dates not confirmed for 1986.

✱ 35p (ch 15p).

P (in street) ✗

WINCHESTER
Hampshire
Map **4** SU42
See also **Avington**

Guildhall Gallery Broadway
☎ (0962) 68166 ext 296
On show are local topographical views. Temporary exhibitions.

Open during exhibitions, Tue–Sat 10–5, Sun & Mon 2–5. (Closed Mon in winter). Subject to alteration.

Free.

P (100 yds) ⚗ ⚙ shop ✗

Hospital of St Cross
(S of city, off St Cross Rd)
☎ (0962) 51375
Founded originally in 1136, and extended in 1446, the oldest charitable institution in Britain still functioning. The Wayfarer's Dole of bread and ale is given at the Porter's lodge, during opening hours. Brother's hall, old kitchen, church and garden.

Open daily (ex Sun & PHs) Apr–Sep 9.30–12.30 & 2–5; Oct–Mar 10.30–12.30 & 2–3.30.

60p (ch 25p, students & pen 40p).

P ⚙ (gardens only) shop ✗

Royal Hussars Museum Southgate St
☎ (0962) 61781 ext 239
Outstanding uniforms and photo displays lead from the founding in 1715 through Victorian periods of service in India, the Crimea and Africa to the 20th century. Of special interest is the great cupboard in which Trooper Fowler was concealed for 3 years during World War I, and a life-size reconstruction of a dug-out. Many

Winchcombe
–
Windsor

magnificent paintings including Wollen's 'The Scouts'.

Open Tue after Etr–Oct Tue–Fri 11–4, Sat & Sun 2–4.

20p (ch & pen 10p). Party 20 + .

P (City Parks, 200 yds) shop ✗

Serle's House Southgate St
☎ (0962) 61782 ext 261
A fine Baroque-style 18th-century house, now incorporating the Royal Hampshire Regiment museum and memorial garden.

Open Mon–Fri 10–12.30 & 2–4. (Closed BH).

Free.

P ⚙ (ground floor only) ✗

Westgate Museum High St
☎ (0962) 68166 ext 269
The medieval west gate of the city, containing exhibition of armour.

Open daily Mon–Sat 10–5 & Sun 2–5 (4pm Nov–Mar). (Closed Mon Nov–Mar; Good Fri, Xmas & New Years day).

15p (ch 5p). Party (school) free.

P (Tower St, 100 yds) shop ✗

The Great Hall of Winchester Castle
Castle Avenue, off High St
☎ (0962) 54411 ext 366
The only surviving portion of the castle is the notable great hall of 1235 with Purbeck marble columns. At the west end is the legendary Round Table of King Arthur and his knights.

Open all year daily 10–5. (Closed Good Fri & Xmas).

Free (contributions).

P (100 yds) ⚙ shop ✗

Winchester City Museum The Square
☎ (0962) 68166 ext 269
Well-laid out display relating to the archaeology and history of the city and central Hampshire. Reconstructed 19th-century chemist's shop.

Open Mon–Sat 10–5, Sun 2–5 (4pm Nov–Mar). (Closed Good Fri, Xmas, New Year's day & Mons Nov–Mar).

20p (ch free).

P ⚙ (ground floor only) shop ✗

Winchester College College St
☎ (0962) 64242
One of England's oldest public schools, founded by William of Wykeham in 1382. Of special interest is the chapel, and during school terms, Fromond's chantry and the cloisters, which are accessible weekdays 10–6 (Sun 2–6) in summer; 10–4 (Sun 2–4) in winter.

Guided tours (ex Sun am) 11, 2 & 3.15 (also 4.30 May–Aug) subject to alteration.

20p. Guided tours 50p (ch 16 25p).

P (limited) ⚙ (ground floor only) dogs discouraged

WINDERMERE
Cumbria
Map **7** SD49
(see also BOWNESS ON WINDERMERE)

Lake District National Park Visitor Centre Brockhole (on A591)
☎ (09662) 2231
19th-century house in 32 acres of gardens and woodland on the eastern shore of Lake Windermere. National Park Visitor Centre with audio-visual displays, films, 'Living Lakeland' exhibition and information centre and bookshop. Special family events during schools hols. Lake launch trips daily in summer and garden tours Wed & Fri, May to September. 'Teddy Bears Picnics' in spring and summer. World of Beatrix Potter, through the season. Children's,Squirrel Nutkin Trail. Lake shore nature trail. Play area.

Open late Mar–early Nov daily from 10am (closing time varies with season). Winter opening for parties by arrangement.

£1.20 (ch 5–18 60p). Party.

⚠ ⚗ ⊓ ⚙ (ground floor & gardens only, on request) shop

Steamboat Museum Rayrigg Rd
☎ (09662) 5565
Unique collection of Victorian and Edwardian steamboats and other historic sail- and motor-boats. Many still afloat and in working order in our wet dock. Various displays concerning life on and around the lake. Model Boat Regatta May 17 & 18. Steamboat Rally July. Education facilities on request.

Open Apr–Oct, Mon–Sat 10–5, Sun 2–5. Steamboat trips subject to availability and weather, Mon–Sat.

£1.50 (ch 85p, pen £1.25). Family ticket £4. Party.

⚠ ⚗ ⊓ ⚙ shop

WINDSOR
Berkshire
Map **4** SU97

Household Cavalry Museum
Combermere Barracks, St Leonards Rd
☎ (07535) 68222 ext 203
One of the finest military museums in Britain. Uniforms, weapons, horse furniture and armour of the Household Cavalry from 1600 to the present.

Open all year Mon–Fri (ex BH) 10–1 & 2–5; Sun, 2nd wknd in May–1st wknd Sep (ex BH Suns) 10–1 & 2–4.

Free.

P (in road) ⚙ shop

Madame Tussaud's Royalty & Empire Exhibition Windsor and Eton Central Railway Station
☎ (07535) 57837
Exhibition in original station buildings

depicting Queen Victoria's Diamond Jubilee Celebrations with full-size replica of Royal Train and theatre presentation. Open daily 9.30–5.30. (Closed Xmas day). ✻ £2.35 (ch 15 £1.60, pen £2). Party 20+. P (100 yds) & (ground floor only) shop ✕

Windsor Castle
☎ (07535) 68286

A restored Norman royal castle with 19th-century additions for George IV by Wyattville. (See also below).

Castle precinct open daily Jan–29 Mar 10–4.15; 30 Mar–30 Apr. (Closed am 21 Apr) 10–5.15; May–Aug 10–7.15. (Closed 16 Jun); Sep–25 Oct 10–5.15; 26 Oct–Dec 10–4.15.

Always subject to closure, sometimes at very short notice.

Free.

P (400 yds) & shop ✕

St George's Chapel
☎ (07535) 65538

Open weekdays 10.45–3.45 (4pm 30 Mar–25 Oct), Suns 2–3.45. (closed 2–24 Jan, 20, 21 & 27 Apr, 13–17 Jun, Xmas Eve & Xmas day & occasionally at short notice.)

£1.30 (ch 5 free. Ch 16 & pen 60p).

P (500 yds) & shop ✕

State Apartments
☎ (07535) 68286

Open Mon–Sat, 3 Jan–9 Mar 10.30–3;

Windsor

daily 10 May–1 Jun & 28 Jun–23 Oct 10.30–5 (Suns 1.30–5); Mon–Sat, 26 Oct–7 Dec 10.30–3.

Always subject to closure, sometimes at very short notice.

£1.40 (ch 5 free, ch 15 & pen 60p).

P (400 yds) & (by prior arrangement) shop ✕

Queen Mary's Dolls House & Exhibition of Drawings
☎ (07535) 68286

Open 26 Oct–30 Apr, Mon–Sat 10.30–3 (5pm 30 Mar–30 Apr); May–25 Oct, daily 10.30–5, Sun 1.30–5. (Closed 1 & 2 Jan, Good Fri, 17 June & 21–26 Dec). 60p (ch 5 free, ch 15 & pen 20p).

P (400 yds) & by prior arrangement) shop ✕

Royal Mews Exhibition Windsor Castle
☎ (07535) 68286

Open 26 Oct–30 Apr, Mon–Sat 10.30–3 (5pm 30 Mar–30 Apr); May–25 Oct daily. (Sun 1–9 May 1.30–5). (Closed 1 & 2 Jan, Good Fri & 21–26 Dec.)

60p (ch 5 free, ch 15 & pen 20p).

P (400 yds) & shop ✕

Savill Garden (Windsor Great Park)
(reached via Wick Ln, Engelfield Green, near Egham)
☎ (07535) 60222

A famous woodland garden at its peak in spring but producing a wealth of colour and interest throughout the seasons. A formal area of roses and herbaceous borders offers much beauty in summer.

Open daily 10–6 (or sunset if earlier). (Closed 25–28 Dec).

£1.50 (ch 16 accompanied free, pen £1.30), half price Nov–Feb. party.

⚠ ⚟ (licensed, Mar–Oct) & shop garden centre ✕ Ⓥ

See advertisement on page 288

Valley Gardens (Windsor Great Park)
near Virginia Water
☎ (07535) 60222

An area of some 300 acres noted especially for an outstanding range of rhododendrons, camellias, magnolias and other woodland trees and shrubs. Outstanding beauty at all seasons of the year.

Open all year 8–sunset.

Free to pedestrians.

⚠'(£1) ⚟ (licensed, Mar–Oct) & ⚙

Windsor Safari Park and Seaworld
Winkfield Rd (SW of town on B3022)
☎ (07535) 69841

Drive through wild animal reserves. Shows include: killer whale and dolphin, →

If you missed Queen Victoria's Diamond Jubilee in 1897, don't miss it now.

Madame Tussaud's have re-created this spectacular historic moment in its original surroundings, which is climaxed by a breathtaking theatre show spanning Queen Victoria's 60 Glorious Years.

OPPOSITE WINDSOR CASTLE

MADAME TUSSAUD'S -AT WINDSOR-

ROYALTY & EMPIRE

Queen Victoria's Diamond Jubilee 1897

AT WINDSOR & ETON CENTRAL RAILWAY STATION OPEN EVERY DAY (except Christmas Day) 9.30 a.m.– 5.30p.m.

287

parrot, high diving (summer only), birds of prey, sealion, daily feeding of big cats. Walk through Butterfly House. Children's farmyard, boating lakes, soft play centre and more.

Open daily from 10am. (Closed Xmas day).

✱ £4.50 (ch 4–14 & pen £3.50). Party 20 + .
⚲ ⏛ (licensed) ⟊ ♿ shop ✘ (free kennels provided). Ⓥ

WING
Buckinghamshire
Map **4** SP82

Ascott

A 19th-century mansion housing notable works of art including French and Chippendale furniture and oriental porcelain. There is also a fine garden.

House & gardens open 22 Jul–21 Sep; Tue–Sun 2–6, also Aug BH Mon. (Closed 26 Aug). Garden only Apr–17 Jul; Thu & last Sun in each month also 28 Sep 2–6. Garden only last Sun in each month.

House & garden £2. Garden only £1.20 (NT) & (NGS)

WINSLOW
Buckinghamshire
Map **4** SP72

Winslow Hall
☎ (029671) 3433

Windsor
—
Wisley

Built in 1700 the Hall was almost certainly designed by Wren. It retains most of its original features and has recently been restored and redecorated. 18th-century English furniture. Chinese art and some fine clocks and pictures. Garden.

Open Jul–15 Sep daily ex Mon (& weekends only 15–30 Sep), also BH ex Boxing day 2–5.30. Gardens only Sun in May & Jun 2–5. Other times by appointment. Details not confirmed for 1986.

£1.50 (ch 12 free). Garden only 75p. Party.

⚲ ⏛ (Jul–Sep) ♿ (garden only) shop ✘ 🍴 (ex by appointment) Ⓥ

WINSTER
Derbyshire
Map **8** SK26

Market House

Stone-built 17th- or 18th-century market house in main street of village.

Open Apr–Sep, Sat, Sun & BH Mon 2–6 (or sunset).

Free.

P shop ✘ (NT)

WISBECH
Cambridgeshire
Map **5** TF40

Packover House
☎ (0945) 583463

The house dates from 1722 and its interior has Rococo decoration in plaster and wood. The garden is a delightful and colourful example of Victorian planting.

Open 29 Mar–12 Oct. May–Sep daily ex Thu & Fri. Apr & Oct wknds & BH only.

£1.20 (ch 60p pen 90p).

✘ (NT) (NGS)

Wisbech and Fenland Museum
☎ (0945) 583817

Contains fine collection of ceramics and objects d'art. Also archaeology, natural history and Fenland life.

Open Tue–Sat 10–5 (4pm Oct–Mar). (Closed BH).

Free. Museum library and archives available by appointment only.

P (200 yds) shop ✘ coaches by appointment

WISLEY
Surrey
Map **4** TQ05

Wisley Garden
☎ Guildhall (0483) 224163

The famous and extensive garden of the

288

*Royal Horticultural Society. Showing
every aspect of gardening at its best.
Ornamental, fruit, vegetables,
glasshouses and specialist gardens.
Advisory service.*

Open all year Mon–Sat 10–7 or dusk
(4.30pm Jan, Nov & Dec), Sun 2–7 or
dusk. (Closed 25 Dec). Glasshouses close
at 4.15 or sunset Mon–Fri & 4.45 wknds &
BH.

£1.80 (ch 6 90p). Party 20+ (booked in
advance).

🅐 ⬛ (licensed) ⟋⟍ ♿ shop & garden
centre ✖

WITCHINGHAM, GREAT (Lenwade)
Norfolk
Map **9** TG01

Norfolk Wildlife Park
(1m NW off A1067)
☎ Norwich (0603) 872274

*Zoological park of 50 acres, with
comprehensive collection of British and
European mammals in natural
surroundings. Great variety of birds in
specially built aviaries. Children's model
farm & pets corner, exciting play area with
modern equipment. Trained reindeer pull
a wheeled sleigh round the park most
afternoons and can be seen being
harnessed and worked.*

Open daily 10.30–6 (sunset if earlier).

£1.90 (ch 90p, pen £1.70). Party.

Wisley
—
Woburn

🅐 ⬛ (licensed) (Apr–Oct) ⟋⟍ ♿ shop
(Apr–Oct) ✖ Ⓥ

WITCOMBE, GREAT
Gloucestershire
Map **3** SO91

Witcombe Roman Villa

*A large courtyard Roman Villa in which a
hypocaust and several mosaic pavements
are preserved.*

Open at any reasonable time. (Keys at
farmhouse adjoining).

Free.

♿ (AM)

WITNEY
Oxfordshire
Map **4** SP31

Cogges Farm Museum
Cogges (½m SE off A4022)
☎ (0993) 72602

*Farm set in Edwardian period exhibiting
the agriculture of Oxfordshire, together
with local breeds of livestock. Farmhouse
kitchens, dairy and walled gardens.
Agricultural and craft demonstrations
weekends. Historic trail.*

Open 29 Apr–26 Oct, Tue–Sun & BH Mon
10.30–5.30 daily.

£1.50 (ch, pen & students 80p). Party
10+.

🅐 ⬛ (licensed) ⟋⟍ ♿ (ground floor only)
shop

WOBURN
Bedfordshire
Map **4** SP93

Woburn Abbey and Deer Park
☎ (052525) 666

*Woburn Abbey is a palatial 18th-century-
mansion with State apartments and
pictures. The private apartments are
shown when not in use by the family. It
stands in a 3000 acre park, famous for its
collection of wildlife. A programme of
events from May to September.*

Abbey open Sat & Sun only 4 Jan–23 Mar,
11–4.45; daily 24 Mar–26 Oct, 11–5.45
(6.15pm Sun). Last admission 45 minutes
before closing time. **Deer Park** open Sat
& Sun only 4 Jan–23 Mar, 10.30–3.45,
daily 24 Mar–26 Oct 10–4.45 (5.45 Sun).

✳ **Abbey & Deer Park** £2.80 (ch 5–15 £1,
pen £2.20). Family Ticket (2 adults & 2–4
ch) £6.50–£8.50. **Deer Park only** car &
passengers £1.50. Motorcycles &
passengers £1.

🅐 ⬛ ♿ (park & gardens only) shop &
garden centre ✖ (in house ex guide dogs)
Ⓥ

WOBURN ABBEY

OPENED AND RUN BY OUR FAMILY...
FOR YOU AND YOUR FAMILY

Set in a beautifully landscaped deer park, the Abbey contains a most impressive and important
private collection of furniture, paintings, porcelain and silver. There are attractive gardens and
grounds with extensive picnic areas. Unique 40-shop Antiques Centre, a Pottery and a Garden
Centre and Camping Exhibition. Gift Shops.

OPEN Saturdays & Sundays Only from 4th January to 23rd March
1986 Every Day from 24th March to 26th October

Situated 4/5 miles between M1 (exits 12/13) and A5 (turn at Hockliffe)
with London, Oxford, Cambridge and Leicester only approximately 1 hour by road.
WOBURN ABBEY, WOBURN, BEDFORDSHIRE, MK43 0TP. TELEPHONE: WOBURN (052525) 666.

Woburn Wild Animal Kingdom and Leisure Park
☎ (052525) 407

Lies a short distance from Woburn Abbey and is a safari and leisure complex with lions, tigers, monkeys, giraffes and elephants and many other species in the collection; the many other attractions include the Carousel, Rainbow Ride, Boating Lakes, Cabin Lift, Amusements Centre, Sea Lion Show and Pets Corner.

Open daily 15 Mar–2 Nov (weather permitting) from 10am (closing times vary).

Inclusive admission charge £4 (ch 4–15 & pen £3). Party.

⚠ 🍴 (licensed) 🚻 ♿ shop ✖ Ⓥ

WOLVERHAMPTON
West Midlands
Map **7** SO99

Bantock House Museum
Bantock Park, Bradmore Rd
☎ (0902) 24548

This 19th-century house contains important collections of English enamels, japanned tin and paper-maché products of the Midlands. Also shown are early Worcester porcelain, pottery, English and foreign dolls and toys.

Open Mon–Fri 10–7, Sat 10–6 & Sun 2–5. BH Mon & Tue 2–5 (Closed Good Fri, Etr Sun, Xmas & New Years day).

Free.

⚠ ♿ (ground floor only) ✖

Bilston Museum & Art Gallery
Mount Pleasant, Bilston
☎ (0902) 49143

Houses a large collection of fine English painted and transfer printed enamels from 18th and 19th centuries. Also iron and steel artefacts relating to the industrial history of the area. Staffordshire pottery. Frequent exhibitions of contemporary interest.

Open Mon–Sat 10–5. (Closed BH).

Free.

⚠ ✖

Central Art Gallery Lichfield St
☎ (0902) 24549

18th- and 19th-century English water colours and oil paintings. Modern paintings, sculpture and prints. Fine Oriental collections and full programme of temporary exhibitions including Chinese Art 8 Mar–19 Apr. Artists in Industry 14 Jun–12 Jul.

Open Mon–Sat 10–6. (Closed BH).

Free.

P (Civic Centre, 150 yds) ♿ (ground floor only) ✖

Wightwick Manor

A 19th-century house with a collection of pre-Raphaelite works of art, including Morris Fabric and de Morgan ware. Terraced gardens.

Open Thu, Sat & BH Sun & Mon 2.30–5.30. (Closed 25, 26 Dec, 1 & 2nd Jan & Feb). Parties by arrangement. (Due to maintenance, it is likely that only two rooms will be on view during Jul, Aug & Sep.)

£1.80 (ch 90p, must be accompanied). Sat (extra rooms) £2.20 (students 80p). Gardens only 80p. No children under 10.

(NT)

WOLVESNEWTON
Gwent
Map **3** ST49

Model Farm Folk Collection & Craft Centre (1½m off B4235 at Llangwm)
☎ (02915) 231

Late 18th-century cruciform barn housing a collection of unusual and entertaining items used in everyday life from the reign of Queen Victoria onwards. Also agricultural implements, a Victorian bedroom and a medical section. Craft workshops, picture gallery, 'naughty postcard' collection, work sheets for children.

Open Etr week then until Jun, Sat–Mon 11–6; Jul–Sep daily 11–6; Oct & Nov, Sun only 2–5.30. Open at any time for booked parties.

£1.75 (ch 95p).

⚠ 🍴 (licensed) ♿ shop ✖ Ⓥ

WOODBRIDGE
Suffolk
Map **5** TM24

Woodbridge Tide Mill
☎ (03943) 2548

The machinery of this 18th-century mill has been completely restored. There are photographs and working drawings on display. Situated on a busy quayside, this unique building looks over towards the romantic site of the Sutton Hoo Ship Burial.

Open Etr; May Day; Spring BH; Jun, wknds only; Jul–Sep, daily; Oct, wknds only 11–1 & 2.30–5.

Admission fee payable.

P ♿ (ground floor only) shop ✖

WOODHENGE
Wiltshire
Map **4** SU14

(1m N of Amesbury)

Consisted formerly of six concentric rings of timber posts within a ditch. Positions of the posts are marked by concrete pillars. Discovered accidentally by aerial reconnaissance in 1925.

Accessible at all reasonable times.

Free.

♿ (AM)

WOODSTOCK
Oxfordshire
Map **4** SP41

Blenheim Palace
☎ (0993) 811325

Started 1705 by Vanbrugh for first Duke of Marlborough. Palatial baroque-style mansion in park landscaped by Henry Wise and Capability Brown. Fine furnishings, china, pictures and terraced water gardens below Long Library, Sir Winston Churchill born here in 1874 and buried in 1965 in village churchyard of Bladon on southern fringe of park. Plant centre, adventure playground and Butterfly House.

Palace & gardens open 15 Mar–Oct daily 11–6 (last admission 5pm). Park open all year 9–5. Charity cricket 26 May, horse show 27 May.

£3 (ch 16 & 17 & pen £2.30), ch 5–15 £1.40, ch 5 free). Park only, car including occupants £1.70. Pedestrians 20p.

⚠ 🍴 ♿ shop & garden centre

WOOKEY HOLE
Somerset
Map **3** ST54

Wookey Hole Caves & Mill
☎ Wells (0749) 72243

Only two miles from Wells are the famous Wookey Hole Caves. They are best known for the Great Cave lived in by man over 2,000 years ago, and haunted so legend says, by a wicked witch in medieval times. From there a canal path leads to the mill where paper is still made by hand as it has been since the 17th century. Also in the mill is the unique fairground by night exhibition and Madame Tussaud's storerooms. The 'Old Penny Pier Arcade' houses one of the country's largest collections of vintage 1d slot machines, all in full working order.

Open daily, Mar–Oct 9.30–5.30, Nov–Feb 10.30–4.30. (Closed week before Xmas).

✳ £2.65 (ch 4–16 £1.75, ch 4 free, pen £2.15). Family ticket £7.80. Party 20+.

⚠ 🍴 🚻 ♿ (mill & exhibitions only) shop ✖

WOOLSTHORPE
Lincolnshire
Map **8** SK92

Woolsthorpe Manor
☎ Grantham (0476) 860338

A fine stone-built 17th-century house, the birthplace in 1642 of Sir Isaac Newton.

Open 29 Mar–end Oct Sun–Thu, 1.30–6.

£1.30 (ch 60p).

⚠ ✖ (NT)

WORCESTER
Hereford and Worcester
Map **3** SO85

The Commandery Sidbury
☎ (0905) 355071

England's premier Civil War Centre. This fine 15th-century timber framed building was Charles II's H.Q. at Battle of Worcester 1651. Spectacular audio-visuals, rooms showing strategy, arms and armour, period household, Charles II escape route. Education service, doll-making centre with working craftsman. Home of Worcester Militia who stage regular 17th-century live action weekends.

Open Mon–Sat 10.30–5, Sun 2–5. Also open BH Mons.

£1 (ch, pen & students 50p).

P (50 yds) ⬚ ♬ ♿ (ground floor & gardens only) shop ✻

City Museum & Art Gallery Foregate St
☎ (0905) 25371

Temporary art exhibitions from local and national sources. Natural history and geology displays. 19th-century chemists shop. Also collections of Worcestershire Regiment and Worcestershire Yeomanry Cavalry.

Open Mon, Tue, Wed & Fri 9.30–6, Sat 9.30–5.

Free.

P shop ✻

Worcester

Dyson Perrins Museum of Worcester Porcelain Severn St
☎ (0905) 23221

The finest collection of Worcester china in the world, with pieces dating from 1751 to the present day.

Open all year Mon–Fri 9–5 & Sat (Apr–Sep) 10–5. Tours of works Mon–Fri by prior arrangement.

Free. ✶ Tours £1.80 (ch 8–16 90p).

⚠ ⬚ ♿ shop ✻

Elgar's Birthplace Museum
Crown East Ln, Broadheath (3m W of Worcester off A44 to Leominster)
☎ Cotheridge (090566) 224

Cottage where Sir Edward Elgar was born in 1857, now a museum displaying scores, photographs, letters and personalia.

Open daily ex Wed, May–Sep 10.30–6; Oct–15 Jan & 16 Feb–30 Apr 1.30–4.30

£1.20 (ch 14 40p, pen & students 80p).

P (Plough Inn, 50 yds) ♿ (ground floor only) shop ✻ (ex in garden)

Guildhall High St
☎ (0905) 23471

The Guildhall has a fine Early Georgian frontage and from June will become a major Heritage Centre. Worcester's history and personalities are vividly portrayed in sight and sound, including Edward Elgar, Woodbine Willie, Vesta Tilley, the Music Halls and the seven ages of Worcester.

Open Mon–Fri 9.30–5 & occasional Sat in Summer. (Closed BH).

Free.

P (50 yds) ⬚ (summer only) ♿ (ground floor only) ✻

Hawford Dovecote (3m N on A449)

16th-century half-timbered dovecote.

Open daily until sunset.

✶ 20p

(NT)

Tudor House Friar St
☎ (0905) 25371

500-year-old timber-framed house, with a squint, and an ornate plaster ceiling. Now museum of local life featuring social and domestic history, including children's room, Edwardian bathroom and World War II Home Front Displays. Large agricultural exhibits displayed in yard at rear.

Open Mon–Wed & Fri–Sat 10.30–5.

Free.

P (200 yds) ♿ (ground floor only) shop ✻

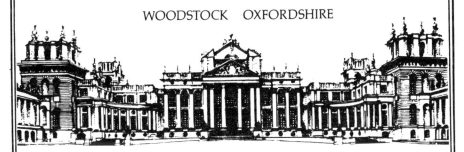

BLENHEIM PALACE
WOODSTOCK OXFORDSHIRE

Home of the Eleventh Duke of Marlborough · Birthplace of Sir Winston Churchill

ATTRACTIONS IN BLENHEIM PARK INCLUDE
BUTTERFLY HOUSE ★ MOTOR LAUNCH ★ PLANT CENTRE
RAILWAY ★ ADVENTURE PLAYGROUND ★ GARDEN RESTAURANT

Open daily 11am–6pm (last admission 5pm) from mid-March–31st October Blenheim Palace, Woodstock, Oxford OX7 1PX. Telephone (0993) 811325

WORDSLEY
West Midlands
Map **7** SO88

Stuart Crystal Red House Glassworks
☎ Brierley Hill (0384) 71161.

*The Redhouse Cone and Museum
opened Easter 1984 represents 200 years
of glassmaking history. The factory tour
enables the visitor to see at close hand
the glassmaking process from the
provision of the initial raw materials to the
finished items.*

Redhouse Cone & Museum open daily 9–
5. Factory Tours. Mon–Fri 10–11.15 &
1.30–3.15. (Fri close at 2.30pm). Closed
for tours 26–31 May & 28 Jul–8 Aug. All
facilities closed 23–27 Dec & 1 Jan.

Free.

⚠ ⚧ & shop ✖

WORKINGTON
Cumbria
Map **11** NY02

Helena Thompson Museum
Park End Rd
☎ (0900) 62598

*Costume, furniture and other decorative
art in 18th-century house. Temporary
exhibitions in former stable block.*

Open Mon–Sat 11–3.

& (ground floor & garden only) shop ✖

WORKSOP
Nottinghamshire
Map **8** SK57

Worksop Priory Church & Gatehouse
☎ (0909) 472180

*Church has unique Norman west front
with twin towers and 12th-century
Transitional nave, with 20th-century
additions, 14th-century scroll ironwork on
doors in south porch. Remarkable 14th-
century double archway with large upper
room which from 1623 housed earliest
elementary school in county. Elaborate
façade with statues, and 15th-century
wayside shrine and chapel.*

Church open daily 7.30–12 & 1.30–4.30.
Gatehouse open Mon–Wed 9.30–1 & 2–4.

Free.

P (50 yds) & (ground floor only) shop &

WORTHING
West Sussex
Map **4** TQ10

Worthing Museum & Art Gallery
Chapel Rd
☎ (0903) 39999 ext 121. Sat only (0903)
204229

*Archaeology, geology, history of
Worthing, pictures and pottery. Large
costume collector. Frequent exhibitions.*

Open Mon–Sat 10–6 (summer), 10–5
(winter).

Free.

P (multi-storey 400 yds) & shop ✖

WRAWBY
Humberside
Map **8** TA00

Wrawby Postmill
☎ Brigg (0652) 53699

*The last surviving example of its type in
the north of England, built c 1780 and
restored to working order in the 1960s.*

Open 31 Mar, 5 & 26 May, 29 Jun, 27 Jul &
25 Aug 1–5pm.

30p (ch 20p ch 5 free). Party (school).

⚠ & (ground floor only) shop

WREXHAM
Clwyd
Map **7** SJ35

Bersham Industrial Heritage
Bersham (2m SW)
☎ (0978) 261529

*An interpretative centre housed in a
Victorian school building which is situated
along an eight-mile industrial history trail.
Exhibitions on John Wilkinson, the
Bersham iron-works, the Davies Brothers,*

gatesmiths of Croes Foel and a reconstructed forge.

Open Etr–Oct Tue–Sat & BH 10–12.30 & 1.30–4, Sun 2–4; Nov–Etr Tue–Fri 10–12.30 & 1.30–4, Sat 12.30–3.30.

Free.

🅰 ⚭ shop ✖

Erddig
(off the A525, 2m S of Wrexham)

Late 17th-century house with 18th-century additions and containing much of its original furniture. Garden restored to its 18th-century formal design containing old varieties of fruit. Domestic outbuildings include laundry, bakehouse, sawmill and smithy, all in working order, plus Agricultural Museum.

Open 28 Mar–19 Oct. Closed Fri 12–5.30 (last admission 4.30pm). School & Youth groups mornings only, by arrangement. Due to extreme fragility Tapestry and Chinese Rooms open only on Wed & Sat.

House, Garden & Museum £2 (ch 75p) Museum & Garden only £1 (ch 35p). Family Ticket £4.75. Party 20+.

P ⌇ ⚭ ✖ (NT)

WROXALL
Isle of Wight
Map **4** SZ57

Appuldurcombe House

Erected in 1710 on site of earlier house, roofless shell of mansion designed in classical style standing in ornamental grounds.

Open see end of gazetteer.

✳ 50p (ch 16 & pen 25p).

(AM)

WROXETER
Shropshire
Map **7** SJ50

Roman Town

Remains of the Roman town of 'Viroconium' dating probably from AD 140–150 including public baths and a colonnade.

Open † see end of gazetteer.

✳ 50p (ch 16 & pen 25p).

🅰 ⚭ (AM)

WROXHAM
Norfolk
Map **9** TG31

Beeston Hall (2½m NE off A1151)
☎ Horning (0692) 630771

18th-century mansion in Gothic style with Neo-Classical interiors. Descendants of the Preston family have resided here since 1640.

Open 30 Mar–14 Sep, Fri, Sun & BH Mon 2–5.30.

£1.30 (ch 60p, pen £1).

🅰 shop ✖ ⓥ

Wrexham
—
Yarmouth, Great

WYCH CROSS
East Sussex
Map **5** TQ43

Ashdown Forest Farm
☎ Nutley (082571) 2040

An extensive collection of rare breeds of farm animals in a traditional setting at the heart of Ashdown Forest. The collection includes 50 breeds of farm animals and poultry, many of which are in danger of extinction, together with a collection old farm machinery and implements.

Open daily 11–6 or dusk. (Closed Xmas day).

£1.50 (ch & pen 80p) party 10+ by arrangement.

🅰 ⌇ ⚭ ⏚ shop ✖

YARMOUTH
Isle of Wight
Map **4** SZ38

Fort Victoria Country Park
Sconce Point (½m W)
☎ (0983) 760860

Remains of fort built in 1852–3 to protect the western approach to Portsmouth. Now being developed as a Country Park with free guided walks, exhibition, picnic and barbecue facilities. Spectacular views of the Solent. The Marine Aquarium shows a cross section of local marine life.

Park open daily. Aquarium open daily 10–6 (ex closed Jan & Feb).

Free. Aquarium 70p (ch 40p pen 50p).

🅰 (coaches for access only) ⌇ ⏚ ⚭ (ground floor & grounds only)

Yarmouth Castle

A Tudor castle built by order of Henry VIII. Repaired in 1609 and 1632.

Open † see end of gazetteer. Apr–Sep only.

✳ 50 (ch 16 & pen 25p).

⚭ (ground floor only) (AM)

YARMOUTH, GREAT
Norfolk
Map **5** TG50

Elizabethan House Museum
4 South Quay
☎ (0493) 855746

Built in 1596. It has a late Georgian front, and contains panelled 16th-century room with a magnificent plaster ceiling. Other rooms have features from later periods, some containing contemporary furniture and illustrating domestic life in the 19th century. Victorian children's toys, Lowestoft porcelain and a collection of 18th- & 19th-century drinking glasses.

Open all year Jun–Sep daily (ex Sat) 10–1 & 2–5.30; Oct–May (Mon–Fri) 10–1 & 2–

5.30. (Closed Good Fri, Xmas & New Year).

20p (ch 5p, students & UB40s 10p) 24 May–Sep; 10p (ch 5p students & UB40s 5p) Oct–23 May.

P (200 yds) shop ✖

Maritime Museum For East Anglia
Marine Parade
☎ (0493) 842267

Maritime history of East Anglia including the herring fishery, the wherry, life-saving and the oil and gas industry.

Open all year (ex Good Fri, Xmas & New Year). Jun–Sep daily (ex Sat) 10–5.30; Oct–May, Mon–Fri 10–1 & 2–5.30.

30p (ch 5p students & UB40s 15p) 24 May–Sep; 5p (ch 5p students & UB40s 10p) Oct–23 May.

P (100 yds) shop ✖

Merrivale Model Village
(near Wellington Picr)
☎ (0493) 842097

Comprehensive village layout including 2¼ inch-gauge model railway and radio-controlled boats. Models on scale of 1:12, set in landscaped gardens and illuminated after dusk from Jun–Oct. Also remote-controlled tanks. Amusements.

Open late May–Sep, daily 9.30am–10pm.

Admission fee payable.

P (20 yds) ⌇ ⚭ shop

Museum Exhibition Galleries
Central Library, Tolhouse St
☎ (0493) 858900

Travelling and local art exhibitions.

Open Mon–Sat 9.30–5.30. (Closed Etr, Late May & Aug BH wknds, Xmas & New Year).

Free.

🅰 ✖

Old Merchants House Row 117
☎ (0493) 857900

Restored 300-year-old house with examples of 17th- to 19th-century local building craftmanship, situated in one of the old narrow lanes of Rows leading from town wall to quay.

Open Apr–Sep, Mon–Fri guided tour only starting from Row 111 Houses at 9.45, 11.20, 2.15 & 3.45.

✳ 50p (ch 16 & pen 25p). Tickets include Row 111 Houses and Greyfriars Cloister.

(AM)

Tolhouse Museum Tolhouse St
☎ (0493) 858900

Late 13th-century building with old dungeons and exhibits on local history. brass rubbing centre with wide range of replica brasses.

Open all year (ex Good Fri, Xmas & New Year). Mon–Fri 10–1 & 2–5.30, also Sun Jun–Sep only.

Free. Charge for brass rubbing.

P (200 yds) shop ✖

YEALMPTON
Devon
Map **2** SX55

National Shire Horse Centre
Dunstone
☎ Plymouth (0752) 880268

*A 60-acre farm worked by shire horses.
See the shire horses, and their foals. Craft
centre with saddler, potter and
wheelwright. Film show, pets area, cart
rides & assualt course. Daily parades
11.30, 2.30 and 4.15. Many special events
held throughout the year at no extra
charge.*

Open daily 10–5. (Closed 24–26 Dec).
£2 (ch £1.25, pen £1.75).

⚠ ⚲ (licensed) ♁ ⅋ shop & garden
centre ⓥ

YELVERTON
Devon
Map **2** SX56

Paperweight Centre
4 Buckland Terrace, Leg O'Mutton
☎ (0822) 854250

*Exhibition of over 800 paperweights.
Beautiful antique and modern glass.
Millefiori, faceted, diamond-cut dated and
signed 'investment' paperweights, many
for sale (from £3–£300).*

Open week before Etr–Oct, Mon–Sat 10–
5. Winter opening Wed 1–5.

Free.

⚠ ⅋ (ground floor only) shop

YEOVIL
Somerset
Map **3** ST51

Yeovil Museum Hendford Manor Hall
☎ Mon–Fri (0935) 75171 Sat (0935) 24774

*Local history and archaeology and
specialised collections of costumes and
firearms.*

Open Mon–Wed, Fri & Sat 9.30–1 & 2–5.

Free.

⚠ (limited) shop

YEOVILTON
Somerset
Map **3** ST52

**Fleet Air Arm Museum & Concorde 002
Royal Naval Air Station**
☎ Ilchester (0935) 840565.

*A collection of more than 50 historic
aircraft, plus ship and aircraft models,
paintings and photographs of the Royal
Naval Air Service and the Fleet Air Arm
telling the story of the development of
aviation at sea from 1903. Special
Falkland Islands Exhibition. Concorde 002
can be seen in an exhibition hall where the
development of passenger supersonic
flight is graphically portrayed. Children's
play area, flying view area. Coaches and
caravans welcome.*

Yealmpton
—
York

Open daily (ex 24 & 25 Dec) 10–5.30
(4.30pm Nov–Feb).

✳ £1.80 (ch & pen 90p).

⚠ ⚲ (licensed) ♁ ⅋ shop ✶

YORK
North Yorkshire
Map **8** SE65

**Borthwick Institute of Historical
Research**
St Anthony's Hall, Peasholme Green
☎ (0904) 642315

*Originally a late 15th-century Guildhall, it
has served in turn as poor-house,
hospital, armoury, and Blue-Coat school.
Now the Borthwick Institute of Historical
Research, part of York University, with a
collection of ecclesiastical archives.
Exhibition of documents.*

Hall open Mon–Fri 9.30–1 & 2–5.

(Closed Xmas, Etr. Search rooms closed
week of Aug BH & preceding week).

Free.

P 50 yds) ⅋ (ground floor & gardens only)
✶

Castle Museum Tower St
☎ (0904) 33932

*An outstanding folk museum including
period rooms, a cobbled street,
Edwardian park, domestic and
agricultural equipment, early crafts,
costumes, toys, arms and armour.
Yorkshire militaria, an Edwardian street
and a water-driven corn mill. 'Every Home
Should Have One' is a new gallery of
domestic gadgets and equipment from
Victorian times to 1960s.*

Open all year Apr–Sep, Mon–Sat 9.30–
6.30, Sun 10–6.30; Oct–Mar, Mon–Sat
9.30–5, Sun 10–5. Last admission 1 hour
before closure. (Closed 25–26 Dec & 1
Jan).

✳ £2 (ch pen & students £1). Joint ticket
with York Story £2.40 (ch pen & students
£1.20). Family joint ticket £6.50

P ⚲ shop ✶

See advertisement on page 296

City Art Gallery Exhibition Square
☎ (0904) 23839

*Treasure house of European and British
paintings. Particularly known for the
Lycett Green collection of Old Masters,
but also contains paintings and drawings
by York Artists, notably William Etty, RA.
Also modern pottery and a regular
programme of temporary exhibitions.*

Open all year Mon–Sat 10–5, Sun 2.30–5.
Last admission 4.30 pm. (Closed Good
Fri, 25–26 Dec & 1 Jan).

✳ 50p (free to students, pen & ch).

P (¼ & ½m) ⅋ shop ✶

Fairfax House Castlegate
☎ (0904) 55543

*An outstanding mid 18th-century interior
and collection of Georgian furniture and
clocks.*

Open Tue–Sat & BH Mon 11–5, Sun 1.30–
5. Last admission 4.30. (Closed Jan &
Feb). Special Connoisseur tours &
evening visits available by arrangement.
£1.30 (ch 60p). party 15+.

P ⅋ shop ✶

Friargate Wax Museum Lower Friargate
☎ (0904) 58775

*Sixty of the World's best known
characters re-created in wax in realistic
surroundings including sound effects.*

Open Mar–Nov daily 10–5. Dec 10–dusk
(subject to change). (Closed Xmas day,
Jan & Feb).

✳ £1.50 (ch & pen 75p). Party.

P (200 yds) shop

Guildhall off Coney St
☎ (0904) 59881 ext 208

*A 15th-century building, restored after
severe war damage. Hall with notable
timbered roof. Underground passage
leading to the river.*

Open May–Oct, Mon–Thu 9–5, Fri 9–4.30,
Sat 10–5, Sun 2.30–4.30; Nov–Apr, Mon–
Thu 9–5, Fri 9–4.30. (Closed Good Fri, 25
& 26 Dec. & 1 Jan).

Free.

⚠ ⅋ (ground floor only) ✶ (ex guide
dogs) ♨

Jorvik Viking Centre Coppergate
☎ (0904) 643211

*Jorvik is the Viking city that
archaeologists uncovered in Coppergate,
shedding a totally new light on the
northern Viking Kingdom based on York.
The first stage of a visit to the centre is an
audio-visual display then visitors board
their electric 'time-cars' at the starting
platform. Watch the 20th century
receding further and further into the
distance until you reach a Viking city,
recreated beneath modern York. A
bustling market, dark, smokey houses, a
busy wharf: everything is recreated in the
most colourful and accurate detail. Turn a
corner and find yourself on the famous
Viking dig reconstructed on site, with the
preserved 10th-century buildings put
back where they were found. Many of the
magnificent objects found are also on
view in a treasure hall displayed in
purpose-built cases. A commentary
explains all that you see and hear.*

Open Apr–Oct daily 9–7; Nov–Mar, daily
9–5.30.

£2.50 (ch 16 £1.25 & pen £1.75 Nov–Mar).
Party 20+.

P (shortstay 150 yds, longstay 440 yds) ⅋
shop ✶ (ex guide dogs)

See advertisement on page 296

294

YORK CITY ART GALLERY
Exhibition Square

You haven't seen York until you've seen the Art Gallery.
Discover a treasure-house of European and British paintings
spanning seven centuries and including the world-famous Lycett
Green collection of Old Masters as well as works by the
remarkable York-born painter of the nude, William Etty. See too
the unrivalled Milner-White collection of stoneware pottery and
watch for details of an exciting programme of temporary
exhibitions, lectures and recitals.

Monday — Saturday 10-5, Sunday 2.30-5
(last admission 4.30)

Closed 1 January, Good Friday, 25 and 26 December

Small admission fee but free to York residents, students,
children, OAPs and Friends of York Art Gallery

For further information telephone (0904) 23839

King's Manor Exhibition Square
☎ (0904) 59861

Former home of Abbot of St Mary's Abbey, later stopping place of James VI of Scotland on way to become James I of England, and of Charles I at time of Civil War. Much altered in early 17th century, and fully restored to become part of university in 1964.

Courtyards open daily (ex 25 Dec) 9–5. Principal rooms open on certain days only during Spring & Summer. Check with porter.

Free.

P (300 yds) ⚲ (ex PH) & (gardens) only

Merchant Adventurers' Hall Fossgate
☎ (0904) 54818 or 51328

Dating from 1357–68 to Tudor times, the major part is 15th century. Belonged to the wealthy and influential Company of the Merchant Adventurers.

Open Apr–Oct daily 9.30–4.30 (restricted viewing when Hall is in use); Nov–Mar Mon–Sat 9.30–1.

70p (ch 16, pen & students 40p). Party 10+.

P (multi-storey, 100 yds) & (ground floor only)

National Railway Museum Leeman Rd
☎ (0904) 21261

Illustrates the history and development of British railway engineering including social aspects. Collection contains some 25 locomotives and about 20 items of rolling stock as well as signalling equipment etc. Small exhibits feature models of locomotives (many working) and rolling stock. Also variety of railway equipment and material, plus collections

of paintings, posters, drawings and films. Reference library service by appointment. Lecture theatre seating 80, is incorporated in the building and an education programme is available. Please apply for details.

Open all year Mon–Sat 10–6, Sun 2.30–6. (Closed Good Fri, May Day BH, 24–26 Dec & 1 Jan).

Free.

△ J & (ground floor & gardens only) shop ✝ (ex guide dogs)

Rail Riders World York BR Station, Tearoom Sq
☎ (0904) 30169

One of the biggest and best model railway layouts in Britain. Set in town and country landscape. Models include the Orient Express, Royal Train, Inter City 125 and the latest freight and passenger trains.

Open Apr–Oct daily 10–6. Restricted opening winter.

£1 (ch & pen 50p). Family £2.25 (more than 2 ch 25p each).

P (500 yds) & shop

Treasurer's House Chapter House St

A mainly 17th- and 18th-century house with fine paintings, furniture and garden. Exhibition and tape/slide show.

Open 29 Mar–Oct, daily 10.30–5. (Closed Good Fri). Last admission 4.30.

£1.30.

Shop (NT)

York Castle off Tower St

Clifford's Tower, a two-storeyed 13th-century keep, built on an 11th-century motte raised by William the Conqueror.

York – Zennor

Open † see end of gazetteer.
✱ 50p (ch 16 & pen 25p).
△ (AM)

The York Story
The Heritage Centre, Castlegate
☎ (0904) 33932

Britain's finest Heritage Centre, interpreting the social and architectural history of the City of York. The exhibition, which includes many notable pieces by modern artists and craftsmen, is equipped with audio-visual units and a display of the treasures of the city. A Heritage 'Walk Around York' is available, guiding visitors to the major buildings in the city.

Open all year Mon–Sat 10–5; Sun 1–5. (Closed 25–26 Dec & 1 Jan).

✱ 80p (ch, pen & students 40p). Joint ticket with Castle Museum £2.40 (ch, pen & students £1.20).

P shop ✝

Yorkshire Museum & Gardens
Museum St
☎ (0904) 29745

Roman, Saxon, Viking, medieval, geological, natural history and ceramic collections. In the gardens are the ruins of St Mary's Abbey, nearby stands the Roman Wall, multangular tower, and St Leonard's Hospital. Roman Exhibition Jun–Dec (special prices).

Museum open Mon–Sat 10–5, Sun 1–5. Observatory open Wed–Sun summer only. Gardens open daily. (Closed 25 & 26 Dec).

✱ 80p (ch & pen 40p). Family ticket £2.

P shop ✝

Yorkshire Museum of Farming
Murton (3m E)
☎ (0904) 489966

Eight acres of farmland where farming past and present can be seen. Livestock Building has displays of the shepherd, farrier and dairy farmer along with live farm animals and the James Herriot surgery which is a special feature. There are more farm animals in the paddocks, also a dovecote and a bee garden where beekeepers give periodic demonstrations. There is also an ironmonger's, a chapel and a granary.

Open 2 Mar–26 Oct, daily 10.30–5.30 (last admission 4.30pm). Special events are numerous & include craft demonstrations, spinning, weaving, sheep shearing, sheepdog displays.

£1.50 (ch 16 & pen 75, ch 5 free).

△ J & (ground floor & gardens only) shop

ZENNOR
Cornwall
Map **2** SW43

Wayside Museum
☎ Penzance (0736) 796945

A unique private museum founded in 1935 covering every aspect of life in Zennor and district from 3000 BC–1930s.

Open daily, Etr–Oct 10—dusk.

60p (ch 30p).

P (25 yds) $. & (ground floor & gardens only) shop ✝

National Trust, National Trust for Scotland, English Heritage and National Gardens Scheme.

English Heritage

AM Ancient Monuments in England are in the care of the Historic Buildings and Monuments Commission for England, popularly known as English Heritage, with the exception of seven properties in and around London which are administered by the Department of the Environment. A twelve-month season ticket giving admission to all English Heritage properties is available from English Heritage Membership Dept., PO Box 43, Ruislip, Middlesex HA4 0XW.

Ancient Monuments in Scotland (with the exception of Holyrood House) are the responsibility of the Scottish Development Department, 3–11 Melville St, Edinburgh EH3 7QD. Membership of the Friends of the Scottish Monuments can be purchased from the above address.

Ancient Monuments in Wales are the responsibility of Cadw, Brunel House, Fitzalan Rd, Cardiff CF2 1UY. Heritage in Wales Membership, entitling the subscriber admission to all the Welsh sites, can be purchased from the above address.

Except where otherwise stated, the standard times of opening for all Ancient Monuments, except Scotland, are as follows:

16 Oct–14 Mar:	weekdays	Sunday
	9.30–4	2–4
15 Mar–15 Oct:	weekdays	Sunday
	9.30–6.30	2–6.30

Certain standard times for Ancient Monuments now include Sunday opening from 9.30 between April and September only; these entries have in each case been marked with a † after the word 'open' in the gazetteer. Standard times of opening for all Ancient Monuments in Scotland are as follows:

Apr–Sep:	weekdays	Sundays
	9.30–7	2–7
Oct–Mar:	weekdays	Sundays
	9.30–4	2–4

All monuments in England and Wales are closed on 1 January and 24–26 December. Those in Scotland are closed on 25 and 26 December, also 1 and 2 January. Some of the smaller monuments may close for the lunch hour and may be closed for one or two days a week. It is advisable to check before visiting. Pre-booked parties of 11 and over (15 in Wales) may obtain a 10% discount on admission at most of the monuments. Children under 5 are admitted free to all monuments.

The National Trusts

NT Indicates properties in England and Wales administered by the National Trust for Places of Historic Interest or Natural Beauty, 42 Queen Anne's Gate, London SW1H 9AS.

NTS National Trust for Scotland, 5 Charlotte Square, Edinburgh EH2 4DU.

The National Gardens Scheme

NGS National Gardens Scheme, 57 Lower Belgrave St, London SW1W 0LR.
Over 1,700 gardens (some entries are in this book) open to the public, mostly for one or two days a year. Proceeds for charity. Booklet £1.35 including postage.

Symbols and abbreviations

Other symbols and abbreviations used throughout this publication will be found inside the covers, whilst an explanation of how to use the gazetteer section appears on page 5.

192 Centre for Alternative Technology, *Machynlleth*
281 Chalcot House, *Westbury*
39 Chalk Pits Museum, *Amberley*
141 Chambercombe Manor, *Ilfracombe*
83 Charlecote Park, *Charlecote*
225 Charles Dickens Birthplace Museum, *Portsmouth & Southsea*
235 Charles Dickens Centre, *Rochester*
240 Charlestown Visitor Centre, *St Austell*
83 Chartwell
83 Chatham Historic Dockyard Visitor Centre, *Chatham*
83 Chatsworth
256 Chatterley Whitfield Mining Museum, *Stoke-on-Trent*
268 Chavenage, *Tetbury*
84 Cheddar Caves, *Cheddar*
83 Cheddar Caves Museum, *Cheddar*
84 Chelmsford & Essex Museum, *Chelmsford*
183 Chelsea Physic Gardens, *London SW3*
85 Chepstow Castle, *Chepstow*
85 Chepstow Museum, *Chepstow*
85 Chertsey Museum, *Chertsey*
86 Cheshire Military Museum, *Chester*
86 Chessington Zoo, *Chessington*
86 Chester Heritage Centre, *Chester*
86 Chester Visitors Centre, *Chester*
277 Chesters Roman Fort & Museum, *Walwick*
87 Chicheley Hall, *Chicheley*
88 Chiddingstone Castle, *Chiddingstone*
48 Child Beale Wildlife Trust, *Basildon (Berks)*
88 Chilham Castle, *Chilham*
88 Chillingham Wild Cattle, *Chillingham*
88 Chillington Hall
83 Chiltern Open Air Museum, *Chalfont St Giles*
89 Chirk Castle, *Chirk*
185 Chiswick House, *London W4*
89 Cholmondeley Castle Gardens, *Cholmondeley*
89 Christchurch Castle & Norman House, *Christchurch*
143 Christchurch Mansion, *Ipswich*
204 Churche's Mansion, *Nantwich*
180 Church Farm House Museum, *London NW4*
250 Church Farm Museum, *Skegness*
136 Churchill Gardens Museum & Brian Hatton Art Gallery, *Hereford*
124 Chwarel Wynne Mine & Museum, *Glyn Ceiriog*
89 Chysauster Ancient Village
89 Cilgerran Castle, *Cilgerran*
110 City Art Centre, *Edinburgh*
194 City Art Gallery, *Manchester*
294 City Art Gallery, *York*
124 City Eastgate, *Gloucester*
212 City Hall, *Norwich*
154 City Museum, *Lancaster*
239 City Museum, *St Albans*
247 City Museum, *Sheffield*
58 City Museum & Art Gallery, *Birmingham*
67 City Museum & Art Gallery, *Bristol*
124 City Museum & Art Gallery, *Gloucester*
223 City Museum & Art Gallery, *Plymouth*
225 City Museum & Art Gallery, *Portsmouth & Southsea*
256 City Museum & Art Gallery, *Stoke-on-Trent*
291 City Museum & Art Gallery, *Worcester*
221 City of Peterborough Museum & Art Gallery, *Peterborough*
41 Clan Donald Centre, *Armadale*
69 Clan Donnachaidh (Robertson) Museum, *Bruar*
281 Clandon Park, *West Clandon*
110 Clan Macpherson House & Museum, *Newtonmore*
97 Clapton Court Gardens, *Crewkerne*
115 Claremont, *Esher*
115 Claremont Landscape Garden, *Esher*

90 Clava Cairns
200 Claydon House, *Middle Claydon*
106 Claypotts Castle, *Dundee*
90 Clearwell Castle, *Clearwell*
90 Clearwell Caves Ancient Iron Mines, *Clearwell*
279 Cleeve Abbey, *Washford*
38 Clergy House, *Alfriston*
90 Clevedon Court, *Clevedon*
90 Clevedon Craft Centre, *Clevedon*
158 Clickheinen, *Lerwick*
103 Click Mill, *Dounby*
146 Cliffe Castle Museum, *Keighley*
90 Clitheroe Castle Museum, *Clitheroe*
91 Cliveden
249 Clive House Museum, *Shrewsbury*
239 Clock Tower, *St Albans*
247 Clock Warehouse, *Shardlow*
91 Clouds Hill, *Clouds Hill*
91 Clun Town Trust Museum, *Clun*
144 Coalbrookdale Museum & Furnace Site, *Ironbridge*
144 Coalport China Works Museum, *Ironbridge*
109 Coastal Defence Museum, *Eastbourne*
218 Coats Observatory, *Paisley*
89 Cobbaton Combat Vehicle Museum, *Chittlehampton*
91 Cobham Hall, *Cobham (Kent)*
289 Cogges Farm Museum, *Witney*
91 Coity Castle, *Coity*
109 Coker Court, *East Coker*
92 Colchester & Essex Museum, *Colchester*
92 Colchester Zoo, *Colchester*
276 Coldharbour Mill, *Uffculme*
205 Coleridge Cottage, *Nether Stowey*
151 Coleton Fishacre Garden, *Kingswear*
80 Colne Valley Railway & Museum, *Castle Hedingham*
150 Colzium House & Estate, *Kilsyth*
92 Combe Martin Motorcycle Collection, *Combe Martin*
202 Combe Sydenham Hall, *Monksilver*
291 Commandery, The, *Worcester*
186 Commonwealth Institute, *London W8*
76 Compton Acres Gardens, *Canford Cliffs*
92 Compton Castle, *Compton (Devon)*
93 Conisborough Castle, *Conisborough*
276 Conishead Priory, *Ulverston*
158 Constable Burton Hall Gardens, *Leyburn*
93 Conwy Castle, *Conwy*
54 Conwy Valley Railway Museum, *Betws-y-Coed*
93 Conwy Visitor Centre, *Conwy*
150 Cookworthy Museum of Rural Life, *Kingsbridge*
94 Corby Castle, *Corby (Great)*
94 Corfe Castle, *Corfe Castle*
94 Corfe Castle Museum, *Corfe Castle*
94 Corgarff Castle, *Corgarff*
89 Corinium Museum, *Cirencester*
224 Cornish Engines, *Pool*
158 Cornucopia—Caswell's Cornish Heritage, *Lelant*
134 Cornwall Aero Park & Flambards Victorian Village, *Helston*
130 Corrigall Farm Museum, *Harray*
94 Corsham Court, *Corsham*
76 Cotehele House, *Calstock*
95 Coton Manor Gardens, *Coton*
210 Cotswold Countryside Collection, *Northleach*
128 Cotswold Farm Park, *Guiting Power*
71 Cotswold Wildlife Park, *Burford (Oxon)*
62 Cotswolds Motor Museum, *Bourton-on-the-Water*
95 Coughton Court, *Coughton*
116 Country Life Museum, *Exmouth*
272 Countryside Centre, *Torridon*
228 County Council Demonstration Garden, Arboretum & Rural Studies Centre, *Probus*
274 County Museum & Art Gallery, *Truro*

193 Courage Shire Horse Centre, *Maidenhead*
187 Courtauld Institute Galleries, *London WC1*
186 Court Dress Collection, *London W8*
188 Courthouse, *Long Crendon*
139 Courts, The, *Holt*
95 Coventry Cathedral, *Coventry*
95 Coventry Toy Museum, *Coventry*
215 Cowper & Newton Museum, *Olney*
134 Craft/Heritage Centre, *Heckington*
154 Craigcleuch Scottish Explorers' Museum, *Langholm*
236 Cragside House & Country Park, *Rothbury*
96 Craigievar Castle, *Craigievar*
110 Craigmillar Castle, *Edinburgh*
68 Crampton Tower Museum, *Broadstairs*
96 Cranbourne Manor Private Gardens & Garden Centre, *Cranbourne*
201 Crarae Gardens, *Minard*
96 Crathes Castle & Garden, *Crathes*
251 Craven Museum, *Skipton*
210 Creake Abbey, *North Creake*
96 Creetown Gem Rock Museum & Art Gallery, *Creetown*
96 Creswell Crags Visitor Centre, *Creswell*
97 Criccieth Castle, *Criccieth*
97 Crichton Castle, *Crichton*
180 Cricket Memorial Gallery, *London NW8*
97 Croft Castle, *Croft*
52 Crofton Beam Engines, *Bedwyn, Grt*
97 Cromer Museum, *Cromer*
141 Cromwell Museum, *Huntingdon*
121 Crookston Castle, *Glasgow*
197 Crossraguel Abbey, *Maybole*
160 Croxteth Hall & Country Park, *Liverpool*
163 Cruachan Power Station, *Lochawe*
35 Cruickshank Botanic Gardens, *Aberdeen*
118 Culcreuch Castle, *Fintry*
98 Culloden Battlefield, *Culloden Moor*
98 Culross Palace, *Culross*
98 Culzean Castle, *Culzean*
98 Culzean Country Park, *Culzean*
226 Cumberland House Natural Science Museum & Aquarium, *Portsmouth & Southsea*
276 Cumbria Crystal, *Ulverston*
182 Cuming Museum, *London SE17*
45 Curraghs Wild Life Park, *Ballaugh*
98 Cusworth Hall Museum, *Cusworth*
181 Cutty Sark Clipper Ship, *London SE10*
283 Cwmmau Farmhouse, *Brilley, Whitney-on-Wye*
199 Cyfarthfa Castle Museum & Art Gallery, *Merthyr Tydfil*
45 Cyffdy Farm Park, *Bala*
98 Cymer Abbey
99 Dalemain, *Dacre*
99 Dalkeith Park, *Dalkeith*
230 Dalmeny House, *Queensferry, South*
141 Danny, *Hurstpierpoint*
35 Dan-yr-Ogof & Cathedral Showcaves, *Abercraf*
99 Darlington Museum, *Darlington*
99 Darlington Railway Museum, *Darlington*
272 Dartington Glass Factory, *Torrington, Gt*
99 Dartington Hall, *Dartington*
223 Dartmoor Wild Life Park, *Plympton*
99 Dartmouth Castle, *Dartmouth*
70 Dart Valley Railway, *Buckfastleigh*
60 David Livingstone Centre, *Blantyre*
256 Dawyck Botanic Garden, *Stobo*
226 D-Day & Overlord Embroidery, *Portsmouth & Southsea*
100 Deal Castle, *Deal*
149 Dean Castle, *Kilmarnock*
191 Dean Forest Railway Society, *Lydney*
252 Dean Heritage Museum, *Soudley*
100 Deddington Castle, *Deddington*
100 Deene Park, *Deene*
215 Deer Abbey, *Old Deer*
210 Delapre Abbey, *Northampton*

Index

305

Report Form

It is our aim to make this guide the best and most comprehensive of its kind and in order to achieve this we are constantly on the lookout for new places to include. If you should know of any places which are open to the public and which are not already in the book, we would be most interested to hear about them. Just fill in the details below and return this form to:

Guidebook Publications Unit,
The Automobile Association,
Fanum House,
Basing View,
Basingstoke, Hants RG21 2EA.

Name

Address

Name of Establishment

Address of Establishment

Location (if outside town)

Date of visit

Description

Facilities

Parking

Refreshments

Picnic area

Shop

Access for wheelchair-bound visitors

Other comments

Report Form

It is our aim to make this guide the best and most comprehensive of its kind and in order to achieve this we are constantly on the lookout for new places to include. If you should know of any places which are open to the public and which are not already in the book, we would be most interested to hear about them. Just fill in the details below and return this form to:

Guidebook Publications Unit,
The Automobile Association,
Fanum House,
Basing View,
Basingstoke, Hants RG21 2EA.

Name

Address

Name of Establishment

Address of Establishment

Location (if outside town)

Date of visit

Description

Facilities

Parking

Refreshments

Picnic area

Shop

Access for wheelchair-bound visitors

Other comments

Useful Addresses

National Trust Information Offices

London Information Officer,
Mrs Sukie Hemming,
National Trust, 36 Queen Anne's Gate,
London SW1H 9AS
Tel 01-222 9251

REGIONAL INFORMATION OFFICERS:

CORNWALL   Giles Clotworthy,
Lanhydrock, Bodmin, Cornwall PL30 4DE
Tel Bodmin (0208) 4281

DEVON   Anthony Adam,
Killerton House, Broadclyst, Exeter, Devon
EX5 3LE
Tel Exeter (0392) 881691

WESSEX   Tom Burr,
Stourton, Warminster, Wiltshire BA12 6QD
Tel Bourton (Dorset)
(0747) 840560/840224

SOUTHERN   Norman Price,
Polesden Lacey, Dorking, Surrey RH5 6BD
Tel Bookham (0372) 53401

KENT & EAST SUSSEX   Miss Pam Horner,
Scotney Castle, Lamberhurst, Tunbridge
Wells, Kent TN3 8JN
Tel Lamberhurst (0892) 890651

EAST ANGLIA   Christopher Hanson-Smith,
Blickling, Norwich RH11 6NF
Tel Aylsham (0263) 733471

THAMES & CHILTERNS   Ian C. Lamaison,
Hughenden Manor, High Wycombe, Bucks
HP14 4LA
Tel High Wycombe (0494) 28051

SEVERN   Miss Barbara Morley,
34–36 Church Street, Tewkesbury, Glos
GL20 5SN
Tel Tewkesbury (0684) 292919/292427

SOUTH WALES   Roddy Rees,
22 Alan Road, Llandeilo, Dyfed SA19 6HU
Tel Llandeilo (055882) 3530

NORTH WALES   John Alwyn-Jones,
Trinity Square, Llandudno,
Gwynedd LL30 2DE
Tel Llandudno (0492) 74421

MERCIA   David Brown,
Attingham Park, Shrewsbury, Shropshire
SY4 4TP
Tel Upton Magna (074377) 202
OR   Philip Browning,
The Stamford Estate Office, Market Street,
Altrincham, Cheshire WA14 4SJ
Tel Altrincham (061928) 0075

EAST MIDLANDS   Alex Youel,
Clumber Park Stableyard, Worksop, Notts
S80 3BE
Tel Worksop (0909) 486411

YORKSHIRE   Miss Tiffany Hunt,
Goddards, 27 Tadcaster Road, Dringhouses,
York YO2 2QG
Tel York (0904) 702021

NORTH WEST   Nigel Sale,
Rothay Holme, Rothay Road, Ambleside,
Cumbria LA22 0EJ
Tel Ambleside (0966) 33883

NORTHUMBRIA   Paul Dickson,
Scots' Gap, Morpeth, Northumberland
NE61 4EG
Tel Scots' Gap (067074) 691

JUNIOR DIVISION

Acorn Camps and Young National Trust
Groups:
The Old Grape House, Cliveden, Taplow,
Maidenhead, Berks SL60HZ
Tel Burnham (Bucks) 4228

Education Advisor,
8 Church Street, Lacock, Wiltshire
Tel Lacock 430

National Trust for Scotland

REGIONAL INFORMATION OFFICERS:

CENTRAL, FIFE AND LOTHIAN:
National Trust for Scotland HQ, 5 Charlotte
Square, Edinburgh EH2 4DU
Tel 031-226 5922

GLASGOW AND WEST OF SCOTLAND:
Hutchesons' Hall, Ingram Street, Glasgow
G1 1EJ
Tel 041-552 8391

GRAMPIAN AND ANGUS:
Pitmedden House, Ellon, Aberdeenshire
AB4 0PD
Tel Udny 2352

HIGHLAND:
109 Church Street, Inverness IV1 1EY
Tel Inverness 232034

PERTHSHIRE:
Castle Cleirach, The Cross, Dunkeld
PH8 0AN
Tel Dunkeld 460
AND The Branklyn House, Dundee Road,
Perth PH2 7BB
Tel Perth 25535

Historic Houses Association
38 Ebury Street, London SW1
Tel 01-730 9419

National Gardens Scheme
57 Lower Belgrave Street, London SW1
Tel 01-730 0359

The Museums Association
34 Bloomsbury Way, London WC1
Tel 01-404 4767

English Tourist Board
4 Grosvenor Gardens, London SW1W 0DU
Tel 01-730 3400

English Regional Tourist Boards
Cumbria Tourist Board,
Ashleigh, Holly Road, Windermere,
Cumbria LA23 2AQ
Tel (09662) 4444

Northumbria Tourist Board,
9 Osborne Terrace, Jesmond, Newcastle
upon Tyne NE2 1NT
Tel (0632) 817744

North West Tourist Board,
The Last Drop Village, Bromley Cross,
Bolton, Lancashire BL7 9PZ
Tel (0204) 591511

Yorkshire & Humberside Tourist Board,
312 Tadcaster Road, York, North Yorkshire
YO2 2HF
Tel (0904) 707961

Heart of England Tourist Board,
PO Box 15, Worcester, Worcestershire
WR1 2JT
Tel (0905) 29511

East Midlands Tourist Board,
Exchequergate, Lincoln, Lincolnshire
LN2 1PZ
Tel (0522) 31521/3

Thames & Chilterns Tourist Board,
8 The Market Place, Abingdon, Oxfordshire
OX14 3UD
Tel (0235) 22711

East Anglia Tourist Board,
14 Museum Street, Ipswich, Suffolk IP1 1HU
Tel (0473) 214211

London Tourist Board,
26 Grosvenor Gardens, London SW1W 0DU
Tel 01-730 3488

West Country Tourist Board,
Trinity Court, 37 Southernhay East, Exeter,
Devon EX1 1QS
Tel (0392) 76351

Southern Tourist Board,
Town Hall Centre, Leight Road, Eastleigh,
Hampshire SO5 4DE
Tel (0703) 616027

Isle of Wight Tourist Board,
21 High Street, Newport, Isle of Wight
PO30 1JS
Tel (0983) 524343

South East England Tourist Board,
1 Warwick Park, Tunbridge Wells, Kent
TN2 5TA
Tel (0892) 40766

Scottish Tourist Board
23 Ravelston Terrace, Edinburgh EH4 3EU
Tel 031-332 2433

Wales Tourist Board
Brunel House, 2 Fitzalan Road, Cardiff
CF2 1UY
Tel (0222) 499909

Isle of Man Tourist Board
13 Victoria Street, Douglas, Isle of Man
Tel (0624) 4323 (winter) (0624) 4328/9
(May–Sept)

Channel Islands
JERSEY
Weighbridge, St Helier, Jersey
Tel (0534) 78000; 31958 (accommodation)
24779 (local information)

GUERNSEY
Crown Pier, St Peter Port
Tel (0481) 23552 (enquiries) 23555
(accommodation)

The Airport, La Villiaze Forest
Tel (0481) 37267

Your Opinions Please

Reader Questionnaire

Stately Homes, Museums, Castles and Gardens in Britain 1986

Tell us what you think of this book and you can obtain the 1987 edition at a substantial discount. We try to tailor our books to meet our readers' needs and this questionnaire will help us keep in touch with what you find interesting and useful. Please tell us what your reactions are to this book and return the completed questionnaire (no stamp needed) to us by 15th November 1986, to the following address:

Automobile Association
Department PMD (SHG)
Freepost
Basingstoke RG21 2BR

How did you acquire this guide?

AA shop ☐
Bookshop ☐
Mail Order ☐
Other (please specify)_____

Please indicate your usage of the guide

Every week ☐
Once a month ☐
Less than once a month ☐
Never ☐

Does the book contain enough information about establishments for your needs?

Yes ☐   No ☐

If the answer is no, please tell us what further information you would like

_____
_____
_____
_____

Do you find the illustrated features at the front of the book interesting?

Yes ☐   No ☐

Do you find the Money-off Vouchers useful?

Yes ☐   No ☐

Did the Money-off Vouchers affect your decision to buy this book?

Yes ☐   No ☐

Please tell us which of the other features of the book you like

_____
_____
_____

Please tell us about any aspects of this book which could be improved

_____
_____
_____

What other publications or other sources of information do you use to find out about places of interest?

_____
_____
_____

What other AA books do you possess?

_____

_____

_____

Are you   Male   ☐

                 Female   ☐

                 Under 21   ☐

                 21 - 30   ☐

                 31 - 45   ☐

                 46 - 60   ☐

What is your occupation?

_____

Do you have any previous editions of this guide? If so, please state which year(s):

_____

_____

How many people, apart from yourself, have consulted this guide?

_____

Please fill in your name and address in block capitals

NAME_____

ADDRESS_____

_____

To thank you for returning this questionnaire we will supply you with next year's edition at a substantial discount. An order form will be sent to you shortly before publication. **Answering this questionnaire however, imposes no obligation to purchase.**

AA MOTORWAY MOTORING

The National Grid

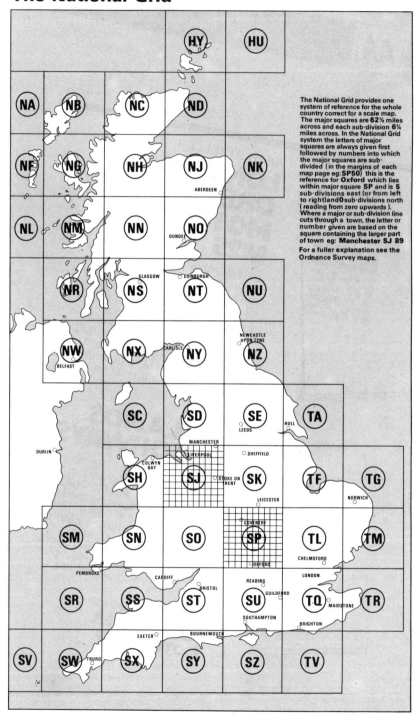

The National Grid provides one system of reference for the whole country correct for a scale map. The major squares are 62½ miles across and each sub-division 6¼ miles across. In the National Grid system the letters of major squares are always given first followed by numbers into which the major squares are sub-divided (in the margins of each map page eg: **SP50**) this is the reference for **Oxford** which lies within major square **SP** and is **5** sub-divisions east (or from left to right) and **0** sub-divisions north (reading from zero upwards). Where a major or sub-division line cuts through a town, the letter or number given are based on the square containing the larger part of town eg: **Manchester SJ 89**

For a fuller explanation see the Ordnance Survey maps.

Key to Atlas

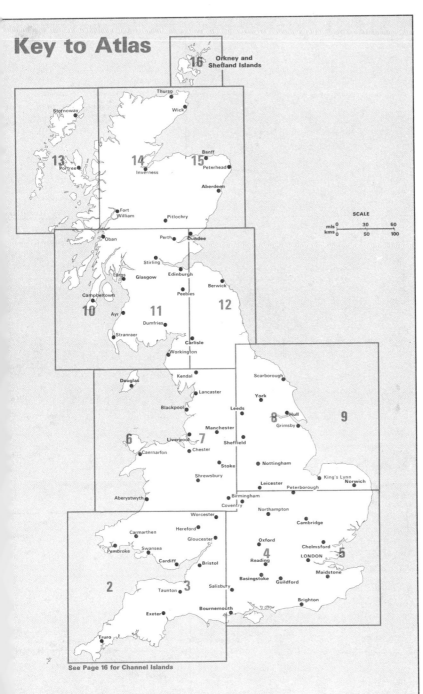

16 Orkney and Shetland Islands

Thurso
Wick
Stornoway
Banff
13 Portree **14** Inverness **15** Peterhead
Aberdeen
Fort William
Pitlochry

SCALE

| mls | 0 | 30 | 60 |
| kms | 0 | 50 | 100 |

Oban Perth Dundee
Stirling
Larbs Glasgow Edinburgh
Campbeltown Peebles Berwick
10 Ayr **11** **12**
Dumfries
Stranraer
Carlisle
Workington

Douglas Kendal Scarborough
Lancaster York
Blackpool Leeds Hull
8 Grimsby **9**
Manchester
6 Liverpool **7** Sheffield
Caernarfon Chester Stoke Nottingham
Shrewsbury Leicester King's Lynn Norwich
Peterborough
Aberystwyth Birmingham
Coventry Northampton Cambridge
Worcester
Carmarthen Hereford
Gloucester Oxford Chelmsford
Pembroke Swansea Reading LONDON **5**
Cardiff Bristol Basingstoke Guildford Maidstone
2 **3** Salisbury
Taunton Brighton
Exeter Bournemouth

Truro

See Page 16 for Channel Islands

Maps produced by
The AA Cartographic Department
(Publications Division), Fanum House,
Basingstoke, Hampshire RG21 2EA

*This atlas is for location purposes Only:
see Member's Handbook for current road
and AA road services information*

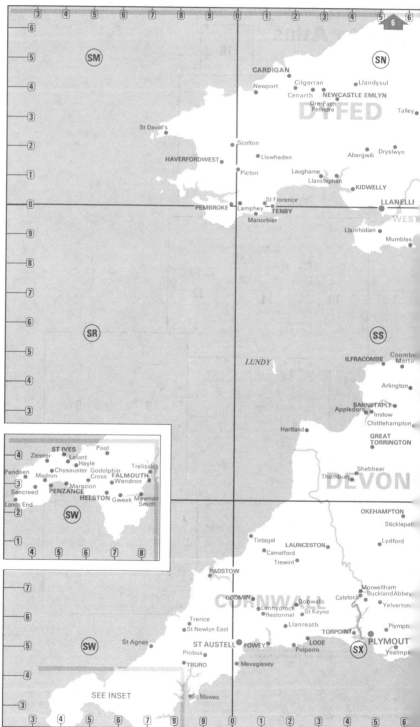

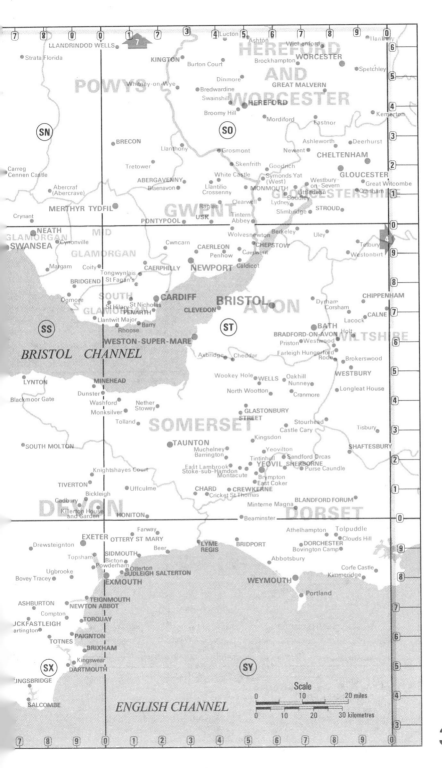

4

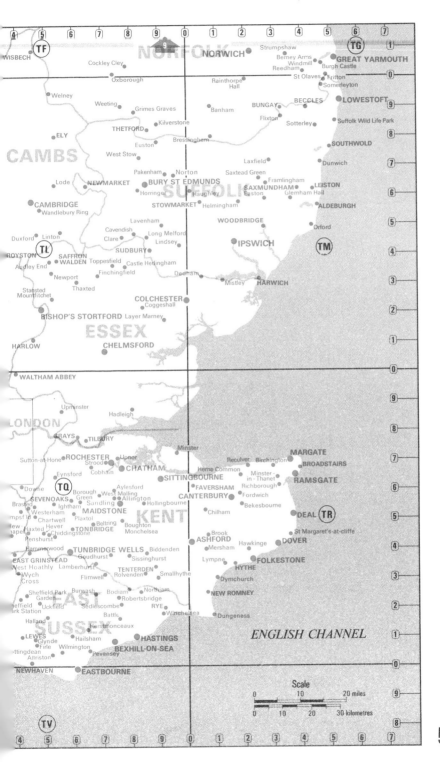

5

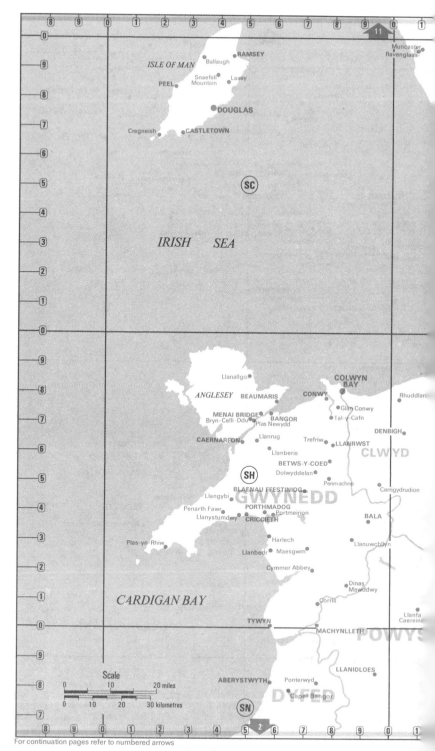

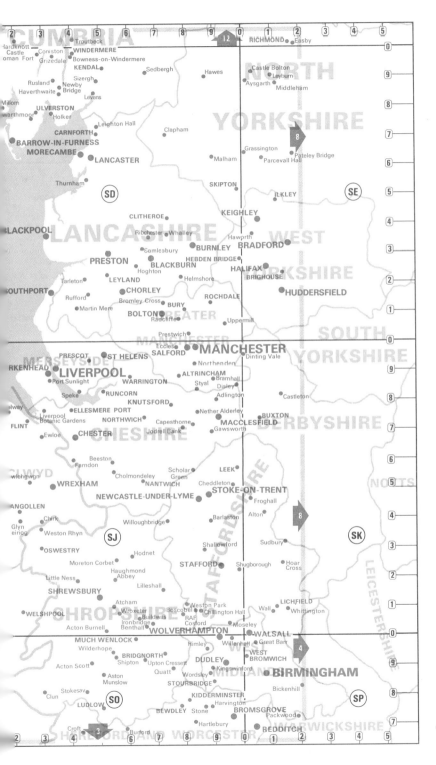

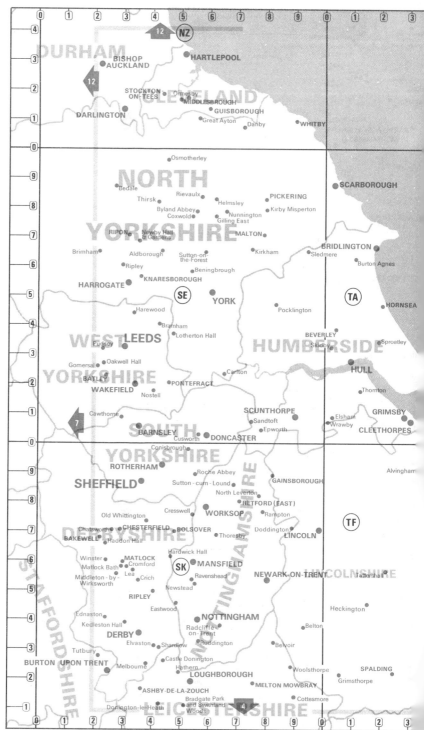

8

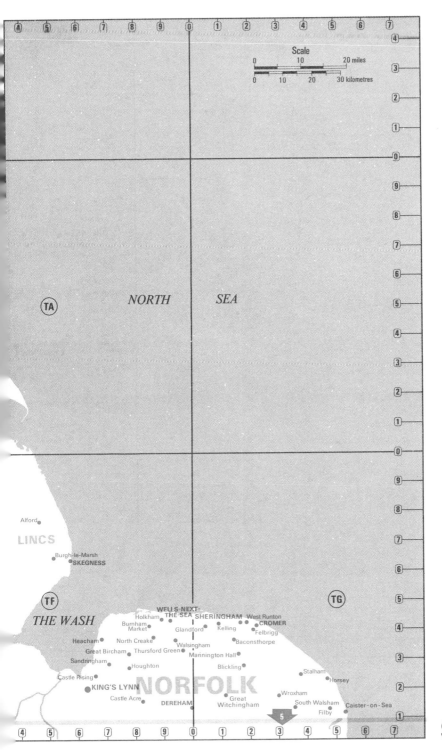

Scale

0   10   20 miles

0   10   20   30 kilometres

NORTH   SEA

TA

NORTH SEA

Alford

LINCS

Burgh-le-Marsh
SKEGNESS

TF

THE WASH

TG

WELLS-NEXT-
THE-SEA   SHERINGHAM   West Runton
Holkham   CROMER
Burnham   Glandford   Kelling   Felbrigg
Market
Heacham   North Creake   Baconsthorpe
Great Bircham   Thursford Green   Walsingham
Sandringham   Mannington Hall

Houghton   Blickling   Stalham
Castle Rising   Horsey

KING'S LYNN   NORFOLK
Castle Acre   Wroxham
DEREHAM   Great   South Walsham
Witchingham   Filby   Caister-on-Sea

5

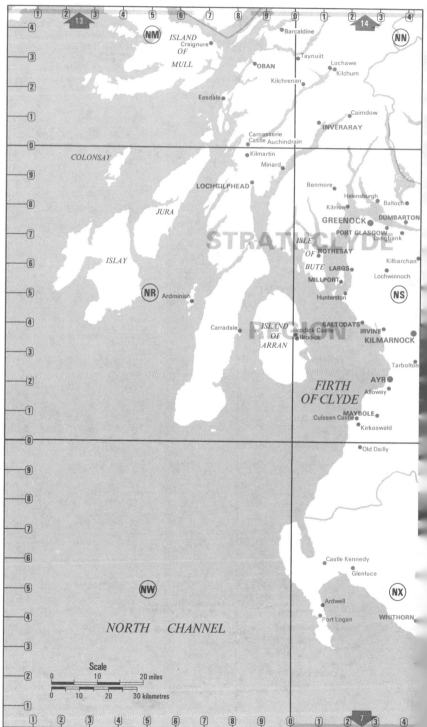

ISLAND
OF
MULL

Craignure
Barcaldine
Taynuilt
Lochawe
Kilchurn
OBAN
Kilchrenan
Cairndow
Easdale
INVERARAY
Carnasserie
Castle Auchindrain
Kilmartin
Minard
COLONSAY

Benmore
LOCHGILPHEAD
Helensburgh
Balloch
Kilmun
GREENOCK   DUMBARTON
JURA
PORT GLASGOW
Langbank
ISLE
OF ROTHESAY
BUTE LARGS   Kilbarchan
ISLAY
Lochwinnoch
MILLPORT
Hunterston

NR Ardminish

Carradale
SALTCOATS
ISLAND Brodick Castle   IRVINE
OF Brodick   KILMARNOCK
ARRAN

Tarbolton

FIRTH   AYR
OF CLYDE   Alloway

MAYBOLE
Culzean Castle
Kirkoswald

Old Dailly

Castle Kennedy
Glenluce

NW   NX

Ardwell
NORTH   CHANNEL   Port Logan   WHITHORN

Scale
0   10   20 miles
0   10   20   30 kilometres

10

TAYSIDE

REGION

NN

Lawers

Dunkeld

Meigle

NO

DUNDEE

Scone

PERTH

Comrie   CRIEFF

Muthill

AUCHTERARDER

CUPAR
Ceres

FIFE

FALKLAND

REGION

CALLANDER

Milnathort
KINROSS

Port of
Menteith   DOUNE

Blair Drummond

DOLLAR

Causewayhead   Menstrie

STIRLING
Bannockburn

DUNFERMLINE

KIRKCALDY

Fintry

CULROSS

Aberdour

KILSYTH   FALKIRK

BO'NESS

LINLITHGOW

QUEENSFERRY (South)

PRESTONPANS

Bearsden

Torphichen

EDINBURGH

GLASGOW

BATHGATE

LOTHIAN   REGION

Inglistor
Gogar

Inveresk
Balerno   MUSSELBURGH

PAISLEY

Lasswade

DALKEITH

PENICUIK

Newtongrange
Crichton

Uddingston
Blantyre   Bothwell

HAMILTON

NS

NT

PEEBLES

Stobo
Broughton

Traquair   Walkerburn

BORDERS

BIGGAR

REGION

Wanlockhead

12

MOFFAT

Thornhill

DUMFRIES

Moniaive

Ellisland Farm

LOCHMABEN

LANGHOLM

AND GALLOWAY

DUMFRIES

Ecclefechan

REGION

Drumcoltran Tower
New Abbey

Ruthwell

Creetown

CASTLE DOUGLAS

Caerlaverock

Cardoness
Castle

Kirkbean

Tongland   Palnackie

NX   KIRKCUDBRIGHT

Dundrennan

NY

MARYPORT

CUMBRIA

COCKERMOUTH

WORKINGTON

KESWICK

WHITEHAVEN

Grasmere
Rydal

7

NORTHUMBERLAND

DURHAM

Scale

0 ——— 10 ——— 20 miles
0 —— 10 —— 20 —— 30 kilometres

ARBROATH

NO

Leuchars
ST ANDREWS

FIFE

REGION

Lochty
Kellie Castle
ANSTRUTHER

FIRTH OF FORTH

11

NORTH BERWICK

Aberlady Dirleton
East Fortune **DUNBAR**
EAST LINTON
HADDINGTON

LOTHIAN

REGION

EYEMOUTH

NORTH SEA

NT LAUDER

DUNS

Norham
BERWICK-UPON-TWEED

NU

Holy Island

Gordon
COLDSTREAM
Smailholm Ford
MELROSE **KELSO**
Dryburgh
St Boswells
SELKIRK

Bamburgh

BORDERS

Chillingham

Embleton

REGION **JEDBURGH**

HAWICK

ALNWICK Howick

Whittingham Warkworth

Rothbury

Hermitage

Brinkburn

DUMFRIES

AND

GALLOWAY

REGION

NORTHUMBERLAND

Cambo
MORPETH

11

Carrawbrough
Housesteads Walwick **TYNEMOUTH**
Brampton Bardon Mill **NEWCASTLE UPON TYNE** **SOUTH SHIELDS**
Corbridge JARROW
Newton **PRUDHOE** **WEAR**
CARLISLE Rowlands **NZ**
Great Gill **WASHINGTON**
Corby Bearmish **SUNDERLAND**
Ryhope
NY

Alston

DURHAM

8

CUMBRIA

Skelton

DURHAM

Brougham
Dacre Temple Sowerby
Lowther Staindrop
8
Shap
Brough **CLEVELAND**
BARNARD CASTLE
Bowes

12

7

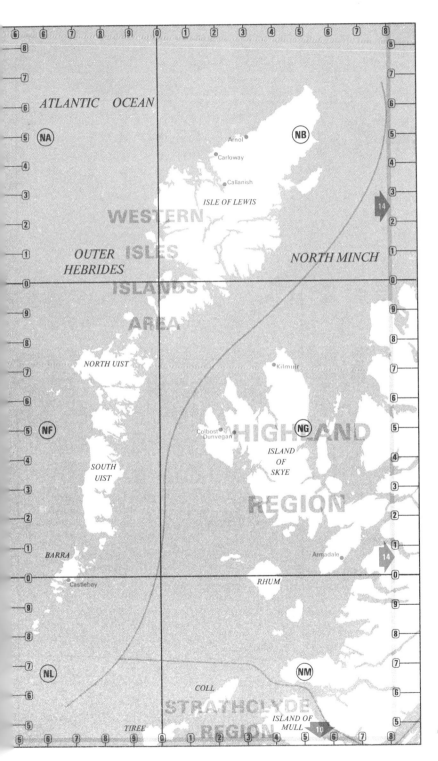

ATLANTIC OCEAN

NA

NB

Arnol

Carloway

Callanish

ISLE OF LEWIS

WESTERN

OUTER ISLES
HEBRIDES

ISLANDS

AREA

NORTH MINCH

NORTH UIST

Kilmuir

NF

Colbost
Dunvegan

NG

HIGHLAND

SOUTH
UIST

ISLAND
OF
SKYE

REGION

BARRA

Armadale

Castlebay

RHUM

NL

NM

COLL

STRATHCLYDE

TIREE

REGION

ISLAND OF
MULL

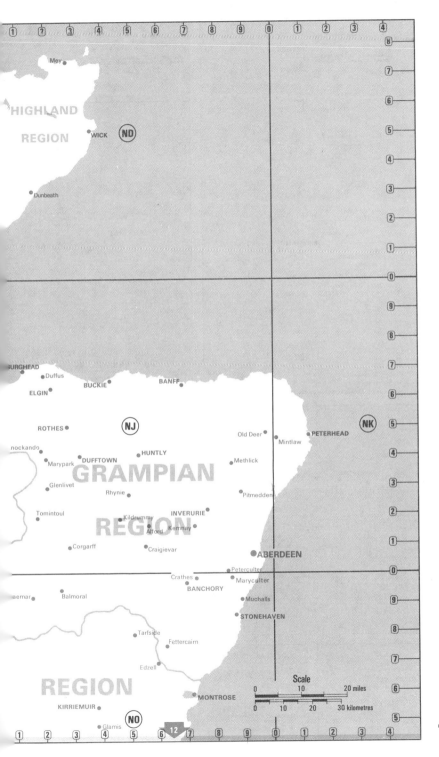

Scale

0   10   20 miles

0   10   20   30 kilometres

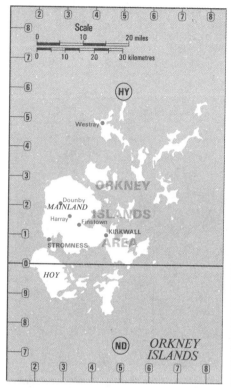

ORKNEY ISLANDS

Scale
0   10   20 miles
0 10 20 30 kilometres

HY

Westray

ORKNEY
MAINLAND   ISLANDS
Dounby
Harray Finstown
KIRKWALL
STROMNESS   AREA

HOY

ND   ORKNEY
ISLANDS

SHETLAND ISLANDS

Scale
0   10   20 miles
0 10 20 30 kilometres

HP

YELL

SHETLAND
ISLANDS
MAINLAND
AREA   HU

Scalloway   LERWICK

Mousa Island

Sumburgh   SHETLAND
ISLANDS

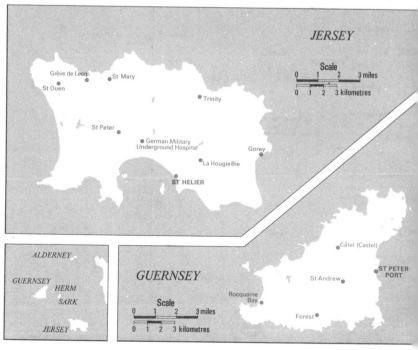

JERSEY

Scale
0   1   2   3 miles
0 1 2 3 kilometres

Grève de Lecq   St Mary
St Ouen

Trinity

St Peter

German Military
Underground Hospital
Gorey
La Hougie Bie
ST HELIER

ALDERNEY

GUERNSEY   HERM
SARK

JERSEY

GUERNSEY

Scale
0   1   2   3 miles
0 1 2 3 kilometres

Câtel (Castel)

ST PETER
PORT

St Andrew

Rocquaine
Bay

Forest

16